THE STORY OF JESUS
IN THE WORLD'S LITERATURE

BOOKS BY EDWARD WAGENKNECHT

Lillian Gish, An Interpretation (1927)

Values in Literature (1928)

Geraldine Farrar, An Authorized Record of Her Career (1929)

Utopia Americana (1929)

A Guide to Bernard Shaw (1929)

The Man Charles Dickens, A Victorian Portrait (1929)

Jenny Lind (1931)

Mark Twain, The Man and His Work (1935)

Cavalcade of the English Novel (1943)

Cavalcade of the American Novel (in preparation)

EDITOR, ETC.

The Chimes, by Charles Dickens (1931)
(Limited Editions Club)

The College Survey of English Literature (1942)
(with Others)

Life on the Mississippi, by Mark Twain (1944)

Six Novels of the Supernatural (1944)

The Fireside Book of Christmas Stories (1945)

When I Was a Child (1946)

Six Novels of Crime and Mystery (1946)

THE STORY OF

JESUS

IN THE WORLD'S

LITERATURE

Edited by

EDWARD WAGENKNECHT

═

With Illustrations by

FRITZ KREDEL

New York

CREATIVE AGE PRESS · INC.

Christmas, by Sigrid Undset. *From Christmas and Twelfth Night,* by Sigrid Undset. Longmans, Green and Co., 1932. Reprinted by permission of the publishers.

The Holy Child, by Charles Carroll Albertson. Reprinted by permission of the author.

A Christmas Hymn, The Anger of Christ, Cost, The Song of a Heathen, Holy Land, by Richard Watson Gilder. From *The Poems of Richard Watson Gilder.* Houghton Mifflin Co., 1908. Reprinted by permission of the publishers.

Christmas Song, by Bliss Carman. From *Bliss Carman Poems.* Reprinted by permission of Dodd, Mead & Co. Copyright, 1929, by Bliss Carman.

A Carol, by Lizette Woodworth Reese. Copyright by Lizette Woodworth Reese, and reprinted by permission of Rinehart & Co. A Christmas Folk-Song, Bible Stories, by Lizette Woodworth Reese. From *Selected Poems of Lizette Woodworth Reese.* Copyright, 1926, by Lizette Woodworth Reese, and reprinted by permission of Rinehart & Co.

A Christmas Carol, by Algernon Charles Swinburne. From *Swinburne's Poems.* Reprinted by permission of Harper & Bros.

A Christmas Carol, In the Carpenter's Shop, by Sara Teasdale. From *The Collected Poems of Sara Teasdale.* Reprinted by permission of The Macmillan Co.

In The Bleak Mid-Winter, "The Love of Christ Which Passeth Knowledge", Good Friday, A Better Resurrection, Mary Magdalene and the Other Mary, Despised and Rejected, by Christina Rossetti. From Christina Rossetti's *Collected Poems.* Reprinted by permission of The Macmillan Co.

Carol, Poem for Epiphany, The Ride to Jerusalem by Norman Nicholson. From *Five Rivers,* by Norman Nicholson. Published and copyright, 1945, by E. P. Dutton & Co.

The Donkey, A Christmas Carol, by G. K. Chesterton. From *The Wild Knight and Other Poems,* published by E. P. Dutton & Co.

While Shepherds Watched Their Flocks by Night, by Margaret Deland. From *The Old Garden and Other Verses,* by Margaret Deland. Houghton Mifflin Co., 1887. Reprinted by permission of the Estate of Margaret Deland.

A Cradle Song, by Padraic Colum. From *Poems,* by Padraic Colum. Reprinted by permission of The Macmillan Co.

The Song of a Shepherd-Boy At Bethlehem, The Fishers, by Josephine Preston Peabody. From *The Collected Poems of Josephine Preston Peabody,* Houghton Mifflin Co., 1927. Reprinted by permission of the publishers.

The Three Kings of Cologne, by Eugene Field. From *A Second Book of Western Verse,* by Eugene Field. Reprinted by permission of Charles Scribner's Sons. The First Christmas Tree, by Eugene Field. From *A Little Book of Profitable Tales,* by Eugene Field. Reprinted by permission of Charles Scribner's Sons. The Holy Cross, by Eugene Field. From *The Holy Cross,* by Eugene

Field. Reprinted by permission of Charles Scribner's Sons.

The Journey of the Magi, by T. S. Eliot. From *Collected Poems of T. S. Eliot.* Copyright, 1934, 1936, by Harcourt Brace & Co. Copyright in Canada by Faber & Faber Ltd.

The Gift, by Laura Spence Portor. Reprinted from the *Atlantic Monthly,* by permission of the author and publishers. The Windflowers and the Sage, The Christ-Child, by Laura Spence Portor. Reprinted from the *Woman's Home Companion,* by permission of the author and the publishers. The Vigil of Joseph, by Elsa Barker. Reprinted by permission of Dodd, Mead & Co.

The Winds At Bethlehem, by W. M. Letts. From *The Spires of Oxford and Other Poems,* by Winifred M. Letts. Published by E. P. Dutton & Co.

The Oxen, by Thomas Hardy. From *Collected Poems,* by Thomas Hardy. Reprinted by permission of The Macmillan Co.

The Little Christmas Donkey, The Shepherd's Madrigal, The Easter Robin, by Geraldine Farrar. Reprinted by permission of the author and of Charles Foley, music publisher. The Legend of the Dogwood Tree, "What Think Ye of Christ?", by Geraldine Farrar. Reprinted by permission of the author.

The Innocents, Peter and John, by Elinor Wylie. Reprinted from *Collected Poems,* by Elinor Wylie. Reprinted by permission of Alfred A. Knopf, Inc. Copyright, 1928, by Alfred A. Knopf, Inc.

The Sphinx: Le Repos En Egypte, by Agnes Repplier. Reprinted by permission of the author and the *Catholic World.*

Out of Egypt Have I Called My Son, The Wilderness, by Caroline Hazard. From *A Scallop-Shell of Quiet,* by Caroline Hazard, published by Houghton Mifflin Co. Reprinted by permission of the Estate of Caroline Hazard.

That Holy Thing, The Woman Who Came Behind Him In the Crowd, Lost and Found, by George MacDonald. From *George MacDonald's Poetical Works.* Reprinted by permission of Colonel Maurice MacDonald.

No Sudden Thing of Glory, Christmas Night, Unto Us A Son Is Given, Easter Night, Christ In the Universe, by Alice Meynell. From *The Poems of Alice Meynell.* Reprinted by permission of Charles Scribner's Sons, and Burns, Oates & Washbourne, Ltd.

The Consecration of the Common Way, A Guard of the Sepulcher, The Ascension, by Edwin Markham. Reprinted by permission.

How Can They Honor Him? by Anderson M. Scruggs. From *Glory of Earth,* by Anderson M. Scruggs, Ogelthorpe University Press. Reprinted by permission of the author and of *Holland's, The Magazine of the South.*

To Jesus on His Birthday, by Edna St. Vincent Millay. Copyright, 1927, by Edna St. Vincent Millay. From *The Buck In The Snow and Other Poems,* published by Harper & Bros.

After Christmas A Landlord Remembers, by Elizabeth Coatsworth. From *Country Poems,* by Elizabeth Coatsworth. Reprinted by permission of The Macmillan Co.

The Maid-Servant At the Inn, by Dorothy Parker. From *The Portable Dorothy Parker.* Copyright, 1944, by Dorothy Parker. Reprinted by permission of the Viking Press.

The Well of the Star, by Elizabeth Goudge. Reprinted by permission of Coward-McCann, Inc. Copyright, 1941, by Elizabeth Goudge.

The Other Wise Man, by Henry van Dyke. Copyright, 1895, by Harper & Bros. Copyright, 1923, by Henry van Dyke.

Christmas Morning, by Elizabeth Madox Roberts. From *Under the Tree,* by Elizabeth Madox Roberts. Copyright, 1922, by B. W. Huebsch. Reprinted by permission of the Viking Press.

Little Jesus, Desiderium Indesideratum, by Francis Thompson. Reprinted from *The Collected Works of Francis Thompson,* by permission of the Newman Bookshop, Westminster, Maryland.

Christmas, by Elizabeth Stanton Rice. From *Poems,* by Elizabeth Stanton Rice. Copyright, 1937, by T. H. Rice.

The Second Christmas, by John Haynes Holmes. From *The Second Christmas,* by John Haynes Holmes. Reprinted by permission of the Macmillan Co.

At Nazareth, A Stranger in Scythopolis, by Katharine Lee Bates. From *Selected Poems of Katharine Lee Bates.* Copyright, 1930, by George S. Burgess and Dorothy Burgess, and published by Houghton Mifflin Co. Reprinted by permission of Mrs. George S. Burgess. Tempted, Alone Into the Mountain, reprinted by permission of Mrs. George S. Burgess.

The Boy Christ, Thirty Pieces of Silver for Jesus, by Helene Mullins. *Earthbound and Other Poems,* by Helene Mullins. Copyright, 1929, by Harper & Bros.

The Boy Jesus, Robin Redbreast, Mater Dolorosa, Holy Sanctuary, Two Easter Lilies, Christ and the Winds, Holy Saturday, by John Banister Tabb. From *The Poetry of Father Tabb.* Copyright 1902, 1923, 1928, by Francis Litz. Reprinted by permission of Dodd, Mead & Co.

Mary At Nazareth, The Wife of Judas Iscariot, by Cale Young Rice. From *Collected Poems and Plays,* by Cale Young Rice. Reprinted by permission of Dr. L. L. Rice.

The Seventh Christmas, by Coningsby Dawson. From *When Father Christmas Was Late,* by Coningsby Dawson. Copyright, 1917, 1920, 1929. Reprinted by permission of Doubleday & Co.

Jesus In His Family, The Young Carpenter, by Winifred Kirkland. From *Discovering the Boy of Nazareth,* by Winifred Kirkland. Reprinted by permission of The Macmillan Co.

Child, by Carl Sandburg. From *Chicago Poems,* by Carl Sandburg. By permission of Henry Holt & Co.

The editor and the Publishers thank the many authors, agents, and publishers whose interest and co-operation has made possible the preparation of this book.

In addition to the specific acknowledgments made elsewhere, we wish to express our thanks to the Oxford University Press for unusual kindness and understanding in permitting us to quote from certain seventeenth-century poets of whose works they have published copyrighted texts.

We have tried our best to trace the ownership of all copyrighted material included in this volume. We offer our sincere apologies in the event of any accidental infringements of anyone's rights.

Journey To Jerusalem, by Maxwell Anderson, is reprinted by permission of Anderson House. The non-professional acting rights of this play are controlled exclusively by Dramatists Play Service, Inc., 6 East 39th St., New York City, without whose permission in writing no performance of it may be made.

The Little Miracle, by Zoë Akins. Copyright, 1936, by Curtis Publishing Co. Copyright, 1936, by Zoë Akins Rumbold.

His Youth, On The Road, The Crowning Wonder, by John Oxenham. From "Gentlemen—The King!" by John Oxenham. Reprinted by permission of Erica Oxenham. Credo by John Oxenham. From Bees in Amber. Reprinted by permission of Erica Oxenham.

Carpenter, by Isabel Fiske Conant. Reprinted from Voices: A Journal of Poetry, by permission of the author and of Harold Vinal, publisher.

The Nazareth Shop, by Robert McIntyre. Reprinted by permission from the Christian Advocate.

Departure from Nazareth, The Young Man of Nain. The Praetorians, by Edwin McNeill Poteat. From These Shared His Cross, by Edwin McNeill Poteat. Copyright, 1941, by Harper & Bros. The Feast is Prepared, The Disciples in the Garden, Troubled by Dreams, by Edwin McNeill Poteat. From These Shared His Passion, by Edwin McNeill Poteat. Copyright, 1940, by Harper & Bros.

The Cherry-Tree Carol, The Carnal and the Crane. Anonymous. From English and Scottish Popular Ballads, edited by Francis James Child. Reprinted by permission of Houghton Mifflin Co.

The Beasts of the Fields, The Virgin of the Angels, by Jules Lemaitre. Reprinted from On the Margin of Old Books, by Jules Lemaitre; translated by Clarence Stratton. Copyright, 1929, by Coward-McCann.

The Flight into Egypt, by Selma Lagerlöf. From Christ Legends, by Selma Lagerlöf. Translated from the Swedish by Velma Swanston Howard. Reprinted by permission of Henry Holt & Co.

The Flight Into Egypt, by Thornton Wilder. Reprinted from The Angel That Troubled the Waters, by Thornton Wilder. Copyright, 1928, by Coward-McCann.

The Joyous Miracle, by Frank Norris. From The Joyous Miracle, by Frank Norris. Copyright, 1906. Reprinted by permission of Doubleday & Co.

A Ballad of Christmas, by Walter de la Mare. Reprinted from Collected Poems, by Walter de la Mare, by permission of the author and of Henry Holt & Co. The Burning-Glass, by Walter de la Mare. From The Burning-Glass. Copyright, 1945, by Walter de la Mare. Reprinted by permission of the author and of the Viking Press.

The Fairy Tree, by Temple Lane. To Miss Temple Lane and The Talbot Press, Dublin, for "The Fairy Tree" from Fisherman's Wake, by Temple Lane, the lyric set to music by Dr. Vincent O'Brien, and published by Messrs. J. and W. Chester, Ltd., of London.

The Ocean Christ, by Anatole France. From Golden Tales of Anatole France. Copyright, 1909, by Dodd, Mead & Co. Reprinted by permission of Dodd, Mead & Co. Copyright in Canada by John Lane, Ltd.

The Travelling Man, by Lady Gregory. From Seven Short Plays, by Lady Gregory, courtesy of G. P. Putnam's Sons.

A Christmas Night, To and Fro About the City, by John Drinkwater. From Poems, 1908-1919. Reprinted by permission of Houghton Mifflin Co.

The Golden Legend, by Don Marquis. From Chapters for the Orthodox, by Don Marquis. Copyright, 1934. Reprinted by permission of Doubleday & Co.

The Sacred Fire Burns, Jesus Expands His Gospel, by Ivan Nazhivin. From According to Thomas, by Ivan Nazhivin. Translated by Emile Burns. Copyright, 1931, by Harper & Bros. Reprinted by permission of the publishers.

A Ballad of Trees and the Master, by Sidney Lanier. From Poems, by Sidney Lanier. Reprinted by permission of Charles Scribner's Sons.

The Mysticism of Jesus, by Sheldon Cheney. From Men Who Have Walked With God, by Sheldon Cheney. Reprinted by permission of Alfred A. Knopf, Inc. Copyright, 1945, by Sheldon Cheney. The title of this selection has been supplied by the editor.

Religion and Doctrine, by John Hay. From Poems, by John Hay. Reprinted by permission of Houghton Mifflin Co.

The Ten Lepers, by Katharine Tynan. From Flower of Peace, by Katharine Tynan. Reprinted by permission of Charles Scribner's Sons, and Burns Oates & Washbourne, Ltd. Sheep and Lambs, by Katharine Tynan. From Collected Poems. Reprinted by permission of The Macmillan Co.

The Ten Lepers in the Wilderness, Told in the Stars, by Manuel Komroff. From In the Years of Our Lord, by Manuel Komroff. Copyright, 1942, by Manuel Komroff.

The Demoniac and the Swine, The Great Decision, Nicodemus Sums It Up. Anonymous. From By An Unknown Disciple. Copyright, 1919, by Harper & Bros. Reprinted by permission of the publishers.

John the Six, by Josephine Johnson. From Winter Orchard and Other Stories, by Josephine Johnson; published by Simon and Schuster.

The Conversion of Mary Magdalene. Anonymous. From The Life of Saint Mary Magdalene. Translated by Valentina Hawtrey. Published by John Lane, The Bodley Head, 1904. Reprinted by permission of the publisher. The title of this selection has been supplied by the editor.

The Woman of Samaria, by Edmond Rostand. From The Plays of Edmond Rostand. Translated by Henderson Daingerfield Norman. Reprinted by permission of The Macmillan Co.

What Went Ye Out For to See? by Arthur Hugh Clough. From Poems, by Arthur Hugh Clough. Reprinted by permission of The Macmillan Co.

The Prodigal Son, by James Weldon Johnson. From God's Trombones, by James Weldon Johnson. Copyright, 1927, by the Viking Press. O Black and Unknown Bards, by James Weldon Johnson. From Saint Peter Relates an Incident. Copyright, 1917, 1921, by James Weldon Johnson. Reprinted by permission of the Viking Press.

Jesus as a Story-Teller, The Humor of Jesus, by William Ellery Leonard. From The Poet of Galilee, by William Ellery Leonard. Copyright, 1909, by B. W. Huebsch. Reprinted by permission of the Viking Press.

The Teaching of Jesus, by J. Middleton Murry. From Jesus Man of Genius, by J. Middleton Murry. Copyright, 1926, by J. Middleton Murry.

Jesus As the Pharisees Saw Him, by Edmond Fleg. From Jesus, by Edmond Fleg, translated by Phyllis Megroz. Copyright, 1935, by E. P. Dutton & Co.

The Originality of Jesus, by George A. Gordon. Reprinted from the Atlantic Monthly by permission of the publishers.

The Search, A Christmas Carol, by James Russell Lowell. From The Complete Poetical Works of James Russell Lowell. Reprinted by permission of Houghton Mifflin Co.

Simon the Cyrenian Speaks, by Countee Cullen. From Color, by Countee Cullen. Copyright, 1925, by Harper & Bros. Litany of the Black People, by Countee Cullen. From Copper Sun, by Countee Cullen. Copyright, 1927, by Harper & Bros.

The Jew to Jesus, by Florence Kiper Frank. From The Jew to Jesus and Other Poems, by Florence Kiper Frank. Reprinted by permission of Mitchell Kennerly, publisher.

The Refugee From Judea, by William Zukerman. From the Menorah Journal, Winter, 1941. Copyright, 1941, by the Menorah Association, Inc. Reprinted by permission of the publishers.

A Little Child of Mary, by H. T. Burleigh. Reprinted by permission of G. Ricordi & Co., Inc., music publishers.

The Christ of the Andes, by Florence Earle Coates. From Poems, by Florence Earle Coates, published by Houghton Mifflin Co., and reprinted by permission of the Estate of Florence Coates.

The White Comrade, by Robert Haven Schauffler. From New and Selected Poems, by Robert Haven Schauffler. Copyright, 1942, by Robert Haven Schauffler. Reprinted by permission of Dodd, Mead & Co.

Above the Battle's Front, Where is the Real Non-Resistant? by Vachel Lindsay. From Collected Poems, by Vachel Lindsay. Reprinted by permission of The Macmillan Co.

The Terrible Meek, by Charles Rann Kennedy. Copyright, 1912, 1933, 1939 (in renewal), by Charles Rann Kennedy. The Terrible Meek was written for the furtherance of World Peace, and may be performed, recited, broadcast by anybody without payment of royalty. The author would appreciate, however, the courtesy of a notification in all such cases, such notification to be addressed to Samuel French, 25 West 45th Street, New York

IN MEMORY OF
MY MOTHER AND FATHER

CONTENTS

Part One · His Coming

CONTENTS

Part Two · The Hidden Years

Part Three · Legends

Part Four · His Work on Earth

CONTENTS

Part Five · The Social Gospel

Part Six · The Passion Drama

Part Seven · Christ as Redeemer and Savior

INTRODUCTION

Religion has long lived close to the printing press. When Mr. Edward Weeks, the Editor of *The Atlantic Monthly,* a number of years ago compiled his now famous list of best-selling modern American books, most "well-read" Americans rubbed their eyes upon reading that Charles M. Sheldon's novel, *In His Steps,* though mentioned neither in Quinn's history of American fiction nor in Van Doren's, had been far and away the king of best-sellers, circulating, at the very lowest estimate, some 8,000,000 copies, and outdistancing its closest competitor by a cool 6,000,000! Not so long afterwards, a revolutionary young American announced to an uninterested world that his history of American literature, when he should write it, would deal only with the books that had been "read." I wonder how much more space he intends to devote to Charles M. Sheldon than to Nathaniel Hawthorne!

Mr. Weeks's discovery about *In His Steps* had nothing of the anomalous about it. Booksellers' catalogues show that even during the period that we call the Restoration the backbone of the English book business was made up of religious books and not of the scandalous play-books to which many moderns imagine the age to have given its exclusive devotion.

Puritanism has often been judged during these latter years as hostile to artistic expression; yet two of the very great narrative poems of the world—*The Faerie Queene* and *Paradise Lost*—were either produced by or strongly influenced by Sixteenth and Seventeenth Century English Puritanism; I really doubt that anything the Impuritans have to show, even in this untrammelled Twentieth Century, is so very much better!

I am not sure that men of letters in any period have ever paid quite such a magnificent tribute to Jesus as Italian painters did in the time of Raphael or composers of sacred oratorios in the days of Händel; but the poets at least have not been silent by any means, and an astonishingly high proportion of the great singers of the last three hundred years have found their natural and inevitable place between the covers of this book.

I once heard S. Parkes Cadman publicly lament that few men of genius had really loved God. Though no man has ever loved God as God deserves to be loved, perhaps Dr. Cadman's statement would have come closer to the truth had he said that few men of genius have loved God in the precise terms in which a clergyman defines or understands the love of God. Tennyson loved God in that way, and so did Browning; and neither one was a less impressive poet because of that fact. The same thing is, of course, even more obviously true of such essentially devotional poets as George Herbert, Christina Rossetti, and George MacDonald. It is not true of Shakespeare or of Shelley or of Keats; but if God is the Creative Power of the universe, it is ridiculous to think of such richly endowed spirits as anything less than vessels filled with the strength of God, nor is it possible to doubt that the love of God possessed them. Caroline Spurgeon, studying Shakespeare's imagery as a means of recovering some aspects of his personality, concluded among other things that Shakespeare was profoundly anti-war. Of course he was! It needed no study of his imagery to tell us that. Shakespeare was anti-war as all creative spirits are anti-war—and I care nothing about what his consciously held "opinions" on the matter of war and peace may have been, for an artist does not create with his opinions—because the creative spirit is necessarily on the side of life and against death. As Miss Mary Garden once remarked, there are only two kinds of people in the world—the builders and the destroyers; the whole of the artist's morality is implicit in that statement. A student of music once asked another great singer, the late Madame Emma Calvé, what was the most important thing for a girl to remember if she wanted to become a great singer herself. Without a moment's hesitation, the great Carmen replied that the most important thing was to believe in God. If the creative spirit is necessarily anti-war, by the same token he is necessarily and profoundly pro-God, and never more so than when he understands himself so little as to sign his name in a fit of youthful bravado as "Percy Bysshe Shelley, Atheist."

The lyrical poet has the advantage of being able to express his religious emotion simply and directly; the novelist or playwright who chooses to retell a Biblical story, on the other hand, finds himself up against the impossible task of competing, or seeming to compete, with his sources. All Passion Plays are interesting because of the magnificent tale they have to tell, and all suffer by comparison with the Gospels upon which they are based. Thomas Mann met distinguished success with the Joseph-saga because, preserving the outlines of one of the finest narratives ever written, he was yet able to fill it full of philosophical significance, creating as it were a summary or synthesis of the experiences of the modern spirit as it faces the great ultimate questions of life and death. And Walter de la Mare, though working on a much more modest scale in his *Stories from the Bible*, achieved something very like a miracle because he had the selflessness not to be at all concerned about his "originality." To all the strength of the Biblical writers' conceptions, he added all the grace of his own delicate art: one could not ask much more from literature than the eclectic narrative which was the result.

But both these writers, be it observed, have confined themselves to the Old Testament; Mr. de la Mare, indeed, has heroically resisted the urging of friends and publishers who have begged him to apply the same method to the life of Jesus. No writer of his calibre has ever written that life—in the English language at any rate. Dickens's *The Life of Our Lord,* made for the use of his own children and long withheld from publication, was awaited with many hopes, none of which were satisfied; for while Dickens got much of his goodness into *The Life of Our Lord,* he kept his genius out; there is nothing in the book to indicate that it was written by a great writer.

Excessive reverence is no doubt the explanation for Dickens's failure and Mr. de la Mare's refusal, a reverence which in Mr. de la Mare's case seems more than likely to deprive the world of a masterpiece. We see the same thing in the interpretations of Jesus which are offered upon stage and screen; even that fine actor, Mr. H. B. Warner seemed (in the film, *The King of Kings*), perpetually to be holding himself in, lest he should, by any chance, do something wrong or something that might offend the Catholics or the Christian Scientists or any considerable group in between.

Only the iconoclasts can quite escape this sense of constraint in the presence of the Master of the Christian World—oddly enough, the biographers and trained Biblical scholars come much closer to overcoming it than the creative writers!—and the iconoclastic solution of the problem does not get us far. *The Brook Kerith,* by George Moore, and *The Man Who Died,* by D. H. Lawrence, are both brilliant works of the imagination. Only, unfortunately, the characters presented in them bear not the remotest resemblance to what everybody knows Jesus of Nazareth must have been like.

Some novelists and dramatists have felt this so strongly that—like the author of *Ben-Hur*—they have refused to bring Jesus himself upon the stage at all. This method is no solution, yet it can be used with telling effect. Viewing Jesus through the eyes of his family, for example, the play, *Family Portrait,* by Lenore Coffee and William Joyce Cowen, has illuminated many things.

There are many problems, too, which never can be solved because the data needed to settle them simply do not exist. Who, for example, can ever be sure that he knows the truth about Judas Iscariot? Charles Lamb gave it up in despair, not being able to understand how any man who had dipped bread in the same dish with the Son of Man could ever bring himself to betray him. Was Judas simply a monster of perfidy? Or was he a tragically misguided idealist who was trying to force Jesus' hand and compel him to declare himself king in Israel? We shall never know, but Eric Linklater's novel *Judas* presents a fascinating hypothesis.

In the light of all the problems and difficulties, it is no wonder that most modern playwrights and novelists should choose to devote themselves to other themes, rather than to telling this story—the great story of the Western world—over and over again, illuminating it with every resource of genius and of art until the last ounce of its significance should have been extracted from it. That is what they would do, of course, if they were to treat the story as the Greek dramatists handled the immortal legends of their race. But we must not forget that to the Greeks the drama was a religious ceremonial.

We think of modern art as secular rather than sacred in its point of view, yet this is not completely true. Insofar as the novel and the drama ever achieve any really complete or profound or penetrating interpretation of life, they are inevitably religious, for there is no truth that is not religious truth. Take the novel, for example; take the criticisms of life that have been made in fiction, as I have tried to describe them in my *Cavalcade of the English Novel.* George Eliot was the first major novelist in England who did not profess the Christian religion; but none of her predecessors had ever set forth the Christian ethic with such penetrating power. Among George Eliot's successors have been men of all shades of belief and of unbelief; but there is a level at which all men who have lived profoundly and thought profoundly are agreed; Christianity is so profoundly true an interpretation of human life that only the man who misses the boat completely can be positively unchristian. John Galsworthy, for example, made no profession whatever of Christian faith, but what writer ever set forth the Christian view of sacrifice more touchingly than he did at the climax of Fleur's and Soames's pilgrimage?

The arrangement of the material in this book is mainly chronological, though some sections like V and VII do not exist in terms of a chronological framework. There is also, inevitably, some overlapping; the fact that Section III is devoted wholly to Legends does not mean that legendary material has been altogether excluded elsewhere. No two editors would have chosen exactly the same material for this book, and no two editors would have arranged their material in exactly the same way; all I can say is that I have tried to place each selection where it would be most effective in relation to all the other selections.

This is a book of creative literature about Jesus, not a book of opinions about Jesus or of theological speculations. It is, I think, the first book of its kind that has ever been published; Mr. Norman Ault has, indeed, given us *The Poets' Life of Christ;* there are other anthologies of poetry about Jesus, to some of which I am considerably indebted. This volume, however, embraces many types of literature. There are even a few essays; but the essays have, I think, a literary quality, and while they will not command universal agreement, I think none of them run off into religious controversy. The creative imagination has been allowed to run its own course: Selma Lagerlöf, Geraldine Farrar, and Thornton Wilder have each treated the theme of the Flight to Egypt, but each has treated it very differently; I can no more conceive of any intelligent reader being troubled by Miss Farrar's placing the flight of the Holy Family before the birth of Jesus rather than after it than I can conceive of any sane person being offended by Mr. Wilder's humor. If any should be, I can only suggest that he turn over to William Ellery Leonard's paper on "The Humor of Jesus"!

I may add that it was because my book was not conceived as a controversial work—and not at all because I felt that Jesus needed to be "protected" —that I excluded the iconoclasts; such literary expressions of unbelief as the works by George Moore and D. H. Lawrence which I have already mentioned were left out because they could not be made to fit into the scheme of the book.

EDWARD WAGENKNECHT

Evanston, Illinois
March 26, 1946

PART ONE

His Coming

————

Some say that ever 'gainst that season comes
Wherein our Saviour's birth is celebrated,
The bird of dawning singeth all night long;
And then, they say, no spirit can walk abroad;
The nights are wholesome; then no planets strike,
No fairy takes, nor witch hath power to charm,
So hallow'd and so gracious is the time.

HAMLET

1. ADESTE FIDELES

CHRISTMAS

Sigrid Undset

The old masters are not afraid to paint the little new-born Lord Jesus quite realistically. The sweet, downy child's head is large in relation to the body, the limbs are painfully thin. He has one finger in His mouth, and lies sucking it while He thoughtfully rubs one rosy-heeled little foot against the other. The tiny infant lies on the bare, cold, earthy floor; at the best He is given only a handful of straw or a little white cloth spread out under Him.

One feels tempted to follow the example of the shepherds in the old mystery-plays and give the young mother good advice about child management. But the upright and slender young Virgin Mary kneels, deeply sunk in meditation and prayer. She looks at her little Son whom she has borne in her womb and to whom she has given a body from her body, and in Him she sees her God and Saviour, the Creator who has chosen this world as His throne—the night sky above, with its myriad of stars, being but a corner of His mantle which He has cast around His mother and Himself.

St. Joseph, faithful and upright, stands on guard; and near him are the angels, trusty advisers to the carpenter. They have arrayed themselves in visible shapes, and made themselves very beautiful for the feast. They are wearing richly folded white linen tunics, like ministers at a festal mass, and their hair falls in luxuriant curls round their smiling, red-cheeked faces. To keep their unruly locks tidy they have put on their heads crowns of gold and garlands of flowers.

It is only their Master and their King who can come to such a festival without being thus decked out. The heavens are His and the earth. He has laid the foundations of this ball of earth and all that is upon it, and now He is coming to us as the lowest of us all to serve us; for so it was foreordained in God's counsels from all eternity—God's secret counsels, at which we, in our smallness and weakness, so often take offence.

"Let not your heart be troubled," says Jesus to His disciples. "Fear not," is one of the last things He bids them. He says it also when He comes to earth, and He says it more emphatically than with words. Who can be afraid of a tiny baby? The half-crazy Idumean ruler in the castle up in Jerusalem—but he has been for so long a prisoner in his own wild kingdom of dreams that he has lost the taste for the sweet and simple everyday things of life. And the wild riders of the sky are afraid. But to men of goodwill the King of Peace has come as a newborn babe in a crib, and He has chosen to come to us so weak and naked in order that we may each one do something for Him.

Is not this the last and most mysterious reason for the joy of Christmas—that the world has been turned upside down; that the Almighty has laid aside His insignia of office and receives our gifts, if we want to give them to Him? The mystery of the Atonement is introduced with a Christmas play, the real meaning of which is far beyond our poor comprehension; but for almost two thousand years the world has echoed every Christmas with the noise and merriment of the children who come to visit the stable, and humanity has played itself warm and full of laughter around the Son of God who has become a little child for its sake.

Through the poetry and dreams of the Middle Ages one vision persists: Anti-Christ when he comes will suddenly appear as a full-grown man. He cannot make himself so small and humble as to become the son of a woman, for has he not brooded for æons over his great plan of revolt and world destruction? He cannot, therefore, possibly find time to play in a village street with other children in a land which is only a small province of a world power. It is only the Almighty who has created and upheld the universe who can afford to lie and rest among the shavings on the floor of St. Joseph's workshop and hold Mary's hand when she goes to the well outside the town walls to fetch Him water.

The devil pops up at any time disguised in some human form or other. The most important point is, however, that the whole thing is a disguise. The tempter, the spy, worms himself in everywhere in possible and impossible shapes. It is quite thinkable that he himself, for reasons we do not know, has rather a predilection for appearing as the man with small crooked horns on his forehead, and goat-legged; but he can always easily dress himself up as a beautiful woman or venerable monk, or a sort of poodle-dog or a staring pig or a headless cock. As long as the disguise is suitable. . .

It is God who comes to us from eternity, faithful and loving, and binds Himself to us in chains of flesh and blood so as to fight with the human race for the human race, true God and true man among men. His heart, in which dwells all the fullness of the Godhead, has throbbed below Mary's heart. His mouth, from which St. John saw issuing the sword of judgement, has sucked at Mary's breast.

The maiden has lifted up her adored son, has wrapped Him in swaddling clothes, and holds Him in her arms. The Child Jesus leans His head against His mother's breast, and His serious infant eyes look down upon us all over Mary's supporting hand. Then He nestles up to her closer still and lifts His little right hand—now it is raised in blessing over the shepherds who come in. She must sit down with the Child so that the visitors can look at Him properly. The old chieftain from the East creeps forward on his knees towards the two and holds out a golden censer—perhaps the Child Jesus might find delight in playing with it; listen how nicely the chain rattles! The Child's hand waves in the air for a moment and He kicks contentedly, then His hand sinks in a fleeting caress down upon the old man's head.

Humanity had made for itself pictures of goddesses with their children, the offspring of gods, in their arms. It had worshipped them—goddesses of Egypt, Babylon, China. Not one of them had the power to give any hope of peace to the children of men. They were wild and munificent, cruel and capricious, like the human nature they were meant to represent .

Then steps forward a child of the race—a woman. A young virgin full of grace, who meekly answers the angel who brings her tidings from Him who has created both the maid and the angel. "Lo, I am the handmaid of the Lord; be it done to me according to thy word." And the Word became flesh and dwelt among us. Mary holds out to us her Child, the Child who is true God and true Man, and He has come to save us, because each immortal soul is worth more than all the transient glory of the earth and the stars. And Mary's son tells us that all that we do or do not do for one of the smallest of His little ones, that we do or do not do for Him.

The old pictures of goddesses decay, forsaken and forgotten. The memory of the orgies and bloody rites and dirges of their followers comes down to us in confused myths and in adventure stories for the children who run, playing and smiling, around the Mother of compassion as she walks forward with Jesus in her arms.

Where she is driven out, the ghost of Herod steps in, and the people are bemused by the Idumean's dream of dominion and glory, feastings in newly built palaces and deeds of violence in dark cellars, and in their hearts awaken Herod's hatred of his own offspring and his fear of children. And the old visions come up again, of goddesses, of the fruitfulness of earth, the breaking of the buds, and the fall of the leaf.

Each one presses her own child to her breast, ready to fight for it against the others. The children of Leto draw the bow again and there is no mercy for the sons and daughters of Niobe.

So let us follow the children who sing at the top of their voices:

> Adeste, fideles,
> Laeti triumphantes,
> Venite, venite in Bethlehem.

And when we give one another our Christmas presents in His name, let us remember that He has given us the sun and the moon and the stars, the earth with its forests and mountains and oceans and all that lives and moves upon them. He has given us all green things and everything that blossoms and bears fruit—and all that we quarrel about and all that we have misused. And to save us from our own foolishnesses and from all our sins He came down to Earth and gave Himself.

> Venite adoremus Dominum.

2. SALUTATION

THE HOLY CHILD

Charles Carroll Albertson

He is the Ancient Wisdom of the World,
  The Word Creative, Beautiful and True,
The Nameless of Innumerable Names,
  Ageless forever, yet Forever New.

A HYMN FOR
THE NATIVITY OF MY SAVIOR

Ben Jonson

I sing the birth was born tonight,
The Author both of life and light;
  The angels so did sound it.
And like the ravished shepherds said,

Who saw the light and were afraid,
  Yet searched, and true they found it.

The Son of God, the eternal King,
That did us all salvation bring,
  And free the soul from danger;
He whom the whole world could not take,
The Word which heaven and earth did make,
  Was now laid in a manger.

The Father's wisdom willed it so,
The Son's obedience knew no No,
  Both wills were in one stature:
And as that wisdom had decreed,
The Word was now made flesh indeed,
  And took on Him our nature.

What comfort by Him do we win,
Who made Himself the price for sin,
  To make us heirs of Glory!
To see this Babe all innocence,
A martyr born in our defence;
  Can man forget this story?

FOR THE NATIVITY
OF OUR LORD

William Drummond

O than the fairest day, thrice fairer night,
Night to best days, in which a sun doth rise,
Of which the golden eye, which clears the skies,
Is but a sparkling ray, a shadow light;
And blessed ye, in silly pastor's sight,
Mild creatures, in whose warm crib now lies
That heaven-sent youngling, holy maid-born wight,
Midst, end, beginning of our prophecies:
Blest cottage, that hath flowers in winter spread;
Though wither'd, blessed grass, that hath the grace
To deck and be a carpet to the place.
Thus singing to the sound of oaten reed,
Before the Babe the shepherds bow'd their knees,
And springs ran nectar, honey dropped from trees.

HYMN ON THE MORNING
OF CHRIST'S NATIVITY

John Milton

It was the winter wild,
While the heaven-born child
    All meanly wrapt in the rude manger lies;
Nature, in awe to him,
Had doffed her gaudy trim,
    With her great Master so to sympathize:
It was no season then for her
To wanton with the sun, her lusty paramour.

Only with speeches fair
She woos the gentle air
    To hide her guilty front with innocent snow,
And on her naked shame,
Pollute with sinful blame,
    The saintly veil of maiden white to throw;
Confounded, that her Maker's eyes
Should look so near upon her foul deformities.

But he, her fears to cease,
Sends down the meek-eyed Peace;
    She, crowned with olive green, came softly sliding
Down through the turning sphere,
His ready harbinger,
    With turtle wing the amorous clouds dividing;
And waving wide her myrtle wand,
She strikes a universal peace through sea and land.

No war, or battle's sound,
Was heard the world around;
    The idle spear and shield were high uphung;
The hooked chariot stood
Unstained with hostile blood;
    The trumpet spake not to the armed throng;
And kings sat still with awful eye,
As if they surely knew their sovran Lord was by.

But peaceful was the night
Wherein the Prince of Light
    His reign of peace upon the earth began:
The winds, with wonder whist,
Smoothly the waters kissed,
    Whispering new joys to the mild ocean,
Who now hath quite forgot to rave,
While birds of calm sit brooding on the charmed
    wave.

The stars, with deep amaze,
Stand fixed in steadfast gaze,
    Bending one way their precious influence,
And will not take their flight,
For all the morning light,
    Or Lucifer that often warned them thence;
But in their glimmering orbs did glow,
Until their Lord himself bespake and bid them go.

And though the shady gloom
Had given day her room,
    The sun himself withheld his wonted speed,
And hid his head for shame,
As his inferior flame
    The new-enlightened world no more should need:
He saw a greater Sun appear
Than his bright throne or burning axletree could
    bear.

The shepherds on the lawn,
Or ere the point of dawn,
    Sat simply chatting in a rustic row;

Full little thought they than,
That the mighty Pan
  Was kindly come to live with them below:
Perhaps their loves, or else their sheep,
Was all that did their silly thoughts so busy keep.

When such music sweet
Their hearts and ears did greet
  As never was by mortal finger strook,
Divinely-warbled voice
Answering the stringed noise,
  As all their souls in blissful rapture took:
The air, such pleasure loath to lose,
With thousand echoes still prolongs each heavenly
    close.

Nature that heard such sound
Beneath the hollow round
  Of Cynthia's seat the airy region thrilling,
Now was almost won
To think her part was done,
  And that her reign had here its last fulfilling:
She knew such harmony alone
Could hold all heaven and earth in happier union.

At last surrounds their sight
A globe of circular light,
  That with long beams the shamefaced night
    arrayed;
The helmed cherubim
And sworded seraphim
  Are seen in glittering ranks with wings displayed,
Harping in loud and solemn quire,
With unexpressive notes, to Heaven's new-born heir.

Such music (as 'tis said)
Before was never made,
  But when of old the sons of morning sung,
While the Creator great
His constellations set,
  And the well-balanced world on hinges hung,
And cast the dark foundations deep,
And bid the weltering waves their oozy channels
    keep.

Ring out, ye crystal spheres!
Once bless our human ears
  (If ye have power to touch our senses so),
And let your silver chime
Move in melodious time;
  And let the bass of heaven's deep organ blow;

And with your ninefold harmony
Make up full consort to the angelic symphony.

For if such holy song
Enwrap our fancy long,
  Time will run back and fetch the age of gold;
And speckled Vanity
Will sicken soon and die,
  And leprous Sin will melt from earthly mould;
And Hell itself will pass away,
And leave her dolorous mansions to the peering day.

Yea, Truth and Justice then
Will down return to men,
  Orbed in a rainbow; and, like glories wearing,
Mercy will sit between,
Throned in celestial sheen,
  With radiant feet the tissued clouds down steer-
    ing;
And Heaven, as at some festival,
Will open wide the gates of her high Palace Hall.

But wisest Fate says no,
This must not yet be so;
  The Babe yet lies in smiling infancy
That on the bitter cross
Must redeem our loss,
  So both himself and us to glorify:
Yet first, to those ychained in sleep,
The wakeful trump of doom must thunder through
    the deep,

With such a horrid clang
As on Mount Sinai rang,
  While the red fire and smouldering clouds out-
    brake:
The aged earth, aghast
With terror of that blast,
  Shall from the surface to the centre shake,
When at the world's last session,
The dreadful Judge in middle air shall spread his
    throne.

And then at last our bliss
Full and perfect is,
  But now begins; for from this happy day
The old Dragon under ground,
In straiter limits bound,
  Not half so far casts his usurped sway;

And wroth to see his kingdom fail,
Swinges the scaly horror of his folded tail.

The oracles are dumb;
No voice or hideous hum
    Runs through the arched roof in words deceiving.
Apollo from his shrine
Can no more divine,
    With hollow shriek the steep of Delphos leaving.
No nightly trance, or breathed spell,
Inspires the pale-eyed priest from the prophetic cell.

The lonely mountains o'er,
And the resounding shore,
    A voice of weeping heard and loud lament;
From haunted spring, and dale
Edged with poplar pale,
    The parting Genius is with sighing sent;
With flower-inwoven tresses torn,
The Nymphs in twilight shade of tangled thickets
    mourn.

In consecrated earth,
And on the holy hearth,
    The Lars and Lemures moan with midnight
        plaint;
In urns and altars round,
A drear and dying sound
    Affrights the flamens at their service quaint;
And the chill marble seems to sweat,
While each peculiar power forgoes his wonted seat.

Peor and Baalim
Forsake their temples dim,
    With that twice-battered god of Palestine;
And mooned Ashtaroth,
Heaven's queen and mother both,
    Now sits not girt with tapers' holy shine;
The Lybic Hammon shrinks his horn;
In vain the Tyrian maids their wounded Thammuz
    mourn.

And sullen Moloch, fled,
Hath left in shadows dread
    His burning idol all of blackest hue;
In vain with cymbals' ring
They call the grisly king,
    In dismal dance about the furnace blue;
The brutish gods of Nile, as fast,
Isis and Orus and the dog Anubis, haste.

Nor is Osiris seen
In Memphian grove or green,
    Trampling the unshowered grass with lowings
        loud;
Nor can he be at rest
Within his sacred chest;
    Naught but profoundest Hell can be his shroud;
In vain, with timbrelled anthems dark,
The sable-stoled sorcerers bear his worshipped ark.

He feels from Juda's land
The dreaded infant's hand;
    The rays of Bethlehem blind his dusky eyn;
Nor all the gods beside
Longer dare abide,
    Not Typhon huge ending in snaky twine:
Our Babe, to show his Godhead true,
Can in his swaddling bands control the damned
    crew.

So when the sun in bed,
Curtained with cloudy red,
    Pillows his chin upon an orient wave,
The flocking shadows pale
Troop to the infernal jail,
    Each fettered ghost slips to his several grave,
And the yellow-skirted fays
Fly after the night-steeds, leaving their moon-loved
    maze.

But see! the Virgin blest
Hath laid her Babe to rest.
    Time is our tedious song should here have end-
        ing:
Heaven's youngest-teemed star
Hath fixed her polished car,
    Her sleeping Lord with handmaid lamp attending;
And all about the courtly stable
Bright-harnessed angels sit in order serviceable.

CHRIST'S NATIVITY

Henry Vaughan

Awake, glad heart! get up and sing!
It is the birth-day of thy King.
    Awake! awake!

The sun doth shake
Light from his locks, and, all the way
Breathing perfumes, doth spice the day.

Awake, awake! hark how th' wood rings;
Winds whisper, and the busy springs
    A concert make;
    Awake! awake!
Man is their high-priest, and should rise
To offer up the sacrifice.

I would I were some bird, or star,
Flutt'ring in woods, or lifted far
    Above this inn
    And road of sin!
Then either star or bird should be
Shining or singing still to thee.

I would I had in my best part
Fit room for thee! or that my heart
    Were clean as
    Thy manger was!
But I am all filth, and obscene;
Yet, if thou wilt, thou canst make me clean.

Sweet Jesu! I will then. Let no more
This leper haunt and soil thy door!
    Cure him, ease him,
    O release him!
And let once more, by mystic birth,
The Lord of life be born in earth.

THE CHILD JESUS

Francis Quarles

Hail, blessèd Virgin, full of heavenly grace,
Blest above all that sprang from human race;
Whose heaven-saluted womb brought forth in one
A blessèd Saviour, and a blessèd son:
O! what a ravishment 't had been to see
Thy little Saviour perking on thy knee!
To see him nuzzle in thy virgin breast!
His milk-white body all unclad, undrest;
To see thy busy fingers clothe and wrap

His spradling limbs in thy indulgent lap!
To see his desperate eyes, with childish grace,
Smiling upon his smiling mother's face!
And, when his forward strength began to bloom,
To see him diddle up and down the room!
O, who would think so sweet a babe as this
Should e'er be slain by a false-hearted kiss!

A CHRISTMAS HYMN

Richard Watson Gilder

Tell me what is this innumerable throng
Singing in the heavens a loud angelic song?
    These are they who come with swift and shining
        feet
    From round about the throne of God the Lord of
        Light to greet.

O, who are these that hasten beneath the starry sky,
As if with joyful tidings that through the world shall
    fly?
    The faithful shepherds these, who greatly were
        afeared
    When, as they watched their flocks by night, the
        heavenly host appeared.

Who are these that follow across the hills of night
A star that westward hurries along the fields of light?
    Three wise men from the east who myrrh and
        treasure bring
    To lay them at the feet of him their Lord and
        Christ and King.

What babe new-born is this that in a manger cries?
    Near on her bed of pain his happy mother lies?
        O, see! the air is shaken with white and
            heavenly wings—
        This is the Lord of all the earth, this is the King
            of Kings.

Tell me, how may I join in this holy feast
With all the kneeling world, and I of all the least?
    Fear not, O faithful heart, but bring what most
        is meet:
    Bring love alone, true love alone, and lay it at his
        feet.

3. SONGS AND CAROLS

CHRISTMAS SONG

Bliss Carman

Above the weary waiting world,
Asleep in chill despair,
There breaks a sound of joyous bells
Upon the frosted air.
And o'er the humblest rooftree, lo,
A star is dancing on the snow.

What makes the yellow star to dance
Upon the brink of night?
What makes the breaking dawn to glow
So magically bright,—
And all the earth to be renewed
With infinite beatitude?

The singing bells, the throbbing star,
The sunbeams on the snow,
And the awakening heart that leaps
New ecstasy to know,—
They all are dancing in the morn
Because a little child is born.

A CAROL

Lizette Woodworth Reese

Joseph was an old man;
  Simple and tall was he,
Who went about in Bethlehem
  To find, if it might be,

A little space beneath a roof,
  For Jesus Christ to lie,
Safe, on His tender Mother's breast,
  Until the dark went by.

He asked of women; he asked of men;
  He asked of ox and ass,
All in a small and broken shed,
  Out in the village grass.

The women said nay; the men said nay;
  And nay the great inn said;
There was no otherwhere to go
  But that ramshackled shed.

A-many a wind about it blew;
  Its roof was withered and thin;
Oh, was that not a poor place
  To house Christ Jesus in?

A CHRISTMAS CAROL

Sara Teasdale

The kings, they came from the south,
  All dressed in ermine fine,
They bore Him gold and chrysoprase,
  And gifts of precious wine.

The shepherds came from out the north,
  Their coats were brown and old;
They brought Him little new-born lambs—
  They had not any gold.

The wise men came from out the east,
  And they were wrapped in white;
The star that led them all the way,
  Did glorify the night.

The angels came from Heaven high,
  And they were clad with wings,
And lo! they brought a joyful song
  The host of heaven sings.

The kings they knocked upon the door;
  The shepherds entered in;
The wise men followed after them,
  To hear the song begin.

The angels sang throughout the night,
  Until the rising sun,
But little Jesus fell asleep
  Before the song was done.

A CHRISTMAS CAROL

Algernon Charles Swinburne

Three damsels in the queen's chamber,
  The queen's mouth was most fair;
She spake a word of God's mother
  As the combs went in her hair.
    Mary that is of might,
    Bring us to thy Son's sight.

They held the gold combs out from her,
  A span's length off her head;
She sang the song of God's mother
  And of her bearing-bed.
    Mary most full of grace,
    Bring us to thy Son's face.

When she sat at Joseph's hand,
  She looked against her side;
And either way from the short silk band
  Her girdle was all wried.
    Mary that all good may,
    Bring us to thy Son's way.

Mary had three women for her bed,
  The twain were maidens clean;
The first of them had white and red,
  The third had riven green.
    Mary that is so sweet,
    Bring us to thy Son's feet.

She had three women for her hair,
  Two were gloved soft and shod;
The third had feet and fingers bare,
  She was the likest God.
    Mary that wieldeth land,
    Bring us to thy Son's hand.

She had three women for her ease,
  The twain were good women:
The first two were the two Maries,
  The third was Magdalen.
    Mary that perfect is,
    Bring us to thy Son's kiss.

Joseph had three workmen in his stall,
  To serve him well upon;
The first of them were Peter and Paul,
  The third of them was John.
    Mary, God's handmaiden,
    Bring us to thy Son's ken.

"If your child be none other man's,
  But if it be very mine,
The bedstead shall be gold two spans,
  The bedfoot silver fine."
    Mary that made God mirth,
    Bring us to thy Son's birth.

"If the child be some other man's,
  And if it be none of mine,
The manger shall be straw two spans,
  Betwixen kine and kine."
    Mary that made sin cease,
    Bring us to thy Son's peace.

Christ was born upon this wise,
  It fell on such a night,
Neither with sounds of psalteries,
  Nor with fire for light.
    Mary that is God's spouse,
    Bring us to thy Son's house.

The star came out upon the east
  With a great sound and sweet:
Kings gave gold to make him feast
  And myrrh for him to eat.
    Mary, of thy sweet mood,
    Bring us to thy Son's good.

He had two handmaids at his head,
  One handmaid at his feet;
The twain of them were fair and red,
  The third one was right sweet.
    Mary that is most wise,
    Bring us to thy Son's eyes. Amen.

Angels and archangels
  May have gathered there,
Cherubim and seraphim
  Thronged the air,
But only his mother
  In her maiden bliss
Worshipped the Beloved
  With a kiss.

What can I give Him,
  Poor as I am?
If I were a shepherd
  I would bring a lamb,
If I were a Wise Man,
  I would do my part,—
Yet what I can I give Him,
  Give my heart.

IN THE BLEAK MID-WINTER

Christina Rossetti

In the bleak mid-winter
  Frosty wind made moan,
Earth stood hard as iron,
  Water like a stone;
Snow had fallen, snow on snow,
  Snow on snow,
In the bleak mid-winter
  Long ago.

Our God, heaven cannot hold him,
  Nor earth sustain;
Heaven and earth shall flee away
  When he comes to reign:
In the bleak mid-winter
  A stable-place sufficed
The Lord God Almighty
  Jesus Christ.

Enough for him whom cherubim
  Worship night and day,
A breastful of milk
  And a mangerful of hay;
Enough for him whom angels
  Fall down before,
The ox and ass and camel
  Which adore.

CAROL

Norman Nicholson

Mary laid her Child among
  The bracken-fronds of night—
And by the glimmer round His head
  All the barn was lit.

Mary held her Child above
  The miry, frozen farm—
And by the fire within His limbs
  The resting roots were warm.

Mary hid her Child between
  Hillocks of hard sand—
By singing water in His veins
  Grass sprang from the ground.

Mary nursed her Child beside
  The gardens of a grave—
And by the death within His bones
  The dead became alive.

A CHRISTMAS CAROL

G. K. Chesterton

The Christ-child lay on Mary's lap,
  His hair was like a light.
(O weary, weary were the world,
  But here is all aright.)

The Christ-child lay on Mary's breast,
  His hair was like a star.

(O stern and cunning are the kings,
  But here the true hearts are.)

The Christ-child lay on Mary's heart,
  His hair was like a fire.
(O weary, weary is the world,
  But here the world's desire.)

The Christ-child stood at Mary's knee,
  His hair was like a crown,
And all the flowers looked up at Him,
  And all the stars looked down.

4. THE HUMBLE MEN OF EARTH . . .

"WHILE SHEPHERDS WATCHED THEIR FLOCKS BY NIGHT"

Margaret Deland

Like small curled feathers, white and soft,
  The little clouds went by,
Across the moon, and past the stars,
  And down the western sky:
In upland pastures, where the grass
  With frosted dew was white,
Like snowy clouds the young sheep lay,
  That first, best Christmas night.

The shepherds slept; and, glimmering faint,
  With twist of thin, blue smoke,
Only their fire's crackling flames
  The tender silence broke—
Save when a young lamb raised his head,
  Or, when the night wind blew,
A nesting bird would softly stir,
  Where dusky olives grew—

With finger on her solemn lip,
  Night hushed the shadowy earth,
And only stars and angels saw
  The little Saviour's birth;
Then came such flash of silver light
  Across the bending skies,
The wondering shepherds woke, and hid
  Their frightened, dazzled eyes!

And all their gentle sleepy flock
  Looked up, then slept again,
Nor knew the light that dimmed the stars
  Brought endless Peace to men—
Nor even heard the gracious words
  That down the ages ring—
"The Christ is born! the Lord has come,
  Good-will on earth to bring!"

Then o'er the moonlit, misty fields,
  Dumb with the world's great joy,
The shepherds sought the white-walled town,
  Where lay the baby boy—

And oh, the gladness of the world,
  The glory of the skies,
Because the longed-for Christ looked up
  In Mary's happy eyes!

THE SHEPHERDS

Samuel Taylor Coleridge

The shepherds went their hasty way,
  And found the lowly stable-shed,
Where the virgin-mother lay:
  And now they checked their eager tread,
For to the babe, that at her bosom clung,
A mother's song the virgin-mother sung.

They told her how a glorious light,
  Streaming from a heavenly throng,
Around them shone, suspending night,
  While, sweeter than a mother's song,
Blest angels heralded the Saviour's birth,
Glory to God on high! and peace on earth.

She listened to the tale divine,
  And closer still the babe she pressed;
And while she cried, "The babe is mine!"
  The milk rushed faster to her breast:
Joy rose within her, like a summer's morn;
Peace, peace on earth! the Prince of peace is born.

A CRADLE SONG

Padraic Colum

O, men from the fields!
Come gently within.
Tread softly, softly,
O! men coming in.

Mavourneen is going
From me and from you,
Where Mary will fold him
With mantle of blue!

From reek of the smoke
And cold of the floor,
And the peering of things
Across the half-door.

O, men from the fields!
Soft, softly come through—
Mary puts round him
Her mantle of blue.

OUTLANDERS,
WHENCE COME YE LAST?

William Morris

Outlanders, whence come ye last?
  The snow in the street and the wind on the door.
Through what green sea and great have ye passed?
  Minstrels and maids, stand forth on the floor.

From far away, O masters mine,
  The snow in the street and the wind on the door.
We come to bear you goodly wine:
  Minstrels and maids, stand forth on the floor.

From far away we come to you,
  The snow in the street and the wind on the door.
To tell of great tidings strange and true:
  Minstrels and maids, stand forth on the floor.

News, news of the Trinity,
  The snow in the street and the wind on the door.
And Mary and Joseph from over the sea:
  Minstrels and maids, stand forth on the floor.

For as we wandered far and wide,
  The snow in the street and the wind on the door.

What hap do ye deem there should us betide?
  Minstrels and maids, stand forth on the floor.

Under a bent when the night was deep,
  The snow in the street and the wind on the door.
There lay three shepherds tending their sheep:
  Minstrels and maids, stand forth on the floor.

"O ye shepherds, what have ye seen,
  The snow in the street and the wind on the door.
To slay your sorrow and heal your teen?"
  Minstrels and maids, stand forth on the floor.

"In an ox-stall this night we saw,
  The snow in the street and the wind on the door.
A Babe and a maid without a flaw."
  Minstrels and maids, stand forth on the floor.

"There was an old man there beside,
  The snow in the street and the wind on the door.
His hair was white and his hood was wide."
  Minstrels and maids, stand forth on the floor.

"And as we gazed this thing upon,
  The snow in the street and the wind on the door.
Those twain knelt down to the Little One."
  Minstrels and maids, stand forth on the floor.

"And a marvellous song we straight did hear,
  The snow in the street and the wind on the door.
That slew our sorrow and healed our care."
  Minstrels and maids, stand forth on the floor.

News of a fair and a marvellous thing,
  The snow in the street and the wind on the door.
Nowell, nowell, nowell, we sing!
  Minstrels and maids, stand forth on the floor.

THE SONG OF A SHEPHERD-BOY AT BETHLEHEM

Josephine Preston Peabody

Sleep, Thou little Child of Mary:
  Rest Thee now.
Though these hands be rough from shearing
  And the plough,
Yet they shall not ever fail Thee,
When the waiting nations hail Thee,
  Bringing palms unto their King.
  Now—I sing.

Sleep, Thou little Child of Mary,
  Hope divine,
If Thou wilt but smile upon me,
  I will twine
Blossoms for Thy garlanding.
Thou'rt so little to be King,
  God's Desire!
  Not a brier
Shall be left to grieve Thy brow;
  Rest Thee now.

Sleep, Thou little Child of Mary.
  Some fair day
Wilt Thou, as Thou wert a brother,
  Come away
Over hills and over hollow?
All the lambs will up and follow,
  Follow but for love of Thee.
  Lov'st Thou me?

Sleep, Thou little Child of Mary;
  Rest Thee now.
I that watch am come from sheep-stead
  And from plough.
Thou wilt have disdain of me
When Thou'rt lifted, royally,
  Very high for all to see:
  Smilest Thou?

5. . . . AND THE MIGHTY

THE THREE KINGS OF COLOGNE

Eugene Field

From out Cologne there came three kings
  To worship Jesus Christ, their King.
To Him they sought fine herbs they brought,
  And many a beauteous golden thing;
They brought their gifts to Bethlehem town,
And in that manger set them down.

Then spake the first king, and he said:
  "O Child, most heavenly, bright, and fair!
I bring this crown to Bethlehem town
  For Thee, and only Thee, to wear;
  So give a heavenly crown to me
When I shall come at last to Thee!"

The second, then. "I bring Thee here
  This royal robe, O Child!" he cried;
"Of silk 'tis spun, and such an one
  There is not in the world beside;
  So in the day of doom requite
Me with a heavenly robe of white."

The third king gave his gift, and quoth:
  "Spikenard and myrrh to Thee I bring,
And with these twain would I most fain
  Anoint the body of my King;
  So may their incense sometime rise
To plead for me in yonder skies!"

Thus spake the three kings of Cologne,
  That gave their gifts and went away;
And now kneel I in prayer hard by
  The cradle of the Child today;
  Nor crown, nor robe, nor spice I bring
As offering unto Christ, my King.

Yet have I brought a gift the Child
  May not despise, however small;
For here I lay my heart today,
  And it is full of love to all.
Take Thou the poor but loyal thing,
My only tribute, Christ, my King!

JOURNEY OF THE MAGI

T. S. Eliot

A cold coming we had of it,
Just the worst time of the year
For a journey, and such a long journey:
The ways were deep and the weather sharp,
The very dead of winter.
And the camels galled, sore-footed, refractory,
Lying down in the melted snow.
There were times we regretted
The summer palaces on slopes, the terraces,
And the silken girls bringing sherbet.
Then the camel men cursing and grumbling
And running away, and wanting their liquor and
    women,
And the night-fires going out, and the lack of shelters,
And the cities hostile and the towns unfriendly
And the villages dirty and charging high prices:
A hard time we had of it.
At the end we preferred to travel all night,
Sleeping in snatches,
With the voices singing in our ears, saying
That this was all folly.

Then at dawn we came down to a temperate valley,
Wet, below the snow line, smelling of vegetation;
With a running stream and a water-mill beating the
    darkness,
And three trees on the low sky,
And an old white horse galloped away in the
    meadow.
Then we came to a tavern with vine-leaves over the
    lintel,
Six hands at an open door dicing for pieces of silver,
And feet kicking the empty wine-skins.
But there was no information, and so we continued
And arrived at evening, not a moment too soon
Finding the place; it was (you may say) satisfactory.

All this was a long time ago, I remember,
And I would do it again, but set down
This set down
This: were we led all that way for
Birth or Death? There was a Birth, certainly,
We had evidence and no doubt. I had seen birth and
    death,
But had thought they were different; this Birth was
Hard and bitter agony for us, like Death, our death.
We returned to our places, these Kingdoms,
But no longer at ease here, in the old dispensation,
With an alien people clutching their gods.
I should be glad of another death.

And he beheld
The landscape like an empire and found in
Even a sycamore leaf the plan of his domain.
And he offered the gold of his sight
The regimen of his thought
To the Child born that night.

A King stepped out of my breast
Who had the bearing of a priest.
To him the moon's movement
Was a sacrament,
And the taste of water and of wine,
The touch of bread and the weight of a stone.
And he offered the frankincense of the heart,
Prayer swung in the censer on the charcoal alight,
To the Child born that night.

A King stepped out of my loins,
And black as grapes were his skin and his veins.
In him was the anger of sex
Where the blood like a sea on the shingle breaks,
The pride of living, the longing for further birth
Because of the presentiment of death.
And he offered the myrrh of tiredness, the untight'n-
    ing of the fingers from the nerve's root
To the Child born that night.

Three Kings stepped out of my body
But only my two eyes between the three—
Only my two eyes and the wild skies to see.

POEM FOR EPIPHANY

Norman Nicholson

Three Kings stepped out of my body,
Walked across the sand by the wild sea
From December into January.

A King stepped out of my head,
And before him the sand was red
And the sea gold,

THE GIFT

Laura Spencer Portor

Caspar, Melchior, Balthazar,
These are they who followed the star.

Myrrh, and incense, gems and gold,
These are the gifts they brought of old;—

THE STORY OF JESUS

These are the precious wonderful things
They brought, as befitting three wise Kings.

The humble Shepherds were quite too poor
To lay such gifts on the stable floor;

But one left his cloak, and mittens; another
His shepherd's crook and cap; and his brother,

Who had carried a lamb across the wild,
Left that as gift for the Holy Child.

Oh, Mary might better have liked a gem—
(For the best of women are fond of them)—

And Joseph no doubt the gold approved;—
'Tis a thing men's hearts have always loved;

These things I suspect;—but sure I am
The Little Lord Christ preferred the lamb.

THE VIGIL OF JOSEPH

Elsa Barker

After the Wise Men went, and the strange star
Had faded out, Joseph the father sat
Watching the sleeping Mother and the Babe,
And thinking stern, sweet thoughts the long night
    through.

"Ah, what am I, that God has chosen me
To bear this blessed burden, to endure
Daily the presence of this loveliness,
To guide this Glory that shall guide the world?

"Brawny these arms to win Him bread, and broad
This bosom to sustain Her. But my heart
Quivers in lonely pain before that Beauty
It loves—and serves—and cannot understand!"

6. . . . *JOIN WITH NATURE AND HER CREATURES*
TO HAIL HIM

THE SNOW

Joseph Beaumont

His softest feathers winter thither sent
  To be a pillow for the infant's head;
For sure no harm the honest season meant
When in the cave his fluttering snow he spread:
  But at his presence into tears it fell,
  Checked by a whiter, chaster spectacle.

THE GLORY OF THE GRASS

Claire Wallace Flynn

"And she brought forth her first-born son, and wrapped
him in swaddling clothes, and laid him in a manger. . . ."
               LUKE 2:7

In what far, Judean field
Did these upgrowing grasses yield

Their promises of gentle strength
When they should cradle Him at length?

What secret grace did earth produce,
That made those grasses for His use?
What glory from the sun they drew,
And what of pity from the dew?

What lad with sudden singing heart,
From all the other lads apart,
Cut them and bound them in the sun
And went his way—his work all done?

What tender girl, dark-haired and brown,
Carried the sheaves into the town;
Nor felt the weight of all that load
Along the narrow, hilly road?

And then the night, when Mary's face
Grew pallid in that lowly place,
Who filled the manger, made the bed,
Where only dumb beasts long had fed?

The humblest thing that grows on earth,
You gave Him comfort at His birth,
And kept Him warm, and made a nest,
Wherein His tiny limbs might rest!

Still with strange blindness have we trod
Amongst the common fields of God,
Seeing but dimly as we pass
The ancient glory of the grass!

THE WINDS AT BETHLEHEM

W. M. Letts

When Jesus lay on Mary's knee
    There was no wind nor breeze that stirred,
For Heaven then made minstrelsy
    And all the earth in silence heard.

There was no wind on sea or land,
    No boisterous gale blew loud and wild,
The four great winds came hand in hand
    And stood about the Holy Child.

The four great winds, their pinions furled.
    Came softly in with humble tread;
They saw the Maker of the World
    Upon His lowly manger bed.

The South wind looked with radiant eyes
    Upon this King so small and sweet;
He softly sang Him lullabies
    And knelt adoring at His feet.

The West wind like a shepherd clad
    Had brought his pastoral pipes to play;
He piped his music wild and glad
    Until the shadows fled away.

The North wind bowed and knelt him down
    To gaze upon this sight so fair;
He gave the Babe the frosty crown
    That lay upon his tangled hair.

Before that shrine the East wind bent,
    He had strange gifts beyond all price,
Of gold and gems of Orient
    And gums and frankincense and spice.

There was no wind on sea or land,
    But round about the manger bed
The four great winds stood hand in hand
    And worshipped there with wings outspread.

THE OXEN

Thomas Hardy

Christmas Eve, and twelve of the clock.
"Now they are all on their knees,"
An elder said as we sat in a flock
By the embers in hearthside ease.

We pictured the meek, mild creatures where
They dwelt in their strawy pen.
Nor did it occur to one of us there
To doubt they were kneeling then.

So fair a fancy few would weave
In these years! Yet, I feel,

If someone said on Christmas Eve,
"Come, see the oxen kneel

"In the lonely barton by yonder coomb
Our childhood used to know,"
I should go with him in the gloom
Hoping it might be so.

A CHRISTMAS FOLK-SONG

Lizette Woodworth Reese

The Little Jesus came to town;
The wind blew up, the wind blew down;
Out in the street the wind was bold;
Now who would house Him from the cold?

Then opened wide a stable door,
Fair were the rushes on the floor;
The Ox put forth a hornèd head;
"Come, little Lord, here make Thy bed."

Uprose the Sheep were folded near;
"Thou Lamb of God, come, enter here."
He entered there to rush and reed,
Who was the Lamb of God indeed.

The little Jesus came to town;
With ox and sheep He laid Him down;
Peace to the byre, peace to the fold,
For that they housed Him from the cold!

THE LITTLE CHRISTMAS DONKEY

Geraldine Farrar

Great Herod on his golden throne
    Did in his wrath and fear
Decree that every tiny babe
    Should perish far and near.

Sweet Mary's gentle heart stood still,
    Oppressed by such a plight;

But God's bright angel came to her
    And counselled secret flight.

The little donkey stood close by.
    His soft eyes seemed to say:
"O trust in me, and have no fear,
    For I will lead the way."

Then gently on his furry back,
    Was cradled Mary sweet;
And so she rode to music
    Of the little donkey's feet.

He plodded o'er the desert sand,
    And bravely made his way,
Until before an inn they stopped,
    To ask if they might stay.

Alas, the inn was crowded full!
    There was no room at all,
Save in the lowly stable there,
    Beside the oxen stall.

Sweet Mary sank upon the straw,
    And lo! a wondrous sight!
For as the Holy Child was born,
    The world grew dazzling bright.

The splendid wings of angels
    Did brush the sleeping earth,
Their joyous carols telling
    The news of Jesus' birth.

One shining star shone out above,
    And in its silver ray,
The little donkey also kneeled
    On this first Christmas day.

And there he lay beside the Child;
    His feet were sore and worn;
Yet never counted he the pain,
    The burden he had borne.

His was a true if humble way
    To give his very best.
He did his nearest duty,
    And to God left all the rest.

So, little children, when you see him,
    Patient, with good will,
Remember how he served our Lord,
    And *never* use him ill.

7. PERIL AND FLIGHT

HEROD'S SUSPICIONS

Richard Crashaw

Why art thou troubled, Herod? what vain fear
  Thy blood-revolving breast to rage doth move?
Heaven's King, who doffs himself weak flesh to
    wear,
  Comes not to rule in wrath, but serve in love;
Nor would he this thy feared crown from thee tear,
  But give thee a better with himself above.
    Poor jealousy! why should he wish to prey
    Upon thy crown, who gives his own away?

Make to thy reason, man, and mock thy doubts;
  Look how below thy fears their causes are;
Thou art a soldier, Herod; send thy scouts,
  See how he's furnished for so feared a war.
What armour does he wear? A few thin clouts.
  His trumpets? tender cries. His men, to dare
    So much? rude shepherds. What his steeds? alas,
    Poor beasts! a slow ox and a simple ass.

THE INNOCENTS

Elinor Wylie

When the cock in the dish
Crew "Christus natus est!"
I saddled a wish
And rode from the west.

The ditches were piled
With young children dying:
I saw Herod's child
In a gold cradle lying.

At high white noon
In a tower turned south;
A silver spoon
Was in the child's mouth.

It was bright as a candle
And heavy as lead:
Carved on the handle
Was John Baptist's head.

I climbed like a cat;
I stole the metal;
I hammered it flat
To a silver petal.

I curled the leaf
To a silver bell
To echo the grief
Of Israel.

The dead were dumb
But it spoke for them:
By night I was come
To Bethlehem.

Mary's mantle
Covered the Christ:
With myrrh and santal
His hair was spiced.

I kissed the ground
Where the gold was tossed:
The bell made a sound
Like a young child lost.

"This bell is a bird
Or a shaken bud;
It speaks a word
The colour of blood.

"This bell is a cup
Or a thorny cap . . ."
The Christ sat up
In Mary's lap.

"O take this bell
And stifle its breath,
For Israel
Is tired of death.

"When Herod's boy
Lies broken and dying,
Give him this toy
To quiet his crying."

THE SPHINX:
LE REPOS EN EGYPTE

Agnes Repplier

All day I watch the stretch of burning sand;
  All night I brood beneath the golden stars;
Amid the silence of a desolate land,
  No touch of bitterness my reverie mars.
Built by the proudest of a kingly line,
  Over my head the centuries fly fast;
The secrets of the mighty dead are mine;
  I hold the key of a forgotten past.
Yet, ever hushed into a rapturous dream,
  I see again that night. A halo mild
Shone from the liquid moon. Beneath her beam
  Traveled a tired young Mother and the Child.

Within mine arms she slumbered, and alone
  I watched the Infant. At my feet her guide
Lay stretched o'er-wearied. On my breast of stone
  Rested the Crucified.

THE INCARNATION

Giles Fletcher

A child He was, and had not learned to speak,
That with His word the world before did make;
His mother's arms Him bore, He was so weak,
That with one hand the vaults of Heav'n could shake.
See how small room my infant Lord did take,
  Whom all the world is not enough to hold,
  Who of His years, or of His age hath told?
Never such age so young, never a child so old.
And yet but newly He was infanted,
And yet already He was sought to die;
Yet scarcely born, already banished;
Not able yet to go, and forced to fly:
But scarcely fled away, when by and by
  The tyrant's sword with blood is all defil'd,
  And Rachel for her sons, with fury wild,
Cries, "O thou cruel king, and O my sweetest child!"

Egypt His nurse became, where Nilus springs,
Who straight, to entertain the rising sun,
The hasty harvest in his bosom brings:
But now for drought the fields were all undone,
And now with waters all is overrun:
  So fast the Cynthian mountains pour'd their snow
  When once they felt the sun so near them glow
That Nilus Egypt lost, and to a sea did grow.
The angels caroll'd loud their song of peace,
The cursèd oracles were strucken dumb;
To see their Shepherd the poor shepherds press,
To see their King the kingly sophies come;
And them to guide unto his Master's home,
  A star comes dancing up the Orient,
  That springs for joy over the strawy tent,
Where gold, to make their Prince a crown, they all
  present.

OUT OF EGYPT
HAVE I CALLED MY SON

Caroline Hazard

The mighty river flows as when Thine eyes
  Thy baby eyes, in wonder saw it flow.
  The Pyramids stand there; no one may know
Their countless years, or ancient builders wise;
Thy childish gaze was caught in glad surprise

To see the haughty camels come and go;
The ass thy mother rode still ambles slow;

Unmoved by centuries the country lies.
Up from the calm, the peace, the mystic land,
  Back to the scene of conflict and of strife,
  Thy parents journeyed at the Lord's command.
A touch of glory rests upon the place
  Which gave its shelter to Thine infant grace,
  And nourished Thee to be the Life of Life.

8. THE MEANING OF CHRIST'S COMING

NO SUDDEN THING OF GLORY

Alice Meynell

No sudden thing of glory and fear
Was the Lord's coming; but the dear
  Slow nature's days followed each other
  To form the Saviour from his mother—
One of the children of the year.

The earth, the rain, received the trust,—
The sun and dews, to frame the Just.
  He drew his daily life from these
  According to his own decrees,
Who makes man from the fertile dust.

Sweet summer and the winter wild,
These brought him forth, the Undefiled.
  The happy springs renewed again
  His daily bread, the growing grain,
The food and raiment of the child.

CHRISTMAS TREES

Violet Alleyn Storey

I saw along each noisy city street
The trees for Christmas, standing dark and still,
The pines and firs come down from field and hill,
Old trees and young that had known sun and sleet.

Soft needles fell on hard, dull pavement there,
And forest rose in a most treeless place;
And there was gladness in each passing face,
And there was balsam fragrance everywhere.

O, lovely way to celebrate Your Birth
Whose Birth Star glistened through Judea's trees;
Whom Joseph taught the skilful use of these;
Who, on a Tree, once overcame the earth!

Grant then Your blessing, Friend of Trees, we pray,
On those who deck green boughs for Christmas Day!

[23]

CHRISTMAS NIGHT

Alice Meynell

"If I cannot see thee present I will mourn thee absent, for this also is a proof of love."

THOMAS à KEMPIS

We do not find Him on the difficult earth,
  In surging human-kind,
In wayside death or accidental birth,
  Or in the "march of mind."

Nature, her nests, her prey, the fed, the caught,
  Hide Him so well, so well,
His steadfast secret there seems to our thought
  Life's saddest miracle.

He's but conjectured in man's happiness,
  Suspected in man's tears,
Or lurks beyond the long, discouraged guess,
  Grown fainter through the years.

But absent, absent now? Ah, what is this,
  Near as in child-birth bed,
Laid on our sorrowful hearts, close to a kiss?
  A homeless childish head.

THE BURNING BABE

Robert Southwell

As I in hoary winter's night
  Stood shivering in the snow,
Surprised I was with sudden heat
  Which made my heart to glow;
And lifting up a fearful eye
  To view what fire was near,
A pretty babe all burning bright
  Did in the air appear:
Who, scorchèd with excessive heat,
  Such floods of tears did shed
As though His floods would quench His flames
  With which His tears were bred:

"Alas!" quoth He, "but newly born
  In fiery heats I fry,
Yet none approach to warm their hearts
  Or feel my fire but I.

"My faultless breast the furnace is;
  The fuel wounding thorns;
Love is the fire, and sighs the smoke;
  The ashes, shames and scorns;
The fuel Justice layeth on,
  And Mercy blows the coals,
The metal in this furnace wrought
  Are men's defilèd souls:
For which, as now on fire I am
  To work them for their good,
So will I melt into a bath,
  To wash them in my blood."
With this He vanish'd out of sight
  And swiftly shrunk away,
And straight I callèd unto mind
  That it was Christmas Day.

NEW PRINCE, NEW POMP

Robert Southwell

Behold a little, tender Babe,
  In freezing winter night,
In homely manger trembling lies;
  Alas! a piteous sight.
The inns are full; no man will yield
  This little Pilgrim bed;
But forced He is with silly beasts
  In crib to shroud His head.

Weigh not His crib, His wooden dish,
  Nor beasts that by Him feed;
Weigh not His mother's poor attire,
  Nor Joseph's simple weed.
This stable is a Prince's court,
  This crib His chair of state;
The beasts are parcel of His pomp,
  The wooden dish His plate.

The persons in that poor attire
His royal liv'ries wear;
The Prince Himself is come from Heav'n;
This pomp is praised there.
With joy approach, O Christian wight!
Do homage to thy King;
And highly praise this humble pomp,
Which He from Heav'n doth bring.

Yet on the road thy wheels are not,
  Nor on the seas thy sail!

My fancied ways why shouldst thou heed?
  Thou com'st down thine own secret stair;
Com'st down to answer all my need,
  Yea, every bygone prayer!

AVE MARIA GRATIA PLENA

Oscar Wilde

Was this His coming! I had hoped to see
A scene of wondrous glory, as was told
Of some great god who in a rain of gold
Broke open bars and fell on Danaë:
Or a dread vision as when Semele,
Sickening for love and unappeased desire,
Prayed to see God's clear body, and the fire
Caught her brown limbs and slew her utterly.
With such glad dreams I sought this holy place,
And now with wondering eyes and heart I stand
Before this supreme mystery of Love:
Some kneeling girl with passionless pale face,
An angel with a lily in his hand,
And over both the white wings of a Dove.

THAT HOLY THING

George MacDonald

They all were looking for a king
  To slay their foes and lift them high,
Thou cam'st, a little baby thing
  That made a woman cry.

O son of man, to right my lot
  Nought but thy presence can avail;

THE CONSECRATION
OF THE COMMON WAY

Edwin Markham

The hills that had been lone and lean
Were pricking with a tender green,
And flocks were whitening over them
From all the folds of Bethlehem.

The King of Heaven had come our way,
And in a lowly stable lay:
He had descended from the sky
In answer to the world's long cry—
Descended in a lyric burst
Of high archangels, going first
Unto the lowest and the least,
To humble bird and weary beast.
His palace was a wayside shed,
A battered manger was his bed:
An ox and ass with breathings deep
Made warm the chamber of his sleep.

Three sparrows with a friendly sound
Were picking barley from the ground:
An early sunbeam, long and thin,
Slanted across the dark within,
And brightened in its silver fall
A cart-wheel leaning to the wall.
An ox-yoke hung upon a hook:
A worn plow with a clumsy crook
Was lying idly by the wheel.
And everywhere there was the feel
Of that sweet peace that labor brings —
The peace that dwells with homely things.

Now have the homely things been made
Sacred, and a glory on them laid.
For He whose shelter was a stall,
The King, was born among them all.
He came to handle saw and plane,
To use and hallow the profane:
Now is the holy not afar
In temples lighted by a star,
But where the loves and labors are.
Now that the King has gone this way,
Great are the things of every day!

A paper wreath; a day at home for me.
The merry bells ring out, the people kneel;
Up goes the man of God before the crowd;
With voice of honey and with eyes of steel
He drones your humble gospel to the proud.
Nobody listens. Less than the wind that blows
Are all your words to us you died to save.
O Prince of Peace! O Sharon's dewy Rose!
How mute you lie within your vaulted grave.
  The stone the angel rolled away with tears
  Is back upon your mouth these thousand years.

HOW CAN THEY HONOR HIM?

Anderson M. Scruggs

How can they honor Him—the humble lad
  Whose feet struck paths of beauty through the
    earth—
With all the drunken revelry, the mad
  Barter of goods that marks His day of birth?
How can they honor Him with flame and din,
  Whose soul was peaceful as a moon-swept sea,
Whose thoughts were somber with the world's great
    sin
  Even while He trod the hill to Calvary?

I think if Jesus should return and see
  This hollow blasphemy, this day of horror,
The heart that languished in Gethsemane
  Would know again as great and deep a sorrow,
And He who charmed the troubled waves to sleep
With deathless words—would kneel again and weep.

TO JESUS ON HIS BIRTHDAY

Edna St. Vincent Millay

For this your mother sweated in the cold,
For this you bled upon the bitter tree:
A yard of tinsel ribbon bought and sold;

GUESTS *

Anonymous

Yet if his majesty, our sovereign lord,
  Should of his own accord
  Friendly himself invite,
And say, "I'll be your guest to-morrow night,"
How should we stir ourselves, call and command
All hands to work! "Let no man idle stand!

"Set me fine Spanish tables in the hall;
  See they be fitted all;
  Let there be room to eat
And order taken that there want no meat.
See every sconce and candlestick made bright,
That without tapers they may give a light.

"Look to the presence: are the carpets spread,
  The dazie o'er the head,
  The cushions in the chairs,
And all the candles lighted on the stairs?
Perfume the chambers, and in any case
Let each man give attendance in his place!"

Thus, if the king were coming would we do;
  And 'twere good reason too;
  For 'tis a duteous thing
To show all honor to an earthly king,
And after all our travail and our cost,
So he be pleased, to think no labor lost.

* Probably before 1625.

But at the coming of the King of Heaven
  All's set at six and seven:
  We wallow in our sin.
Christ cannot find a chamber in the inn.
We entertain him always like a stranger,
And, as at first, still lodge him in the manger.

From HELLAS

Percy Bysshe Shelley

A power from the unknown God,
  A Promethean conqueror, came;
Like a triumphal path he trod
  The thorns of death and shame.
  A mortal shape to him
  Was like the vapor dim
Which the orient planet animates with light;
  Hell, Sin, and Slavery came,
  Like bloodhounds mild and tame,
Nor preyed, until their Lord had taken flight;
  The moon of Mahomet
  Arose, and it shall set:
While blazoned as on Heaven's immortal noon
  The cross leads generations on.

Swift as the radiant shapes of sleep
  From one whose dreams are Paradise
Fly, when the fond wretch wakes to weep,
  And Day peers forth with her blank eyes;
  So fleet, so faint, so fair,
  The Powers of earth and air

Fled from the folding-star of Bethlehem:
  Apollo, Pan, and Love,
  And even Olympian Jove
Grow weak, for killing Truth had glared on them:
  Our hills and seas and streams,
  Dispeopled of their dreams.
Their waters turned to blood, their dew to tears,
  Wailed for the golden years.

UNTO US A SON IS GIVEN

Alice Meynell

Given, not lent,
And not withdrawn—once sent,
This Infant of mankind, this One,
Is still the little welcome Son.

New every year,
New born and newly dear,
He comes with tidings and a song,
The ages long, the ages long;

Even as the cold
Keen winter grows not old,
As childhood is so fresh, foreseen,
And spring in the familiar green.

Sudden as sweet
Come the expected feet.
All joy is young, and new all art,
And He, too, Whom we have by heart.

9. LOOKING BACKWARD

AFTER CHRISTMAS
A LANDLORD REMEMBERS

Elizabeth Coatsworth

All day my wife, the maids, the men
And I ran to and fro,
What had been done we did again,
We served both high and low.

At last we lay in weary beds,
Then boomed a staff on door,
"O Landlord, here's a desperate head!"
The inn could hold no more.

He took her to the stable near,
I woke before the day,
For with her cry our cock crowed clear,
The little ass did bray.

There seemed to come a sound of song,
I could not get to sleep,
And then the shepherds came along
And brought their bleating sheep.

That meant more runnings to and fro,
More things to eat and drink,
The work was hard, the pay was low,
We had no time to drink.

With beasts rejoicing, peering swains,
Guests calling, new-born boys,
It was enough to turn our brains
Run-running through the noise.

Then came the kings with camels, too,
And horses white as milk,
And all their gorgeous retinue
Clad in brocades and silk.

The star that troubled us by night
Had led them all the way.
We worked like mad, but it was right—
At least the kings would pay.

All's past, we've time to take our ease
And try to figure out
Why our old ox fell to his knees
And what it was about.

She looked like any maid at all
Brought to her labor here,
But there's gold buried near the wall
And the beasts still act queer.

THE MAID-SERVANT AT THE INN

Dorothy Parker

"It's queer," she said, "I see the light
    As plain as I beheld it then,
All silver-like and calm and bright—
    We've not had stars like that again!

"And she was such a gentle thing
    To birth a baby in the cold.
The barn was dark and frightening—
    This new one's better than the old.

"I mind my eyes were full of tears,
　For I was young, and quick distressed,
But she was less than me in years
　That held a son against her breast.

"I never saw a sweeter child—
　The little one, the darling one!—

I mind I told her, when he smiled
　You'd know he was his mother's son.

"It's queer that I should see them so—
　The time they came to Bethlehem
Was more than thirty years ago;
　I've prayed that all is well with them."

10. TWO CHRISTMAS STORIES

THE WELL OF THE STAR

Elizabeth Goudge

On the road to Bethlehem there is a well called the Well of the Star. The legend goes that the three Wise Men, on their journey to the Manger, lost sight of the star that was guiding them. Pausing to water their camels at the well they found it again reflected in the water.

David sat cross-legged by himself in a corner of the room, separated from the other children, clasping his curly toes in his lean brown hands, and wished he were a rich man, grown-up and strong, with bags full of gold and thousands of camels and tens of thousands of sheep. But he was not rich, he was only a diminutive, ragged, shepherd boy who possessed nothing in the world except the shepherd's pipe slung round his neck, his little pipe upon which he played to himself or the sheep all day long and which was as dear to him as life itself.

At the moment he was very miserable. Sighing, he lifted his hands and placed them on his stomach, pushing it inward and noting the deflation with considerable concern. How soon would he be dead of hunger? How soon would they all be dead of hunger, and safely at rest in Abraham's bosom? It was a very

nice place, he had no doubt, and suitable to grandparents and people of that type, who were tired by a long life and quite ready to be gathered to their fathers, but hardly the place for a little boy who had lived for only a few short years in this world, who had seen only a few springs painting the bare hills purple and scarlet with the anemone flowers, only a few high summer suns wheeling majestically through the burning heavens.

If only it were summer now, instead of a cold night in mid-winter! If only mother would light a fire for them to warm themselves by, a bright fire that would paint the walls of the dark little one-roomed house orange and rose color, and chase away the frightening shadows. But there was no light in the room except the flickering, dying flame that came from a little lamp, fast burning up the last of their oil, set on the earth floor close to his mother, where she sat crouched beside her sick husband, swaying herself ceaselessly from side to side, abandoned to her grief and oblivious of the wails of four little cold and hungry children, younger than David, who lay all together on their matting bed.

If only he were a rich man, thought David, then it would not matter that storms had destroyed the barley, that their vines had failed, or that their father, the carpenter of this tiny village on a hill top, could no longer ply his trade. Nothing would matter if he were a rich man and could buy food and wine and oil and healing salves; they would be happy then, with food in their stomachs, their father well, and comforting light in this horrible darkness of mid-winter.

How could he be a rich man?

Suddenly there came to David's mind the thought of the wishing well far down below on the road to Bethlehem. It was a well of clear sparkling water, and it was said that those who stood by it at midnight, and prayed to the Lord God Jehovah from a pure heart, were given their heart's desire. The difficulty, of course, was to *be* pure in heart. They said that if you were, and your prayer had been accepted, you saw your heart's desire mirrored in the water of the well; the face of someone you loved, maybe, or the gold that would save your home from ruin, or even, so it was whispered, the face of God himself. . . . But no one of David's acquaintance had ever seen anything, though they had visited and prayed time and again.

Nevertheless he jumped up and crept noiselessly through the shadows to the door. He had no idea whether his heart was pure or no, but he would give it the benefit of the doubt and go down to the well. He pulled open the door and slipped out into the great cold silent night.

And instantly he was terribly afraid. All around him the bare hills lay beneath the starlight in an awful, waiting, attentive loneliness, and far down below the terraces of olive trees were drowned in pitch-black shadow. But the sky was streaming with light, so jeweled with myriads of blazing stars that it seemed the weight of them would make the sky fall down and crush the waiting earth to atoms. The loneliness, the darkness, the cold and that great sky above, turned David's heart to water and made his knees shake under him. He had never been out by himself so late at night before, and he had not got the courage, hungry and cold as he was, to go down over the lonely hills and through the darkness of the olive trees to the white road below where they said that robbers lurked, wild sheep stealers and murderers who would cut your throat as soon as look at you just for the fun of it.

Then he bethought him that just over the brow of a near-by hill a flock of sheep were folded, and their shepherds with them. His own cousin Eli, who was teaching David to be a shepherd, would be with them, and Eli would surely be willing to leave the sheep to the other shepherds for a short time and go with David to the well. . . . At least David would ask him to.

He set off running, a little flitting shadow beneath the stars, and he ran hard because he was afraid. . . . For surely, he thought, there was something very strange about this night. . . . The earth lay so still, waiting for something, and overhead that great sky was palpitating and ablaze with triumph. Several times, as he ran, he could have sworn he heard triumphant voices crying, "Glory to God! Glory to God!" as though the hills themselves were singing, and a rushing sound as though great wings were beating over his head. Yet when he stopped to listen there was nothing, only the frail echo of a shepherd's pipe and a whisper of wind over the hills.

He was glad when he saw in front of him the rocky hillock behind which the sheep were folded. "Eli!" he cried, giving a hop, skip and a jump, "Are you there? Jacob? Tobias? It's David."

But there was no answering call from the friendly shepherds, though there was a soft bleating from the sheep, only that strange stillness with its undercurrent of triumphant music that was heard and yet not heard. With a beating heart he bounded round the corner and came out in the little hollow in the hills that was the sheepfold, his eyes straining through the darkness to make out the figures of his friends.

But they were not there; no one was there except a tall, cloaked stranger who sat upon a rock among the sheep leaning on a shepherd's crook. . . . And the sheep, who knew their own shepherds and would fly in fear from a stranger whose voice they did not know, were gathered closely about him in confidence and love. . . . David halted in blank astonishment.

"Good evening to you," said the stranger pleasantly. "It's a fine night."

David advanced with caution, rubbing his nose in perplexity. Who was this stranger? The sheep seemed to know him, and he seemed to know David, yet David knew no man with so straight a back and so grand a head or such a deep, ringing, beautiful voice. This was a very great man, without doubt; a soldier, perhaps, but no shepherd.

"Good evening," said David politely, edging a little closer. "'Tis a fine evening, but cold about the legs."

"Is it? Then come under my cloak," said the stranger, lifting it so that it suddenly seemed to spread about him like great wings, and David, all his fear suddenly evaporated, scuttled forward and found himself gathered in against the stranger's side, under the stranger's cloak, warm and protected and sublimely happy.

"But where are the others?" he asked. "Eli and Jacob and Tobias?"

"They've gone to Bethlehem," said the stranger. "They've gone to a birthday party."

"A birthday party, and didn't take me?" ejaculated David in powerful indignation. "The nasty, selfish brutes!"

"They were in rather a hurry," explained the stranger. "It was all rather unexpected."

"Then I suppose they had no presents to take?" asked David. "They'll feel awkward, turning up with no presents. . . . Serve them right for not taking me."

"They took what they could," said the stranger. "A shepherd's crook, a cloak, and a loaf of bread."

David snorted with contempt, and then snorted again in indignation. "They shouldn't have gone," he said, and indeed it was a terrible crime for shepherds to leave their sheep, with those robbers prowling about in the shadows below and only too ready to pounce upon them.

"They were quite right to go," said the stranger. "And I have taken their place."

"But you're only one man," objected David, "and it takes several to tackle robbers."

"I think I'm equal to any number of robbers," smiled the stranger. He was making a statement, not boasting, and David thrilled to the quiet confidence of his voice, and thrilled, too, to feel the strength of the arm that was round him and of the knee against which he leant.

"Have you done a lot of fighting, great lord?" he whispered in awe.

"Quite a lot," said the stranger.

"Who did you fight?" breathed David. "Barbarians?"

"The devil and his angels," said the stranger nonchalantly.

David was momentarily deprived of the power of speech, but, pressing closer, he gazed upward at the face of this man for whom neither robbers nor devils seemed to hold any terrors, and once he began to look he could not take his eyes away, for never before had he seen a face like this man's, a face at once delicate and strong, full of power yet quick with tenderness, bright as the sky in early morning yet shadowed with mystery. . . . It seemed an eternity before David could find his voice.

"Who are you, great lord?" he whispered at last. "You're no shepherd."

"I'm a soldier," said the stranger. "And my name is Michael. . . . What's your name?"

"David," murmured the little boy, and suddenly he shut his eyes because he was dazzled by the face above him. . . . If this was a soldier, he was a very king among soldiers.

"Tell me where you are going, David," said the stranger.

Now that they had told each other their names David felt they were lifelong friends, and it was not hard to tell his story. He told it all: his father's illness, his mother's tears, the children's hunger and the cold home where there was no fire and the oil was nearly finished; his longing to be a rich man that he might help them all, and the wishing well that gave their heart's desire to the pure in heart.

"But I hadn't meant to go down to the road alone, you see," he finished. "I thought Eli would have gone with me, and now Eli has gone to that birthday party."

"Then you'll have to go alone," said Michael.

"I suppose the sheep wouldn't be all right by themselves?" hinted David gently.

"They certainly would not," said Michael firmly.

"I'm not afraid, of course," boasted David and shrank a little closer against that strong knee.

"Of course not," concurred Michael heartily. "I've noticed that Davids are always plucky. Look at King David fighting the lion and the bear when he was only a shepherd boy like you."

"But the Lord God Jehovah guided and protected him," said David.

"And the Lord God will protect you," said Michael.

"I don't *feel* as though he was protecting me," objected David.

"You haven't started out yet," said Michael, and laughed. "How can he protect you when there's nothing to protect you from? Or guide you when you don't take to the road? Go on now. Hurry up." And with a gentle but inexorable movement he withdrew his knee from beneath David's clinging hands, and lifted his cloak from David's shoulders so that it slid back with a soft rustling upward movement, as though great wings were folded against the sky. . . . And the winter wind blew cold and chill about the little boy who stood ragged and barefoot in the blackness of the night.

"Good-by," said Michael's deep voice; but it seemed to be drifting away as though Michael too were withdrawing himself. "Play your pipe to yourself if you are afraid, for music is the voice of man's trust in God's protection, even as the gift of courage is God's voice answering."

David took a few steps forward, and again terror gripped him. Again he saw the bare lonely hills, and the shadows down below where the robbers lurked. He glanced back over his shoulder, ready to bolt back to the shelter of Michael's strong arm and the warmth of his cloak. . . . But he could no longer see Michael very clearly, he could only see a dark shape that might have been a man but that might have been only a shadow. . . . But yet the moment he glanced back he knew that Michael was watching him, Michael the soldier who was afraid neither of robbers nor of the devil and his angels, and with a heart suddenly turned valiant he turned and scuttled off down the hill toward the valley.

Nevertheless he had the most uncomfortable journey. Going down the hill he cut his feet on the sharp stones, and fell down twice and barked his knees, and going through the olive grove below he saw robbers hiding behind every tree. There were times when he was so frightened that his knees doubled up beneath him and he came out in a clammy perspiration, but there were other times when he remembered Michael's advice and stopped a minute to play a few sweet notes on his precious pipe, and then he was suddenly brave again and rushed through the terrifying shadows whooping as though he were that other David going for the lion and the bear. . . . But all the same it was a most uncomfortable journey, and he was overwhelmingly thankful when with final jump he landed in the road and saw the water of the well gleaming only a few feet away from him.

He leaned against the stone parapet and looked at it gravely. . . . Water. . . . In this land that in the summer months was parched with drought and scorched with heat water was the most precious thing in the world, the source of all growth and all purification, the cure of sickness, the preserver of life itself. It was no wonder that men came to water to pray for their heart's desire, to water, the comforter and lord of all life. "Comfort ye, comfort ye, my people." It seemed to him that he heard voices singing in the wind among the olive trees, as though the trees themselves were singing, voices that sang not to the ear but to the soul. "He shall feed his flock like a shepherd: he shall gather the lambs with his arm, and carry them in his bosom. Wonderful! Counselor! The mighty God! The everlasting Father! The Prince of Peace!" Surely, he thought, if the Lord God Jehovah cared so for the little lambs he would care also for David's sick father and weeping mother and the little hungry children, and covering his face with his brown fingers he prayed to the Lord God that he might have gold to buy food and wine and oil for that stricken house up above him on the hill. And so hard did he pray that he forgot everything but his own longing, forgot his fears and the cold wind that nipped him through his rags, saw nothing but the darkness of his closed eyes and heard nothing but his own desperate whispering.

Then, sighing a little like a child awaking from sleep, he opened his eyes and peeped anxiously through his fingers at the water in the well. Would he have his heart's desire? Had he prayed from a pure heart? Was that something glittering in the well? He dropped his hands from his face and leaned closer, the blood pounding so in his ears that it sounded like drums beating. Yes, it was gold! Circles of gold lying upon the surface of the water, as though the stars had dropped down from heaven. With a cry of joy he leaned nearer, his face right over the water, as though he would have touched with his lips those visionary gold pieces that promised him his heart's desire. . . . And then, in an instant of time, his cry of joy changed to a cry of terror, for framed in those twinkling golden points of light he saw the reflection of a man's face, a bearded swarthy face with gleaming teeth and eyes, the face of a foreigner.

So the Lord God had not protected him. So the robbers had got him. He stared at the water for a long minute, stark with terror, and then swung round with a choking cry, both his thin hands at his throat to protect it from the robber's knife.

"Do not cry out, little son. I will not hurt you." The man stretched out a hand and gave David's shoulder a reassuring little shake. "I but looked over your shoulder to see what you stared at so intently."

The voice, deep-toned, kindly, strangely attractive with its foreign inflection, chased away all David's fears. . . . This was no robber. . . . His breath came more evenly, and he wiped the sweat of his terror off his forehead with his tattered sleeve while he looked up with bulging eyes at the splendid stranger standing in front of him.

He was tall, though not so tall as that other splendid stranger keeping the sheep up on the hill, and he wore a purple robe girdled at the waist with gold and a green turban to which were stitched gold ornaments that shook and trembled round his proud, hawk-nosed face. David had one pang of agonized disappointment as he realized that it was only the reflection of these gold ornaments he had seen in the water, and not God's answer to his prayer, and then amazement swept all other thoughts from his mind.

For the star-lit road to the well that a short while ago had been empty was now full. While David prayed, his ears closed to all sounds, a glittering cavalcade had come up out of the night. There were black men carrying torches, richly caparisoned camels, and two more splendid grave-faced men even more richly dressed than his friend. The torch light gleamed on gold and scarlet, emerald green and rich night blue, and the scent of spices came fragrant on the wind. This cavalcade might have belonged to Solomon, thought David, to Solomon in all his glory. . . . Surely these men were kings?

But the camels were thirsty, and the first king drew David gently away from the well that they might drink. Yet he kept his hand upon his shoulder and looked down upon him with kindly liking.

"And for what were you looking so intently, little son?" he asked.

"For my heart's desire, great lord," whispered David, nervously pleating his ragged little tunic with fingers that still shook from the fright he had had.

"So?" asked the stranger. "Is it a wishing well?"

"They say," said David, "that if you pray to God for your heart's desire from a pure heart, and if God has granted your prayer, you will see a vision of it in the water."

"And you saw yours?"

David shook his head. "You came, great lord," he explained. "I saw you."

One of the other kings, an old white-bearded man in a sea-green robe, was listening smiling to their talk. "We three have lost a star, little son," he said to David. "Should we find it again in your well?"

David thought it must be a joke, for what could three great lords want with a star? But when he looked up into the fine old eyes gazing down into his he saw trouble and bewilderment in them.

"If your heart is pure, great lord."

A shadow passed over the old man's face and he turned back to the third king, a young man with a boy's smooth skin and eyes that were bright and gay.

"Gaspar," he said. "You are young and pure of heart, you look."

Gaspar laughed, his white teeth flashing in his brown face. "Only an old wives' tale," he mocked. "We've lost the star twenty times in the blaze of the night sky and twenty times we have found it again. Why should we look for it now in a well?"

"Yet pray," said the old man sternly. "Pray and look."

Obediently Gaspar stepped up to the well, his scarlet robe swirling about him and the curved sword that he wore slapping against his side, bowed his head in prayer, then bent over the well.

"I can see only a part of the sky," he murmured, "and each star is like another in glory—no—yes." He paused and suddenly gave a shout of triumph. "I have found it, Melchior! It shines in the center of the well, like the hub of a wheel or the boss of a shield."

He straightened himself and flung back his head, his arms stretched up toward the sky. "There! There!" he cried, and David and the elder kings, gazing, saw a great star blazing over their heads, a star that was mightier and more glorious than the sister stars that shone around it like cavaliers round the throne. . . . And as they gazed it suddenly moved, streaking through the sky like a comet.

"Look! Look!" cried David. "A shooting star!" And he danced out into the middle of the road to follow its flight. "Look! It is shining over Bethlehem!"

The three kings stood behind him, gazing where he pointed, and saw at the end of the road, faintly visible in the starlight, slender cypress trees rising above the huddled roofs of a little white town upon a hill, and above them the blazing star.

Gaspar, young and excited, suddenly swung round and began shouting to the servants to bring up the camels, but the two older kings still stood gazing.

"Praise be to the Lord God," said the old king tremulously, and he bowed his head and crossed his hands upon his breast.

"Bethlehem," said the king who was David's friend. "The end of our journey."

His voice was infinitely weary, and for the first time it occurred to David that these great lords had come from a long way off. Their beautiful clothes were travel-stained and their faces drawn with fatigue. They must, he decided suddenly, be lunatics; no sane men, he thought, would come from so far away to visit an unimportant little place like Bethlehem; nor be in such a taking because they had lost sight of a star. Nevertheless he liked them and had no wish to lose their company.

"I'll take you to Bethlehem," he announced, and flung back his head and straddled his legs as though it would be a matter of great difficulty and danger to guide them the short way along the straight road to a town that was visible to the naked eye.

"And so you shall," laughed his friend. "And you shall ride my camel in front of me and be the leader of the caravan."

David jigged excitedly from one foot to the other. He had never ridden a camel, for only well-to-do men had camels. He could not contain himself and let out a shrill squeak of joy as a richly caparisoned beast was led up and made to kneel before them; a squeak that ended rather abruptly when the camel turned its head and gave him a slow disdainful look, lifting its upper lip and showing its teeth in a contempt so profound that David blushed hotly to the roots of his hair, and did not recover himself until he was seated on the golden saddle cloth before his friend, safe in the grip of his arm, rocking up toward the stars as the camel got upon its feet.

It was one of the most wonderful moments of that wonderful night when David found himself swaying along toward the cypresses of Bethlehem, the leader of a caravan. Because he was so happy he put his pipe to his lips and began to play the gay little tune that shepherds have played among the hills since the dawn of the world, and so infectious

was it that the men coming behind began to hum it as they swung along under the stars.

"It is right to sing upon a journey, great lord," said David, when a pause fell, "for music is the voice of man's trust in God's protection, even as the gift of courage is God's voice answering."

"That is a wise child you have got there, Balthasar," said old Melchior, who was riding just behind them.

"I didn't make that up for myself," David answered truthfully. "A man up in the hills told it to me. A man who came to mind the sheep so that Eli and the other shepherds could go with their presents to a birthday party in Bethlehem."

"Does all the world carry gifts to Bethlehem tonight?" questioned Balthasar softly. "Wise men from the desert with their mysteries, shepherds from the hills with their simplicities, and a little boy with the gift of music."

"Do you mean that we are all going to the same place?" asked David eagerly. "Are you going to the birthday party too? And am I going with you? Me too?"

"A king has been born," said Balthasar. "We go to worship him."

A king? The world seemed full of kings tonight, and kings doing the most unsuitable things, too, keeping sheep on the hills and journeying along the highway travel-stained and weary. On this wonderful topsy-turvy night nothing surprised him, not even the news that the birthday party was a king's; but desolation seized him as he realized that he wouldn't be able to go to it himself. . . . For how could he go inside a grand palace when his clothes were torn and his feet were bare and dirty? They wouldn't let him in. They'd set the dogs on him. . . . Disappointment surged over him in sickening waves. He gritted his teeth to keep himself from crying, but even with all his effort two fat tears escaped and plowed two clean but scalding furrows through the grime on his face.

They were at Bethlehem before he realized it, for he had been keeping his head bent for fear Balthasar should see his two tears. Looking up suddenly he saw the white walls of the little town close in front of him, the cypress trees like swords against the sky and that star shining just ahead of them, so bright that it seemed like a great lamp let down out of heaven by a string. The gate of the town was standing wide open and they clattered through it without hindrance, which surprised David until he remembered that just at this time Bethlehem would be full of people who had come in from the country to be taxed. They would not be afraid of robbers to-night, when the walls held so many good strong countrymen with knives in their girdles and a quick way with their fists. The visitors were still up and about, too, for as they climbed the main street of the little hill town David could see lines of light shining under doors and hear laughter and voices behind them. . . . And a good thing too, he thought, for at any other time the arrival of this strange cavalcade in the dead of night might have caused a disturbance. . . . The Lord God, he thought, had arranged things very conveniently for them.

"Which way are we going?" he whispered excitedly to his king.

"We follow the star," said Balthasar.

David looked up and saw that the star must have been up to its shooting tricks again, for it had now moved over to their right, and obediently they too swerved to their right and made their way up a narrow lane where houses had been built over caves in the limestone rock. Each house was the home of poor people, who kept their animals in the cave below and lived themselves in the one room above reached by its flight of stone steps.

"The king can't be *here!*" said David disgustedly, as the cavalcade, moving now in single file, picked its way over the heaps of refuse in the lane. "Only poor people live *here*."

"Look!" said Balthasar, and, looking, David saw that the star was hanging so low over a little house at the end of the lane that a bright beam of light caressed its roof.

"The star is making a mistake," said David firmly, "if it thinks a king could be born in a place like that."

But no one was taking any notice of him. A great awe seemed to have descended upon the three kings, and a thankfulness too deep for speech. In silence the cavalcade halted outside the house at the end of the lane, and in silence the servants gathered round to bring the camels to their knees and help their masters to the ground. David, picked up and set upon his feet by a sturdy Nubian whose black face gleamed in the torchlight like ebony, stood aside and watched, something of the awe that gripped the others communicating itself to him, so

that the scene he saw stamped itself upon his memory forever. . . . The torchlight and starlight lighting up the rich colors of the kings' garments and illuminating their dark, intent faces, as though they were lit by an inner light; the stir among the servants as three of them came forward carrying three golden caskets, fragrant with spices and so richly jeweled that the light seemed to fall upon them in points of fire, and gave them reverently into their masters' hands. . . . The birthday presents, thought David, the riches that Balthasar had spoken of, and he looked hastily up at the poor little house built above the stable, incredulous that such wealth could enter a door so humble.

But the door at the top of the stone steps was shut fast and no line of light showed beneath it, or shone out in welcome from the window. The only light there was showed through the ill-fitting door that closed in the opening to the cave below, and it was toward this that Melchior turned, knocking softly on the rotten wood and standing with bent head to listen for the answer.

"But that's the *stable!*" whispered David. "He couldn't be there!"

But no one answered him, for the door opened and the three kings, their heads lowered and their long dark fingers curved about their gifts, passed into the light beyond, the door closing softly behind them, shutting David outside in the night with the strange black servants and the supercilious camels.

But his curiosity was too strong for him to feel afraid. There was a hole quite low in the door and kneeling down he pressed his dirty little face against the wood and squinted eagerly through it.

Of course there was no king there; he had said there wouldn't be and there wasn't; looking beyond the kings he saw there was nothing there but the stable and the animals and a few people, poor people like himself. The animals, a little donkey with his ribs sticking through his skin and an old ox whose shoulders bore the marks of the yoke they had carried through many hard years, were fastened to iron rings in the wall of the cave, but both of them had turned their sleepy heads toward the rough stone manger filled with hay, and toward a gray-bearded man who held a lighted lantern over the manger and a woman with a tired white face, muffled in a blue cloak, who lay on the floor leaning back against the wall. . . . But though she was so tired she was smiling at the men who were kneeling together on the hard floor, and she had the loveliest and most welcoming smile that David had ever seen.

And then he saw that the men she was smiling at were Eli, Jacob, and Tobias, kneeling with heads bent and hands clasped in the attitude of worship. And before them on the hard floor, just in front of the manger, they had laid their gifts: Eli's shepherd's crook that had been his father's, Jacob's cloak lined with the lamb's wool that he set such store by, and Tobias's little loaf of bread that he always ate all by himself in the middle of the night when he was guarding sheep, never giving a crumb to anyone else no matter how hard they begged. And beside these humble men knelt the kings in their glory, and beside the simple gifts were the three rich fragrant caskets, just as though there were no barrier between rich people and poor people, and no difference in value between wood and bread and gold and jewels.

But what could be in that manger that they were all so intent upon it? David had another peep through his hole and saw to his astonishment that there was a baby in it, a tiny newborn baby wrapped in swaddling clothes. Normally David took no interest at all in babies, but at the sight of this one he was smitten with such awe that he shut his eyes and ducked his head, just as though he had been blinded by the sight of a king with eyes like flame sitting upon a rainbow-encircled throne.

So this was the king, this tiny baby lying in a rough stone manger in a stable. . . . It struck David that of all the extraordinary places where he had encountered kings this night this was the most extraordinary of all. . . . And then he gave a joyous exclamation. On the journey here he had cried because he had thought a barefoot dirty little boy would not be able to go to a king's birthday party, but surely even he could go to a birthday party in a stable. He leaped to his feet, dusted his knees, pulled down his rags, laid his hands on the latch of the door, and crept noiselessly in.

And then, standing by himself in the shadows by the door, he bethought him that he had no present to give. He had no possessions in the world at all, except his beloved shepherd's pipe, and it was out of the question that he should give that for he loved it as his own life. Noiseless as a mouse he turned to go out again, but suddenly the mother in the blue cloak, who must have known all the time that he was

there, raised her face and smiled at him, a radiant smile full of promise, and at the same time the man with the gray beard lowered the lantern a little so that it seemed as though the whole manger were enveloped with light, with that baby at the heart of the light like the sun itself.

And suddenly David could not stay by himself in the shadows, any more than he could stay in a dark stuffy house when the sun was shining. No sacrifice was too great, not even the sacrifice of the little shepherd's pipe that was dear as life itself, if he could be in that light. He ran forward, pushing rudely between Balthasar and Tobias, and laid his shepherd's pipe joyously down before the manger, between Balthasar's jeweled casket and Tobias's humble loaf of bread. . . . He was too little to realize, as he knelt down and covered his face with his hands, that the birthday gifts lying there in a row were symbolic of all that a man could need for his life on earth: a cloak for shelter, a loaf of bread for food, a shepherd's crook for work, and a musical instrument to bring courage in the doing of it; and those other gifts of gold and jewels and spices that symbolized rich qualities of kingliness and priestliness and wisdom that were beyond human understanding. "Wise men from the desert with their mysteries," Balthasar had said, "shepherds from the hills with their simplicities, and a little boy with the gift of music." But David, peeping through his fingers at the baby in the manger, did not think at all, he only felt, and what his spirit experienced was exactly what his body felt when he danced about on the hills in the first hot sunshine of the year; warmth was poured into him, health and strength and life itself. He took his hands away from his face and gazed and gazed at that baby, his whole being poured out in adoration.

And then it was all over and he found himself outside Bethlehem, trailing along in the dust behind Eli, Jacob, and Tobias, footsore and weary and as cross as two sticks.

"Where's my camel?" he asked petulantly. "When I went to Bethlehem I was the leader of a caravan, and I had three great lords with me, and servants and torches."

"Well, you haven't got them now," said Eli. "The great lords are still at Bethlehem. . . . When Jacob and Tobias and I saw you there in the stable we made haste to take you home to your mother, young truant that you are."

"I don't want mother," grumbled David. "I want my camel."

Eli glanced back over his shoulder at the disagreeable little urchin dawdling at his heels. Was this the same child who had knelt in the stable wrapped in adoration? How quick can be the fall from ecstasy! "You keep your mouth shut, little son," he adjured him, "and quicken your heels; for I must get back to those sheep."

"Baa!" said David nastily, and purposely lagged behind.

So determinedly did he lag that by the time he had reached the well he found himself alone again. The well! The sight of it brought home to him his desperate plight. From his night's adventure he had gained nothing. Up there on the hill was the little house that held his sick father, his weeping mother, and his hungry little brothers and sisters, and he must go home to them no richer than he went. . . . Poorer, in fact, for now he had lost his shepherd's pipe, thrown away his greatest treasure in what seemed to him now a moment of madness. . . . Now he had nothing, nothing in all the world.

He flung himself down in the grass beside the well, and he cried as though his heart were breaking. The utter deadness of the hour before dawn weighed on him like a pall, and the cold of it numbed him from head to foot. He felt himself sinking lower and lower, dropping down to the bottom of some black sea of misery, and it was not until he reached the bottom that comfort came to him.

His sobs ceased, and he was conscious again of the feel of the earth beneath the grass where he lay, hard and cold yet bearing him up with a strength that was reassuring. He thought of the terraces of olive trees above him and of the great bare hills beyond, and then he thought of the voices he had heard singing in the wind up in the hills, and singing down below among the trees, and then suddenly he thought he heard voices in the grass, tiny voices that were like the voices of all growing things, corn and flowers and grasses. "They that sow in tears, shall reap in joy," they whispered. "He that goeth forth and weepeth, bearing precious seed, shall doubtless come again rejoicing, bringing his sheaves with him."

He got up, his courage restored, and stumbled over to the well, faintly silvered now with the first hint of dawn. He did not pray to be a rich man, he did not look in it for his heart's desire, he simply went to it to wash himself, for he did not intend to appear before his mother with dirty tear stains all over his face. . . . If he could not arrive back home with bags full of gold and thousands of camels and tens of thousands of sheep he would at least arrive with a clean and cheerful face to comfort them.

Like all small boys David was a noisy washer, and it must have been the sound of his splashings that prevented him from hearing the feet of a trotting camel upon the road; nor could the surface of the well, much agitated by his ablutions, show him at first the reflection of the man standing behind him; it had to smooth itself out before he could see the swarthy face framed in the twinkling golden ornaments. When he did see it he blinked incredulously for a moment and then swung round with a cry of joy.

"So you thought I had forgotten you, did you, little son?" smiled Balthasar. "I would not forget so excellent a leader of a caravan. When you left the stable I followed after you as quickly as I could. See what I have for you."

He gave a bag to David, and the little boy, opening it, saw by the first light of the dawn the shine of golden pieces. . . . Lots of golden pieces, enough to buy medicines and healing salves for his father and food and warmth for all of them for a long time to come. . . . He had no words to tell of his gratitude, but the face that he tilted up to Balthasar, with eyes and mouth as round in wonder as coins themselves, was in itself a paean of praise.

Balthasar laughed and patted his shoulder. "When I saw you give your shepherd's pipe to the little king," he said, "I vowed that you should not go home empty-handed. . . . I think it was the little king himself who put the thought into my head. . . . Now I must go back to my country, and you to your home, but we will not forget each other. Fare you well, little son."

As he went up through the shadows of the olive trees David was no longer frightened of robbers, for he was far too happy. The trees were singing again, he thought, as the dawn wind rustled them. "Comfort ye, comfort ye, my people," they sang. And when he got out beyond the trees, and saw the great bare stretches of the hills flushed rose and lilac in the dawn, it seemed as though the hills themselves were shouting, "Glory to God!"

THE OTHER WISE MAN

Henry van Dyke

THE SIGN IN THE SKY

In the days when Augustus Cæsar was master of many kings and Herod reigned in Jerusalem, there lived in the city of Ecbatana, among the mountains of Persia, a certain man named Artaban, the Median. His house stood close to the outermost of the seven walls which encircled the royal treasury. From his roof he could look over the rising battlements of black and white and crimson and blue and red and silver and gold, to the hill where the summer palace of the Parthian emperors glittered like a jewel in a sevenfold crown.

Around the dwelling of Artaban spread a fair garden, a tangle of flowers and fruit trees, watered by a score of streams descending from the slopes of Mount Orontes, and made musical by innumerable birds. But all color was lost in the soft and odorous darkness of the late September night, and all sounds were hushed in the deep charm of its silence, save the plashing of the water, like a voice half sobbing and half laughing under the shadows. High above the trees a dim glow of light shone through the curtained arches of the upper chamber, where the master of the house was holding council with his friends.

He stood by the doorway to greet his guests—a tall, dark man of about forty years, with brilliant eyes set near together under his broad brow, and firm lines graven around his fine, thin lips; the brow of a dreamer and the mouth of a soldier, a man of sensitive feeling but inflexible will—one of those who, in whatever age they may live, are born for inward conflict and a life of quest.

His robe was of pure white wool, thrown over a tunic of silk; and a white, pointed cap, with long lapels at the sides, rested on his flowing black hair. It was the dress of the ancient priesthood of the Magi, called the fire-worshipers.

"Welcome!" he said, in his low, pleasant voice, as one after another entered the room—"welcome, Abdus; peace be with you, Rhodaspes and Tigranes, and with you my father, Abgarus. You are all welcome, and this house grows bright with the joy of your presence."

There were nine of the men, differing widely in age, but alike in the richness of their dress of many-colored silks, and in the massive golden collars around their necks, marking them as Parthian nobles, and in the winged circles of gold resting upon their breasts, the sign of the followers of Zoroaster.

They took their places around a small black altar at the end of the room, where a tiny flame was burning. Artaban, standing beside it, and waving a barsom of thin tamarisk branches above the fire, fed it with dry sticks of pine and fragrant oils. Then he began the ancient chant of the Yasna, and the voices of his companions joined in the beautiful hymn to Ahura-Mazda:

We worship the Spirit Divine,
*   all wisdom and goodness possessing,*
Surrounded by Holy Immortals,
*   the givers of bounty and blessing,*
We joy in the works of His hands,
*   His truth and His power confessing.*

We praise all the things that are pure,
*   for these are His only Creation;*
The thoughts that are true, and the words
*   and deeds that have won approbation;*
These are supported by Him
*   and for these we make adoration.*

Hear us, O Mazda! Thou livest
*   in truth and in heavenly gladness;*
Cleanse us from falsehood, and keep us
*   from evil and bondage to badness;*
Pour out the light and the joy of Thy life
*   on our darkness and sadness.*

Shine on our gardens and fields,
*   Shine on our working and weaving;*
Shine on the whole race of man,
*   Believing and unbelieving;*
Shine on us now through the night,
*   Shine on us now in Thy might,*
The flame of our holy love
*   and the song of our worship receiving.*

The fire rose with the chant, throbbing as if it were made of musical flame, until it cast a bright illumination through the whole apartment, revealing its simplicity and splendor.

The floor was laid with tiles of dark blue veined with white; pilasters of twisted silver stood out against the blue walls; the clearstory of round-arched windows above them was hung with azure silk; the vaulted ceiling was a pavement of sapphires, like the body of heaven in its clearness, sown with silver stars. From the four corners of the roof hung four golden magic-wheels, called the tongues of the gods. At the eastern end, behind the altar, there were two dark-red pillars of porphyry; above them a lintel of the same stone, on which was carved the figure of a winged archer, with his arrow set to the string and his bow drawn.

The doorway between the pillars, which opened upon the terrace of the roof, was covered with a heavy curtain of the color of a ripe pomegranate, embroidered with innumerable golden rays shooting upward from the floor. In effect the room was like a quiet, starry night, all azure and silver, flushed in the east with rosy promise of the dawn. It was, as the house of a man should be, an expression of the character and spirit of the master.

He turned to his friends when the song was ended, and invited them to be seated on the divan at the western end of the room.

"You have come to-night," said he, looking around the circle, "at my call, as the faithful scholars of Zoroaster, to renew your worship and rekindle your faith in the God of Purity, even as this fire has been rekindled on the altar. We worship not the fire, but Him of whom it is the chosen symbol, because it is the purest of all created things. It speaks to us of one who is Light and Truth. Is it not so, my father?"

"It is well said, my son," answered the venerable Abgarus. "The enlightened are never idolaters. They lift the veil of the form and go in to the shrine of the reality, and new light and truth are coming to them continually through the old symbols."

"Hear me, then, my father and my friends," said Artaban, very quietly, "while I tell you of the new light and truth that have come to me through the most ancient of all signs. We have searched the secrets of nature together, and studied the healing virtues of water and fire and the plants. We have read also the books of prophecy in which the future is dimly foretold in words that are hard to understand. But the highest of all learning is the knowledge of the stars. To trace their courses is to untangle the threads of the mystery of life from the beginning

to the end. If we could follow them perfectly, nothing would be hidden from us. But is not our knowledge of them still incomplete? Are there not many stars still beyond our horizon—lights that are known only to the dwellers in the far south-land, among the spice-trees of Punt and the gold-mines of Ophir?"

There was a murmur of assent among the listeners.

"The stars," said Tigranes, "are the thoughts of the Eternal. They are numberless. But the thoughts of man can be counted, like the years of his life. The wisdom of the Magi is the greatest of all wisdoms on earth, because it knows its own ignorance. And that is the secret of power. We keep men always looking and waiting for a new sunrise. But we ourselves know that the darkness is equal to the light, and that the conflict between them will never be ended."

"That does not satisfy me," answered Artaban, "for, if the waiting must be endless, if there could be no fulfilment of it, then it would not be wisdom to look and wait. We should become like those new teachers of the Greeks, who say that there is no truth, and that the only wise men are those who spend their lives in discovering and exposing the lies that have been believed in the world. But the new sunrise will certainly dawn in the appointed time. Do not our own books tell us that this will come to pass, and that men will see the brightness of a great light?"

"That is true," said the voice of Abgarus; "every faithful disciple of Zoroaster knows the prophecy of the Avesta and carries the word in his heart. 'In that day Sosiosh the Victorious shall arise out of the number of the prophets in the east country. Around him shall shine a mighty brightness, and he shall make life everlasting, incorruptible, and immortal, and the dead shall rise again.'"

"This is a dark saying," said Tigranes, "and it may be that we shall never understand it. It is better to consider the things that are near at hand, and to increase the influence of the Magi in their own country, rather than to look for one who may be a stranger, and to whom we must resign our power."

The others seemed to approve these words. There was a silent feeling of agreement manifest among them; their looks responded with that indefinable expression which always follows when a speaker has uttered the thought that has been slumbering in the hearts of his listeners. But Artaban turned to Abgarus with a glow on his face, and said:

"My father, I have kept this prophecy in the

secret place of my soul. Religion without a great hope would be like an altar without a living fire. And now the flame has burned more brightly, and by the light of it I have read other words which also have come from the fountain of Truth, and speak yet more clearly of the rising of the Victorious One in his brightness."

He drew from the breast of his tunic two small rolls of fine linen, with writing upon them, and unfolded them carefully upon his knee.

"In the years that are lost in the past, long before our fathers came into the land of Babylon, there were wise men in Chaldea, from whom the first of the Magi learned the secret of the heavens. And of these Balaam, the son of Beor, was one of the mightiest. Hear the words of his prophecy: 'There shall come a star out of Jacob, and a sceptre shall arise out of Israel.'"

The lips of Tigranes drew downward with contempt, as he said:

"Judah was a captive by the waters of Babylon, and the sons of Jacob were in bondage to our kings. The tribes of Israel are scattered through the mountains like lost sheep, and from the remnant that dwells in Judea under the yoke of Rome neither star nor sceptre shall arise."

"And yet," answered Artaban, "it was the Hebrew Daniel, the mighty searcher of dreams, the counsellor of kings, the wise Belteshazzar, who was most honored and beloved of our great King Cyrus. A prophet of sure things and a reader of the thoughts of God, Daniel proved himself to our people. And these are the words that he wrote." (Artaban read from the second roll:) "'Know, therefore, and understand that from the going forth of the commandment to restore Jerusalem, unto the Anointed One, the Prince, the time shall be seven and three-score and two weeks.'"

"But, my son," said Abgarus, doubtfully, "these are mystical numbers. Who can interpret them, or who can find the key that shall unlock their meaning?"

Artaban answered: "It has been shown to me and to my three companions among the Magi—Caspar, Melchior, and Balthazar. We have searched the ancient tablets of Chaldea and computed the time. It falls in this year. We have studied the sky, and in the spring of the year we saw two of the greatest stars draw near together in the sign of the Fish, which is the house of the Hebrews. We also saw a new star there, which shone for one night and then vanished. Now again the two great planets are meeting. This night is their conjunction. My three brothers are watching at the ancient Temple of the Seven Spheres, at Borsippa, in Babylonia, and I am watching here. If the star shines again, they will wait ten days for me at the temple, and then we will set out together for Jerusalem, to see and worship the promised one who shall be born King of Israel. I believe the sign will come. I have made ready for the journey. I have sold my house and my possessions, and bought these three jewels—a sapphire, a ruby, and a pearl—to carry them as tribute to the King. And I ask you to go with me on the pilgrimage, that we may have joy together in finding the Prince who is worthy to be served."

While he was speaking he thrust his hand into the inmost fold of his girdle and drew out three great gems—one blue as a fragment of the night sky, one redder than a ray of sunrise, and one as pure as the peak of a snow mountain at twilight—and laid them on the outspread linen scrolls before him.

But his friends looked on with strange and alien eyes. A veil of doubt and mistrust came over their faces, like a fog creeping up from the marshes to hide the hills. They glanced at each other with looks of wonder and pity, as those who have listened to incredible sayings, the story of a wild vision, or the proposal of an impossible enterprise.

At last Tigranes said: "Artaban, this is a vain dream. It comes from too much looking upon the stars and the cherishing of lofty thoughts. It would be wiser to spend the time in gathering money for the new fire-temple at Chala. No king will ever rise from the broken race of Israel, and no end will ever come to the eternal strife of light and darkness. He who looks for it is a chaser of shadows. Farewell."

And another said: "Artaban, I have no knowledge of these things, and my office as guardian of the royal treasure binds me here. The quest is not for me. But if thou must follow it, fare thee well."

And another said: "In my house there sleeps a new bride, and I cannot leave her nor take her with me on this strange journey. This quest is not for me. But may thy steps be prospered wherever thou goest. So, farewell."

And another said: "I am ill and unfit for hardship,

but there is a man among my servants whom I will
send with thee when thou goest, to bring me word
how thou farest."

But Abgarus, the oldest and the one who loved
Artaban the best, lingered after the others had gone,
and said, gravely: "My son, it may be that the light
of truth is in this sign that has appeared in the skies,
and then it will surely lead to the Prince and the
mighty brightness. Or it may be that it is only a
shadow of the light, as Tigranes has said, and then
he who follows it will have only a long pilgrimage
and an empty search. But it is better to follow even
the shadow of the best than to remain content with
the worst. And those who would see wonderful
things must often be ready to travel alone. I am too
old for this journey, but my heart shall be a companion of the pilgrimage day and night, and I shall
know the end of thy quest. Go in peace."

So one by one they went out of the azure chamber
with its silver stars, and Artaban was left in solitude.

He gathered up the jewels and replaced them in
his girdle. For a long time he stood and watched the
flame that flickered and sank upon the altar. Then he
crossed the hall, lifted the heavy curtain, and passed
out between the dull red pillars of porphyry to the
terrace on the roof.

The shiver that thrills through the earth ere she
rouses from her night sleep had already begun, and
the cool wind that heralds the daybreak was drawing
downward from the lofty, snow-traced ravines of
Mount Orontes. Birds, half awakened, crept and
chirped among the rustling leaves, and the smell
of ripened grapes came in brief wafts from the
arbors.

Far over the eastern plain a white mist stretched
like a lake. But where the distant peak of Zagros
serrated the western horizon the sky was clear.
Jupiter and Saturn rolled together like drops of
lambent flame about to blend in one.

As Artaban watched them, behold, an azure spark
was born out of the darkness beneath, rounding itself with purple splendors to a crimson sphere, and
spiring upward through rays of saffron and orange
into a point of white radiance. Tiny and infinitely
remote, yet perfect in every part, it pulsated in the
enormous vault as if the three jewels in the Magian's
breast had mingled and been transformed into a
living heart of light.

He bowed his head. He covered his brow with
his hands.

"It is the sign," he said. "The King is coming, and
I will go to meet him."

BY THE WATERS OF BABYLON

All night long Vasda, the swiftest of Artaban's horses,
had been waiting, saddled and bridled, in her stall,
pawing the ground impatiently, and shaking her bit
as if she shared the eagerness of her master's purpose, though she knew not its meaning.

Before the birds had fully roused to their strong,
high, joyful chant of morning song, before the white
mist had begun to lift lazily from the plain, the other
wise man was in the saddle, riding swiftly along the
high-road, which skirted the base of Mount Orontes,
westward.

How close, how intimate is the comradeship between a man and his favorite horse on a long journey.
It is a silent, comprehensive friendship, an intercourse beyond the need of words.

They drink at the same wayside springs, and sleep
under the same guardian stars. They are conscious
together of the subduing spell of nightfall and the
quickening joy of daybreak. The master shares his
evening meal with his hungry companion, and feels
the soft, moist lips caressing the palm of his hand as
they close over the morsel of bread. In the gray
dawn he is roused from his bivouac by the gentle
stir of a warm, sweet breath over his sleeping face,
and looks up into the eyes of his faithful fellow-
traveler, ready and waiting for the toil of the day.
Surely, unless he is a pagan and an unbeliever, by
whatever name he calls upon his God, he will thank
Him for this voiceless sympathy, this dumb affection,
and his morning prayer will embrace a double blessing—God bless us both, and keep our feet from falling and our souls from death!

And then, through the keen morning air, the swift
hoofs beat their spirited music along the road, keeping time to the pulsing of two hearts that are moved
with the same eager desire—to conquer space, to
devour the distance, to attain the goal of the
journey.

Artaban must indeed ride wisely and well if he
would keep the appointed hour with the other Magi;
for the route was a hundred and fifty parasangs, and

fifteen was the utmost that he could travel in a day. But he knew Vasda's strength, and pushed forward without anxiety, making the fixed distance every day, though he must travel late into the night, and in the morning long before sunrise.

He passed along the brown slopes of Mount Orontes, furrowed by the rocky courses of a hundred torrents.

He crossed the level plains of the Nisæans, where the famous herds of horses, feeding in the wide pastures, tossed their heads at Vasda's approach, and galloped away with a thunder of many hoofs, and flocks of wild birds rose suddenly from the swampy meadows, wheeling in great circles with a shining flutter of innumerable wings and shrill cries of surprise.

He traversed the fertile fields of Concabar, where the dust from the threshing-floors filled the air with a golden mist, half hiding the huge temple of Astarte with its four hundred pillars.

At Baghistan, among the rich gardens watered by fountains from the rock, he looked up at the mountain thrusting its immense rugged brow out over the road, and saw the figure of King Darius trampling upon his fallen foes, and the proud list of his wars and conquests graven high upon the face of the eternal cliff.

Over many a cold and desolate pass, crawling painfully across the wind-swept shoulders of the hills; down many a black mountain-gorge, where the river roared and raced before him like a savage guide; across many a smiling vale, with terraces of yellow limestone full of vines and fruit trees; through the oak groves of Carine and the dark Gates of Zagros, walled in by precipices; into the ancient city of Chala, where the people of Samaria had been kept in captivity long ago; and out again by the mighty portal, riven through the encircling hills, where he saw the image of the High Priest of the Magi sculptured on the wall of rock, with hand uplifted as if to bless the centuries of pilgrims; past the entrance of the narrow defile, filled from end to end with orchards of peaches and figs, through which the river Gyndes foamed down to meet him; over the broad rice-fields, where the autumnal vapors spread their deathly mists; following along the course of the river, under tremulous shadows of poplar and tamarind, among the lower hills; and out upon the flat plain, where the road ran straight as an arrow through the stubble-fields and parched meadows; past the city of Ctesiphon, where the Parthian emperors reigned and the vast metropolis of Seleucia which Alexander built; across the swirling floods of Tigris and the many channels of Euphrates, flowing yellow through the corn-lands—Artaban pressed onward until he arrived at nightfall of the tenth day, beneath the shattered walls of populous Babylon.

Vasda was almost spent, and he would gladly have turned into the city to find rest and refreshment for himself and for her. But he knew that it was three hours' journey yet to the Temple of the Seven Spheres, and he must reach the place by midnight if he would find his comrades waiting. So he did not halt, but rode steadily across the stubble-fields.

A grove of date-palms made an island of gloom in the pale yellow sea. As she passed into the shadow Vasda slackened her pace, and began to pick her way more carefully.

Near the farther end of the darkness an access of caution seemed to fall upon her. She scented some danger or difficulty; it was not in her heart to fly from it—only to be prepared for it, and to meet it wisely, as a good horse should do. The grove was close and silent as the tomb; not a leaf rustled, not a bird sang.

She felt her steps before her delicately, carrying her head low, and sighing now and then with apprehension. At last she gave a quick breath of anxiety and dismay, and stood stock-still, quivering in every muscle, before a dark object in the shadow of the last palm-tree.

Artaban dismounted. The dim starlight revealed the form of a man lying across the road. His humble dress and the outline of his haggard face showed that he was probably one of the poor Hebrew exiles who still dwelt in great numbers in the vicinity. His pallid skin, dry and yellow as parchment, bore the mark of the deadly fever which ravaged the marshlands in autumn. The chill of death was in his lean hand, and as Artaban released it the arm fell back inertly upon the motionless breast.

He turned away with a thought of pity, consigning the body to that strange burial which the Magians deemed most fitting—the funeral of the desert, from which the kites and vultures rise on dark wings, and the beasts of prey slink furtively away, leaving only a heap of white bones in the sand.

But, as he turned, a long, faint, ghostly sigh came

from the man's lips. The brown, bony fingers closed convulsively on the hem of the Magian's robe and held him fast.

Artaban's heart leaped to his throat, not with fear, but with a dumb resentment at the importunity of this blind delay.

How could he stay here in the darkness to minister to a dying stranger? What claim had this unknown fragment of human life upon his compassion or his service? If he lingered but for an hour he could hardly reach Borsippa at the appointed time. His companions would think he had given up the journey. They would go without him. He would lose his quest.

But if he went on now, the man would surely die. If he stayed, life might be restored. His spirit throbbed and fluttered with the urgency of the crisis. Should he risk the great reward of his divine faith for the sake of a single deed of human love? Should he turn aside, if only for a moment, from the following of the star, to give a cup of cold water to a poor, perishing Hebrew?

"God of truth and purity," he prayed, "direct me in the holy path, the way of wisdom which Thou only knowest."

Then he turned back to the sick man. Loosening the grasp of his hand, he carried him to a little mound at the foot of the palm-tree.

He unbound the thick folds of the turban and opened the garment above the sunken breast. He brought water from one of the small canals near by, and moistened the sufferer's brow and mouth. He mingled a draught of one of those simple but potent remedies which he carried always in his girdle—for the Magians were physicians as well as astrologers— and poured it slowly between the colorless lips. Hour after hour he labored as only a skilful healer of disease can do; and at last the man's strength returned; he sat up and looked about him.

"Who art thou?" he said, in the rude dialect of the country, "and why hast thou sought me here to bring back my life?"

"I am Artaban the Magian, of the city of Ecbatana, and I am going to Jerusalem in search of one who is to be born King of the Jews, a great Prince and Deliverer of all men. I dare not delay any longer upon my journey, for the caravan that has waited for me may depart without me. But see, here is all that I have left of bread and wine, and here is a potion of healing herbs. When thy strength is restored thou canst find the dwellings of the Hebrews among the houses of Babylon."

The Jew raised his trembling hand solemnly to heaven.

"Now may the God of Abraham and Isaac and Jacob bless and prosper the journey of the merciful, and bring him in peace to his desired haven. But stay; I have nothing to give thee in return—only this: that I can tell thee where the Messiah must be sought. For our prophets have said that he should be born not in Jerusalem, but in Bethlehem of Judah. May the Lord bring thee in safety to that place, because thou hast had pity upon the sick."

It was already long past midnight. Artaban rode in haste, and Vasda, restored by the brief rest, ran eagerly through the silent plain and swam the channels of the river. She put forth the remnant of her strength, and fled over the ground like a gazelle.

But the first beam of the sun sent her shadow before her as she entered upon the final stadium of the journey, and the eyes of Artaban, anxiously scanning the great mound of Nimrod and the Temple of the Seven Spheres, could discern no trace of his friends.

The many-colored terraces of black and orange and red and yellow and green and blue and white, shattered by the convulsions of nature, and crumbling under the repeated blows of human violence, still glittered like a ruined rainbow in the morning light.

Artaban rode swiftly around the hill. He dismounted and climbed to the highest terrace, looking out toward the west.

The huge desolation of the marshes stretched away to the horizon and the border of the desert. Bitterns stood by the stagnant pools and jackals skulked through the low bushes; but there was no sign of the caravan of the wise men, far or near.

At the edge of the terrace he saw a little cairn of broken bricks, and under them a piece of parchment. He caught it up and read: "We have waited past the midnight, and can delay no longer. We go to find the King. Follow us across the desert."

Artaban sat down upon the ground and covered his head in despair.

"How can I cross the desert," said he, "with no food and with a spent horse? I must return to Babylon, sell my sapphire, and buy a train of camels, and provision for the journey. I may never overtake my friends. Only God the merciful knows whether I shall not lose the sight of the King because I tarried to show mercy."

FOR THE SAKE OF A LITTLE CHILD

There was a silence in the Hall of Dreams, where I was listening to the story of the Other Wise Man. And through this silence I saw, but very dimly, his figure passing over the dreary undulations of the desert, high upon the back of his camel, rocking steadily onward like a ship over the waves.

The land of death spread its cruel net around him. The stony wastes bore no fruit but briers and thorns. The dark ledges of rock thrust themselves above the surface here and there, like the bones of perished monsters. Arid and inhospitable mountain ranges rose before him, furrowed with dry channels of ancient torrents, white and ghastly as scars on the face of nature. Shifting hills of treacherous sand were heaped like tombs along the horizon. By day, the fierce heat pressed its intolerable burden on the quivering air; and no living creature moved on the dumb, swooning earth, but tiny jerboas scuttling through the parched bushes, or lizards vanishing in the clefts of the rock. By night the jackals prowled and barked in the distance, and the lion made the black ravines echo with his hollow roaring, while a bitter blighting chill followed the fever of the day. Through heat and cold, the Magian moved steadily onward.

Then I saw the gardens and orchards of Damascus, watered by the streams of Abana and Pharpar with their sloping swards inlaid with bloom, and their thickets of myrrh and roses. I saw also the long, snowy ridge of Hermon, and the dark groves of cedars, and the valley of the Jordan, and the blue waters of the Lake of Galilee, and the fertile plain of Esdraelon, and the hills of Ephraim, and the highlands of Judah. Through all these I followed the figure of Artaban moving steadily onward, until he arrived at Bethlehem. And it was the third day after the three wise men had come to that place and had found Mary and Joseph, with the young child, Jesus, and had laid their gifts of gold and frankincense and myrrh at his feet.

Then the other wise man drew near, weary, but full of hope, bearing his ruby and his pearl to offer to the King. "For now at last," he said, "I shall surely find him, though it be alone, and later than my brethren. This is the place of which the Hebrew exile told me that the prophets had spoken, and here I shall behold the rising of the great light. But I must inquire about the visit of my brethren, and to what house the star directed them, and to whom they presented their tribute."

The streets of the village seemed to be deserted, and Artaban wondered whether the men had all gone up to the hill-pastures to bring down their sheep. From the open door of a low stone cottage he heard the sound of a woman's voice singing softly. He entered and found a young mother hushing her baby to rest. She told him of the strangers from the far East who had appeared in the village three days ago, and how they said that a star had guided them to the place where Joseph of Nazareth was lodging with his wife and her new-born child, and how they had paid reverence to the child and given him many rich gifts.

"But the travelers disappeared again," she continued, "as suddenly as they had come. We were afraid at the strangeness of their visit. We could not understand it. The man of Nazareth took the babe and his mother and fled away that same night secretly, and it was whispered that they were going far away to Egypt. Ever since, there has been a spell upon the village; something evil hangs over it. They say that the Roman soldiers are coming from Jerusalem to force a new tax from us, and the men have driven the flocks and herds far back among the hills, and hidden themselves to escape it."

Artaban listened to her gentle, timid speech, and the child in her arms looked up in his face and smiled, stretching out its rosy hands to grasp at the winged circle of gold on his breast. His heart warmed to the touch. It seemed like a greeting of love and trust to one who had journeyed long in loneliness and perplexity, fighting with his own doubts and fears, and following a light that was veiled in clouds.

"Might not this child have been the promised Prince?" he asked within himself, as he touched its soft cheek. "Kings have been borne ere now in lowlier houses than this, and the favorite of the stars may rise even from a cottage. But it has not seemed good to the God of Wisdom to reward my search so soon and so easily. The one whom I seek has gone before me; and now I must follow the King to Egypt."

The young mother laid the babe in its cradle, and rose to minister to the wants of the strange guest that fate had brought into her house. She set food before him, the plain fare of peasants, but willingly offered, and therefore full of refreshment for the soul as well as for the body. Artaban accepted it gratefully; and, as he ate, the child fell into a happy slumber, and murmured sweetly in its dreams, and a great peace filled the quiet room.

But suddenly there came the noise of a wild confusion and uproar in the streets of the village, a shrieking and wailing of women's voices, a clangor of brazen trumpets and a clashing of swords, and a desperate cry: "The soldiers! the soldiers of Herod! They are killing our children."

The young mother's face grew white with terror. She clasped her child to her bosom, and crouched motionless in the darkest corner of the room, covering him with the folds of her robe, lest he should wake and cry.

But Artaban went quickly and stood in the doorway of the house. His broad shoulders filled the portal from side to side, and the peak of his white cap all but touched the lintel.

The soldiers came hurrying down the street with bloody hands and dripping swords. At the sight of the stranger in his imposing dress they hesitated with surprise. The captain of the band approached the threshold to thrust him aside. But Artaban did not stir. His face was as calm as though he were watching the stars, and in his eyes there burned that steady radiance before which even the half-tamed hunting leopard shrinks and the fierce blood-hound pauses in his leap. He held the soldier silently for an instant, and then said in a low voice:

"I am all alone in this place, and I am waiting to give this jewel to the prudent captain who will leave me in peace."

He showed the ruby, glistening in the hollow of his hand like a great drop of blood.

The captain was amazed at the splendor of the gem. The pupils of his eyes expanded with desire, and the hard lines of greed wrinkled around his lips. He stretched out his hand and took the ruby.

"March on!" he cried to his men, "there is no child here. The house is still."

The clamor and the clang of arms passed down the street as the headlong fury of the chase sweeps by the secret covert where the trembling deer is hidden. Artaban re-entered the cottage. He turned his face to the east and prayed:

"God of truth, forgive my sin! I have said the thing that is not, to save the life of a child. And two of my gifts are gone. I have spent for man that which was meant for God. Shall I ever be worthy to see the face of the King?"

But the voice of the woman, weeping for joy in the shadow behind him, said very gently:

"Because thou hast saved the life of my little one, may the Lord bless thee and keep thee; the Lord make His face to shine upon thee and be gracious unto thee; the Lord lift up His countenance upon thee and give thee peace."

IN THE HIDDEN WAY OF SORROW

Then again there was a silence in the Hall of Dreams, deeper and more mysterious than the first interval, and I understood that the years of Artaban were flowing very swiftly under the stillness of that clinging fog, and I caught only a glimpse, here and there, of the river of his life shining through the shadows that concealed its course.

I saw him moving among the throngs of men in populous Egypt, seeking everywhere for traces of the household that had come down from Bethlehem, and finding them under the spreading sycamore trees of Heliopolis, and beneath the walls of the Roman fortress of New Babylon beside the Nile—traces so faint and dim that they vanished before him continually, as footprints on the hard river-sand glisten for a moment with moisture and then disappear.

I saw him again at the foot of the pyramids, which lifted their sharp points into the intense saffron glow of the sunset sky, changeless monuments of the perishable glory and the imperishable hope of man. He looked up into the vast countenance of the crouching Sphinx, and vainly tried to read the meaning of the calm eyes and smiling mouth. Was it, indeed, the mockery of all effort and all aspiration, as Tigranes had said—the cruel jest of a riddle that has no answer, a search that never can succeed? Or was there a touch of pity and encouragement in that inscrutable smile—a promise that even the defeated should attain a victory, and the disappointed should discover a prize, and the ignorant should be made wise, and the blind should see, and the wandering should come into the haven at last?

I saw him again in an obscure house of Alexandria, taking counsel with a Hebrew rabbi. The venerable man, bending over the rolls of parchment on which the prophecies of Israel were written, read aloud the pathetic words which foretold the sufferings of the promised Messiah—the despised and rejected of men, the man of sorrows and the acquaintance of grief.

"And remember, my son," said he, fixing his deep-set eyes upon the face of Artaban, "the King whom you are seeking is not to be found in a palace, nor among the rich and powerful. If the light of the world and the glory of Israel had been appointed to come with the greatness of earthly splendor, it must have appeared long ago. For no son of Abraham will ever again rival the power which Joseph had in the palaces of Egypt, or the magnificence of Solomon throned between the lions in Jerusalem. But the light for which the world is waiting is a new light, the glory that shall rise out of patient and triumphant suffering. And the kingdom which is to be established forever is a new kingdom, the royalty of perfect and unconquerable love.

"I do not know how this shall come to pass, nor how the turbulent kings and peoples of earth shall be brought to acknowledge the Messiah and pay homage to Him. But this I know. Those who seek Him will do well to look among the poor and the lowly, the sorrowful and the oppressed."

So I saw the other wise man again and again, traveling from place to place, and searching among the people of the dispersion, with whom the little family from Bethlehem might, perhaps, have found a refuge. He passed through countries where famine lay heavy upon the land and the poor were crying for bread. He made his dwelling in plague-stricken cities where the sick were languishing in the bitter companionship of helpless misery. He visited the oppressed and the afflicted in the gloom of subterranean prisons, and the crowded wretchedness of slave-markets, and the weary toil of galley-ships. In all this populous and intricate world of anguish, though he found none to worship, he found many to help. He fed the hungry, and clothed the naked, and healed the sick, and comforted the captive; and his years went by more swiftly than the weaver's shuttle that flashes back and forth through the loom

while the web grows and the invisible pattern is completed.

It seemed almost as if he had forgotten his quest. But once I saw him for a moment as he stood alone at sunrise, waiting at the gate of a Roman prison. He had taken from a secret resting-place in his bosom the pearl, the last of his jewels. As he looked at it, a mellower lustre, a soft and iridescent light, full of shifting gleams of azure and rose, trembled upon its surface. It seemed to have absorbed some reflection of the colors of the lost sapphire and ruby. So the profound, secret purpose of a noble life draws into itself the memories of past joy and past sorrow. All that has helped it, all that has hindered it, is transfused by a subtle magic into its very essence. It becomes more luminous and precious the longer it is carried close to the warmth of the beating heart.

Then, at last, while I was thinking of this pearl, and of its meaning, I heard the end of the story of the Other Wise Man.

A PEARL OF GREAT PRICE

Three-and-thirty years of the life of Artaban had passed away, and he was still a pilgrim, and a seeker after light. His hair, once darker than the cliffs of Zagros, was now white as the wintry snow that covered them. His eyes, that once flashed like flames of fire, were dull as embers smouldering among the ashes.

Worn and weary and ready to die, but still looking for the King, he had come for the last time to Jerusalem. He had often visited the holy city before, and had searched through all its lanes and crowded hovels and black prisons without finding any trace of the family of Nazarenes who had fled from Bethlehem long ago. But now it seemed as if he must make one more effort, and something whispered in his heart that, at last, he might succeed.

It was the season of the Passover. The city was thronged with strangers. The children of Israel, scattered in far lands all over the world, had returned to the Temple for the great feast, and there had been a confusion of tongues in the narrow streets for many days.

But on this day there was a singular agitation visible in the multitude. The sky was veiled with a portentous gloom, and currents of excitement seemed to flash through the crowd like the thrill which shakes the forest on the eve of a storm. A secret tide was sweeping them all one way. The clatter of sandals, and the soft, thick sound of thousands of bare feet shuffling over the stones, flowed unceasingly along the street that leads to the Damascus gate.

Artaban joined company with a group of people from his own country, Parthian Jews who had come up to keep the Passover, and inquired of them the cause of the tumult, and where they were going.

"We are going," they answered, "to the place called Golgotha, outside the city walls, where there is to be an execution. Have you not heard what has happened? Two famous robbers are to be crucified, and with them another, called Jesus of Nazareth, a man who has done many wonderful works among the people, so that they love him greatly. But the priests and elders have said that he must die, because he gave himself out to be the Son of God. And Pilate has sent him to the cross because he said that he was the 'King of the Jews.'"

How strangely these familiar words fell upon the tired heart of Artaban! They had led him for a lifetime over land and sea. And now they came to him darkly and mysteriously like a message of despair. The King had arisen, but He had been denied and cast out. He was about to perish. Perhaps He was already dying. Could it be the same who had been born in Bethlehem thirty-three years ago, at whose birth the star had appeared in heaven, and of whose coming the prophets had spoken?

Artaban's heart beat unsteadily with that troubled, doubtful apprehension which is the excitement of old age. But he said within himself: "The ways of God are stranger than the thoughts of men, and it may be that I shall find the King, at last, in the hands of His enemies, and shall come in time to offer my pearl for His ransom before He dies."

So the old man followed the multitude with slow and painful steps toward the Damascus gate of the city. Just beyond the entrance of the guard-house a troop of Macedonian soldiers came down the street, dragging a young girl with torn dress and dishevelled hair. As the Magian paused to look at her with compassion, she broke suddenly from the hands of her tormentors and threw herself at his feet, clasping him around the knees. She had seen his white cap and the winged circle on his breast.

"Have pity on me," she cried, "and save me, for the sake of the God of purity! I also am a daughter of the true religion which is taught by the Magi. My father was a merchant of Parthia, but he is dead, and I am seized for his debts to be sold as a slave. Save me from worse than death."

Artaban trembled.

It was the old conflict in his soul, which had come to him in the palm-grove of Babylon and in the cottage at Bethlehem—the conflict between the expectation of faith and the impulse of love. Twice the gift which he had consecrated to the worship of religion had been drawn from his hand to the service of humanity. This was the third trial, the ultimate probation, the final and irrevocable choice.

Was it his great opportunity or his last temptation? He could not tell. One thing only was clear in the darkness of his mind—it was inevitable. And does not the inevitable come from God?

One thing only was sure to his divided heart—to rescue this helpless girl would be a true deed of love. And is not love the light of the soul?

He took the pearl from his bosom. Never had it seemed so luminous, so radiant, so full of tender, living lustre. He laid it in the hand of the slave.

"This is thy ransom, daughter! It is the last of my treasures which I kept for the King."

While he spoke the darkness of the sky thickened, and shuddering tremors ran through the earth, heaving convulsively like the breast of one who struggles with mighty grief.

The walls of the houses rocked to and fro. Stones were loosened and crashed into the street. Dust clouds filled the air. The soldiers fled in terror, reeling like drunken men. But Artaban and the girl whom he had ransomed crouched helpless beneath the wall of the Prætorium.

What had he to fear? What had he to live for? He had given away the last remnant of his tribute for the King. He had parted with the last hope of finding Him. The quest was over, and it had failed. But even in that thought, accepted and embraced, there was peace. It was not resignation. It was not submission. It was something more profound and searching. He knew that all was well, because he had done the best that he could, from day to day. He had been true to the light that had been given to him. He had looked for more. And if he had not found it, if a failure was all that came out of his life, doubtless that was the best that was possible. He had not seen the revelation of "life everlasting, incorruptible and immortal." But he knew that even if he could live his earthly life over again, it could not be otherwise than it had been.

One more lingering pulsation of the earthquake quivered through the ground. A heavy tile, shaken from the roof, fell and struck the old man on the temple. He lay breathless and pale, with his gray head resting on the young girl's shoulder, and the blood trickling from the wound. As she bent over him, fearing that he was dead, there came a voice through the twilight, very small and still, like music sounding from a distance, in which the notes are clear but the words are lost. The girl turned to see if someone had spoken from the window above them, but she saw no one.

Then the old man's lips began to move, as if in answer, and she heard him say in the Parthian tongue:

"Not so, my Lord: For when saw I thee an hungered and fed thee? Or thirsty, and gave thee drink? When saw I thee a stranger, and took thee in? Or naked, and clothed thee? When saw I thee sick or in prison, and came unto thee? Three-and-thirty years have I looked for thee; but I have never seen thy face, nor ministered to thee, my King."

He ceased, and the sweet voice came again. And again the maid heard it, very faintly and far away. But now it seemed as though she understood the words:

"Verily I say unto thee, Inasmuch as thou hast done it unto one of the least of these my brethren, thou hast done it unto me."

A calm radiance of wonder and joy lighted the pale face of Artaban like the first ray of dawn on a snowy mountain-peak. One long, last breath of relief exhaled gently from his lips.

His journey was ended. His treasures were accepted. The Other Wise Man had found the King.

11. THE CHILD AND THE BLESSING

CHRISTMAS MORNING

Elizabeth Madox Roberts

If Bethlehem were here today,
Or this were very long ago,
There wouldn't be a winter time
Nor any cold or snow.

I'd run out through the garden gate,
And down along the pasture walk;
And off beside the cattle barns
I'd hear a kind of gentle talk.

I'd move the heavy iron chain
And pull away the wooden pin;

I'd push the door a little bit
And tiptoe very softly in.

The pigeons and the yellow hens
And all the cows would stand away;
Their eyes would open wide to see
A lady in the manger hay,
If this were very long ago
And Bethlehem were here today.

And mother held my hand and smiled—
I mean the lady would—and she
Would take the wooly blankets off
Her little boy so I could see.

His shut-up eyes would be asleep,
And he would look just like our John,
And he would be all crumpled too,
And have a pinkish color on.

I'd watch his breath go in and out.
His little clothes would be all white.
I'd slip my finger in his hand
To feel how he could hold it tight.

And she would smile and say, "Take care,"
The mother, Mary, would; "Take care";
And I would kiss his little hand
And touch his hair.

While Mary put the blankets back
The gentle talk would soon begin.
And when I'd tiptoe softly out
I'd meet the wise-men going in.

LITTLE JESUS

Francis Thompson

Ex ore infantium Deus et lactentium perfecisti laudem.

Little Jesus, wast Thou shy
Once, and just so small as I?
And what did it feel like to be
Out of heaven, and just like me?
Didst Thou sometimes think of *there,*
And ask where all the angels were?

I should think that I would cry
For my house all made of sky;
I would look about the air,
And wonder where my angels were;
And at waking 'twould distress me—
Not an angel there to dress me!

Hadst Thou ever any toys,
Like us little girls and boys?
And didst Thou play in heaven with all
The angels, that were not too tall,
With stars for marbles? Did the things
Play *Can you see me?* through their wings?

Didst Thou kneel at night to pray,
And didst Thou join Thy hands, this way?

And did they tire sometimes, being young,
And make the prayer seem very long?
And dost Thou like it best, that we
Should join our hands to pray to Thee?
I used to think, before I knew,
The prayer not said unless we do.
And did Thy Mother at the night
Kiss Thee, and fold the clothes in right?
And didst Thou feel quite good in bed,
Kissed, and sweet, and Thy prayers said?

Thou canst not have forgotten all
That it feels like to be small;
And Thou know'st I cannot pray
To thee in my father's way—
When Thou wast so little, say,
Couldst Thou talk Thy Father's way?

So, a little Child, come down
And hear a child's tongue like Thy own;
Take me by the hand and walk,
And listen to my baby-talk.
To Thy Father show my prayer
(He will look, Thou art so fair),
And say: "O Father, I, Thy Son,
Bring the prayer of a little one."

And He will smile, that children's tongue
Has not changed since Thou wast young!

CHRISTMAS

Elizabeth Stanton Rice

There's a wondrous peace lies on this earth,
A snow white Christmas day;
All the brethren feel its spell
As they hush their souls to pray:

*Oh, Jesus, Holy Jesus
We call upon your love,
Forgive our sins, oh bless us—
We would ascend above.*

The snow gleams softer, gentler
While the sun beats in the air,
*Peace on Earth to all of you—
A Merry Christmas There!*

PART TWO

The Hidden Years

———————

But what was the sun like, before it came up?

WALTER DE LA MARE

1. HIS CHILDHOOD

THE SECOND CHRISTMAS

John Haynes Holmes

"And when they had performed all things according to the law of the Lord, they returned into Galilee, to their own city of Nazareth. . . .

"But Mary kept all these things, and pondered them in her heart."

LUKE II:39, 19

It had been a dreary year for Mary. Such a disappointment after that thrilling experience in Bethlehem! Was there ever such a birthday? Had ever a mother been so blessed?

Of course, Mary did not understand it all. She was a simple maiden—young, untaught, quite unprepared. Furthermore, it had all come so suddenly, and when she was nearly dead with pain. That night in the stable!—she did not dare to think of it at times, it had been so terrible. All day she had traveled in the dust and heat, knowing that her hour was upon her. Joseph had been so kind. The little donkey had hurried along so fast on his little clicking hoofs. But it seemed every minute as though she would die. And then, when they had reached Bethlehem, just as the night was falling and the chill was dropping from sky to earth, they could find no shelter. Would she ever forget how they went from door to door? No room, no room! Everything crowded! For the people had gathered for the census, and there was not a corner anywhere.

What they would have done, had that inn-keeper not taken pity on them, she never dared to think. The little Jesus, her darling son, would have been born somewhere out in the fields, under some hedge, per-haps in the gutter of the town, and probably would have died. But the inn-keeper had been kind—perhaps he had seen her agony upon her face! And he had let them go into the stable, where the sheep and the cattle had made it warm with the heat of their bodies and sweet with the breath of their nostrils. And there in the soft straw, close by an ox or an ass, she had yielded to her pangs, and at last had taken the little baby into her arms and laid him in a manger. She was weak and cold—there had been a good deal of blood! So she had not noticed much of what had happened. But Joseph had told her wonderful things, and she had kept all these things in her heart. For there had been miracles that night! Surely, more miracles would come. Her first-born was a wonder-child. God must show new signs to hallow him. She would be ready this time!

So all the long year she had waited. Every night she had watched for visitors from afar, or listened for music from the skies. But nothing had happened. The rains had come—the earlier rains, and then the latter rains. The lilies of the field had blossomed, and the hot summer had ripened the grapes and olives. Now the winter had come again. And she was still waiting—in vain! It was all so disappointing—as if heaven had been opened to her, and then been closed. Yes, it had been a dreary year. She could not understand.

As the months had passed, and life in the little home in Nazareth had settled down into the humdrum of morning, noon and night, breakfast, dinner and supper, the Sabbath, the week-days and the Sabbath again, Mary had fallen into the habit of looking into her heart, and dreaming of that night in Bethlehem. Sometimes in the evening, when the day's work was done, and Jesus was safely cradled, and the supper was cleared away, and Joseph, poor man, was tired and had gone to bed, she would be still wide-awake, especially in these last days before the birthday of her son, and she would climb to the roof of the house—the flat roof that looked up to the stars. And she would sit, and gaze far off to the south, beyond Jerusalem, to that place among the hills which was Bethlehem. It was there that the heavens had opened to the shepherds abiding in the fields. And an angel of the Lord had come upon them, and the glory of the Lord had shone round about them and they were sore afraid. And the angel had told them not to fear, for he brought them good tidings of a child born this day in the city of David, which was Christ the Lord. And suddenly there was with the angel a multitude of the heavenly host praising God, and saying, "Glory to God in the highest, and on earth peace, good-will toward men." Joseph had told her this, just as the shepherds had told him. For they had come to Bethlehem, and found Jesus in the manger, and worshipped him. She remembered those shepherds. They were simple folk, and did not dazzle her like the Magi. She remembered that one of them looked like her brother in Capernaum. He had asked to kiss the baby, and his face had shone with happiness. He was the only one of all the shepherds who was not afraid. Her heart clove to him. And then they had gone—and she had not seen them any more.

Sometimes she would remember it all in the day-time, when she was alone. This was not often, for the baby kept her busy. He was a dear creature—she could play with him now! And she had to watch him, to keep him out of harm's way. For he was toddling across the floor, and just beginning to reach for the pots and water-jars, and even for Joseph's sharp tools on the carpenter's bench. But there was the hour in the morning, when she went to the well to fill her water-jars. She would linger after the other women had gone, and the gossip of the village had died away into silence. Passers-by were frequent, but quiet was about the place. And there, alone, she would recall the Magi, as they came to her that morning out of the East, following the star which had led them to Beth-

lehem. She had not seen their camels and their servants, crowding the little court-yard of the inn; Joseph had told her about them. But the Magi had come to her, tall men in splendid robes, two of them old, and one a shining youth, more like a king than a wise-man. It had all seemed so unreal—like some kind of strange and wonderful dream. But when they had gone, there were the rich gifts for her little son—gold, frankincense, and myrrh. So it must have been true. The Magi had done obeisance to Jesus, and had hailed him as a King.

What did all this mean? Patiently she had waited for an answer but none had come. There were shepherds—but none to seek her out. They were here on the hills of Nazareth, just as they had been there on the Judaean hills a year ago on that night of miracle and wonder. Sometimes during the day they came into the town for food, or for a talk with the towns-folk. But they never asked for Mary and her child. And there were men who came from afar to Nazareth, rich merchants, traveling sages, perhaps kings and princes. Regularly the long camel trains passed by on the road to Egypt, and regularly they came back again on the long journey to the East. Sometimes they stayed the night, and filled the inns and stable-yards, even the streets, with noise and clamor. But there were no magi among them, no man old or young who knew anything about Mary and her son. As for the heavens, they were silent—no angel-songs any more! And the star, after those nights in Bethlehem a year ago, had dimmed and gone. Mary did not dare to tell how many nights, when all Nazareth was still, she had listened for the song and watched for the star. Joseph would laugh at her, and the neighbors think her queer.

Once, when Joseph was away, buying lumber in Tiberias for his carpentry shop, Mary had climbed to the roof-top of her house with the infant Jesus in her arms, and there she had waited, with eager eyes and ears, till the morning light had come. The stars were wonderful that night. They had cast down light so bright that she could see the neighbors' houses, and the streets of Nazareth, and even the outline of the hills. More than once, as the darkness pressed upon her, she thought that she had seen her star, Jesus's star—a planet larger and swifter than the others. Breathless, and with no more motion in her than in a frozen reed, she had looked to see the heavens open again, and an angel-host appear and acclaim her son,

But every time it was the same. Her eyes became dim, and the stars danced and became confused—and nothing happened. She had been deceived—or, rather, had deceived herself. And so all the year had passed, and the birth-night had come again. It was very disappointing.

But this second birth-night was going to be a happy one, even though there were no wonders. She was going to make certain of that! Once, to be sure, she had thought of asking Joseph to go to Bethlehem again, just as they had done a year ago. The little donkey was in his stall, with the cow and the sheep—he would know the way. It would take some money, but there would be no census this time, and thus no extra taxes. Joseph could ill spare the time from his busy shop, but a few days, only a few, would make no real difference. He could work the harder for his rest when he got back. And this time there would be no crowds—the journey would be easy and pleasant. And in Bethlehem they could sleep in an inn, and not in a stable. Yet there was one stable that she would see. In the dead of night, the birth-night, she would go there to the stall where she had lain the year before in pain, and she would wait. Surely the heavens above Judaea would open again, and the angel-host would chant the song of "peace on earth, good-will toward men." And the shepherds would come running to the stall, and they would exclaim that Jesus was now so big, and they would play with him, and talk to him, as well as worship his hands and feet. Perhaps she would see that same shepherd boy who was like her brother and had not been afraid. And if she stayed long enough, perhaps the Magi would come again, and bestow new gifts. If she could only be in Bethlehem, these are the things that would happen, as they had happened before. And she would know, in very truth, that her little son was indeed the King foretold of old. But she had not dared to ask Joseph to make the journey. He would laugh at her. Perhaps even he would be impatient, and rebuke her foolishness. So she had kept these things in her heart, and said nothing.

She even began to fear that perhaps it had only been a dream—that night in Bethlehem. Joseph had told her about the shepherds; but he had been dreadfully frightened when he saw how sick she was, and he was tired after the long and anxious journey; and amid all the noise and the crowds, and the natural excitement over a baby born in such a place,

he may have imagined things. There had been shepherds drawn into the town by the great stir of the throngs that filled the inns, and to the stable to keep warm, but they had heard no angel-songs about a son of David, and knew nothing about cloven skies. If they had pressed about the manger, it was only as they might press about one of their ewe-lambs in labor. Yes, Joseph had imagined things. As for the wise-men, they had imagined things, too. They had been misled in their quest of the King foretold. Yes, it was all a dream. A whole year had brought no sign, and she could be deceived no more. Nor should she be disappointed, for Jesus was her own dear child—her first-born, since already she felt a fresh stirring in her womb—and the loveliest boy in Nazareth. Yes, she would be glad that she was a mother, and had a son, and could make him a rabbi in the synagogue, and thus serve Israel and Israel's God.

And now was the birth-night! She must make everything ready for the morrow, for it was to be a day of feasting and revelry. Joseph, busy as he was, had agreed to lay down his hammer and plane, and make the occasion a holiday. The neighbors had been invited, and would come in—Sarah, and Abigail, and Deborah, and Rachel, and Rebekah, and Leah—each with her little gift of remembrance, and her blessing from the Most High. Even Elizabeth had promised to come, with John, the cousin of Jesus—that handsome lad, whose birth from his mother's barren womb had itself been something of a miracle. It was well for John and Jesus to become acquainted, for they would have much in common in the years to come. As for Mary, she had her secret. For she had baked some shew-bread in the hot oven, and drawn some wine from the oldest jars, those of Jacob, the father of Joseph, pressed from the sweet grapes these many years ago. She had it all planned —that when the company of kinsmen and neighbors were together, and tired from feasting, she would take the bread and break it before Jesus and give him to eat, and pour the wine and give him to drink. And then they would all eat of the bread and drink of the wine—Joseph first, and then Elizabeth, and then the others in their turn, and last of all herself. This they would do in love one for another, and in remembrance of that baby who had been born in Bethlehem. This should be their festival, when on the morrow the little Jesus was a full year old.

It was late when Mary's work was done. The threshold had been swept and the floor cleaned. The chairs and stools were in order about the table, and the cups in their places. Joseph's bench was thrust into a corner, and the tools carefully laid away. Joseph himself was sleeping, for the first peep of dawn must see him up. His shirt, newly washed, was ready, together with the Sabbath robe and the Sabbath shoes. For this was to be as a holy-day, and Joseph must be fitly clothed.

Mary was tired, but she could not sleep. Her mind was filled with the morrow, that everything should be right. There must be nothing forgotten, nothing undone. Also she was excited in recollection of a year ago. Perhaps that star had shone, after all! Perhaps it might shine again tonight, just in celebration! Suppose she looked, to see! Softly Mary crept to the door, wrapped herself against the cold, and went out. All was dark, except for a light in Rebekah's house, where she was tending her sick child. All was quiet, except for an occasional bark from the wolves, and a call from some shepherd to his sheep upon the hills. Was that shepherd watching, as she was watching? Would he be frightened, as the Bethlehem shepherds were frightened, if the heavens opened in song? But there was no sign, no sound. The sky, so black in its impenetrable depths, was studded with galaxies of stars. They were all there, just as she had seen them since childhood. As she gazed upon them, she saw it was about a half-hour to midnight. It was all as it had been on all the nights in all this year gone by. Nothing wonderful any more!

Mary turned away—and found herself walking not toward the house, but toward the little stable in the rear. Why should she not go there and lie down for a moment in the straw, just as she had done a year ago, when Jesus came? There was Toto, the donkey that had carried her all that long way to Bethlehem, and the cow, and the sheep close folded from the cold. The Bethlehem stable had been larger, and there had been oxen there, and camels, and horses. But the stall would be the same, and the manger. She could imagine it was that same stable where the inn-keeper had given them shelter. And perhaps, if she closed her eyes, she would see the shepherds again; and, if she listened intently, would hear them telling their story; and, if she folded her arms in the old familiar way, would feel the wee babe against

her bosom. She would go in, and wait till midnight. Then she would creep back again—and Joseph would never know.

It was dark as she lifted the wooden pin, and opened the door. She could hear the slow chewing of the cow upon her cud; there was a nervous crowding among the sheep; Toto gave a sharp stamp of his hoof, as though in recognition. She could see nothing—only feel how cold it was! But she knew the byre—that empty stall, close by the cow and the ass, where they kept the hay for the feeding! Quickly she found her way to it, and nestled down just under the manger, and pulled the fragrant hay about her to keep her warm. This was the way it was a year ago. It seemed as though time had rolled back, and she was in Bethlehem again. Of course, Joseph was not here; and there were no crowds, no noise, no confusion. All was quiet—just as it had been that night after the babe had come, and the shepherds had returned to their flocks, and the crowds at last had fallen to sleep. She could think now, as she thought then, of Jesus, her boy; she could sing to him the old lullaby of her mother's home; and then, perhaps, she could sink once more, just for a few moments, into that blissful oblivion of consciousness which comes so easily after the birth-pangs. It must be midnight now, just as it was when Joseph lifted the new baby from the straw, and placed him against her breast . . . How still it was—and warm! If only she had the baby in her arms again! . . .

Mary never knew just what happened. Joseph never believed; the neighbors only smiled. But before she went to sleep—yes, before she closed her eyes!—there came a kind of glow across the stable near the door. At first she thought it was Joseph come to seek her with his lamp. But she saw only the light—at first soft and dim, then brightening and spreading, like the sun in the east at dawn. It moved along the walls of the byre, until the walls were all aflame. But it did not burn, for the light was cold, like stars against the night. At first it seemed as though the light were shining *through* the walls, as light shines through a curtain. Then she thought it was shining *on* the walls, like the bright glow of the holy vessels in the synagogue. But soon she saw it was *in* the walls, and then in the stable, and through it, and all about it. The animals were as clear as when they stood in moonlight, only this light was a radiance which streamed not from one direction but from all. Mary could see her hands, and the stall, and the manger. She felt as though she were bathed in light—as though the whole stable were being flooded by the sea. Then slowly, silently, the light seemed to gather together where she lay. The rest of the stable grew gradually dark, but here the light was so dazzling she could scarcely see. It was "a burning and a shining light," a shaft of flame leaping sheer from the floor to the roof of the little stable. It must have been something like this that the Children of Israel saw when the fiery pillar led them through the desert wastes of Sinai!

And it was no dream, for the animals beheld it. Mary could not see the sheep, but the ass and the cow were close beside her. And they were not frightened. For lo, as she looked upon them, they bowed their heads; and then they kneeled, like worshippers before an altar—ass and cow side by side, and fronted toward the light.

How long the animals kneeled, or what they did at all, poor Mary never knew, for her eyes were now fixed upon the light which seemed to burst into a kind of final effulgence of glory, and then take shape into the bright form of an angel. How tall and beautiful he was! She knew she should be frightened before such celestial presence. But how could she be frightened, when she gazed upon such a radiant countenance and looked into such gentle eyes. This must be God's messenger, and God was good, and his spirit peace. So she was not afraid, though she was full of marvel and amaze.

But it was not long for her to wonder, for no sooner was the Angel clear in form than he found voice, and spoke. Like a psalm of David was his word, and like the harp of David his utterance.

"Mary, blessed of women," said the Angel, "thou hast been sad through all this year. Thou hast not found joy in thy child, nor content within thine heart. For always thou hast looked for miracle and sign . . ."

"But, my Lord," interrupted Mary, "there *was* miracle and sign, when Jesus was born in Bethlehem of Judaea this night a year ago."

"Yea, miracle and sign," said the Angel, gently; "such miracle and sign as accompany the wonder of every birth. To those who have eyes to see, a star shines when any child is born. To those who have ears to hear, the morning stars sing together and all the sons of God shout for joy, when a new soul comes into the world. There is hope for man whenever man is young, and for the world whenever another life appears."

"But I have believed, my Lord," said Mary, "that Jesus was King, Messiah, Christ . . ."

"Not so," said the Angel. "Thou hast borne not a king, but a greater than a king. Thy son is destined to be a prophet of the Most High. He has come to speak the word and do the will of God, and, if he have strength, to rear His kingdom. He will not rule, but suffer; he will be not the master, but the servant of all; he will command not by the sword, but by the spirit. It has been foretold that Israel shall be led and the world saved by a Suffering Servant of Yahweh, who shall surpass all conquerors, destroy all tyrants, outlive all empires, and subdue mankind to love. Thy son is he, if thou wilt have him so, for God has blessed him beyond other men."

"But, my Lord, these wonders in Bethlehem—did they not mark him as the son of David, to bring in his kingdom once again?"

"Not David," replied the Angel, "but Elias! The Magi came not to do obeisance to royalty, but to acclaim wisdom. The angels sang not of power, but of peace. O Mary, look not for wonders in the heavens or on the earth—for cloven skies and marching stars, for earthquakes and famines, for wars and victories of arms. These show not God! Look rather for wonders within—for a mind that dwells apart in mystic rapture, for a heart that enfolds the race as a hen gathers her chickens under her wings, for lips that speak the very word of God, for a soul that dares all for His kingdom.

"Delve deep into thy son's life, as a miner delves deep into the earth for precious treasure. What thou findest guard, though thou art dazzled and afraid. For Jesus, thy son, is given thee of God to rear and fashion for His service. Bind him fast to the Law of Israel; teach him the words and works of the holy prophets; turn him from violence and vengeance, and all the ways of hate; keep his hands clean and his heart pure; show him the path of love, and lead his feet therein; and give him courage to dare, and faith to endure, even unto the end. Then will he be not the son of David, a king, but the true Messiah, the Savior of the world.

"Be strong, Mary, for thy task is grievous. Thou must suffer greatly for thy son. Thou wilt see him despised and rejected of men, a man of sorrows and acquainted with grief. The world will fear him and hate him—beat him with rods, crown him with thorns, pierce him with nails. Men will repeat his words, and do them not; they will accept his commandments, and break them; they will hail his name, and betray him. Greed and power and war will everywhere prevail, and the kingdom never come.

"But be not dismayed, for thy son, though dead, shall live; and, though despised, shall be honored first of all men upon earth. Above the clash of arms his word shall sound; and in the darkness of lust and hate, his face shall shine. The world will not be able to forget him, nor mankind to escape him. For even where he is most denied, he is the Truth; where he is least followed, he is the Way; where he is dead in fear and hate, he is the Life.

"So long as the earth shall swing among the stars, men will return to him upon the day that he was born. In every stable of the world, upon the birth-night, his light will shine, and the dumb creatures kneel they know not why. And on the morning of the birthday, in every home and heart of man, love will be born again, and there, for a fleeting hour, do its blessed work. On this day will men live, in Jesus's name, as they would wish to live on every day. Secretly they will weep, that they still fight and steal and kill; and secretly they will resolve to fight and steal and kill no more. It will be long ere the kingdom come. God must be very patient. A thousand, two thousand years will pass, and men will still be taking the name of thy son and doing not his will. Wars and rumors of wars will fly upon the wind; darkness will enshroud the earth, and gross darkness the people; the nations will furiously rage, and imagine vain things; hatred and violence will do as ever the awful work of death. But thy son will live as the rebuke of all men's work; he will be remembered and reverenced in despite of all earth's wicked ways; and his words, like beacons, will point the way of life.

"Be patient, Mary, as God is patient. Be brave as God is brave. Though there be no sign nor wonder more, thy work is sure."

There was a silence, and the light began to dim. The Angel faded, like the dying sun at evening. The stable was suddenly dark again, and Mary cold. She trembled, and looked about her. But she saw nothing that she had not earlier seen. The animals were the same; they seemed not to be restless, or fright-

ened. She rose quickly from the stall, and hastened to the door, and stepped into the night. The stars were there, wheeling their silent way, and pointing to a few minutes after midnight. It was late—and she had been asleep, and dreaming. Or was it true—that, on this second birth-night, she had seen an angel of the Lord and heard his voice? She did not know. She only knew that she must hurry. She had been away too long; the baby might be fretting, and Joseph awake. She sped to the house, and listened. Not a sound. She pulled the latch-pin, opened the door, and entered. All was still! She must go to Jesus, and feel if he was asleep . . .

But what was this? The little cradle all aglow with light? No, it could not be! It was dark now. There was not a shimmer of light. But she had seen him, her baby, just as though a star were lit upon him. And she remembered what she had seen. The baby's feet drawn down straight and stiff, and his arms flung out wide on either side—as though he were stretched upon a cross . . . And on his face, his dear sweet face—a smile!

AT NAZARETH

Katharine Lee Bates

A little Child, a Joy-of-heart, with eyes
    Unsearchable, he grew in Nazareth,
His daily speech so innocently wise
    That all the town went telling: "Jesus saith."

THE BOY CHRIST

Helene Mullins

Exquisite face that agony must tear,
    Exquisite flesh that scarlet blood must stain,
Hide, hide, while yet the rabble does not dare
    To visit you, with implements of pain.

Unsullied hair, shrink from the candid touch
  Of friend and enemy, for both will be
With those who do not love you overmuch,
  Upon the crowded hill at Calvary.

Brave eyes that choose unworthy men to bless,
  Nor seek their gratitude, now turn away,
And learn to love your precious loneliness.
  Kind hearts, be more reserved and do not lay
Yourselves upon less loving hands that will
  Not fail to strike you on that shameful hill.

THE BOY JESUS

John Banister Tabb

Once, measuring his height, he stood
  Beneath a cypress tree,
And, leaning back against the wood,
  Stretched wide his arms for me;
Whereat a brooding mother-dove
Fled fluttering from her nest above.

At evening he loved to walk
Among the shadowy hills, and talk
    Of Bethlehem;
But if perchance there passed us by
The paschal lambs, he'd look at them
In silence, long and tenderly;
And when again he'd try to speak,
I've seen the tears upon his cheek.

IN THE CARPENTER'S SHOP

Sara Teasdale

Mary sat in the corner dreaming,
  Dim was the room and low,
While in the dusk the saw went screaming
  To and fro.

Jesus and Joseph toiled together,
  Mary was watching them,
Thinking of Kings in the wintry weather
  At Bethlehem.

Mary sat in the corner thinking,
  Jesus had grown a man;
One by one her hopes were sinking
  As the years ran.

Jesus and Joseph toiled together,
  Mary's thoughts were far—
Angels sang in the wintry weather
  Under a star.

Mary sat in the corner weeping,
  Bitter and hot her tears—
Little faith were the angels keeping
  All the years.

MARY AT NAZARETH

Cale Young Rice

I know, Lord, Thou hast sent Him—
Thou art so good to me!—
But Thou hast only lent Him,
  His heart's for Thee!

I dared—Thy poor hand-maiden—
Not ask a prophet-child:
Only a boy-babe laden
  For earth—and mild.

But this one Thou hast given
Seems not for earth—or me!
His lips flame truth from heaven,
  And vanity

Seem all my thoughts and prayers
When He but speaks Thy Law;
Out of my heart the tares
  Are torn by awe!

I cannot look upon Him,
So strangely burn His eyes—
Hath not some grieving drawn Him
   From Paradise?

For Thee, for Thee I'd live, Lord!
Yet oft I almost fall
Before Him—Oh, forgive, Lord,
   My sinful thrall!

But e'en when He was nursing,
A baby at my breast,
It seemed He was dispersing
   The world's unrest.

Thou bad'st me call Him "Jesus,"
And from our heavy sin
I know He shall release us,
   From Sheol win.

But, Lord, forgive! the yearning
That He may sometimes be
Like other children, learning
   Beside my knee,

Or playing, prattling, seeking
For help—comes to my heart. . . .
Ah sinful, Lord, I'm speaking—
   How good Thou art!

THE SEVENTH CHRISTMAS

Coningsby Dawson

I

It was the Seventh Christmas. In the village of Nazareth, which some say means "Flowery," all the children save one had wakened that morning quite unexcited and without any hope of presents. Grown people had gone as usual about their daily work. All the shops were open. No one felt any kinder than was ordinary. No one said, "Seven years ago today

Jesus was born in Bethlehem." No one had forgiven his enemy, for it was not over Nazareth that the angels had sung, "Peace, good will toward men." Had you wandered down that quiet village street, where no snow had fallen and no windows were decorated with holly, where sandal-footed girls were coming out from houses balancing pitchers on their heads, you would never have guessed that it was the morning of the Seventh Christmas.

Even in the carpenter's cottage, where the little Jesus dwelt, his father and mother seemed to have forgotten. And perhaps his father had, for bread was hard to earn. But his mother, though she did not show it, had remembered. On this day, of all days, she pondered in her heart the wonders that had been foretold about her son at his birth. On this day, of all days, she watched for the angels to return. But the wonders were long in commencing, and had she told any of her neighbors the miracle that had happened at Bethlehem they would have thought it an idle tale she had invented.

Though she had remembered that it was Jesus' birthday, she was ashamed to own it, for she had no present for him and scarcely any food in the house. So, when the one child in Nazareth, the only child in all the world who knew that it was Christmas, had awakened that morning, it had seemed to him that the world did not care. At first he was disappointed; but when he saw the trouble in his mother's eyes he sang to make her glad.

Before the day was ended something was sure to happen; something unexpected always did happen on his birthdays. Two years ago a shepherd had come all the way from Bethlehem, a four days' journey, carrying a lamb in his bosom. Still longer ago, before he could remember, someone had given him three golden caskets. His mother took care of them; she had never let him see inside them, and she had never told him their story. His father, Joseph, had been offered much money for them; but though they were poor his mother had always refused to sell.

All day he had waited for the unexpected to occur. As he helped his father at the carpenter's bench he watched his mother seated in the doorway, clad in her striped robe and wrapped in a white linen shawl as in a shroud. Every time a camel train shuffled by, stirring up the dust on the road to Damascus, he could hear the coins jingle on her forehead. She, too, was waiting—for what, he wondered.

The day dragged on. There was no midday meal. His seventh birthday and no one had remembered! What did the birthday of a little boy matter when times were so hard in Nazareth? It was winter; flowers had perished from the fields; brooks were white with dashing water; a bleak look was over everything, and work was scarce. Younger carpenters were always passing down to the coast towns with the caravans; they were glad to ply their trade for the smallest hire. Joseph could not compete with them. He could no longer stoop for his tools or move quickly. If no one was at hand to remember for him he would often make mistakes in his measurements; then all the materials that he had worked upon were wasted. So Mary used to send the little Jesus with Joseph when people wanted to give him orders for doors and milk pails and beds and chests. But because he was so often in error they wanted him less frequently; and when they did they beat him down in price because he was infirm.

"Ah, friend Joseph," they would say, "thou wast once a good carpenter before thou didst journey into Egypt. The hot roads robbed thee of thy strength. If thou hadst only stayed in Nazareth——"

As Joseph turned away the little Jesus would look up into his dim eyes and question, "Why didst thou not stay in Nazareth, Father?"

And his father would reply, as though defending himself, "It was for thy sake that I went."

"And did I go with thee? And was it there that they did give me the golden caskets?"

But the old man would shake his head. "Perchance it was a dream. When thou art a man thou mightest laugh at me if today I were to tell."

Because Joseph was so old there were times when he would fall asleep over his work; he gave the little Jesus orders always to stay near him to awake him. Then Jesus would try to bring comfort, saying, "I will grow up quickly, Father; when I am a man thou shalt rest." But his mother, who was young and more beautiful than any of the mothers of Nazareth, would show fear at his words and clasp him to her, whispering, "Nay, little son, thou shalt be a child for long years yet."

So it had gone on, and as Joseph's strength had failed him they had grown poorer, till now, on the Seventh Christmas, there was no food left in the carpenter's house. All day Joseph had toiled ceaselessly and Jesus had done his best to help, that the ox yoke might be finished by evening and they might have the money to buy bread. All day Mary had sat in the doorway gazing up and down the sunlit village street, listening and watching. At times she would turn her eyes into the shop and ask a question: "And they sang 'Glory in the highest,' so the shepherds said. Was it not so, Joseph?"

"It was so, if we did not dream it."

He answered as one who was sure of nothing; as he bent his head, his white beard caught up the chips that lay upon the bench.

"But the gifts from the East—the golden caskets—they are proofs. We still have them."

"Aye. They are worth a king's ransom. Merchants going down to Damascus would purchase. Wilt thou not consent? If we were to sell——"

Her eyes rested on him sorrowfully—the soft, dark eyes of a woman who had lived always in loneliness.

"A king's ransom! And shall we sell the ransom of our King without his knowing?"

She turned her gaze back to the village street, still desperately hoping. He should rule over nations and sit upon the throne of David. That was what angels, shepherds, rich strangers had declared in Bethlehem on the night of his birth. Since that first Christmas there had been no more signs or portents—only escapes, long journeys and uneventful poverty. It was as though with his birth the clouds had sealed up the stairway to the heavens and God had forgotten. No wonder Joseph was half persuaded that all the prophecies had been imagined. To the three golden caskets Mary's faith clung. At any moment royal messengers might come riding from Jerusalem to take her son away and crown him. Far down the road through bare olive groves, she would see the smoke of their chariots. She had the little robe ready, which she had worked for him secretly in silk and silver thread. But if they were to come and the caskets were sold, how would they know that Jesus was the king for whom they were seeking?

And yet Joseph was weak for want of bread. With the money that merchants would give them for the caskets they might live all their lives in plenty.

Seeing that his parents' hearts were troubled, again the little Jesus sang, "The Lord is my shepherd; I shall not want." From gray hillsides, where shepherds sat among the flocks, the bleating of sheep answered. Women passing by to draw water at the well and lean camel drivers of a halted caravan paused to stare in at the carpenter's shop, arrested by the boy's clear singing. Their glances traveled from Jesus to his mother. "Blessed art thou among women," their eyes said. Then Mary felt rich, though she was hungry and had given her son no present.

As the day faded and shadows lengthened, boys gathered about the doorway, crying to Jesus to come out among the cypresses and play at "kings" with them. He smiled gravely and shook his head. As they went away he followed their voices out past the threshing floor to the wide, sweet silences where brooks babbled, and in summertime the country was golden with oranges and silver with the quivering leaves of the olives. There, had he gone with them, they would have spread their sheepskin coats for a throne, and he would have sung to them. They would have plaited a crown and set it on his head as though he had been Herod. He would have molded sparrows out of clay for them, so like to life that it seemed he had but to toss them in the air for them to spread their wings and vanish. When evening was a blue smoke blown among the sheepfolds and lights were twinkling in windows in Nazareth, they would have brought him back, riding on their shoulders and shouting before him. But the ox yoke was not yet finished. Their voices died out in the distance.

"I am too old. I cannot."

The tools fell from Joseph's hands. For a moment he swayed above the carpenter's bench; then, gathering his cloak before his face, he slipped to the bed of shavings that strewed the floor and slept.

"Thou must wake him as he bid thee," Mary whispered.

Jesus bent over him. "He is weary. Would that I were a man; then would I finish the yoke myself."

"But thou art still a child, and there is no bread in the house. Thou must wake him."

Jesus stood up and spread abroad his arms; the shadow of the cross fell behind him. Mary covered her eyes with her hands. Jesus ran to her and threw his arms about her. "See, I will sit beside thee and protect thee; but he shall rest. Hadst thou forgotten, Mother? This day I am seven and nearly a man."

"Little one, I had not forgotten; but all day my heart hath ached for thee. I have nothing that I can give thee. I had hoped that thou hadst not remembered."

He laid his face against her breast. The memory of the cross faded. Again he was the tiny babe with whom she had fled into strange countries, seeing nothing of the perils that beset her because of the hopes she had had.

Once more beneath the sunset she cast her eyes along the road, watching for the smoking wheels of chariots. The road was empty; the heavens silent. No sign save the cross had been vouchsafed to her of the promised splendors.

Slowly, like sheep following into a meadow, the stars came out. One by one, in windows of the village street, lights were extinguished. The closing of doors and rustling of lowered curtains were heard. The chill of the Eastern December night crept into the air. In the darkness, at the back of the carpenter's shop, Joseph slept. It seemed in that shuttered world that of all those faithful ones who had greeted the babe at Bethlehem she alone was left to worship. They had given him gold and frankincense then; but now——

Did he slumber? She glanced down; through the dusk his eyes were gazing up at her. She remembered her own girlhood and the excitement of her birthdays. He should not be disappointed. She must give him something, but what, when she was so poor that she could not even give him bread?

II

"Art thou sleepy?"

He shook his head against his mother's breast. He had been listening to the bleating of the sheep; it was like waves beating among the misty hills. Far beyond white walls of the village, as far as eyes could reach, he could see the blur of sheepfolds, the glow of camp fires and the shadowy outlines of watchful figures standing crook in hand beneath the stars. He was thinking of the song that had been with him all day, "The Lord is my shepherd; I shall not want." Lest he should feel the cold, his mother drew him closer, spreading her linen shawl about him like a tent.

"When thou playest at 'kings' with the village boys, thou art always the king—is it not so?" she whispered. "I will tell thee the story of a king who was born on the same day as thou wast."

"Then today will be his birthday?"

She smiled in the darkness. "Today he too is seven. It is a very marvelous story."

"A true story?"

"A true story, but so marvelous that thou mightest not believe it were it not I who told thee."

Jesus remembered Joseph's words, "When thou art a man thou mightest laugh at me if today I were to tell thee." He sat very breathless, for he knew that now he was to learn why his father had taken that long journey into Egypt. And he thought that if he listened intently he might learn whence had come the mysterious golden caskets which his mother would not sell though much money had been offered.

"I, Mary, knew the mother of this king." Her lips trembled against his cheek, and her voice came tenderly. "Doth it seem strange to thee, little Jesus, that thy mother should have known the mother of a king? Every morning and evening with the village girls she would go to draw water at the well. As she went down the street with her empty pitcher she had to pass a carpenter's shop. The carpenter would pause in his work to smile at her; sometimes, when she was returning, he would lay aside his tools and step out to gaze after her. There came a day when he took the pitcher from her hand. 'It is too heavy for thee,' he said. After that, whenever he saw her returning, he would carry the brimming pitcher for her. But this, all this, was before the King's coming and is not what I meant to tell thee."

She ceased; in the quiet of her heart she was dreaming to herself that part of the story.

"One evening," she said, "when the air was sweet with flowers, she was sitting alone in her garden. In the stillness she heard a rush of wings, like to the sound of swallows darting. With the sound of wings came a light that was dazzling. When she looked up, standing in the path before her was an angel who had been sent to her from God."

Jesus pressed against her eagerly. "And did he tell her aught of the golden caskets?"

Mary laughed gently. Remembering had made her happy, so that she had forgotten her poverty. Stooping, she kissed the uplifted face. "Nay, be patient. The golden caskets come later. He told her that she should be the mother of a king and that among women she should be called blessed; for the King, when he came should be the Son of God, and should bring love into the world."

"To be the mother of a king must be very blessed." The little boy spoke gravely. "And after that, Mother, what did he tell her?"

"Spreading his wings, he flew away till the flash of his going grew faint above the palm trees in the gold of the sunset. Next morning the carpenter watched for her to pass; when she did not go to draw water at the well he came in search of her. She was still sitting where the angel had left her, gazing straight before her; for, as thou sayest, to be the mother of a king is very blessed, but it is very terrible to be the mother of the Son of God. Then the carpenter asked her why she had not been to draw water. Now, though he was a good man, he had never seen an angel; and so, when she told him——"

Behind, in the darkness, Joseph stirred. "I cannot," he muttered; "I cannot." In his dreams he was still troubled because the ox yoke was unfinished. Through the shadows Mary spoke to him. Sighing like a child, he ceased from his muttering and slept peaceably.

"And because he had never seen an angel?" Jesus questioned.

Mary turned back from gazing into the dimness of the shop. "Because he was a good man he came to understand at last. Through the summer, while the oranges were yellowing, they lived very happily. In the evenings, in the garden where the angel had appeared to her, the carpenter carved a royal cradle, with cherubim upon it, and she wove robes in preparation for the King's coming. It was in the winter, just before he was expected, that a decree went out from Caesar Augustus that all the world should go, everyone to his own city, to be taxed. Having closed his shop, the carpenter bought an ass and set the mother of the unborn King upon it."

"Was it not a camel, Mother, all covered with gold and purple, such as princes from far countries ride when they pass through Nazareth to the bazaar at Damascus?"

She bowed her head. It was the question she herself would have asked. "It is a true story," she whispered, "and very marvelous—more marvelous as it goes on. The mother of God's Son set out riding on an ass, and the carpenter walked beside her with his staff. Roads were thronged with merchants and soldiers and caravans—with people traveling like the carpenter, everyone to his own city, to be taxed. As the mother of God's Son passed no one noticed her. Men in the fields did not look up from their plowing. Often the carpenter would have to draw the ass aside lest she should be splashed by the wheels of a chariot. She watched them all; she had never known that there were so many people in the world. 'All these my son shall rule,' she thought.

"Through the rose gardens of Jericho she traveled, till on the fourth day, as the sun was setting, Jerusalem blazed up like a golden temple. 'It is here that he will come to be crowned,' she thought; 'perchance it is here he will be born.'

"But Jerusalem was crowded, and the carpenter had kinsfolk in Bethlehem, which was but a six miles' journey; so, though she was weary and the ass stumbled in his steps and the carpenter's feet were sore, they left the domes of Jerusalem behind them and hurried on."

Mary sighed at the remembered pain of that Hebron road, the jolting of the rough track through the mountains, and the forlornness of her thoughts.

Jesus lifted up his arms, drawing down his mother's face to him. Thus they sat in silence. "Had I been there, I would have helped thee," he said at last.

"Thou!" She peered into his eyes, frightened by his quietness. "Little Jesus, thou hast guessed?"

It was as though, beneath the gay seriousness of his childishness, he had always known that he was the Son of God. The earthly mother in her shrank from the thought, as she had shrunk from the shadow of the cross. It made him too little hers in making him so largely God's.

"There is much that thou canst not understand," she faltered. "Someday, when thou art older—"

"Yet tell me," he pleaded. "Am I not nearly a man? Today I am seven."

"Yea, today thou art seven, and I have no present for thee; therefore, I will tell thee. It was growing dark as we climbed up to Bethlehem; far away in the clouds, like a white palace hewn from the moonlight, it shone. Every window was illumined, and all along the road we met travelers turning back. 'There is no room,' they called to us, 'no room.' But Joseph pressed forward, for he had kinsfolk living there; he thought they would take pity on my necessity. We came to the last ascent and the gateway; we entered. He went from door to door, inquiring for shelter, that I might find rest. His kinsfolk and friends with one accord began to make excuses: 'If we had but known of thy coming; if thou hadst but arrived earlier.' Even at the inn there was no place left for us. When my strength was gone, hard by the courtyard of the inn we found a cave in the rocks, where cattle were stalled. The kindly beasts made

way for us, and there, on such a starry night as this is, thou—thou who shalt be ruler over all the world—wast born."

He raised himself in her lap, leaning against her breast and turning her face toward him. "Dost thou believe it?"

Again the question that oppressed her heart! "Why dost thou ask?"

His child's eyes reached up to hers through the dark. "Because we are poor."

"I was poor then." Her voice broke and sank. "I was Mary of Nazareth, as I am now. Ah, but I believed it, for there were signs and portents and wonders in the heavens! Yea, and I still believe it. Have I not treasured all these memories in my heart? I wrapped thee in swaddling clothes and laid thee in a manger because there was no room for thee in the abodes of men—no room for the Son of God! Come near to me, Little Jesus. When I hold thee so I can still believe that I, Mary of Nazareth, am rich and blessed. For seven long years, as many years as thou art, I have kept silent; but now I will tell thee.

"There were shepherds in the fields of Bethlehem, keeping watch over their flocks that night. Dost thou remember how one of them came to Nazareth, a four days' journey, bringing thee a lamb in his arms? And lo, as they watched their flocks, the angel of the Lord came upon them, and the glory of the Lord shone round about them; and they were sore afraid. And the angel said unto them, 'Fear not. For, behold, I bring unto you good tidings of great joy, which shall be to all nations. For unto you is born this day in the city of David a Savior which is Christ the Lord. And this shall be a sign unto you: ye shall find the babe wrapped in swaddling clothes and lying in a manger.'

"And suddenly there was with the angel a multitude of the heavenly host, praising God and saying, 'Glory to God in the highest, and on earth peace, good will toward men.'

"And it came to pass, as the angels were gone away into heaven, the shepherds said one to another, 'Let us now go even unto Bethlehem and see this thing which is come to pass, which the Lord hath made known unto us.' And they came with haste and found thee lying in a manger.

"Scarcely had they departed when a great clamor of trumpets rose upon the night, and the sound of men beating upon doors and demanding, 'Where is he that is born King of the Jews? We have seen his star in the East and are come to worship.'

"So Joseph stepped out from the cave among the rocks and looked down into the courtyard. There he saw a train of camels, caparisoned in gold and purple, like to the camels on which princes ride when they go through Nazareth to the bazaar at Damascus. And from all their necks hung bells that tinkled, and the men who sat upon them waved torches. So great was the company that it spread like a river beneath the city gate and far down the hill. At the head of it rode three kings with shining crowns, and their servants beat upon the doors and shouted, 'Where is he that is born King of the Jews? We have seen his star in the East and are come to worship.'

"Then the householders rose from sleep and looked out from their windows. 'There hath been no king in Bethlehem, my lords, since David.'

"And the master of the inn opened his door, lest his guests should be disturbed and made angry. 'No king hath been born in Bethlehem,' he said, 'but, perchance, in Jerusalem, it may have happened.'

"Then the three lords lifted up their arms and pointed. 'It hath led us from the East,' they chanted; 'for many nights it hath moved before us.'

"And while they yet spake, a star was let down from heaven and came to rest like a lantern above the cave where thou wast lying.

" 'It is naught but a hole in the rocks where beasts are stalled,' said the innkeeper.

"But when the three kings saw the star, they rejoiced with exceeding great joy and made haste to descend from their camels. And when they were come into the cave and saw thee lying in my arms as I sat among the oxen, they fell on their faces and worshipped.

" 'My lords, whence are ye come to me?' I asked.

"Then they uncovered their faces. And I saw that one was a boy, smooth of face and ruddy of countenance. And one was a man in the power of his strength, tanned by the desert and black-bearded. One was white as snow, with eyes that blazed like fires, and so old that his voice was like a reed shaken. And it was he who answered.

" 'Mother of mothers, from the East have we journeyed, and all the gods of Persia have called thee blessed. Long have we waited for thy son to be born, for our prophet, Zoroaster, foretold his coming; and we have a book, which bears the name of Seth the son of Adam, wherein all things are written concerning the star. And in the land of Persia we have a temple, in which are kept the images of our gods and goddesses. On the night on which the star, long awaited, appeared, all our gods and goddesses were heard talking together; in the morning, when we entered the temple, all the images were fallen on their faces. Then we rode forth following the star. Hither we have come bearing presents.'

"Then three slaves appeared, each standing behind his lord and bearing in his arms a golden casket. And the oldest lord took from his slave his casket and lifted therefrom a crown, which he set upon thy forehead, saying, 'This crown I give unto thee for Power. The gold whereof it is made consisteth of thirty pieces, which were a funeral offering unto Adam. It was carried with his body in the Ark, and afterward was coined by Terah. It was for these pieces, also, that Joseph was sold into Egypt by his brethren. Next they were paid as tribute unto Pharaoh, and with them Joseph bought from Sheba the perfumes for the body of his father, Jacob. In aftertimes the Queen of Sheba made a present of them unto Solomon, and so they remained at Jerusalem till Israel was carried captive into Babylon. Now that thou art come, the East yields them back to thee.'

"Then the second lord, who was black-bearded, took from his slave his casket; and when he had opened it there stole forth a sweet fragrance. 'This frankincense,' he said, and his voice was like a strong wind blowing, 'the East yields unto thee for worship.'

"Then the third lord, who was smooth of face, with the foreboding of youth in his eyes, took tremblingly from the hands of his slave his casket, and his voice was like the weeping of a woman."

Mary fell silent. Slowly, one by one, her tears crept down till they fell upon the face of Jesus.

"Mother, tell me—nay, Mother, thou didst promise."

" 'From the East,' he said, 'I bring thee myrrh, which signifieth Death—a gift to every man of woman born.'

"Then they each one took thee in his arms and gazed very wonderingly. On account of the smallness of my means I gave unto them one of thy swaddling bands, which those great lords received with every mark of reverence. And when they had bidden thee farewell they would not go into the inn because it had refused to give thee shelter; but they tethered their camels in the courtyard, and they raised their tents beneath the stars. While they slept an angel appeared unto them, saying, 'Get thee up, and depart swiftly another way.' So they arose and set out for the ships at Tarshish; by morning they were gone. And the same angel spake unto Joseph in a dream, 'Arise. Take the young child and escape into Egypt; for Herod will seek the young child to destroy him.'

"And we straightway fled, taking with us the golden caskets. As we hurried along, I riding on the ass and Joseph walking with his staff, soldiers came marching from Jerusalem and entered into Bethlehem, inquiring diligently for a holy child which had been born. And when they found thee not they put all children that were in Bethlehem to the sword. From the white city on the mountain height a cry went up—women weeping for their children, who would not be comforted because they were not.

"In Egypt work was hard to find; the roads were hot, and Joseph grew old through poverty. Homesickness came upon us for Nazareth, for its olive groves, its sheepfolds, and its shadowy twilights. Then word came to us that Herod was dead and that Archelaus reigned in the room of his father. So we returned to the carpenter's shop, with naught left to us of all these glories save only the golden caskets. The rest—the rest thou knowest."

III

From behind them the breathing of Joseph came softly. Upon the face of Jesus the tears of Mary fell.

He sat as one entranced, awestruck and smiling, thinking of the three great Persian lords, and of the many camels which were like a river, and of the waving torches. Whither had they sailed in the ships from Tarshish, and had the star, which was like a lantern, still gone before them? Then he thought of Herod, and of the old age that Egypt had brought upon Joseph.

"I was so small; wherefore did he wish to kill me?"

"Because of the question that the lords had asked, calling thee the King of the Jews."

"It is the game at which I play with the village boys. Mother, but am I—?"

She pressed her lips against him to silence them. "Thou art a child, the son of Mary. Herod was not good; he feared lest God should wrest his throne from him."

Jesus laughed, holding up his hands in the moonlight and spreading wide his fingers.

Mary took his hands and bent over him. "Why dost thou laugh?"

"Because they are so small; yet thou sayest that he feared them. Archelaus is King of the Jews, while I lack bread. Mother, dost thou think that when I am a man I shall wrest his throne from him?"

"Hush!" She clutched him to her. "Say no more. Say nothing of what I have told thee. If any should have heard thee—Thou art young. Think no more of it. Let it be as a dream that thou wilt forget shortly."

"But it was no dream. Thou didst say it was no dream."

"Nay, it was no dream," she whispered.

A true story! He sat in thought. He, who wore a sheepskin coat and helped in the carpenter's shop and went about with Joseph remembering his measurements—he was the Son of God.

"It is my seventh birthday," he said; "let me look into the golden caskets."

In the barrenness of the present her heart cried out for such a confirmation of the glories that were past. Rising, she entered the shop on tiptoe for fear of waking Joseph. From the place where she had hidden them in readiness for the arrival of charioteers and horsemen who should summon her son to his crowning, she brought them forth; with them she brought the royal robe that she had woven. In the shuttered street, with nothing stirring save the distant flocks and none to watch her save the stars, she put the robe upon him. When, looking down at the kingly shadow that he cast, his eyes danced with gladness and he clapped his hands childishly, she caught his excitement. How often she had longed to array him in these splendors! Surely tonight, late though it was, some sign would come to tell her that God's angels still kept guard. Tremblingly opening the first casket, she drew forth the crown and set it shining on his forehead. "It is for Power," she said. From the second she drew forth the frankincense and scattered it upon his raiment. "It is for Worship." But the third casket, containing the gift which signifieth Death, she did not open.

As she watched him on the threshold of the carpenter's shop, palely attired, with the moonlight throwing a halo round him, the sorrow of her long waiting was forgotten. Her thoughts fled back to the garden of her girlhood and the angel who had come to her out of the sunset. It was enough, though all the world was careless, that she was left faithful. Falling on her knees, with her arms about him, she sang whisperingly the hymn of her thankfulness: "My soul doth magnify the Lord and my spirit hath rejoiced in God my Savior. For he that is mighty hath done to me great things—hath done to me great things——"

Her faith stumbled; suddenly she remembered that her child was hungry—her child, whom she shared with God. Then, because he was smiling, she took new courage. "And holy is his name."

She had sung thus far when Jesus held up his hand, listening and saying nothing. At first she thought he had heard Joseph stirring; the sound of a man sleeping still fell gently. She turned her head, supposing that in the street he had seen someone coming. Then she, too, heard it—the thud-thud-thudding of a swiftly approaching camel and a voice which panted on the night, "Where is he? Where is he?" The question got no farther, for the breath of the rider came sobbingly.

Through olive groves, bare of leaves, a dromedary came racing, swaying and staggering from weariness. It was the kind that princes ride when they pass through Nazareth to the bazaar at Damascus; but it came unfollowed and solitary. From its neck hung a silver bell which tinkled. It was caparisoned in purple and gold; but the purple had faded and the gold was tarnished. Upon it sat a man, gaunt and haggard, whose raiment was gray with the dust of travel. He leant peering forward; his throat was parched, so that at times when his lips moved he uttered nothing.

Urging his beast, he rode past the threshing floor and commenced the ascent into Nazareth. Between shuttered houses, casting his eyes from side to side, he whispered as he approached, "Where is he? Where is he?" As though he had been the survivor of a lost army, the memory of defeat clung upon him.

Kneeling beside Jesus, Mary watched. All day she had waited for ambassadors and lordly caravans, for a repetition of that first miraculous Christmas; now, while the world slept, came this lonely man, fleeing through the night like a shadow. He seemed

half blind. He would have gone by the carpenter's shop, but Mary rose to her feet. He halted.

"Where is he who is born King of the Jews?" he questioned hoarsely. "Once, when I was young, on such a night as this I found him. Tonight there are many stars, but no star to guide me."

She came out from the shadow and stared up into the face of the stranger. "Whence art thou?"

Bending down from his dromedary, he gazed at her puzzled, as though she brought memories. "From the East," he whispered; his voice was like the sound of a woman sobbing. "We had waited so long, I who was young, and Melchior who was old, and Balthazar who was midway between us. At last we found him, and all the gods of Persia fell upon their faces and called him blessed. Again we have waited. We have lost him, and the East grows doubting; for the world hath not changed from what it was. It seems a dream—all that we thought once happened. Melchior is dying; he longs for certainty. So with no star to guide me, because my faith is greatest, I, who am the youngest of we three kings, have journeyed forth. Where is he who is born King of the Jews? If thou canst tell me, I will give thee— But I can give thee nothing, for I have spent my all in the searching. Out of kindness canst thou tell me?"

Mary turned her head, glancing back across her shoulder. The gaze of the youngest lord followed. Gropingly he descended. His eyes met the eyes of the child. In the moonlight he saw the crown which shone upon his forehead, the white robe which garbed him, and the three golden caskets, two of them open, which lay at his feet before him. The fragrance of frankincense stole upon the air, making the night a temple.

"It is true. It is true. It was no dream."

Running forward, he would have bowed himself in worship, but something stopped him. Was it his own loneliness, or the loneliness of the childish kingly figure? Instead, he took him in his arms.

"I came to thee before with a lordly train and trumpets blowing," he whispered; "now I come to thee stained with the dust of travel and empty-handed. What is there I can give thee?"

Jesus stroked the haggard face. "It is my seventh birthday, and my mother is hungry."

From about his waist the lord unloosed a pouch in which were bread and dates. Sitting in the doorway of the carpenter's shop, he spread them out before Jesus and his mother.

"Were I in my own country," he said, "I would give thee a palace of white marble, with fountains playing and hanging gardens and slaves to serve thee. Here I am poor; but such as I have I give thee."

When the meal was ended they talked, and Jesus laughed and sang to them; but always softly, for fear of disturbing Joseph. "The Lord is my shepherd; I shall not want." And he taught his song to the young lord that when he returned to his own people he might say, "It is thus that the little Jesus singeth."

The night wore on. The Persian lord would have stayed till morning for the delight he had in holding the son of Mary. But Mary reminded him: "Melchior is old and dying. It is a long journey. What can we send to him to make him certain?"

Then they thought of the crown; but he himself had given it and might be offended. And they thought of the frankincense; but that was all gone. There was nothing in the shop to send him save the carpenter's tools, which would prove nothing; moreover, Joseph would need them for finishing the ox yoke in the morning.

The child spoke: "Let us send him the third casket, for it hath not been opened."

"Nay," said Mary, for she knew what it contained: myrrh, which signifieth Death—a gift to every man of woman born.

But Jesus freed himself from the arms of the young lord and brought it to him. "I will open it," he said, "and look just once, for it was thy gift to me."

When he raised the lid, a dazzling light burst forth, so that all save Jesus were blinded. But Jesus clapped his hands and laughed, for instead of the gift which signifieth Death out from the casket drifted the star. When the Persian lord saw it floating up into the heavens, he fell on his knees and worshipped.

"The star which we had lost!" he cried. "The star which we had lost!"

Halting above the carpenter's shop, dimming even the moon by the brightness of its shining, it waited for him to follow.

Holding the hand of Jesus, Mary stood gazing down the village street, watching him depart. Directly he was mounted the star moved eastward toward the dawn, going to bring faith to the dying eyes of Melchior. Only once, when at the point of vanishing the Persian lord drew up to wave his hand, did it stay its march across the heavens.

When the thudding of the dromedary had died out in the olive groves, they returned to the doorway of the carpenter's shop. As they sat there in the grayness of the morning Mary slumbered, and the little Jesus drew her robe about her to keep her warm. Then he took the crown from off his forehead and set it back in its casket. And he took off his kingly garment and put on his sheepskin jacket; for he knew that soon the people of Nazareth would be stirring, and they would wonder to see him thus appareled. And he said to himself, "I am nearly a man. Am I not seven?" So he did what he had never done before—he took Joseph's tools, and he worked upon the ox yoke.

Now when Mary wakened and remembered, she thought she had been dreaming. But when she searched for the third casket, which had contained the gift that signifieth Death, it was gone.

While she was still troubled in her spirit, Joseph awoke, uttering a glad cry, and called her to him. By the bench she found him marveling, for the ox yoke was finished and the little Jesus lay asleep on the shavings in the corner.

Bending over the childish hands, she saw that they were blistered with toil for her. Then she fell to smiling and weeping. "Of a truth," she whispered, "he is the Son of God."

JESUS IN HIS FAMILY

Winifred Kirkland

Students of Jesus' unknown years have strangely neglected the third verse of the sixth chapter of Mark. There Jesus' townspeople exclaim: "But is not this our carpenter, the brother of James and Joses and Judah and Simon? Are not his sisters living right here with us?" That verse stands in the very earliest and most authentic account of Jesus, but how many painters of the child Jesus seem to have read it? How many writers describing that childhood appear to remember Mark's words? And when you or I try to picture the boy of Nazareth, we, too, are likely to visualize him as a solitary child.

From the first the Bible record has plainly stated that Jesus was one of many children, so that it really appears as if people had persisted in regarding him as alone and apart, simply because they preferred to think of him that way. Jesus has often been described as the Holy Child. It is possible that many persons cannot believe that any child could be holy if exposed to all the rough-and-tumble of a crowded family life. But surely such an idea implies a rather low opinion of family life. A truer notion may be that those years of close domestic intimacy may have helped to make Jesus the sympathetic man he became. Jesus himself must have profoundly valued home relationships or he would not have remained at home for thirty years. Like any other man, Jesus learned to know men and women by first knowing the brothers and sisters, the father and mother, in his own household. Jesus in manhood showed a surprising insight into human nature. Perhaps, even when he was a tiny boy, each opening baby face was for him an absorbing adventure in understanding.

We need to look clear-eyed at that Nazareth home, and at the ten-year-old Jesus in it, in order to realize, first and forever, that the home life of the child Jesus could not have been easy. It was only a one-room house, in it there were at least seven children. Under the combined Roman and Jewish taxation, the family must have been cruelly poor. When Jesus said that two sparrows were sold for a farthing, perhaps he was remembering hungry little toddlers, and himself their brother. When Jesus spoke of the patching of cloth, he was probably recalling how he had watched a toiling mother sew many and many a patch. There is only one way to throw our searchlight back into that dim, far-off Nazareth dwelling, and to guess our way toward some knowledge of the children within it, pushing up, side by side, and inevitably influencing and affecting each other as they grew. The only illumination we can employ is to look at the Gospel narrative and see whether it says anything about the brothers of Jesus when they were men that suggests what they might have been when they were children and then to examine that same account to discover what characteristics of Jesus the man, already present in Jesus the child, might have affected all his family relationships.

The New Testament mentions Jesus' brothers in several different connections. The earliest of all is in the third chapter of Mark. Mark, writing as Peter's secretary, has been describing Jesus' abrupt emergence from obscurity into astounding popularity, a homekeeping carpenter suddenly able to heal, to teach, to preach, so that all the countryside stood amazed and awed. Then in contrast black as night against morning there came hurrying from Nazareth a little band of Jesus' relatives, unbelieving and alarmed. They came with ropes to bind him as a lunatic and to take him home, declaring, "He has gone raving mad!" On another occasion they would have interrupted at a sacred moment of his teaching.

Later Gospel references reveal the brothers of Jesus in the same light. The evangelist John reports a conversation full of taunts and ridicule. No brother rushes to Jesus' side when the Nazareth mob rises against him. No brother is present at the cross. Yet afterward the "brethren of the Lord" are mentioned as members of the brave persecuted church at Jerusalem. The brother James became a leader among the early Christians. Obviously the brothers of Jesus during his lifetime had little sympathy for his work.

We are all well aware that the attitudes of later life begin in early childhood. Just how old were they, those brothers of Jesus, when they first began to scorn him as a dreamer? Just how old was the young Jesus when he first had to learn to forgive, he who afterward when asked, "How many times shall my brother sin against me and I forgive him?" answered, "Until seventy times seven." Perhaps Jesus was no more than ten when with that tragic keenness of his he began to realize, "A prophet is not without honor but in his own country and among his own kin and in his own house."

But surely there were happier aspects of Jesus' home life as a child. There must have been, for Jesus would have been Jesus even then. Already he would have possessed the joyousness that later made him welcome at every feast, so that we may well believe he would have given children some glorious romps when he was still a child himself. He was all his life a lover of out-of-doors, so that we may picture him as marshaling his brood many a time for a walk to the Nazareth hills still today magic with varied wild flowers, and melodious with many birds.

He whose parables still command an audience of half the world, must as a boy have held youngsters breathless with his story-telling. Of all religious leaders in all the world's history Jesus is the one who most loved children and who most emphasized the value of a childlike mind. All through his brief, bitter career Jesus was always turning sunnily aside to the children along his path. What a tender, loving brother the boy Jesus must have been! And at first the little ones of his household must have loved him in return, as the babies later all along his way seem to have done. It was only as they grew older, harder, more critical, that his younger brothers drew away from his outstretched hand, feeling that somehow he was different, and resenting it. But later, when they lost him, they learned all that he had been to them, that once long ago. As old men, looking back, they came to see and love him.

We may conjecture that from his earliest years Jesus had the same attitude toward his family that he later, without exception, showed in all his contacts with all men and women, the attitude of reverent discovery. His readiness to discover his brothers, as they grew beside him, may perhaps have meant constant fresh discovery of himself, and of his capacities for patience and for adaptation. Jesus must have been pliant and self-effacing or else his brothers, when he had gone away from them at thirty, would not have gone after him so confidently to bring him back. But in his self-effacement at home Jesus as a child and boy may have been building up that self-control which was later to make him a supreme master of men. Very lonely the boy Jesus may sometimes have been there in Nazareth with his undiscerning brothers, yet for thirty unbroken years he remained in that village home. Perhaps very early he came to feel that he might miss something of priceless value for his own growth and theirs, if he should run away from those whom God had sent him for his loving.

Ever present, ever tender, as a background for that sprouting horde of children, stand Joseph and Mary. Each would have had a separate influence upon the development of Jesus' thoughts and together they would have had a shared influence, too. Mary's life was no easy one, poverty-stricken, heavy-worked, and often anxious, especially for that first-born son. Household serenity must have been for her a difficult attainment, but surely she achieved a high and holy peace, or so sensitive a child as Jesus could never have grown to be so joyous a man. Mary lived in a period when women were frankly looked down upon. Girls did not attend school as did their brothers. Women did not sit beside their husbands and sons in the synagogue. Masculine occupations that necessitated conversations with women were despised: the hairdresser's, the weaver's, even the millmaker's. In sharp contrast with his contemporaries how did Jesus regard women? How did he treat them as shown in incident after incident of his career? Where did he learn that understanding that made women in his own time his friends, and women of all time his followers? It seems as if a little boy may once have watched a woman in a one-room peasant home, and, watching her, have learned his reverence for all women.

And Joseph's daily life at home is also to be found written upon the teachings of Jesus. In that crowded household Jesus watched a village carpenter, quiet, gentle, tender, humbly trying to guard and rear his brood. What the boy Jesus, watching, came to think about Joseph is to be guessed from what the word "father" came to mean in his teaching.

And together in a devout, high, united endeavor to fulfill God's will for man and wife, Joseph and Mary wrote upon Jesus' mind a conception of marriage so high that even to-day it sets his teaching apart from that of all other men. The home a humble man and woman, true to the ideals of their race, achieved, became a fitting nursery for a child entrusted to them by God for their rearing. What Jesus, looking back, came to think of his own family life is best shown by the fact that he pictured even the kingdom of heaven as a home full of happy children, which no one might enter except as a little child.

2. TO JERUSALEM AND BACK

CHILD

Carl Sandburg

The young child, Christ, is straight and wise
And asks questions of the old men, questions
Found under running water for all children,
And found under shadows thrown on still waters
By tall trees looking downwards, old and gnarled,
Found to the eyes of children alone, untold,
Singing a low song in the loneliness.
And the young child, Christ, goes asking
And the old men answer nothing and only know love
For the young child, Christ, straight and wise.

JESUS IN THE TEMPLE

John Donne

With His kind mother, who partakes thy woe,
Joseph, turn back; see where your Child doth sit,
Blowing, yea blowing out those sparks of wit
Which Himself on the doctors did bestow.
The Word but lately could not speak, and lo!
It suddenly speaks wonders; whence comes it
That all which was, and all which should be writ,
A shallow-seeming child should deeply know?
His Godhead was not soul to His manhood,
Nor had time mellow'd Him to this ripeness;

But as for one which hath a long task, 'tis good,
With the sun to begin His business,
He in His age's morning thus began,
By miracles exceeding power of man.

JOURNEY TO JERUSALEM

Maxwell Anderson

PREFACE

Before I wrote *Journey to Jerusalem* I had come to a realization, along with many others in these bitter years, that there was no answer to Hitler and the rule of force except some kind of faith, faith of men in themselves and in the race of men. A Hitler is only possible in a despairing nation, a nation of men who have lost faith in their dignity and destiny, a nation which has no hope except that of conquest, no aspiration except to climb upon the backs of others. Opposition to Hitler is only possible in a nation which retains or can recapture a belief that there are other values beyond those of the materialist. A materialist has no answer to Hitler. Hitler would not be what he is if he had an answer to himself. He believes, quite simply, that there is no value in this world which cannot be expressed in monetary or scientific symbols. His philosophy is that of Iago, and his attitude toward his fellow men is like that of Iago

[*71*]

toward Desdemona and Othello and Roderigo and Cassio. They are gulls, to be managed and swindled and brought to ruin through their illusions and emotions. It was part of Iago's scheme that he would be more ruthless than the simple people about him could suspect or conceive. That is also part of Hitler's method.

But modern society has laid itself wider open to Hitler than Venice was to Iago, because there has been a general drift among us toward a belief in salvation by science and machinery. We have pinned our hopes on civilization and progress by material change; we have put aside the ancient wisdom of the race as expressed by the prophets and poets, and have thought, when we did not go so far as to say it, that there is no necessity for a morality based in religion. When a man has admitted that, he is Hitler's meat. If science is to take the place of religion and our morals are to be deduced from science, then the Hitler formula holds: Might makes right, those who are best organized and most ruthless should win, pity and humility and the contrite heart have lost all validity.

For if there are no values beyond scientific values, a man is an animal, to be worked, a woman is an animal, to be bred, a child is an animal, to be saved or not according to its usefulness in the practical and piratical scheme of things. The only sources of human dignity and respect for the individual are the great arts, such as poetry, and the great religions, such as Christianity. These are the only bulwarks the race has ever had against despair. Without them we look out on a cold and bleak universe, a complex of revolving forces throughout the sky, a complex of revolving forces within matter, and ourselves here among these forces, quite meaningless to ourselves or to the universe, with no destiny except to eat our quota of meals, sleep our quota of nights, and die meaninglessly at the end of them. This is despair. This is the despair of Hitler and the German people who follow him. Once accepted it leads inevitably to Iago's Machiavellianism, to the glorification of the state, and to mass murder.

If we are to oppose Hitler we must believe in ourselves, as individuals and as a nation. And if we are to believe in ourselves we must—and there is no way out of it—believe that there is purpose and pattern in the universe, that man can contribute to this purpose and that every individual man has a sacred

right to follow his own intuition toward that purpose in so far as his actions are compatible with the liberty and happiness of his neighbors. It should be every man's right and privilege to choose his own faith or work it out from his own flashes of revelation. But faith we must have.

It was reflection along these lines that took me back to a study of the origin of Christianity. Weakened though it has been of late years, Christianity is still the strongest influence among us toward that individual dignity upon which individual freedom is established. I have never been a professing Christian, yet I have always found in the teachings of Jesus the most convincing evidence of what we are accustomed to call inspiration. The words of the Sermon on the Mount seem to cut across the dark sky of Palestine under the Caesars like God's own levin flash, lighting up centuries past and centuries to come. There were many great prophets among the Jews, and their words are still impressive. There have been great prophets and seers in the Occident since that time, but I know of no other poem, book, play, passage or sermon which compresses so much dynamic and shattering wisdom into words. My own faith is that these poised, unhurried words come out of depths of meaning which the scientist cannot plumb, and that these words and others from the same depths will, in their own way and time, annihilate Hitler and all Hitlers by teaching men faith in themselves and in their destiny.

It was a study of the Sermon on the Mount in its relation to the old prophets and its own time that tempted me to set down my version of the mystery of the emergence of Jesus. He came out of the ancient Jewish culture, out of a profound study of the great voices of His race, at a time when despair and unfaith had gripped His own people, when the Roman Empire, ruled by sensualists and materialists, hung over a world of doubting and cynical slave-states. He came at a time much like our own in many ways, only further gone into the abyss of despair and surrender. I wanted modern men and women, sitting in an audience, to grasp the problem of unfaith as it presented itself to Jesus when He pondered the Old Testament in His youth, and by what seemed to me a happy chance I came upon the passage in Luke which describes His visit to the temple at twelve years old. This story of the Child of God in the court of the Sanhedrin, finding His way to the meaning of the universe as He walks alone among the columns— this appeared to me the perfect symbol of the soul of man searching for its own meaning. I still think the symbol perfect. My telling of the story is not perfect, I know, but it was written with reverence and with "a bowed mind." If my version of this haunting episode from the New Testament should offend anyone I am truly sorry, but I know that the moving figure of Jesus is too bright and eternal to be shadowed even for a moment, or take any injury, by reason of comment or re-telling.

NOTES CONCERNING THE BACKGROUND OF THE PLAY

One of the strangest facts about the life of Jesus is that the years between the beginning and the end of His life are left almost a blank in the New Testament biographies. His birth and the flight into Egypt are recorded fully, and His last year and the death are covered with relative completeness, but of all the weeks between we have record of only one—the Passover week when He was twelve years old and went with His family up to Jerusalem to celebrate the annual feast. Luke alone tells this story, and tells it in his usual beautiful way. It is to him alone that we owe the picture of the child Jesus as He stands before the men of the Sanhedrin and answers their questions with the disconcerting frankness of a gifted child. Without following Luke's narrative strictly, *Journey to Jerusalem* is an attempt to tell the story of this Passover pilgrimage to Jerusalem and to take the child Jesus to the threshold of His mission as He walks alone through the corridors of the temple.

During the life of Jesus many languages were spoken along the eastern coast of the Mediterranean. Greek was still the language of diplomacy and culture; Latin was the speech of the Roman soldiers, tax-gatherers and officials who governed the region for the Caesars; Hebrew was spoken among the priests of the temple at Jerusalem and taught in the religious schools of the Jews; but Aramaic was the common speech, known to all, and heard at every market place and street corner. Aramaic was the speech of Jesus Himself, and when He stood as a child in the Sanhedrin and conversed with the

judges, His native dialect and Galilean accent may easily have caused some smiling among the learned men.

According to the historians, Jesus was probably born in 4 B.C. The birth of Jesus was made a starting point in chronology by the monk Dionysius Exiguus, who lived in the sixth century A.D. Before that time, the events and years of the occidental world had been calculated in relation to the founding of Rome or the first Olympic games held in Greece. But these reckonings were inexact and conflicting, and it was not until modern research had combed the records that the facts of ancient history began to assume an exact chronological order. Partly as a consequence of these vague records, an error was made by Exiguus in the date of the birth of Jesus, and the dating of the Christian era was therefore dislocated by four or five years. It follows that Jesus was twelve years old in the year which is known to us as 8 A.D.

Although the revolution of Judah is not mentioned in the New Testament, it was unquestionably the most important public event that took place in Galilee or Judea during the childhood of Jesus. It was a desperate and almost successful revolution against the authority of the Roman governor who had been set over the tribes of Israel after their conquest by Rome. It was suppressed as mercilessly as Hitler has suppressed the resistance of Poland, with thousands crucified and thousands driven into the hills. In those days the mountains along the coast north of Jerusalem were full of bandits and zealots, bands of robbers and companies of holy men who merged with one another, and were often indistinguishable. It is probable that the evangelism of John the Baptist was a flame still smouldering after the conflagration of Judah's revolt. Throughout the New Testament there are many allusions to this underground life of rebellion which seethed under the iron discipline enforced by Rome through the tetrarch of Galilee, Herod Antipas, and the Procurator of Judea, Pontius Pilate.

The two Herods who touched the life of Jesus are often confused with each other. It was Herod the Great who ordered the death of the children born in 4 B.C. in order to cut off the Messiah in his cradle. It was Herod Antipas, a son of Herod the Great,

who, thirty years later, turned Jesus over to the procurator Pilate for execution. Both these Herods derived their power from Rome, for the whole of what
is now Palestine had become a Roman province
sixty-three years before the birth of Jesus. According to their usual plan, the Roman conquerors had
left native rulers behind them to manage these new
and recalcitrant subjects. The Herods were part Jewish, part Idumaean in origin, and as the years passed
they drifted further from their racial allegiance,
tending to imitate the Romans in dress, customs and
speech. Herod Antipas would have been mistaken
for a Roman in any social gathering.

———

Journey to Jerusalem had its first performance on
any stage, in the National Theatre, New York, on
Saturday, October 12, 1940, when the drama was
produced by the Playwrights Co., Inc.

———

ACT ONE

SCENE ONE

SCENE. *Before the Temple at Jerusalem, in the year
8 A.D. It is night, and we see only half of one vast
column of the Temple, which ascends at the right.
At its base are two or three steps leading into the
Temple. At the extreme left there is a low wall which
marks the boundary of a courtyard before the
Temple. A Roman* SOLDIER *is pacing back and forth
between the steps and the wall, looking out occasionally, toward the sky. A* WOMAN, *wearing a Greek
cloak and head-dress, appears at the left.*

THE WOMAN. Soldier!

MARIUS. Yes, woman!

THE WOMAN. I brought the wine.

MARIUS. You're late.

THE WOMAN. No, soldier; you told me to come
when the red star touched the earth.

MARIUS. You probably waited
for the wrong star. Or your husband was awake
and you couldn't leave. They say never trust a
Greek
or a woman, and you're both.

THE WOMAN. I came when I could.

MARIUS. Let me have the wine.

[*She brings out an earthen wine bottle, and a
handful of dates.*]

I've been watching those stars go by
six deadly hours, without one human squeak
or rustle to keep me awake. This Jerusalem—
the Jews must have a good conscience; when they
sleep,
by Jupiter, they sleep!

[*He drinks from the bottle.*]

THE WOMAN. And you sleep a little,
just a little sometimes!

MARIUS. If they caught me asleep here
they'd run a short sword through my lower intestines
and shove me in a corner. No, I don't sleep.
I walk up and down on this sentry path,
and by the procreative gods of Rome,
and the polluted gods of Greece, and the pimping
gods
of Egypt, I keep good watch.

[*He eats.*]

THE WOMAN. But here in the night,
by a Jewish temple, where nobody comes
and nobody cares who comes, why should it matter
if it's not guarded?

[*He sits warily, looking about.*]

MARIUS. Because the king of the Jews
is crazy, my mouse. Herod's crazy, like his father.
He sits there in his palace, and thinks he sees
the walls cracking, and fire leaking up through the
floors,
and devils tearing the curtains. He jumps and glares
and there's nothing there. He thinks the Messiah's
coming
and he'll be snatched down into some Jewish hell
to squirm on a grill—while the Messiah rules
the chosen people. Now Caesar knows Herod's crazy,
and can't trust any Jew to knife the Messiah
when he appears, so Caesar lends a few Romans
to guard key points and satisfy the old dolt
that everything's under control.

THE WOMAN. But this Messiah,
what is he?

MARIUS. Mouse, I never saw a Messiah,
but I gather he's a kind of Jewish god
from the machine, let down from the Jewish heaven
in a golden chariot of fire, to purge
the heathen. And according to the Jews

you're a Greek heathen and I'm a Roman heathen,
and we ought to be purged. So have a drink.
[*She takes the bottle. He starts up suddenly to
look about.*]
THE WOMAN. Any chariots?
Or gods falling in fire?
MARIUS. The centurion sometimes
passes this way to check on me. I thought
I heard the jingle of iron.
THE WOMAN. There's no one.
MARIUS. And twice
Herod Antipas has been here in the night—
in a quilted gown and straw sandals, slopping along
like a market-woman. I knew his yellow face
from seeing it on his shekels.
THE WOMAN. He's in Galilee.
You wouldn't see Herod here.
MARIUS. Oh, he comes down
to spend a night in Jerusalem, and watch
the procurator and myself. He's serious
about this game of "Look, here comes the Messiah!"
I've been posted
three different places watching for that mule's egg
of his to hatch. I stood guard for three months
on the road from Egypt—then for half a year
I stayed awake nights pacing back and forth across
an alley in Bethlehem.—He shifts the guards
without warning. And no matter where you're stationed
you're likely to see him, shuffling by in the dark,
alone always, and peering back as he goes
to make sure you're there.
THE WOMAN. [*Rising*]
What are you supposed to do
if you catch a Messiah?
MARIUS. Well, an intelligent soldier
destroys the enemy upon contact; I'm
an intelligent soldier—you follow me?
THE WOMAN. But suppose
he comes from the sky with an army?
MARIUS. Well, who wants to suppose
a thing like that? Look, the last light's gone out
in the governor's palace. The Sadducees and the
robbers
and the kings are all in bed beside their women.
Sit here a minute.
[*They sit down together.*]
THE WOMAN. Wait! I think I heard—
I thought there was something.

[*She rises, points out left, and runs into the
Temple at the right. MARIUS rises, looks out left,
and resumes his pacing. Not till after he has
walked to the left wall and turned, and has
come half-way back, does HEROD ANTIPAS slip
out of the shadow at the left and stand watching him. HEROD is a middle-aged man, wearing
gown and slippers, and some kind of skull-cap
for sleeping. He stands staring at MARIUS, who
turns at the Temple steps and sees him. For a
space they are motionless, then HEROD turns
slowly and goes out. MARIUS stands transfixed.
The WOMAN emerges from the Temple.*]
MARIUS. [*Not turning*]
Stay where you were! Go in!
We came within a hand's-breadth of it, mouse.
They say he burns them hollow with a hot iron
when he catches them with women. Go in, and be
quiet.
He's climbing down the path.

Curtain

SCENE TWO

SCENE. *The roof of the palace of* HEROD ANTIPAS *in
Tiberias, Galilee. It is surrounded by low white walls,
and looks out over the sleeping city. It is night.*
HEROD *sits on the wall at the rear, and a* SOOTHSAYER
is seated on the roof, facing him.

THE SOOTHSAYER. It is now understood that each
man has
his star, and as this star moves in the heavens
so will the man's life prosper. By his birth in time
his star is known, by the water drop that falls
when the midwife takes his head in her two hands
and brings him forth to earth.
HEROD. My star is known?
THE SOOTHSAYER. To me only.
HEROD. Tell me which is mine.
THE SOOTHSAYER. Just before daybreak
it rises over the lake. At this time of year
dawn is your best hour.
HEROD. I shall remember that.
Go on.
THE SOOTHSAYER. But first, your Highness, is there
any truth
you would not wish to hear?

HEROD. What kind of truth?

THE SOOTHSAYER. The length of life, the threat of
evil fortune
to be avoided—

HEROD. If it can be avoided
tell me then. Yes, tell me all of it.
Only if it should be my death comes soon—
spare me that.

THE SOOTHSAYER. You will outlive your brothers
and they will all die old.

HEROD. I shall outlive them,
and they shall die old. Yes?

[MIRA, *the first wife of* HEROD, *enters silently,
and stands looking off to the right.*]

THE SOOTHSAYER. Your star has been
attacked, and will be attacked again. A comet
returning every twelve years, fights against
your star, attempts to shatter it, to dull it,
to drag it from its course. It was this comet
that burned over Bethlehem twelve years ago
and triumphed over your star a single night;
but that ended well, your father executing
the children born that year in Bethlehem,
who would have endangered you. But now the
twelve year
comes round again. The comet will return
and you must beware.

HEROD. Beware of what?

THE SOOTHSAYER. Whatever
threatened you then, threatens you now again.

HEROD. The star of the Messiah.

THE SOOTHSAYER. It may have been.
I know nothing of that.

HEROD. But if my father
slew the Messiah, among those born that year
in Bethlehem—then there is no Messiah—
and what meaning has the meteor?

THE SOOTHSAYER. I can only say
that if an adverse star returns to plague
your guardian fire, then the evil was not killed
but only countered—somehow warded off
or frightened underground.

HEROD. If the star return.

THE SOOTHSAYER. And it may not appear. For
three nights now
I've stared at the Constellation of the Serpent
all night long, awaiting. It may be
it will not return, for by my own reckoning
it should have come and gone.

HEROD. How would you know it?

THE SOOTHSAYER. Oh, it would brighten the sky
like a chandelier
let down among candles—

HEROD. He would be twelve years old
if he were still alive. His age and birthplace
are identifying marks that could be used
in case a search was made. If this one is not found
then perhaps all should die. Your pardon, Mira,
but if these are your Arab manners, you may keep
them
for your return to the desert! This, as you know,
is my hour alone!

MIRA. Are you alone?

HEROD. Leave us, Mira!
I have no wish to be angry!

MIRA. Your saintly father,
Herod the Great, made a great slaughter of children,
a slaughter of the innocents, and made his name
a horror among men, because he believed
in some fantastic prophecy concerning
the birth of this Messiah.

HEROD. I know this.

MIRA. And remember it?

HEROD. Yes. I hold it in my mind
always—to take no step that will not look sane
to others—to you, to myself, to anyone
looking up from among the people, or from abroad,
from Rome or Egypt. I shall give no order
that might remind them of my father.

MIRA. No?
What do you contemplate?

HEROD. This is the year of the census.
From every part of Israel and Judea
the tribes go up to Jerusalem in spring
to attend the Passover. Once in so many years
we set our enumerators at the gates
and make our count for the tax rolls. It will be easy
to make a special search among the children
for the one who is prophesied.

MIRA. But this prophecy
and your fear of it, and what action you may take
to find out the Messiah—these are all
irrational—

HEROD. You are not of our race; you come
from the desert—

MIRA. And I see you as you are!

HEROD. I must find a way to make sure I'm not endangered

by a Messianic revolution! At present
I am in danger! There's a star crosses mine!

    MIRA. A star!

    HEROD. And not only a star! There's a wind rising—
and if it storms as it may there'll be little left
for any son of ours.

    MIRA. But how are we threatened?
We're at peace with the world.

    HEROD. When a man's a ruler
he feels the tides and currents under him
as a helmsman feels the sea. I keep a lookout.—
The revolution of Judah washed clear up
to the palace walls. The next wave may run higher.
And what do the agitators cry, and the people
whisper, like a wind blowing close to the earth?
Listen and you can hear it—"The Messiah, the Messiah!"
You hear it in the back streets, in the shops, among
    men
employed to dig the foundations of our palace
here in Tiberias. It happens the palace site
was pitched where an ancient Jewish cemetery
had filled the ground with bones. And the workmen,
    piling
the bones together, have a saying among themselves,
"When the Messiah comes these bones will rise
and tear Herod's palace down!"

    MIRA. Then what you fear
is only the Messiah!

    HEROD. I fear him only!
Whatever else God sends a man can meet
and face it like a king! But this seed of fire
that slumbers among the old books, this will breed a
    kingship
that I cannot face and have no weapon for!
I must take him while he is young!
Before he knows his mission, before the people
begin to turn to him! If ten thousand die,
if half my people die, and he die with them,
then I swear it's well done!

    MIRA. Do you remember
how once you woke me in the night to ask
that if ever I saw signs of the old brain-sickness
your father died of, I should save you from it—
shriek it out at you—have you beaten with whips,
chill you with ice and burn you with fire, but somehow
for our old love keep you sane—?

    HEROD. Yes, I remember—

    MIRA. But now it's upon you—this dread of the
    Messiah
surrounds you like a dream—you never see me—
see no one—see only maniacs—
you will bring us all down together if you persist
in this delusion!

    [HEROD *turns to go, then comes back to her.*]

    HEROD. Is it in my mind?
It cannot be all in my mind.

    MIRA. Yes, but it is!

    HEROD. That would be loathsome. To be like my
    father,
To be as he was. And be watched—and know—
and suspect that you're mad—and wonder—

    MIRA. Do you know what they say
about you in the palm-courts and the baths,
sunning themselves on a Sabbath afternoon,
and looking about lest someone hear? They say
he'll die as his father died, choking in the blood
of children—they say Antipater's gone mad
with his father's madness—that you see the Messiah
    rising
out of the very steam of your morning bath,
and scream for your attendants! They say you
    search,
as your father searched, for tokens and entrail-signs
of this mythical Messiah who will descend
to overthrow you—till the soldiers scoff in the barracks,
and Caesar's weary of you—till Caesar says,
"Humor the madman. The Messianic worm
kills quickly. Let him alone!" And you are alone
here with your seers and prophets, like a madman
shut up with keepers!

    HEROD. Oh, God of our fathers,
reveal your truth to me! Let the heavens speak
or the voice from your whirlwind!

    MIRA. It was your misfortune
to be with your father when he died, I think.
His flesh was tunneled through with living worms,
and you saw the bright blood bubbling up in his
    throat
from his many murders! It will be my misfortune
to watch you die as he died!

    HEROD. Take my hand, Mira,
save me! Keep me from that death!

    [*A sudden flooding of light falls round them.*]

    THE SOOTHSAYER. Your Highness,
look toward the Constellation of the Serpent!

MIRA. What is it?
What is this light?

THE SOOTHSAYER. The comet has returned.

HEROD. Then the Messiah lives, and must be dealt with,
and I was not mad! Send for the praetor! Quick,
I shall give the order before his comet dims,
and before my star has risen!

[*He claps his hands. To* MIRA.]
Fool! Fool of a woman!
It's written in the stars the child still lives!
He must be found—and must die!

Curtain

SCENE THREE

SCENE. *The interior of* JOSEPH's *house at Nazareth. The entrance is at the left, and at this end of the house a number of carpenters' tools and appliances hang or lie about. At the rear wall a long low carpenters' bench has been set where it can be used for a seat. In the middle of the room, somewhat to the right, a curtain, half-drawn, divides the shop from the sleeping apartment. Just to the right of the curtain sits* MIRIAM, *weaving at a small hand-loom.* JESHUA, *a boy of twelve, is reading intently in a scroll.* JOSEPH, *the carpenter, sits astride a hurdle, working with a draw-knife on an oxbow.* JACOB, *a younger boy, is reciting a lesson for him.*

JOSEPH. Will you say it again? And remember the third
reason has to do with something to eat. Think hard
about that and it should be easier.

JACOB. "Tell me why this night
should differ from all other nights of the year?
On other nights we may eat either leavened bread
or unleavened, but tonight only the unleavened;
on other nights we may eat of whatever herbs
we find. Tonight we eat only bitter herbs.
On other nights—"

[*He pauses.*]
Why do we always leave
an empty place at Passover?—No, I know
that's not what I'm to say, but why is one place
left empty?

JOSEPH. That's for Elias, if he should come,
or for an angel, if an angel should come in—
or for the Messiah. Or if none of these should come
then for any stranger.

JACOB. But how would one know Elias
or the angel if he came?

JOSEPH. We might not know,
and so anyone who enters is asked to sit
at the vacant place.—But you haven't said the third
reason.—

JACOB. "On other nights—"
[*He pauses.*]
Oh, but I know it perfectly well except
for those two herbs—the names of those herbs run
backward
away from my mind—and as fast as I run they run
faster
so I never catch them—

JOSEPH. The time will come, my Jacob,
when we all sit in Jerusalem with your father,
and as the youngest it becomes your turn
to open the Haggadah. Then you'll be sorry
you haven't listened and learned.

JACOB. But I do know it
except for the words that run away!

MIRIAM. Will you look
at the oven once more, Jeshua, and tell me
if the loaves are brown?

JESHUA. Yes, Mother.

JOSEPH. Before you go
and while I remember it, here are the silver pieces
for the burnt offering. Each child must carry
his portion of silver up to Jerusalem,
and take care of it, and not lose it, for with that
you must purchase the doves for sacrifice.

[*He gives a coin to* JACOB *and then one to* JESHUA.]

JACOB. I shall care for it. And thank you.

JESHUA. Yes, thank you, father.

[*They start to go out.* JACOB *runs ahead of* JESHUA.]

JACOB. [*Turning at the door*]
Then came the butcher and killed the ox
that drank the water that quenched the fire,
that burned the stick that beat the dog,
that bit the cat that ate the kid
my father bought for two zuzim!
An only kid! An only kid!
So you can't say I don't know that!

[*He runs out.*]

JESHUA. He'll know the rest, too, tomorrow. But he likes
to tease you a little first.

[*He goes out.*]

JOSEPH. How many loaves are you baking?

MIRIAM. Only four to eat on the road. Did I hear you say
there's a great census at Jerusalem
this year?

JOSEPH. Yes.

MIRIAM. How is it taken?

JOSEPH. The last time
there was a row of scribes at the city gate
writing at tables. And as each of us passed by
they took down name and age and place of birth
for the Roman tax rolls.

MIRIAM. Can you think what to say
when we bring Jeshua to the gate?

JOSEPH. Well, no,
I can't. It keeps coming back to bother me,
but I never find an answer. It has always seemed
the best thing was the truth.

MIRIAM. And yet the truth—
if we tell it—isn't it possible a soldier
would take him from us—and we'd never hear
what happened?—and torture ourselves forever, thinking
we might have saved him—wondering which dungeon
of Herod's he might lie in?—or might be dead—
or might be better dead?

JOSEPH. Yes, yes, I know.

MIRIAM. In all Bethlehem and round about they say
there are no boys twelve years old. If a lad came down
this spring to Jerusalem, and told the scribes
quite calmly, I was born in Bethlehem,
my age is twelve—

JOSEPH. Then the scribe would say, without doubt,
this is the child the first Herod overlooked—
this is the child our Herod's hunting for—
this is the budding horn of the Messiah
that must be nipped before it grows too tough
for the Roman pincers.

MIRIAM. If it be true—what sometimes
we have said—then it may be God cares for him—
and yet—if it be true—perhaps our God
expects of us that we be doubly careful
of what's so precious.

JOSEPH. Could we speak to him? Could we some way prepare him?
Tell him that this is only a doubtful guess—
and yet it may be true—and he must therefore
be wary in his answers?

MIRIAM. No, truly, Joseph—
Whatever is in him he must find himself—
Whatever he is to be—he must discover—
We must never say it—never until he asks,
I know this
as if I were being warned to let him walk
to the gate without taking thought. Yet if I were wrong,
and he should tell his truth quite innocently,
and never speak again—

JOSEPH. We shall be three days
on the way to Jerusalem. Some thought may come
before we're at the gate.

[*An emaciated* BEGGAR, *bent over and with a sack on his back, appears in the doorway.*]

THE BEGGAR. You're Joseph of Nazareth?

JOSEPH. Yes.

BEGGAR. I won't give my name,
though you might know it. My name wore off me with
the clothes I had when I went into the hills.
I'm one of the few remaining culls left over
from the revolution of Judah. There are thirty of us
still hiding above on Mount Tabor. What we get to eat
I leave you to imagine. We won't trouble you long,
nor anyone. But whatever you have in the house
that you were about to throw away—I'll take it.
A little mould or mildew wouldn't matter,
and we're used to worms in the meal.

MIRIAM. There's half a loaf
left over from our supper.

THE BEGGAR. If it means you go hungry
never mind it. They'll get us before the year's out,
and whether it's better to starve or rot on a cross
we haven't decided yet.

JOSEPH. The revolution
is seven years old. Are there still thirty men
at large in the hills?

THE BEGGAR. There are thousands, one place and another.
But the fight's gone out of us. And the fight's lost, too

The Roman tax is here to stay, and the Romans
are here to stay, at least for our time. And Judah's
dead, and we're dying.

[*He turns.*]

If it's true about
the half loaf, let me have it.

[*As* MIRIAM *fetches the bread the two* BOYS *re-
enter.*]

JOSEPH. I only wish
that it were more.

THE BEGGAR. You could give more, but why
    should you?
You could have fought when we fought, but why
    should you—
because we lost.

JOSEPH. They rejected me from the phalanx.
I wasn't young enough.

THE BEGGAR. I was young enough.
God knows I'm old enough now. The greeting of God
go with you for the half loaf.

[*He goes out.*]

JESHUA. What man was that?

JOSEPH. We're not a free people. Seventy years
    ago
the Romans came this way, and since that time
their governors have ruled our kings. Our high
    priests
are appointed from Rome; we pay a tax to Rome
and another to Herod. But it's all Rome. We're not
    free,
and seven years ago a man named Judah
led a revolt against the Roman census
and the Roman tax. He's dead now, and this man
was one who followed him. Will follow him fur-
    ther,
to the end of what can be done to a man.

[*They are silent for a moment.*]

MIRIAM. Are the loaves ready?

JESHUA. Not yet, I think, Mother.

[*A* VOICE *is heard from beyond the door.*]

THE VOICE. Some of the most unappetizing people
emerge from this residence.

JOSEPH. It's Shadrach and the others.
Come in, come in!

[SHADRACH, *a carpenter, enters with his wife,*
CASSIA. *They are followed by two stone-masons,*
ZEBULON *and* JESSE, *and their wives,* REBA *and*
ESTHER. SHADRACH *carries a torch, which he
puts out.*]

SHADRACH. There was a cabbage-green
sort of bitten-off fellow, with a sack on his back
that came out of here. Have you missed anything?

JOSEPH. No, Shadrach,
only a bit of bread.

SHADRACH. This part of town
will get a bad name, if it allows gangrene beggars
that smell like that.—Now any other color—
but this squeamish-green!

MIRIAM. Come in, all of you.

CASSIA. And don't mind Shadrach;
he has a good heart.

SHADRACH. No, but that was a spoiled man; he
    was mouldy,
he was on his way back into the substance
from which we don't admit we come—

MIRIAM. Sit here
and rest, Mother Reba. See, Cassia, we have
new rush mats, so that all can sleep here tonight
and start early in the morning. And the blessing of
    God
on all of you, since Shadrach must break in
without God's blessing.

[*She smiles at* SHADRACH.]

REBA. God's greeting to the house.

CASSIA *and* ESTHER. And to all here.

[*The two* MASONS *mumble a pious word with
them.*]

SHADRACH. Did I leave that out? The truth is
I've been God's-greeting the wide world today
and I want a place to sit down. The blessing of God
on the house and its accommodations!

[*He settles himself.*]

ZEBULON. We took
to the road before noon.

JOSEPH. Perhaps you'll be too weary
to start again in the morning.

ZEBULON. No, I think not.
We'll make it a three-day journey, and cool our feet
in the river when we're tired.

JESSE. When we were young
Jerusalem was only two days' away
by the path along hither Jordan. Now, of course,
even the young folks take three days to it.

SHADRACH. Yes,
and why not? It's our one holiday. I work
every day in the year, except holy days, and so
does Cassia. But then when the spring comes round
I begin to smell the Passover feast. That's once

we can forget about hammers and nails and prices
and set off across country like young lovers. I tell you
I'm no strict believer—
give me Ecclesiastes for my money—
"Vanity of vanities, all is vanity,"
there's a prophet—of the making of many books
and the laying of many bricks, and even the sawing
of many boards, there's no end—

JOSEPH. You were about
to say something?

SHADRACH. Yes, I was! I was about to say
man is of few days, and evil—he's born to trouble
as the sparks fly upward, and wherever he walks
there's a hollow place preparing in the ground
to house him at the last—so let him have
three days on the way to Jerusalem.—It's spring
and the flowers are out in the desert.

MIRIAM. I'm always grateful
that Passover comes in the spring when the desert
    lilies
are at their best. There's a kind of happiness
in the temple courts; one's happy just to see
the Sanhedrin, and to know that some men are wise
and care for wisdom—but what one remembers most
is sleeping open to the air, and singing
as we did when we were children, then waking to
    find
the Jordan suddenly, and turning inland
and returning to find it again.

JOSEPH. We'll take the three days.

JESSE. Sometimes I wonder about this Ecclesiastes
when he seems to be saying that nothing matters and
    there's
no God, and the life of man is wind. I wonder
about Ecclesiastes.

CASSIA. And about Shadrach?
    [She touches SHADRACH's hair.]

JESSE. Yes,
about Shadrach, too.

CASSIA. Yes, I wonder about him.
For a good husband and a good carpenter
he has some remarkably sharp things to say
about man's evil days.

SHADRACH. Few and evil. All too few
to spend with so lovely a woman.
    [He puts an arm around her.]

MIRIAM. I must look at my loaves.
I'm baking for the journey.

CASSIA. I'll go with you.

MIRIAM. And since we start early, perhaps you
    should choose your own pallets
where you'll sleep. Mother Reba will have my bed,
if she doesn't mind—

REBA. No, girl—I'm for the floor
with the younger pilgrims.
    [MIRIAM, CASSIA and ESTHER go out. A Roman
    CENTURION appears in the entrance.]

THE CENTURION. This is the house of Joseph the
    carpenter,
or so I'm told?

JOSEPH. You wish to see me?

THE CENTURION. [Affably]
You're a fine set of treasonous heathen, you are, live
down here among rocks and ditches, where a Roman
can't find his way even by daylight. I think you do it
to make soldiers break their necks.

JOSEPH. We hardly know
there are stones and ditches, we're so used to them.

THE CENTURION. Well, forget about that. I came
    on another matter.
You're a carpenter, and now I see you have guests,
and they're carpenters and masons. I'm here about
the palace at Tiberias—Herod's new palace,
and the work on it. When I saw you last at the
    market
I told you we'd need carpenters and masons
to work there in the spring. Well, now it's spring,
and we haven't seen you. A female devil take
those rocks! They've cut a strap in two!
    [He works at his sandal.]

JOSEPH. As you know
next week is set aside for our festival
and we shall all be in Jerusalem.

THE CENTURION. I know,
and I have my orders not to interfere
with a Jewish festival. That's understood
between Herod and the governor and whoever else
makes out the edicts. But I'm also told
to damn well get the palace built, and get
the men to do it. And the men aren't there.
And I'm here, as you may have noticed, and my
    neck's
not broken so far.

JOSEPH. Is it not understood
also, that a workman may pick and choose
among the tasks that offer, thinking of the wage,
and whether the overseers are of his race,
and the distance from his home?

THE CENTURION. There's no wage better.
We're authorized to pay the best wage there is.
And as for the overseers, I'll make you one
with your own men under you. You're known around
for an honest man, and we'll trust you.
    JOSEPH. Let me think
and give you an answer.
    THE CENTURION. I won't come again.
Not through your scarps and outworks. Answer me now.
Will you come when you're through with your Passover?
    SHADRACH. If you'll forgive me
I think the Centurion should be told the reason
why we avoid Herod's palace, and prefer
not to work on it.
    THE CENTURION. Why?
    JOSEPH. Have you never heard
that Herod's new palace in Tiberias
is built on the oldest Jewish graveyard known
in Galilee? Our fathers were buried there,
yet I've seen the bones of Jewish patriarchs
corded up by the workmen in long rows
out in the sun and rain!
    THE CENTURION. Well, Herod's your man,
not ours!
    JOSEPH. And not ours! He's no Jew, and wouldn't stay long
where he is without a Roman guard behind him
and Caesar reaching from Rome!
    THE CENTURION. Oh, Mother of Hermes,
are we so touchy about our father's bones?
You'd better take more care of the living skin
that grows on your backs!
    [MIRIAM and CASSIA *re-enter, carrying four loaves of bread.*]
Stand up and bring your faces nearer the light
so that I'll remember them.
    [*The* MEN *stand.*]
You had a helper
when you worked at Capernaum.
    JOSEPH. My son Jeshua.
He acted as my helper.
    THE CENTURION. Let him stand, too.
    [JESHUA *ranges himself with the others.*]
When you've had your holiday,
and taken your time about it, as you will,
no doubt, you'll come to work on Herod's palace,

and I'll hold you responsible for the others. Bring
your son.
    JOSEPH. He's still at school.
    THE CENTURION. Bring him anyway.
I'm being tender with you, my dear Joseph.
The only question is—will you say yes
to a pleasant man like me, or must they send
another less pleasant? You'll have to answer now
because I'm short of time.
    JOSEPH. Sir, there are no slaves
in Galilee.
    THE CENTURION. There are ways around that, too.
There are ways. And since it's no skin off my knuckles
I'm going.
    [*He turns.*]
    MIRIAM. [*Desperate*]
The work's done better when it's done gladly.
What good will come of a building if the masons
pour in a curse with the mortar, and the carpenters
peg the beams with curses?
    THE CENTURION. Curses won't hurt.
The empire stands on curses, and I've stept
on a number of cursing mouths myself. No Roman
dies of the evil eye.
    MIRIAM. But let them answer
after the Passover. Maybe some mind will change.
Let us not run after evil. Let us meet it
when it has caught up with us.
    THE CENTURION. You Jews go out
to meet it, and drag it in with you.
    [*He sees the loaves.*]
Speaking of bread,
somebody gave half a loaf to one of Judah's
outlaws—a known rebel. We took it from him
and here it is.
    [*He pulls a sack from under his arm.*]
Now we know that nobody here
would provision an outlaw, the penalty being death.
Yet he'd been here, and had the bread with him.
    You see,
I'm being tender with you.—
    [*He lays the sack on the bench.*]
You may as well keep it.
The fellow you gave it to is lying down
where he won't be eating bread.—I'll expect to see you
after Passover—in Tiberias.
    [*He goes out.*]
                            Curtain

SCENE FOUR

SCENE. *A desert place below Jericho on the west side of the Jordan. A gigantic rock lifts at the right, and under its foot a fire is smouldering. To the left a smaller boulder encloses the scene. It is the second night's encampment on the way to Jerusalem, and those who were planning the journey in the last scene are preparing for the night or already lying on their shawls and blankets. Someone has begun a chant, and all sing together the last chapter of Ecclesiastes:*

Remember now thy Creator
in the days of thy youth,
while the evil days come not, nor the years draw
    nigh
when thou shalt say, "I have no pleasure in them."

While the sun or the light,
or the moon or the stars, be not darkened,
nor the clouds return after the rain.

Or ever the silver cord be loosed
or the golden bowl be broken,
or the pitcher be broken at the fountain,
or the wheel broken at the cistern.

Then shall the dust return to the earth as it was,
and the spirit unto God who gave it.

CASSIA.
    [*Rising, looking to the left*]
Shadrach!
    ZEBULON. There was a shadow moving among the
        rocks;
he may be taking a look about.
    JESSE. Alone?
He should have carried a light.
    ZEBULON. Surely no wild beast
would come so close to our fire.
    JOSEPH. I'll walk out that way.
I think I hear him.
    [*He steps out left.*]
    JESSE. There were voices along the river
earlier in the evening.
    [*By this time a number have risen and look out
        to the left.*]
    JACOB. Is it true
there are lions in the desert, Mother?

MIRIAM. No,
not here, I think. We're only one day's journey
from Jerusalem city. On the other side of the river
there may be lions.
    JACOB. And leopards?
    MIRIAM. Yes, leopards, too.
    JACOB. Don't you remember in the book of Kings
there were lions this side of the Jordan?
    MIRIAM. Yes, long ago,
there may have been then.
    JACOB. I think there are lions here.
        [*He sits up.*]
I really think so. It's not such a wide river.
They could come right across.
    JESHUA. Did I ever tell you the story
of the lion who wouldn't get his feet wet?
    JACOB. No.
    JESHUA. Once there was a lion who lived alone
in the trans-Jordan country. He lived quite well
there on the other side of the river, and ate
nearly every day. But then there came a season
when all things failed on his side of the river.
        [*JACOB lies back to listen.*]
He couldn't find anything, not even a cony
among the rocks, and so every day he sat empty
and looked across the river at hither-Jordan
and cried because he was hungry, and looked at his
    paws
and licked them, and cried. And he said to him-
    self,
"This hunger
is a terrible thing; it's a thing stronger than lions,
because it's stronger than I am." Then he set one
    paw
in the shallow of the river, and said, "This water
is an ancient enemy, and I dislike it,
but I must cross the river, and taste the sheep
on the hills of hither-Jordan." Then he shook his
    paw,
like this, to shake the water from it, and roared,
and put in another foot, and snarled, and said,
"This hunger is stronger than I am, but I am stronger
than water!" and at that he jumped straight in
and beat the river with his paws, and choked,
and jumped out again. Then the lion said. "It seems
I was mistaken. A great lion like myself
is stronger than hunger. I'm not hungry at all."
So he licked himself all over and lay down
and looked very fierce, but the trouble really was

he was afraid of water. And from that day
there are no lions on this side.

JACOB. But didn't he ever
get anything to eat?

JESHUA. Yes, after a while—
in the rainy season. But no matter how hungry he
was
he never swam the river.

[JOSEPH *returns from the left.*]

JOSEPH. He's not that way.
I think he's walked on up the valley.

CASSIA.

[*Calling*]
Shadrach!

ESTHER. Isn't there a fire? I saw the flash of a
fire.

[*She looks out to the right.*]

ZEBULON. Yes, and that's where he's gone. There's
another encampment
like our own.

REBA. Then what was the need to frighten
the women and children? My legs give way and bend
all the way down, like a pair of tallow candles
in a warm house.

JESSE. Yes, I do see a fire,
and someone coming this way.

ZEBULON. This will be Shadrach.

[*There is a moment's pause. They wait silently.*]

SHADRACH.

[*Entering from the right*]
We must put out our fire and move our camp
toward the path along the river. Gather your things!
Quick, Cassia! Quick, all of you—and the children—
we'll find another place!

CASSIA. But why, Shadrach?

SHADRACH. Never mind—
only we move.

JESSE. What have you seen?

[*The company stirs itself to move.*]

SHADRACH. It wasn't
so much what I saw as what I heard. A nest
of wild men warming their hands around a fire
and estimating gravely what we're worth
in gold or silver—or hides. I've heard of these naked
and hairy bandits in the hills, but these
are hairier than I expected. Come,
if our fire's out, and we've vanished, they'll give up
and turn on somebody else.

JACOB. Maybe they're lions.

SHADRACH. No, they're not lions. They're men,
but not of the sort
I want to talk with.

[*As he speaks, a half-naked emaciated* MAN
*with a sword in his hand appears behind him.
He turns, and two or three other* BANDITS *enter.
Some carry weapons, some staves.*]

ISHMAEL.

[*The 1st* BANDIT]
You are on your way
to the holy city?

SHADRACH. Yes.

ISHMAEL. How many of you?

JOSEPH. Ten.

ISHMAEL. Do you bear offerings?

JOSEPH. No.

ISHMAEL. Have you money
to pay for offerings?

[*They are silent.*]
Answer as if you stood
in the presence of your God, for you are held
responsible in your answers.

JOSEPH. There is no one here
who knows what the others have. What little we
carry
in silver or copper coins we took with us
to buy our sacrifices.

ISHMAEL. And do you not know
that whatever you buy in the temple courts yields
profit
to Hanan the high priest, and that Hanan paid
for his place, giving money to Herod, and Herod in
turn
bought his seat from Augustus? Is it worship of
God
that pays tribute to Rome?

JOSEPH. Sir, we have heard these things,
or guessed at them indirectly. But a man
must worship God, and his family must worship,
and in all the sacred books there is no door open
for access unto God, save the rites of the temple,
and the high priest of our people. If these be corrupt
are we corrupted, worshipping? And if so,
should we then shut ourselves from God entirely,
and eat as the beast eats, without thought or thanks
for Him who made him?

ISHMAEL. How can I answer you, you who have
forgotten Judah?

How can I answer you
who bow your necks to the oxbow and plow for
  Herod
and reap for Caesar?
Who pour out money for burnt offerings
on a captured altar, and think God is pleased?
You and those with you have betrayed your God,
as, when Judah was dying, you betrayed him,
sending no succor to him!

2ND ROBBER. The men will come forward
and give over what money they have.

ISHMAEL. Then if afterward you are searched
and money is found on a man, then by Jéhovah
and by our Judah, that man shall die, and be nailed
to the desert floor with thorn-sticks sharpened in
fire!

JOSEPH. Will you tell me your name?

ISHMAEL. They call me Ishmael
because my hand is raised against every tribe
that sends up tribute to Rome!

JOSEPH. We must pay them quietly, Shadrach,
  for these men
are armed, and we are not.
    [He detaches a purse from his girdle and sur-
    renders it.]

SHADRACH. Very well.
    [He also pays, followed by JESSE and ZEBULON.]

JOSEPH. Were you a follower of Judah?

ISHMAEL. Yes.

JOSEPH. And did Judah hold it righteous
to rob pilgrims in the desert?

ISHMAEL. No, but the days have made it
  righteous!

JOSEPH. And are you a prophet,
to say what is righteous?

ISHMAEL. Come up into the hills with me,
you who travel easily to Jerusalem!
Come into the hills, and I will show you the men
who followed Judah; how some of them are sick
and there is no physician,
how some of them are stricken with the sun
and some with hunger,
and some have died of cold, without covering,
and day and night, when the noon is fire, or the
  darkness
falls like a winter, there are always the Romans, the
  Romans
out of their camps, with metal shields before them,
and short swords thrusting at the belly!

This is our life. And you are soft and have not helped
  us.
You will help now a little. Against your will.

JOSEPH. But even if this is true, could I not
  say,
"Lo, I am a poor man, and my neighbor is rich;
I will go to my neighbor and take from him
lest my child hunger tomorrow?"

ISHMAEL: Would you hear what Judah said when
  he was dying?
This was the message of Judah, "The Messiah is
  born
who will conquer the Romans!
His star has been seen, and he lives,
and he will deliver us!
Whether he come in fire, with wings of iron,
or with chariots over the earth,
whether he come with thousands or alone,
he will deliver Galilee and Judaea!
Therefore wait for the Messiah, and keep watch,
and you who are called Ishmael, keep you my
  men,
this little remnant, keep them and live in hope;
for the old law has been broken like tablets of glass,
and shall bind you under no more!
And no man ever again shall loose or bind
save the Messiah, who now lives among you,
and has not spoken, but will speak, and burn out
the hearts of over-lords, and wither kingships—
till there's neither procurator nor tax
nor Caesar left above you!" This said Judah
when he was dying, and he died above in the hills
of an old wound. And we wait here for the Messiah,
even robbers, even sleepers in the rain,
but doing the will of God!

SHADRACH. It won't help to argue with a madman,
  Joseph,
and these folks are plainly mad.

ZEBULON. Yes, they are mad.

JOSEPH. Then the Messiah lives?

ISHMAEL. This too was promised me when he lay
  dying,
by Judah, that I should see the Messiah, though he
should never see him. Now I am dying too,
for I have a mortal lesion, and can live
but a few days. Yet I shall see him, for this
was prophesied.—But go to Jerusalem!
As the Jordan runs to Bahr Lut—to the Dead Sea,
go down to that sink which is called Jerusalem!

Worship a shame-faced god at his dirtied altar!
Kneel down in the courts where kneeling is at a
    price,
and harken to Pharisees! But remember, rising,
that you have fed for a day those who kneel among
    rocks,
who worship a free God freely, and await
that which is promised, and will come!
    [*He turns to go.*]
    JESHUA. Ishmael!
    JESSE. Be quiet,
and let him go.
    ISHMAEL. Did someone call me?
    SHADRACH. No!
These are insane men, Jeshua, and criminals;
let them go if they will.
    JESHUA. Will you take my silver?
    ISHMAEL. Who was it called me?
    MIRIAM. They have taken enough, Jeshua.
We shall come penniless to my brother's house.
    JESHUA. I should like to give him my silver,
        Mother.
    SHADRACH. Well,
now that they know he has it—
    [*He shrugs and turns away.* JESHUA *crosses to*
    ISHMAEL *and offers him the coin.*]
    ISHMAEL. You give this freely?
    JESHUA. Yes, freely.
    ISHMAEL. You are not frightened?
    JESHUA. No, not frightened.
But I cannot give it unless you put out your hand—
and I wish to give it.
    ISHMAEL. What is your name?
    JESHUA. Jeshua.
    ISHMAEL. And how old are you?
    JESHUA. Twelve.
    ISHMAEL. And where were you born?
    JESHUA. In Bethlehem.
    [ISHMAEL *takes the silver.*]
    ISHMAEL. Let me see your face.
Now blessed be the God
of Judah, who has let me live to this hour.—
Give back what we have taken,
for this is a holy company. And go quickly
into the hills, and bring news there we are gone
to Jerusalem—for our waiting nears an end,
and those who live shall have sight of him!
    [*The 2nd* ROBBER *restores the money to* JOSEPH,
    and goes out.]

Lie down
and rest, and we will guard you. Yes, many more
will come from the hills to guard you. I keep only
this silver penny, as earnest of the kingdom.
    JESHUA.
    [*Coming dowr to his* FATHER *and* MOTHER]
Why does he look at me?
    SHADRACH.
    [*Tapping his forehead*]
He's touched. They're all touched,
But they have their uses.
    JOSEPH. There was some kind of magic
in your gift of silver.
    MIRIAM. It's not a usual thing
that they receive alms.
    ZEBULON. What does this mean to you?
    JESSE. I gather one thing:
They've given the money back.
    SHADRACH. And they're setting a guard.
    ZEBULON. But these are robbers
and desperate men. Do we dare lie down and close
our eyes and let them guard us?
    SHADRACH. I shall lie down,
because I'm tired. Besides, what else can we do?
    JESSE Well, sleep well, Shadrach.
    SHADRACH. Oh, I shall sleep well. I always sleep
        my soundest guarded by robbers.

Curtain

SCENE FIVE

SCENE. *Evening before the city gates of Jerusalem.
A* SCRIBE *sits writing at a small table; a line of people is forming to the right. The party that we know
has arrived and is now answering.* MARIUS, *who has
been posted at the gate, approaches to listen.* JESHUA
*has perched on a rock at the rear, and reads a scroll.
A* WOMAN *passes the group and enters the gates. She
carries bird cages on her back.*

    THE DOVE SELLER. Buy my pigeons and doves! Buy
        my white doves!
Buy my pigeons and doves! Buy my white doves!
    THE SCRIBE.
    [*To* REBA]
Your birthplace?
    REBA. Capernaum.

[*86*]

THE SCRIBE. Your age?

REBA. Sixty-five.

[*He nods to her. She passes on.* JESSE *comes next to the table.* MIRIAM *and* JOSEPH *sit on a stone a little forward from the others.*]

JOSEPH. The soldier has come out from the gate.

MIRIAM. Yes. He listens.
Oh, Joseph—have we trusted too much? My breath fails me—
and my heart. Shall we go back? Shall we turn
and not stay for the Passover?

JOSEPH. But all eyes would be upon us—
and those who thought no harm of us might then wonder
why we had been afraid.

THE SCRIBE.
[*Angry*]
Must you mumble your words
down toward the earth?

JESSE. Sir?

THE SCRIBE.
[*To* MARIUS]
God pity the census-taker.
Humanity poured over him like a vomit;
the infirmity of age, the noses and rears
of inarticulate children, the—

MARIUS. It's a long day
here from sun-up to sun-down and your pen
gets worn down like your patience—

THE SCRIBE. Well, pass on.
I think I have it.

MARIUS. The porter's coming now
to close the gates.

THE SCRIBE. Jesse, the son of Kerith,
living in Nazareth, sixty-nine years old,
a mason.

JESSE. Yes, sir.

THE SCRIBE.
[*Looking at* JACOB, *who is in line behind* JESSE.]
Is this your son?

JESSE. Why, no, sir.

THE SCRIBE. Your grandson?

JESSE. No, sir.

THE SCRIBE. Are you his guardian?

JESSE. No.

THE SCRIBE. Then why does he come pushing in behind you?
Who's with you?

JACOB. I can answer for myself.

I'm Jacob, the son of the judge, Gennesareth,
I was born in Jerusalem, and I live there; see—
I'm here with my kinsman Joseph

MARIUS. Ask his age.

THE SCRIBE. Your age?

JACOB. Ten years old.

THE SCRIBE.
[*To Joseph*]
This boy is with you?

JOSEPH. Yes.

THE SCRIBE. These answers are correct?

JOSEPH. Yes. Quite correct.

THE SCRIBE. Pass in, then. And hurry. The sun has touched the hill,
thank God, and the gates will soon be closing. Come, your name?
[SHADRACH *steps before the table.* JESHUA *continues to read obliviously.*]

SHADRACH. Shadrach of Nazareth, a carpenter.

JOSEPH. We can't leave now.

MIRIAM. No.

JOSEPH. The soldier
wished to know Jacob's age. It would have been better to hide in Egypt—or sleep in a cave of the mountains out toward Phoenicia. To have kept no feasts, and lived only to guard him from them.

MIRIAM. Let us leave now, Joseph.
Jacob will enter the city with the others,
but you and I and Jeshua must turn back,
and find our way home. I feel it strongly—we must—
no matter what may be said—

JOSEPH. Yes, I feel it strongly—
and yet I ask too why there's been no sign
if there was danger.

MIRIAM. We are lost now if we pause!
Come, we will turn together, and, if they call,
we will not enter still, but give quite different names
and be seen no more at Nazareth, be seen
no more in any city—

JOSEPH. I fear even that
may be fatal now. They look at us under brows
and wait for us—
[*They turn to take their places before the* SCRIBE. *At this moment* ISHMAEL *and the 2nd* ROBBER *enter and take their places at the table where Joseph and Miriam would have stood.*]

THE SCRIBE. Speak then. Your name?

ISHMAEL. Ishmael.

THE SCRIBE. And occupation?

ISHMAEL. I gather desert honey, and parch grain
over the fire, and study God's word.

THE SCRIBE. That's three occupations. And none
recognized.
Will you give me one that I can write down here
as a livelihood among civilized men?

ISHMAEL. I will.—
I study God's word.

THE SCRIBE. And are you paid for that?

ISHMAEL. I'm paid in the words
of God, and in understanding of His words.
Are any paid better?

THE SCRIBE.
[*Looking up at him, then smothering his anger*]
Let it go. Where do you live?

ISHMAEL. In Bethábara, in the desert of the Salt
Sea.
I have my brother with me, and my son.
My brother, who stands behind me, is deaf and
dumb,
and cannot speak for himself. His name is Dark,
and we are the sons of Rabbath.
[*The* SCRIBE *writes.*]

THE SCRIBE. And your own son,
do you have him with you?

ISHMAEL. Yonder, reading the scroll,
the lad there yonder.
[JESHUA *looks up and listens.*]

THE SCRIBE. And his name?

ISHMAEL. Jeshua.

THE SCRIBE. And where was he born?

ISHMAEL. Sir, on the slopes of Mount Nebo where
his mother
was tending flock. In no city and no town
but desert born.

MARIUS. Who has taught him to read?

ISHMAEL. I taught him to read.
He reads the word of God.

THE SCRIBE. What is his age?

ISHMAEL. He is thirteen years old.
[JESHUA *gets down and crosses to* MIRIAM, *who
puts her finger to her lips.*]

MIRIAM. Say nothing, and go with him.

THE SCRIBE. And now if you'll kindly pull all
your wits together in an effort to make sense, we'll
have a last try at your occupation. Something must
be set down as the thing you do.—

ISHMAEL. I have told you I gather honey
and parch corn over the fire, and study God's word!

THE SCRIBE. Are you paid for any of these?

ISHMAEL. I am not paid.

THE SCRIBE. But when you need money for taxes,
and all men born
pay taxes, where do you get it?

ISHMAEL. You may set down
that I sell the honey.

THE SCRIBE. Well, I will set it down,
but the desert north of Nebo is full of robbers
and I have no doubt you're among them, both of you,
if the truth were known.

ISHMAEL. And Jerusalem, your city,
is full of robbers, and that truth is known,
full of scribes and Levites and Pharisees
and Sadducees, sucking the very gristle
from children's bones, to make profit of gold and
silver
for Herod and his Arabian wife!

THE SCRIBE. Very well—
but I say you're a robber, as most of them are robbers
across the Jordan, and ripe for crucifixion,
and they'll get you before you're through!

ISHMAEL. But first the scribes
and Levites—and the ravenous house of Hanan—
God will see them hung up first!

THE SCRIBE. As you like. Go in
before they shut the gates.
[*To* JESHUA]
Go in with your father.
[JESHUA *follows Ishmael.*]
Jeshua!

JESHUA. Yes?

THE SCRIBE. That is your name? Jeshua?

JESHUA. Yes.

THE SCRIBE. What is it you read?

JESHUA. This scroll?
The book of Isaiah.
Only these latter chapters of Isaiah
were written by an Unknown Prophet, of whom the
name
even has been lost.

THE SCRIBE. And what does it say in the book?

JESHUA. Here where I read it says that the earth
was better at one time, and will be again.

THE SCRIBE. Do you believe that?

JESHUA. Yes, I believe it.

THE SCRIBE. Go in.
[JESHUA *goes in.* JOSEPH *and* MIRIAM *come to
the table.*]

THE SCRIBE. Yes?

JOSEPH. Joseph of Nazareth,
a carpenter, and his wife Miriam.

THE SCRIBE. There's a boy with you
named Jacob, who went in before you?

JOSEPH. Yes.

THE SCRIBE.

[Writing]

Go in then. The porter may close the gates. The sun
went down some time ago.

[JOSEPH and MIRIAM go inside. The PORTER begins to shut the gates.]

MARIUS. We shall have the old fox Herod
here tomorrow, and we've caught nothing yet.

THE SCRIBE. No.

MARIUS. This last lad—you called him to make
him turn—for a look at his face?

THE SCRIBE. To make him answer his name—
and say what he was reading.

MARIUS. He was reading Isaiah,
Whatever Isaiah is.

THE SCRIBE. It's a holy book. Quite holy enough
to make him the madman's son.

MARIUS.

[To the PORTER]

Let us through before it's locked, boy. Wait, let us
through.

We're too old to pile over it.

[They go in.]

Curtain

❦

ACT TWO

SCENE ONE

SCENE. An inner room of the Temple, used for the
meetings of the Sanhedrin. The session is over for
the day, but a few members linger to discuss an unfinished question.

GENNESARETH. We are all friends of the high
priest—or must seem
to be his friends. Our seats in the Sanhedrin
would soon be filled with others if we dared

dispute his policy. But when you have walked
through the streets of Jerusalem, have you turned
suddenly
by chance and seen the curious eyes upon you
there in the crowd? Eyes that say, "This is a priest,
and I should reverence him," but which also say,
"This man serves under Hanan, and Hanan serves
under Herod, and all three stand together between
my God and me. How can reverence to them
be reverence to my God?" You have seen this question
in people's eyes—and you have wondered, too,
"Do we serve God or do we serve corruption,
here in the temple?"

MALACHI. Only people who are free
may serve God as they please.

GENNESARETH. Then when will our day
of deliverance come? How long will our God be kept
a prisoner at His own altar—and we His jailors,
paid to betray Him in Silence?

ABBAS. A visitor.
The high priest Hanan.

[HANAN enters.]

HANAN. Forgive me, gentlemen. I asked you to
wait
after the others were gone, because I have
a peculiar message for you from our Lord Herod,
a message and a commission. You are men of the
spirit
and he of the flesh—or such is his word to you—
and there are matters wherein he is blind
though you may be able to see. Among these matters
is that of the Messiah's coming. This
has been foretold by seers you study hourly,
and when this prophecy has come to pass
it will be those attuned to it in mind
who will first know—who will feel the first faint
trembling
of earth beneath the footstep of its king
and be aware of him. And your commission
from Herod is only this—when you first know
or first suspect his presence in our midst—
it is his wish that you will send this news
through me to him. Or directly if you will.
For Herod and myself wish to do him honor
and submit ourselves to his kingdom.—I come to ask
for Herod—as from himself—if this magic news
should touch you, will you come first to us, that we
may share your happiness?

ABBAS. If it comes to us
you shall hear, Lord Hanan.

CHORAZIM. And if this revelation
should come to you, a much more likely thing,
you being the high priest and the friend of God,
will you not share it with us then, so that we
may worship with you?

HANAN. You have my word for that, if God should
favor me.

CHORAZIM. Thank you, my lord.

HANAN. Also—I hope you have not mistaken
Herod—
he is a mystic and a dreamer of dreams,
but his dreams are the same as yours. Until tomorrow.
[*He goes out.*]

CHORAZIM. Yes, my lord.

GENNESARETH. The adder in the nest!
A snake could argue quite as plausibly
that he means to worship the bird!

ABBAS. But do you think so?

GENNESARETH. This welcome prepared—

ABBAS. Yes—?

GENNESARETH. Is a quiet murder.
And what he asks is that we join with him
in a conspiracy to destroy the Messiah!

MALACHI. Come!
Come, sir, the head of our church does not conspire
with the head of our state against what might be
called
the flowering of our race. They and all of us
would gain by that flowering.

CHORAZIM. You refer, I believe
to the Messiah as a flower?

MALACHI. I do.

CHORAZIM. Perhaps
another metaphor were more apt. Suppose
he's planted like an acorn in a jar,
which grows and spreads his roots and must become
a tree if he's to live. And then suppose
that we're the pottery that hems him in
and must be shattered when his swelling roots
reach out for earth.

GENNESARETH. But obviously, Chorazim,
we cannot let self-interest affect us
in such a matter. Who values the clay pot
if by its breaking this eternal oak
is set in our soil to flourish forever?

MALACHI. I value my clay pot.

And Herod values his, and Hanan his,
more than any oak or acorn.

GENNESARETH. But think what you say!
You'd let them murder him and make no outcry—

CHORAZIM. Come, come, the word—
the word is strong—murder—

GENNESARETH. Is it stronger than death?
For that's what they mean! Death!

ABBAS. But think what you say,
Gennesareth! Suppose a Messiah comes
and the high priest does not welcome him, but finds
him
worthy of death—are we not bound to believe
that he is worthy of death—that he is not
the true Messiah?

GENNESARETH. If there were grave doubt, perhaps—
But any child or man who appeared and seemed
to be the Messiah, they would seek his death!
Whether he were doubtful or not!

ABBAS. Would there not be doubt always?
What test have we for the true Messiah? None.
None generally accepted.

GENNESARETH. Would you then—
if the Messiah were to stand before us—
if he came here—and revealed himself—would you—
report his presence to Hanan?

CHORAZIM. There is none
among us, my dear Gennesareth, who would care
to have it said, "The Messiah passed this way,
and spoke to you, and then went on, but you
of the Sanhedrin never knew him."

GENNESARETH. Which means
if he came, you would betray him!

ABBAS. Come, again,
the word again—the word is strong—betray—
why should we say betray? Let us say announce,
for that is our meaning. If the Messiah comes
I shall announce him gladly.

CHORAZIM. Yet he will not come—he will not
come—
Be sure of that—the question will not arise.
The children of Israel are fools to hope for him
and the high priest and the king are fools to fear
him—
for he will not come.
[JESHUA *enters behind them.*]

GENNESARETH. There are passages
as early as the pentateuch of Moses

that cannot be interpreted except
as the promise of his coming!

CHORAZIM. It is promised, yes.
And so we wait for it. Meanwhile the Romans
govern us as they like, and pick our pockets
with ease, because we're watching the gates of
    Heaven
for the coming of a god!

MALACHI. My theory is—

ABBAS. There's a child that listens.
Can it be that we are watched?

GENNESARETH. This is Jeshua,
the son of my cousin Joseph of Nazareth,
who stays with me during Passover at my house.

    [To JESHUA]
How did you come here?

JESHUA. I was walking here among the columns,
and thought I was alone till I heard your voices—
You will forgive me?

MALACHI.

    [Continuing]
My theory is that we
of this generation shall not see the Messiah
because he has come and gone. Two centuries
have passed since Judas Maccabaeus marched
to Jerusalem, expelling the foreign legions
that had conquered us. Could not our Maccabaeus
have been the Messiah? He fulfilled the conditions.
I think he was the Messiah, and that we
shall see no other.

JESHUA. But—Judas Maccabaeus
could not have been the Messiah!

CHORAZIM. No?—then why not?
Your kinsman's son has opinions of his own.

JESHUA. I'm sorry. I spoke without thinking. I had
    forgotten—
this is the court of the Sanhedrin—

GENNESARETH. It is indeed not fitting that a child
    should interrupt us.

JESHUA. Yes, I know.

    [He turns to go.]

MALACHI. And yet I should like to know why
    your cousin's son
should say so passionately that Maccabaeus
could not have been the Messiah. For myself,
I cannot see why not.

GENNESARETH. Stay, Jeshua—
stay and answer.

JESHUA. But you can answer this.
You could all answer better than I.

CHORAZIM. No, truly,
we have no answer.

JESHUA. We know the works of men
can be undone. We know that Maccabaeus
once set us free, but we were conquered again.
If Maccabaeus had been sent of God
we should still be free, for the works of God
cannot be undone.

ABBAS. It's a shrewd answer.

CHORAZIM. Yes.
Yes, he has a certain logic
which is not bad.

ABBAS. He lives in Galilee.

MALACHI. Let's not despise the country. As you
    know
it's the shepherd boys come fresh from off the hills
who prosper in Jerusalem.
You learned this from your father, Jeshua,
or was it yours?

JESHUA. I've learned many things, from him,
but, I think not this. Isn't it a plain meaning?
It came to me—if the Messiah stood on earth,
alone, and found himself a man, expecting
no help from God, he could not have much hope.
He could have no hope at all.

CHORAZIM. I don't follow you.
You're too abstruse for me.

JESHUA. If it were given
to you to be the Messiah, and you stood
here in this room, and looked out over the earth,
and saw our poverty of men and things,
and knew that we were a pathway for the empires
that lie to east and west—would you have courage
even to begin?

CHORAZIM. But I am not the Messiah.

JESHUA. If he were a man, and without the help
    of God,
he would be much like you.

CHORAZIM.

    [Smiling]
Ah, a shrewd thrust!
The country boy strikes home! Take him off, some-
    one,
because he bites and scratches!

MALACHI. Well, here's a question
which has puzzled the wise men time out of mind—
When the Messiah comes will he descend

from heaven or be born, a man among men,
here on our earth?

JESHUA. He will be born among men.

ABBAS.

[*Smiling*]

You see! He knows!

MALACHI. Now you must have some reason—
some weighty reason for this answer?

JESHUA. Yes.
I have a reason.

MALACHI. Give it, sir. We await you.

JESHUA. It's written that he's to come of the line
of David,
and David was a man.

MALACHI. A casuist—

[*He throws up his hands in mock despair.*]

an absolutist and a casuist—
I must admit that David was a man,
and according to the prophet the Messiah
will come of the line of David. Some country priest
has worked these riddles out, brooding alone
over his crust of shew-bread and the Torah,
and schooled the boy in his answers.

ABBAS. But now I think
you've stepped into difficulties, Jeshua.
The work of Maccabaeus was undone,
you say, and therefore he was only a man,
and therefore not the Messiah. But you also say
the Messiah will be a man.

JESHUA. With the help of God.
A man with the help of God.

ABBAS. Is that so different?

JESHUA. Isn't it all the difference in the world?

ABBAS. Yes, if a man were ever sure he had it—
it might be.

JESHUA. But a man would know if he had it.

ABBAS. You think he would?

JESHUA. If God should speak to a man
the man would know.

CHORAZIM. I think when you grow up
you'll be among us here in the Sanhedrin—
But answer one last question:
How will you know the Messiah when he comes?

MALACHI. Yes, how shall we know him?
Answer that, Jeshua.

JESHUA. By his victories.
By his great victories.
And by the immortal army from the sky
that fights beneath his banner.

ABBAS. Oh, God will send an army!

JESHUA. He must.

MALACHI. Is there any prophecy
regarding such an army?

JESHUA. No, there is none.
But could our little handful of tribes
win against Rome unless God sent us help
out of his Heaven? If there's to be a Messiah
God must help him!

CHORAZIM. Meanwhile, we've wandered far
from our last question: How shall we know the
Messiah
when he appears? Instead of your vague answer
were it not better to put those facts together
which the prophecies reveal? It's true, as you say,
he's to come of the line of David. His birthplace, too,
has been predicted. No doubt you know it?

JESHUA. No.

CHORAZIM. You cannot name his birthplace?

JESHUA. No.

MALACHI. There are gaps,
my scholar, in your erudition. The place
is named in a passage which you must have
studied—
the fourth chapter of Micah. Let me quote it for
you:
"But thou, town of Bethlehem,
though thou be little among the thousands of Judah,
yet out of thee shall come forth, Bethlehem Ephrata,
him who is to be the ruler of Israel."
Do you know these words?

JESHUA. No, this is new to me.
For I have studied all the other prophets
except only Micah.

[*The music of a chant is heard from a distance.*]

ABBAS. The ritual has begun,
and we shall be expected.

CHORAZIM.

[*To* GENNESARETH]

Yes, we must go.
But bring your kinsman up to Jerusalem
when he's of an age to come.

MALACHI. Yes, bring him when he's older, Gennesareth.

[ABBAS *and* MALACHI *go out.*]

GENNESARETH. Would you care to be one of us,
Jeshua,
when you are older?

JESHUA. To be with you here? Yes, and yet—

if God dwells here, should one not feel his presence
even in passing by?

GENNESARETH. You haven't felt it
here in the Temple?

JESHUA.
    [With self-reproach]
No.

CHORAZIM. Not in this room?

JESHUA. No. Least of all here in this room. But I
shall walk on further—and if I don't find it—then
I shall know the lack is in me, and not in the Temple,
for it is God's house.

Curtain

SCENE TWO

SCENE. *Before the Temple at Jerusalem. It is toward
evening but the court and the steps are still busy
with activities associated with the Passover.*

The GREEK WOMAN *is selling jewelry, and her neck
and arms are loaded with bangles. The* DOVE WOMAN
is offering doves to passers-by, two MONEY-CHANGERS
have set up shop on the steps, a MATZOH-SELLER *is
seated on a step, and a* FRUIT-SELLER *has spread his
wares for sale. A* PHARISEE *stands behind them in
silent prayer.*

JESSE, REBA, ZEBULON, SHADRACH *and* CASSIA *enter
and stand in a group below the Temple steps.*

DOVE WOMAN. Buy my pigeons and doves!
Buy my white doves!

GREEK WOMAN. Bangles, earrings and bracelets!

FRUIT-SELLER. Three sestertia a dozen, if you
    please!
Dates and figs from Syria!

MATZOH-SELLER Shew bread for the festival!
Shew-bread!

1ST MONEY-CHANGER. I can exchange into Greek
    or Roman coinage
at the lowest rates. Copper, silver or gold
in the standard denarius of Rome, the drachma
of Athens, or for those who travel abroad,
the Egyptian obol. Farthings, mites, sestertia,
the Augustan aureus of soft gold, to be handled
lightly, lest you wear it down—

2ND MONEY-CHANGER. My charge
is definite and unvaried. One per cent
of all amounts above one aureus,

and below that, two per cent. My competitor
deducts an indefinite and exorbitant fee
which you feel though you do not see it!

1ST MONEY-CHANGER. If you are wise
you will disbelieve the slanderous attack
of my associate at the next table, a man
of criminal record, the son of an Arab pirate
and a Phoenician strumpet, whose practice it is
to extract full fifty per cent of all he touches
and swear that he took but one!

2ND MONEY-CHANGER. To his other virtues
the brigand on my right adds a practical knowledge
of sleight-of-hand, which enables him to delude you
with copper for gold, and deceive you as to your
    change.
Watch him carefully, I desire you.

JESSE. Why should we part with our shekels?
The shekels are good money!

THE GREEK WOMAN. Gold and silver ornaments
    from Tyre!
Carved ivory combs from Asia! At no price!
For whatever you will pay!
    [Holding a bracelet out to CASSIA.]
This is Persian gold!

CASSIA. Shadrach, I want a bangle.

SHADRACH. Let me see.

CASSIA. This.

SHADRACH. But that's a cheap gaudy bangle. You
    wouldn't want
a cheap, gaudy one like that.

CASSIA. Yes. Yes, I would.

SHADRACH. You don't need to be hung around with
    gew-gaws;
You're still pretty without them.

CASSIA. I know how it is.
When you're young you're handsome enough with-
    out jewels—
and when you're old nobody will buy them for you.

SHADRACH. I think the Pharisee's about to pray.
He's flapping his wings. Watch! Look!

THE PHARISEE. Oh God of Ezekiel,
look down upon these subtle and mischievous men
who parley over money even in thy courts
and bring in dancing women for wives!
    [JESHUA *enters. The vendors call out simul-
    taneously.*]

DOVE WOMAN. Buy my pigeons and doves!
Buy my white doves!

GREEK WOMAN. Bangles, earrings and bracelets!

FRUIT-SELLER. Three sestercia a dozen, if you please!

Dates and figs from Syria!

MATZOH-SELLER. Shew bread for the festival!

1ST MONEY-CHANGER. I can exchange into Greek or Roman coinage—

2ND MONEY-CHANGER. My charge

is definite and unvaried—

THE PHARISEE.

[Silencing them]

Oh Jahveh,

when thou shalt make a desolation of cities,

when thou shalt come suddenly upon the men who dance

and the women who make music,

in that day spare me, who have kept myself perfect

and have not gone about to become unclean!

[MARIUS, the soldier, enters.]

MARIUS. The Tetrarch Herod

has ordered a distribution of alms!

On the first day of Passover in each year

the Tetrarch distributes silver! Today His Highness

is personally at the temple, to assure

that there is no injustice! To the court of the Gentiles

and take your place in the line!

[The MATZOH-SELLER rises, picks up her basket and exits, followed by the GREEK WOMAN, the FRUIT-SELLER with his basket, and the DOVE WOMAN with her cages. The MONEY-CHANGERS pick up their tables and follow, with the PHARISEE behind them and, after him, MARIUS.]

SHADRACH. It looks as if business

was not so good, the way they abandon it.

ZEBULON. Does he indeed give silver?

JESSE. Yes. No doubt Herod learned

this trick from Caesar, a giving of public money

to make all men his servants.

SHADRACH.

[Doubtful]

And yet it is silver;

it's a day's wage. Will I go any more quickly

to the eternal grinding machine because

I took silver from Herod? I think not.

REBA. I think, since it's not an hour for prayer

and nothing is lost in duty or sacrifice,

we may accept the money.

JESSE. Why, let us take it then.

[SHADRACH, CASSIA and ZEBULON go out.]

Perhaps I speak for an older and sterner time

when the patriarchs taught a distrust of the gifts of rulers.

[He and REBA follow the others. JESHUA is left alone on the stage, looking after them. MIRIAM enters.]

MIRIAM. Joseph, he's here.

[JOSEPH enters.]

JESHUA. Father, there are money-changers here in the Temple—

and Herod gives silver here.

JOSEPH. Yes, Jeshua.

But it should not be so—and was not when I was a child.

There was no buying or selling licensed then

within the Temple enclosure.

MIRIAM. We were frightened, Jeshua,

and came to find you.

JESHUA. Mother, something so strange has happened.

I was in the court of the Sanhedrin

and they spoke of a prophecy I've never heard.

Father—why have we never studied Micah?

Why have I never heard of the prophecy

concerning Bethlehem?

JOSEPH. Will you let me tell you

a little later? It goes back so far

into many things that have happened. Many times

I've tried to think of how to tell you. Still—

I'm not sure.

And whatever I said to you—

might mislead. Might mislead you—and ourselves—

might fix our thinking. So that we quite believed

something we only guess. Perhaps this much

I can say now. When you were but a babe

and the first Herod still lived, I had a dream

warning that we must leave the realm of Herod

and carry you secretly to Egypt. Now,

we had no way of knowing whether my dream

was merely a dream—or a dream sent of God.

There is no proof of such things. But we were afraid,

and obeyed it, and went to Egypt. Then it came true—

for Herod killed all the children.

JESHUA. Yes. That I knew.

JOSEPH. But that was not all. When Herod died in this blood

and Herod's sons became governors of his kingdom,

we made our way back from Egypt—and again a dream

warned me against the province of Judea,

and we kept on north, to settle in Galilee
under Herod Antipas. And now we must question,
were we led wisely, was this last dream a delusion—?
Because so far there's no answer.

JESHUA. Only we've been safe.

JOSEPH. Yes. Safe until we came to the city gates.
Then—while we waited—the robber came from the
  desert to take you through.

MIRIAM. And that, in a way, was an answer.

JOSEPH. Or may have been.

JESHUA. I must tell you—in one night
two or three years ago, when I'd been ill,
I felt you bending over me with a light
when I was half asleep—and heard mother saying:
"It's as if there were an ushering of wings
when I come to bring him water—and then a shadow-
  ing
of wings overhead, when I shield him from the sun—"
Do you remember, Mother, what you said?

MIRIAM. Yes, the whole air seemed troubled in
  the room,
as if I were never ministering alone,
but with bright companions.

JOSEPH. You're a child, Jeshua,
but you see how we've been troubled. From the beginning
our race has always held that there would come
a Messiah of our own, to release all Israel
and destroy those who oppress us. Now we're oppressed
as we were in former times, and we hear all about us
the whisper, and the cry, and the prophecy, too—
"The Messiah, the Messiah! . . ." How are we to know
that we have not dreamed because of our desire?
It's not fair to lay the burden of this question on a
  child—
for it's only a question. It may not be true—
but if you were he—in such case would it be fair
to keep it from you?

JESHUA. But, Father, would this be a burden?
Mother, would this be a burden? You speak so
  strangely!
The Messiah is the Promised One, the Anointed
who comes to us with an army, with the bright sword
of justice, to war on evil, and make an end
of weeping in Israel! I have nothing in me
to make me this prince who is promised.—You know
  me well,
and I am only your Jeshua, who reads

too much, and goes about too much in dreams
of the old heroes.—But if the day has come now
for our Messiah—whether it light on me
or another child—is it anything to be feared?
Let us say it is not for me—but it is our hope,
the coming of the Messiah! Isn't it, Mother?

MIRIAM. Yes, Jeshua.

JOSEPH. And yet our race—
our dark, fierce, wistful race will not see the earth
as the earth is. We live in a doubtful legend,
and tell ourselves these tales—

JESHUA. The Messiah's promised
even in the wisdom of Solomon, the latest
of all the wise books we have!

JOSEPH. Yes, I know that.
The sun's dropped below the wall. It's time to go.
We have half an hour.

JESHUA. Could I sit here on the step—
just a few minutes?

JOSEPH. We dare not leave you, Jeshua.

MIRIAM. No, we dare not.
We must take you with us.

JOSEPH. I think it's best that you should come with
  us now
and never go out alone till we return
to our house in Nazareth.

JESHUA. May I not stay in the Temple?
There was something I wished to find here. And
  haven't found.
If I could sit here alone—

MIRIAM. We took no care
at the gates—yet he was cared for. If this is a wish
and from his heart—it may be wrong to take thought—
we may lead him into danger.

JOSEPH. Then we'll leave you, Jeshua.
But come before it's dark.

JESHUA. Yes, Father.

  [JOSEPH *and* MIRIAM *go out.* JESHUA *sits on the
  step with his head in his hand.* FLACCUS, FESTUS
  and MARIUS *enter and cross the stage.* MARIUS
  pauses and looks back at JESHUA, *then the* SOL-
  DIERS *go out.* ISHMAEL *enters with a dagger in
  his hand. When he sees that* MARIUS *has gone,
  he replaces the dagger in his belt.*]

ISHMAEL. Jeshua!

  [JESHUA *rises.*]
You know who I am?

JESHUA. The prophet from the desert.
The prophet Ishmael.

ISHMAEL. Not the robber Ishmael?

JESHUA. Are you not a prophet?

ISHMAEL. I am sent of God.
Whether a prophet or some lesser tongue
I shall not know. But God has given me words
and my message is to you. Listen carefully
for we have little time.

JESHUA. My father and mother have asked me to
    come home
before the service. I fear I shall be late.
Could you come with me?

ISHMAEL. No, I must say it now,
and you must hear it now. Though you be late.
This is the culmination of my life,
and for you it means the beginning. You may stay
    now
or go—to join the others forever.

JESHUA. Then
if I go, I could not see you tomorrow?

ISHMAEL. No.
I shall not speak tomorrow. Only tonight
is illumined with the crossing of two stars,
one dying and one born.

JESHUA. Is it good or evil
you bring me?

ISHMAEL. When you are older you will know good
    from evil.
Tonight you will not know.

JESHUA. Let me go home.

ISHMAEL. Yes.

    [JESHUA *starts to go out, then stops and turns.*]

JESHUA. I must stay to listen.
I do trust you. You took me through the gates
and watched over us in the desert.

ISHMAEL. When I spoke
and knew you in the desert, did you know then
why I watched over you?

JESHUA. No.

ISHMAEL. Do you know now?

    [JESHUA *is silent.*]

Because I saw
The Messiah in your eyes, and, taking your silver,
felt the immortal substance in your hand,
burning my clay. Are you not the Messiah?

JESHUA. I have dreamed I was the Messiah.

ISHMAEL. In the night—
or a waking dream?

JESHUA. First it came in the night—
then I remembered the dream, and called it back

to see the beauty of fiery images
and the men who came from the sky.

ISHMAEL. Tell me your dream.

JESHUA. I have never told it.

ISHMAEL. No, but tell it to me,
for my message has to do with it.

JESHUA. I walked
among the cedars over Lebanon,
and said to myself the words of the Unknown
    Prophet
who has written in Isaiah—"Awake, awake,
put on strength, O arm of the Lord! Awake,
as in the ancient days, in the generations
of olden time!" And, as I said these words,
I heard a distant singing, and a little door
was opened in the sky, high overhead
many roods above me. Out of this small door
came shining warriors clad in steel and silver
who marched out into the clouds. Then a voice said,
"Go up to them." And I said, "I cannot go,
because they walk on cloud," but the voice said,
    "Try,"
and so I essayed a step, and the moving air
had set itself like stone beneath my feet,
so that I could climb. Then I went up the cloud
among the army, and took the sword that hung
above the door in the sky, and we came together
down the steps of air. The Romans had drawn up
across the Phoenician plain, toward the great sea,
but when they saw that we walked above the sunrise
they sent out an embassy. This came to me,
and I said, "Send out the evil men." They sent
the men from galleys and prisons, but all these
I turned back to them, and said again, "Send out
the evil men." This time they sent the beggars
and the panders from the streets, but I turned them
    back,
and said, "This one last time I ask it of you—
send out the evil men!" Then they sent their kings
and the Emperor Augustus, and the tetrarchs,
and the men who are set over at tasks and taxing,
with the officers beneath them. And I came here
to the holy city, to make it my capital,
and rule wisely and justly. This was my dream—
and now I've told it.

    [*There is a pause.*]

ISHMAEL. Child, child, how can I tell you?
I haven't wept since the death of Judah, but now
I find myself weeping.

JESHUA. Was this an evil dream?

ISHMAEL. Not evil, but mistaken. If you wish to go
you should go now—go back to Nazareth
and root yourself there among poor villagers
who are happy with what they have.

JESHUA. Why should I go?

ISHMAEL. Because there's no turning back once
    I've spoken
to you.
Because it is my mission to fill your soul
with a torment that will become an exaltation—
because it is your mission to torment
the earth, and exalt it.
But tonight you will look with a child's eyes into
    darkness
and not see beyond.

JESHUA. How was my dream mistaken?

ISHMAEL. It is true the Messiah
will stand before the officers and the people
and say, "Send out the evil men!" But he
will make this demand alone. There will come no
    army
out of the sky to help. He will have few friends
and they will not understand him. He will have wis-
    dom
and will cry out wisdom to all men in the streets
but they will not hear.
The words that come from his mouth
will scatter on barrens and in meagre places.
He will be defeated. He will cause laughter
and be set aside.

JESHUA. But now I think you speak evil.
You have not read the prophets. I will not believe
    you.
The Messiah will win victories! You know
the Messiah must conquer!

ISHMAEL. Yes, after a thousand years—
or ten thousand.

JESHUA. How could it be he conquered
after a thousand years?

ISHMAEL. Or after ten thousand.
After these years the memory of his face
and the words he said, and his unearned affliction
will move among men—will catch and move among
    them
like fire—and they will turn and follow him—
seeing evil where he saw it.

JESHUA. How can you know this?
This is a dream like mine.

ISHMAEL. I once believed
that he would win his victories in the field,
our Jewish Messiah. But, living in the hills,
with little to eat, and no solace for the mind
save the reading of God's word,
I set myself to study what was said
concerning the Messiah—and I found
that none had understood. You quote to me
the Unknown Prophet in Isaiah. Listen!
These words are his:
"He was oppressed and he was afflicted,
yet he opened not his mouth:
he is brought as a lamb to the slaughter
and, as a sheep before her shearers is dumb,
so he opened not his mouth.
He was taken from prison and from judgment,
and who shall declare his generation?
For he was cut off out of the land of the living,
for the transgression of my people was he stricken."
Do you know what this means?

JESHUA. It seems to me a dark saying.

ISHMAEL. It means that the guiltless
must suffer for the guilty, that the good are those
who live their lives for others—that those who are
    evil,
those who are base, are lifted up and vouchsafed
redemption through this suffering.

JESHUA. But what has this
to do with the Messiah? Or with me?
The Messiah is sent to conquer the Romans!

ISHMAEL. Yes—
but not as you understand the meaning of conquest.
The Messiah is sent to hunt out wisdom and truth,
to speak this wisdom and truth in love to those
who need his love, and in bitterness to those
who have earned bitterness. And in the end
for this love and bitterness with which he speaks
he will become a symbol of those who are guiltless—
and those who are guilty, seeing in him this symbol,
will turn and destroy him. He will suffer for them
and conquer them in their hearts.

JESHUA. The Messiah is not to suffer. He is not
    sent
to suffer for others. I have never heard this said
by my father or in the temple.

ISHMAEL. Remember the prophets—
and listen again. "Yet it hath pleased the Lord
to bruise him.—He hath put him to grief.
Because he hath poured out his soul unto death;

and he was numbered with the transgressors,
and he bore the sin of many." You have read this?

ISHMAEL. Has it any meaning?

JESHUA. Yes, it is true. I have read
these things, and wondered. Yet if this is the Messiah
the elders are wrong—and my father.

ISHMAEL. Yes, they are wrong.

JESHUA. Some of the words seem to say that he
    must die—
that the Messiah must die.

ISHMAEL. Even this is true. He will die early;
a hateful and intolerable death,
and nails will be through his hands.

JESHUA. Who has sent you to me?

ISHMAEL. Who it is that orders the wheeling of
    the nights
and hung your star on the mountain. Do you believe
    me?
Do you believe that I am come from God
and speak his word?

JESHUA. Yes. If I must.—
When must he die?

ISHMAEL. When he has spoken his wisdom, and
    the earth
is roused up against him.

JESHUA. Could he not keep silent?

ISHMAEL. No.
What he has to say he must say, what he has
to do he must do.

JESHUA. There will be torture used
before he dies?

ISHMAEL. Yes.

JESHUA. No, I cannot! I cannot!
I have never borne pain! I cannot bear pain!
And I'm afraid of death!
I cannot face death! I say this is not for me—
to be this Messiah!

ISHMAEL. Yet you will bear it!

JESHUA. No!

ISHMAEL. But if you were frightened—if you were
    afraid—
afraid of Herod and of Herod's men—
and ran—then Herod would win—then you'd die
    quickly
and all men would die with you.

JESHUA. If I were afraid?

ISHMAEL. Yes, if you were afraid.—You will go
    your way

and be a child and forget. Yet in your mind
what we have said will become a leaven that works
in all you are and do.

JESHUA. Why did I trust you?
It's grown dark, and you're a stranger! I must go
home!

ISHMAEL. I've given you all I have. I'm weary now
and empty. Go if you wish.

JESHUA. If there were only someone I could ask!
Someone who could give an answer!

ISHMAEL. Go into the Temple and pray
for your old dream. If your God will give it back
then you may have it still.

JESHUA. Yes, I will pray.

[He goes out. MARIUS enters opposite.]

MARIUS. I heard your conversation with the boy—
the boy who was your son when I first saw you
at the gates of the city. I heard what you said to him.
What kind of madman are you?

ISHMAEL. God knows how mad I am—
and spent and weak and empty—

MARIUS. Something you said
to this boy had a kind of meaning for me;
I've been set here to watch the Temple
and guard against a Messiah. What this is
I never have quite known. But now it seems
you feel quite certain what the Messiah is,
and this lad is he. Is that true?

ISHMAEL.
    [Looks away, then back before he speaks.]
Yes, it is true.
I looked to my God for an answer, and within
I heard his voice: "Speak to the soldier boldly,
and say, 'This is the Messiah.'"

MARIUS. I'm grateful to you,
and to your God, who makes things simple and clear
even to men-at-arms,
    [He crosses toward the Temple. ISHMAEL takes
    out his dagger. MARIUS turns.]
for I should hesitate indeed to strike down
a child without good warrant. But I think your word
is quite sufficient.
    [He draws his sword and goes toward the inner
    Temple. ISHMAEL runs lightly after MARIUS and
    leaps to his back. A knife flashes and MARIUS is
    wounded, but turns and strikes down ISHMAEL
    with his sword. ISHMAEL lies where he falls;
    MARIUS has sunk to one knee but rises and stag-
    gers out.]

MARIUS. Flaccus! Festus! I'm wounded!

[*As he goes*]

Help, Flaccus—the beggar—help!

[*He crashes to the flag-stones offstage.* JESHUA *comes out of the Temple, sees* ISHMAEL *and runs to him.*]

JESHUA. Ishmael! Ishmael! You're hurt!

What is it? There's a trail of blood out toward the
    court!

ISHMAEL. Run back, Jeshua! Run back into the
    Temple!

The soldiers will come and find you here!

JESHUA. But, Ishmael,

I dare not run away! I dare not be frightened!

ISHMAEL. Quick, quick!

JESHUA. You warned me not to run away,

and you spoke for God!

[*He holds* ISHMAEL's *head on his arm.*]

FESTUS.

[*Outside*]

The beggar had a knife!

FLACCUS.

[*Outside*]

There's no life in him!

FESTUS.

[*Entering*]

That's the fellow, there!

FLACCUS.

[*Enters*]

There's a child with him!

FESTUS. Put the spawn out of the way—

the dirty beggar and all his generation!

FLACCUS. Make him run then.

FESTUS. Yes, make him run, that's best,

and cut him down as he runs.

[*They come near* JESHUA.]

Run! Run while you can!

Do you want to die there on the stones?

[JESHUA *rises and faces them.*]

JESHUA. Are you Herod's men?

FESTUS. Yes, we are Herod's men.

JESHUA. I went into the Temple

and prayed to God. I asked him whether Ishmael

was false or a true man. Then a voice spoke out
    loud

and said, "He is a messenger of my word.

Follow him and turn not back." I cannot run

from Herod's men, nor be frightened of them.

[FESTUS *draws sword.*]

FESTUS. This is a clean, sharp sword! Do you want
    your blood to

darken it?

JESHUA. No.

FESTUS. Then let me see you run

while you still can run!

JESHUA. But if I run

from Herod or Herod's men, I shall die quickly,

having displeased my God! I must stay and face you.

[*There is an uncertain pause.*]

FLACCUS. Put up your sword.

You can't strike down a child who looks up at you.

Let them alone. There's some necromancy

with these Jewish gods and temples. And the beg-
    gar's dying.

Let them alone.

FESTUS. Very well.

[FESTUS *and* FLACCUS *go out.* JESHUA *sits and
again pillows the old man's head on his arm.*]

Curtain

ACT THREE

SCENE ONE

SCENE. *The roof of* HEROD's *palace.* HEROD *and* MIRA
are looking out over the city.

MIRA. For ten days now they have done no work.
    The walls

of our new palace stand as they stood then,

below the line of trees. Is it abandoned?

Is it never to be finished?

HEROD. Why do you ask?

MIRA. Because there's been no work done these
    ten days.

HEROD. This is the time of year when all the Jews

go up to Jerusalem. I encouraged them

to go this year—for my purposes. But now

the work will be resumed. Before the end

of summer, you will have your apartments

overlooking the lake. For now the work

will proceed with a vengeance. There's been too
    much talk

among the Jews, and too little done.

[*The* SOOTHSAYER *enters.*]

Yes?

SOOTHSAYER. The high priest, Hanan,
my lord, and a centurion, and with them
the scribe who sat at the gate.

HEROD. Let them enter.

MIRA. Then—
it's better if I leave you.

HEROD. No, stay if you like.

[HANAN, *the* SCRIBE, *and the* CENTURION *enter.*]

With you I put aside all secrecy,
as with these officers.

HANAN. Good evening, my lord.

HEROD. Good evening, my lord Hanan,
and to you, and you. You all know what I seek for.
Give me what evidence you have. I begin
at once, Lord Hanan, and begin with you.
Has the rumor of this presence passed your way?

HANAN. I have had no word.

HEROD. You conveyed my message
to the scribes and priests?

HANAN. Yes. As you said it to me,
Lord Herod.

HEROD. There came no answer—of any sort—
no cryptic message, wrapped in words, which I
might understand if I heard it?

HANAN. Not a whisper
from all the Temple.

HEROD. You were thorough? There has been
no miracle, no sudden apparition
to those that tend the altar, no power of faith
beyond what's human; no wisdom in the Temple
or among the men of the Sanhedrin beyond
what's usual there?

HANAN. I should have heard of it,
of that I'm certain.

HEROD. Then you, sir—taking the census,
some unexpected presence at the gates
disturbed you for a moment—on some day
which may come back to you now I mention it.—
Some child with a strange wisdom on his face
that caused your hair to rise, just for a moment,
and then was forgotten?

SCRIBE. Your Highness, I hesitate
to speak of this, lest I seem negligent,
but there is one face, out of those that passed the
gates,
which haunts me in the night.

HEROD. The face of a child?

SCRIBE. Yes, of a child.

HEROD. Was he of the age and city
which have been specified?

SCRIBE. No, he was not.

HEROD. But bring him to me.

SCRIBE. My lord, although his name
is written in the records, he was born
and lives still on the foot-hills of Mount Nebo—
the son of a bandit or a wild tribesman. This
is desert country, full of desperate men,
impossible to search.

HEROD. Yet we will search there!
We will search the plains of Nebo thoroughly.
I give you this task.

SCRIBE.

[*Bowing and stepping back*]

Yes, my lord.

HEROD. Centurion!

CENTURION. Yes.

HEROD. How did it come that a trusted man was
killed
in the Temple court—a man I myself had set
to guard against the Messiah?

CENTURION. He was struck down
by a wild man from the desert—and the wild man
was killed in his turn. This would seem to end the
matter.

HEROD. Was there a child
about the Temple, or near it, at the time?

CENTURION. Nothing was said of a child.

HEROD. Everywhere he eludes me,
and he does elude me, for he was there.
His hand was in this. Can it be, I wonder
that he has left our kingdom?

SOOTHSAYER. My lord, look where
his star still hangs on the Galilean night,
and out-burns Jupiter, and dims great Mars
along the west. He is here.

HEROD. Try this stratagem,
Centurion—try this! My wife has asked
why the work's slow on our palace. From now on
the work will go rapidly. Use what force you
need;
drive them, listen to no excuses; let
them understand that they are slaves, incite
our Galilee to rebellion if you can.
Then out of this we'll get our palace done,
and out of this, if there should be rebellion,

and it should find a leader, there's our man—
he'll be the one we seek. Do you understand?

CENTURION. Make them desperate, and look for a
    leader.

HEROD. Yes.
And now you may go. Go all of you except
Mira, my wife.

    [*The* SCRIBE, *the* CENTURION, *the* SOOTHSAYER,
    and HANAN *go out.*]

MIRA. We may get our palace done,
and for that I thank you. But let the Messiah go,
for he has escaped you!

HEROD. Escaped me? It's in my star—
that I shall destroy the Messiah! It's in his star
that I shall destroy him! Though he escape me now,
as he may—though he escape me for years, yet soon
or late, I shall be his death.
Yet sometimes it seems
that I seek the impalpable, try to put my finger
on that which walks the streets and is not seen,
on that which pierces to the heart, yet leaves
no wound or scar. Suppose the Messiah came
like the voice of a bird, suppose he came like dawn
across the earth? What man has turned back the
    morning?
What king has taken the measure of the wind?

Curtain

SCENE TWO

SCENE. JOSEPH'S *house at Nazareth. It is morning.*
MIRIAM *has risen from her work to welcome* JESSE
and ZEBULON, *who enter.*

JESSE. Forgive us, Miriam.
Joseph has asked us to go in. The Centurion
wishes to see us all together.

    [SHADRACH *comes down the steps.*]

MIRIAM. Surely.
Come in. Come in, Shadrach.

SHADRACH. I wish I had
the faith I had formerly in Ecclesiastes;
He says, "He that diggeth a pit shall fall therein;
and whoso breaketh through a fence, a serpent
shall bite him." And yet for a good many years now,
    men
have been digging holes for others, and burying
the others in them, without falling in. And men

go right on smashing fences, and meet no snakes—
or no more than honest men. My Ecclesiastes
was an optimist, after all.

    [JESHUA *enters, carrying a scroll.*]

ZEBULON. We stopped
to speak to Jeshua, because the Centurion asked
for Joseph's helper.

MIRIAM. Yes.

JESSE. We heard one bit
of news at the market. There's a fish found living
in the Dead Sea. Not very large, and not
very edible—but a fish, and alive.

SHADRACH. More than one?

ZEBULON. Whole families of them. Up at the
    northern end
where the fresh water comes in.

SHADRACH. And in Galilee
there are still Jews found living. Maybe not
very numerous, or edible, but still
existing among the back streets and high farms
where there aren't too many Romans.

JOSEPH.
    [*Speaking to the* CENTURION *as he comes down
    the steps*]
Come in, sir.
You'll find us all under one roof, and waiting for you.
Whatever you have to say to us can be said
without a waste of voice.

    [*The* CENTURION *enters after* JOSEPH.]

CENTURION. As you remember I was easy with
    you
when I was here last. Things have changed a little.
I can't make you the same offer. You'll come to work,
and you'll take your chance as to who's the overseer
and what you'll get to do.
    [*To* JOSEPH]
You once said to me,
there are no slaves in Galilee.—That's changed.
That's different now. There are slaves.—I want five
    men
from this house at the palace this morning.
If you want to know
what's different now—I'll tell you. You're trouble-
makers.
You've been seen in company we don't like—
men from the desert—and prophets that go about
inciting to revolt. There was a beggar
around this house before you left, and another
was seen with you on the road to Jerusalem.

Judah's men probably—both of them. You know
when you're wanted—and where. You'll come.
> [*He turns, goes up steps and out.*]

ZEBULON. The voice of Caesar.

JOSEPH. Yes,
and of Herod.—I tried to put it from my mind
while we were away. But under the happiness
of our journey, under the ritual of the Temple
and under our holy songs, this undertone
was heard incessantly: We must return
to face the Centurion.

SHADRACH. How can we serve them
and keep our faith—even a shred of faith?

JESSE. But disobedience to a Roman edict
means death for all of us.

SHADRACH. If we had a leader!

JOSEPH. If we had a leader, such as Judah was—
yet even if we had a leader—even then
our revolution would end as Judah's ended—
in death for many, and life on the hills for many—
and nothing gained.

SHADRACH. A leader like Moses then,
who could take us out of this into something better—
something with a hope in it!

JOSEPH. I've heard it said
there are no more promised lands.

JESSE. But easy, Shadrach—
this is a matter of bones in a cemetery.
Bones are not sacred.

SHADRACH. To them it means desecration!
They spit on our lips and our altars! And our God
is up for sale in Jerusalem! We saw it,
and this is all part of it!

JOSEPH. If the men will come with me
we can talk this over better among ourselves.
> [SHADRACH, ZEBULON, JESSE *and* JOSEPH *go to-
> ward the portal.* JESHUA *rises.*]

No, not you, Jeshua.
> [*The men go out.*]

MIRIAM. You should take your eyes
from your book sometimes, my Jeshua. You read
as if there were great haste.

JESHUA. Do I, Mother?

MIRIAM. Yes.
As if you were fevered, and only more and more
    reading
would quench your thirst.

JESHUA. It is like that.

MIRIAM. What water

is it you seek, my son, reading your eyes out
early in the morning, and then into the night,
till the last light's gone?
> [*He is silent.*]

What was it happened
the night you were late at the Temple?

JESHUA. Oh, Mother, tell me—
is it true—or did I imagine it—
that I stayed all night with the prophet before he
    died
in the court of the Temple—and you found me there
in the early morning?

MIRIAM. We came in the early morning
and found you there.

JESHUA. Then it may all be true—
it may be true—even in this bright daylight!
Oh, Mother,
is it so sure—is it certain, Mother, that I—
am this one—who is chosen?

MIRIAM. Your father's not sure.

JESHUA. But you—you, Mother—or was it my
    father alone
who dreamed? Did nothing come to you?

MIRIAM. No dream.

JESHUA. Then was it all his wishing, as he had
    feared,
his own desire?

MIRIAM. Could you believe so, Jeshua?

JESHUA. I could wish to believe so.

MIRIAM. When you are older ·
you shall know all my heart in all these things,
when you're only a little older.

JESHUA. Tell me your heart.
Say it now.

MIRIAM. Why, Jeshua?

JESHUA. Because it's part of my fever—
that I must hear it. Because I must know what I am
and what will come to me. In all this I read
in the holy books it's as if I set my lips
to Dead Sea water, so that I'm thirstier still—
and must know more!

MIRIAM. What do you read?

JESHUA. The prophecies.

MIRIAM. Concerning the Messiah?

JESHUA. Yes.

MIRIAM. If I
could tell you now—
> [*She puts out her hand to* JESHUA. JESHUA *sits on
> floor at her feet.*]

[*102*]

Mine was no dream, but a vision.
I've never said this—
perhaps I can't say it now. When a mother speaks
to a son who is twelve years old, there's a veil woven
between what she may know and he may hear—
it's as it was when you tried to tell your dream—
do you remember?

JESHUA. Yes.

MIRIAM. And now I find
that I cannot speak. Only an angel came
to me in a vision, saying when you were born
your name was to be called Jeshua, and of your
    kingdom
there was to be no end.
This you may keep in your heart, as I have kept it
till now in mine. You are indeed—you are He.
Whatever has been prophesied for Him
will be yours, will come to us—and we shall see it
when you are grown a man.

JESHUA. Oh, Mother, I know
you wouldn't hurt me—

MIRIAM. Hurt you, Jeshua?
But it was you who said in the outer court
of the Temple, that this was not a burden—that it
could mean only happiness.

JESHUA. Yes, I said it then.—
When you spoke with the angel did you learn from
    him
how the Messiah must die?

MIRIAM. I have never heard
that he will die. There is to be no end
to the Messiah's kingdom.

JESHUA. But he must die.
This is what I heard from the robber prophet,
from Ishmael, when he lay dying in the court,
and I held his hand. The Messiah will not live
to see his kingdom. He will be arraigned and tor-
    tured,
and die under torture. He will find a teaching
which can save men, but they will not follow it.
They will despise him, will send soldiers to find him
and set him before the judges. He will die
to save others. This was said to me by the robber,
and I couldn't believe him. But now I read the rolls
day and night—read all the passages
that have to do with his coming. And it's true
if I'm chosen the Messiah then what it means
is that I'm chosen out of all the children
to be tortured for the others when the time comes

for us to be men together. It's not a kingship—
not to lead armies, not to die old, or in battle,
but to be hurried to a sacrifice
and die young, a criminal's death!

MIRIAM. He was evil, evil—
    this man from the desert!

JESHUA. I said he was evil! Yes,
it seemed like madness to me! But all the books
say what he said—it's there to be read by all
who wish to read it!

MIRIAM. But it has no meaning!

JESHUA. Yes,
Mother, it has a meaning. Its meaning is
that the death of the innocent will work in the hearts
of those who murder them, till the murderers
are sorry, and have changed, and never again
take life unjustly! It may mean more, may mean even
that our race is chosen, our poor race of Israel,
to suffer for other races, as the Messiah
must suffer for our own.

MIRIAM. Where have you read this?

JESHUA. In all of them. That's why I've lain awake
to read when light came into the sky at morning,
and at night till my lamp went out. And they do say
    this.
How we could all have missed it, and hoped so long
for angels out of Heaven, I don't know—
for it's plain there in the prophecies; there's to be
no help come down from God. Our help must come
from within, from our hearts, from those who are
    willing to die
rather than accept injustice. And now you tell me
your vision. And I know. I must somehow find
the truth, according to my soul, and speak it,
and die for it—hoping somehow it will prevail
long after I'm dead.

MIRIAM. I will not believe this, Jeshua—

JESHUA. But I wish you would.
Then I wouldn't be alone. In all the world
there was only Ishmael knew this; and he died
for saying it to me. And now I must carry it.
Will you read the books?

MIRIAM. I'll read them if you like.
If it will help.

JESHUA. And then we can talk about them.

MIRIAM. Yes.

JESHUA. The book of Enoch says it clearly.

MIRIAM. I'll read the book of Enoch.

JESHUA. You'll read it first?

MIRIAM. Yes. First of all.—If this were what it
    means
to be the Messiah—to suffer and to die
for others—if it were not an honor—no,
but a dishonored death and misery—
    JESHUA. Yes?
    MIRIAM. Would you choose it then—?
    JESHUA. If I should find
that I'm still chosen and still wanted when
I come to be a man, then it may be God
would help me. Maybe even if I came to you
you could help me then.
    MIRIAM. I, Jeshua?
    JESHUA. We shall be older.
We shall both have learned by then.
I must find my apron and the helper's tools.
    [JOSEPH, SHADRACH, JESSE and ZEBULON enter.]
    JOSEPH. If we are to go
we must go soon. And Jeshua should be ready.
There were five called for.
    SHADRACH. Yet I still say what hope
have we as a nation? Give us a little something
to look forward to, and we can go on! But what is
    there,
unless it's plain slavery?
    MIRIAM. Is our Jeshua
a workman among you?
    JESSE. Yes.
    MIRIAM. Could he speak to you
as if he were a man?
    JESSE. Yes, if he wishes.
Do you wish to speak, Jeshua?
    JESHUA. I have nothing
of my own to say. But just as Shadrach asked
what hope we have, the book of Enoch opened
under my hand, to a part that I've read often.
May I read it?
    SHADRACH. Yes, read it.
    JESHUA. It's the last chapter.
"A city is but the outer hull, or garment,
of the faith which dwells within. Its palaces
and walls that stand up nobly in the air
and seem so tough and durable, are blown
into these shapes by the spirit which inhabits—
blown like a bubble, and will subside again
when the spirit is withdrawn. And what is true
of cities is true of kingdoms. For a cycle of years
they keep their faith, and this faith holds them
    steady

against the winds. But when they cease to believe
only a little while, the high roofs take rain,
and the walls sink to the moat. There was once a city
whose walls were destroyed by music blown against
    them,
but the walls of every city are raised up
by music, and are held foursquare in the sun
by a people's secret singing."
    SHADRACH. I must read the Scriptures.
There are others beside Ecclesiastes.
    JESHUA. Yes. Then he says:
"The palace built by a king without a faith
will not endure—but there are palaces
not built by hands, and those cannot be torn down
by the hands of kings."
    SHADRACH. It's true.
The kings do lose in the end—and that's a hope,
even for the people of Israel. But tell us then;
Are we never to turn on the kings?
Where is the line? How far can a man serve
    Herod?
    JESHUA. Until he asks of you what belongs to God.
    [MIRIAM rises and looks at JOSEPH.]
    JOSEPH. Until he asks of us what belongs to God.
    SHADRACH. What part of a man belongs to God?
    JESHUA. His mind,
his freedom, his freedom to find his way to God
in his own way.
    SHADRACH.
    [Turns to others.]
    Well, shall we go?
    ZEBULON.
    [Rising.]
    Why, yes,
we can go now.
    [He and JESSE go out.]
    JOSEPH. And you've not lost your faith?
    SHADRACH. Lost it? Lost my faith? I've just now
    found it.
Just this moment found it.
    [He goes out.]
    JOSEPH. So have I, I think. Yes, so have I.
    [He follows the others.]
    JESHUA. I must go with them, Mother, I'm needed,
    too.
    MIRIAM. Yes, Jeshua.
    [She kisses his forehead. JESHUA goes out.]

                                        Curtain

THE LITTLE MIRACLE

Zoë Akins

"Are not two sparrows sold for a farthing? and one of them shall not fall on the ground without your Father."
MATTHEW X, 29

A room in which a carpenter lives, as we see by his table and tools in one corner. A family sleeps here, as we see by the cushions edging the floor on opposite sides. A treasure chest hangs on one wall; beneath it, beautifully painted, is the family Ark. The table about which the family gathers for meals and for talk is to the left. Several stools are disposed about it, and about the room. On the table are a jug of wine, cups, a dish of fruit, and an unlighted oil lamp. On the floor, to one side, are several bundles, such as are carried by travelers.

And here are the carpenter's wife, MARY, *and four of her neighbors: Her cousin,* ELIZABETH, *an old, meek woman who sits before the table, her arms seeking support from it;* JOHANNA, *the ruddy, heavy mother of grown sons;* MARIEMME, *a younger woman, gentle and fair; and* ANNA, *a swarthy, handsome creature, who stands back of the table, her water jug on her shoulder, and speaks with the air of one who feels herself privileged.*

ANNA.
I come from the fountain;
There the women are talking of nothing
Except your return from Jerusalem,
Which was more than three days delayed.
During that time—while those at home
Waited and watched for the company which had
    gone up to the city
To pay the accursed Romans their taxes—
Fearing some evil had befallen you on the way,
There was nothing but came into our thoughts;
Some said thieves had waylaid you and taken the
    money
Meant for the Romans;
Others said, "It may be a plague has fallen on the
    city
And our neighbors and kinfolk are among those
    stricken;
And the well are staying to care for the ill."
Still others, that the Romans had sent another army

Into Jerusalem, and our townspeople were among
    those
Taken captive to the Gentiles, and taken
Over the north sea to their strange city, enslaved.
There was no work done,
Because of these dreadful thoughts.
The Greek merchant would now tell us
Of the mercilessness of Rome; and now
How Joseph had promised him a new door for his
    house,
And gone without finishing it; and how, being a
    stranger,
He feared to lie down among his treasures
With no strong lock between him and the night.
Joel, watching the grapes pass the moment
For gathering, told us, wringing his hands,
How Simon and his two sons had promised themselves
For the wine-making the day following
The first night of the full moon;
My own husband's brother had promised
To be in time for the threshing;
But the grain was gathered and waiting
And he came not, as you know.
Old Zebedee brought us no fish—being unable
To manage his new boat without the aid
Of his three sons. . . . In the synagogue
The priests and the readers said prayers;
Many fasted; others brought sacrifices—
Their doves and their oxen; is it not true, Johanna?
    JOHANNA.
She knows it is all true. I have told her, myself.
    ANNA.
And all because this son of yours —
This son whom you never reprove,
This son whom you think perfect—
Ran away, and was lost for three days
Somewhere in the city!
    ELIZABETH. *(Wearily, lifting her head)*
That, too, she knows.
    ANNA. *(Impatiently)*
But she does not know—or does she not care?—
What they are saying—
Those who turned back with her
To search for her son
At the end of their first day's journey homeward;
Or those here at home,
Who offered their doves and their oxen
For their safety when they came not.
These things she should hear.

ELIZABETH.
I was of the company
Which turned back
Searching for my cousin's son;
And I heard only words of joy
When he was found at the end of the third day.

MARY. *(Quietly)*
What is it I should know?
Let Anna tell me.

ANNA. *(Boldly)*
They are saying that the boy
Is less to blame for the great trouble he caused
Than you, Mary, his mother;
They say you have always been too indulgent with
 him;
They say this would never have happened
If you had not spared the rod always
And spoiled your child.

MARIEMME. *(Gently, speaking for the first time)*
That is true, Mary.
I have often wished for the courage to tell you
How my uncle, who is the boy's teacher
In the synagogue, has shaken his head often,
And declared that it does a lad no good
To be given his own way always.

JOHANNA. *(Also gently)*
Do not take what you are learning unkindly,
 Mary;
Now that you have found him
Who was so recently lost, it is natural
You should think only of his dearness
And shudder back
From what might have happened,
Holding him in the strong arms of your joy, safe.
But presently your happiness will be older,
And your thoughts more calm; think then—
Remember—how others were put to much trouble,
And yourself to terror
Because of his heedlessness; and ask of yourself
If you have done well
In looking upon him as one who can do no wrong.

ANNA. *(Gathering the courage to be even more
 severe)*
It will do him no good, Mary,
To treat him as if he were precious
Beyond all other children.
—As you will see, to your sorrow, in time.

MARIEMME. *(Again, very gently)*
I love the boy, Mary;

And my children love him—my little Martha, and
 my son, James;
Even my husband, who is always busy
And often too tired to talk with me,
Will talk with him, when he comes now and then
Into our house at evening.
All the same, my uncle
Will tell you that the child
Is difficult to teach, and shows too little
Reverence for the temple and the law;
He questions many of the sayings of the scribes,
And his indifference to holy things
Has troubled those who wish him well,
And angered those who feel his will too strong.
 (A slight pause; then MARIEMME *continues, as
 if hesitating to say too much)*
At times, my uncle tells me,
He goes into the pastures with the shepherds,
Or lies all day, in dreams, beside the sea
Instead of going to his lessons.
Such a boy, they say,
Will bring his parents sorrow.

MARY. *(Unbelieving)*
So that is what they are saying,
Even now, of my son!

ANNA.
All that, even now; and more.
Even that he will end upon the cross ——

MARY. *(Rising; her voice trembling with anger)*
Be quiet!

ANNA.
I am sorry ——
 (Coldly)
But it is true, ask any of your neighbors.

MARY.
Out of my house! Out of my house!

ELIZABETH.
Cousin!

MARY. *(Pointing to the door at the back)*
Out of my house!
Go!
 (To ANNA, *then to the others)*
You—
And any others—
Who dare to speak in such a fashion
To me or any other
Of my son! Go!

ANNA. *(With a short laugh as she strolls to the
 door)*

I said that I was sorry, but I am not.
If you are such a fool that you take
What is well-meaning as ill-meant,
I have no wish to serve or to spare you; but ——
    (From the doorway)
If you should hear what others hear, you would learn
That this son of yours dares to talk
Of a Father—
A Father who is in heaven!
Stop him. It makes
People laugh at him;
And at you, Mary,
Knowing what they know.
    (Then she goes)
    MARY. *(To heaven, her eyes closed)*
Must I go softly all my years—
All my years—
In the bitterness of my soul, O Lord,
Because of the sign
Thou has put upon me?
    JOHANNA.
Child, child, come,
Do not take what Anna has said
In a moment's vexation
So to heart.
    MARIEMME.
She said more than she meant
Or anyone means ——
    JOHANNA. *(Gently, interrupting* MARIEMME*)*
Everyone knows there is no kinder little soul
In Nazareth than your son;
Everyone knows that he has ways
Which are tender and healing
With the sick and the old.
    MARIEMME.
The sick and the old,
And the little children;
They turn to him to listen
To the comfort of his young voice
Reciting the psalms of the shepherd, David;
Or the curious beautiful sayings
Of our prophets;
Or to hear the day's story, perhaps,
Which he lives again, and they live,
As he speaks to them
Of being out on a rough sea
With the brave fishermen;
Or up in the high pastures
With the careful shepherds;

And though he is still but a child,
As he speaks the world seems,
And he seems, and we seem who listen,
To be all a part
Of a beautiful dream
That the Lord of Judah is dreaming
For his own glory.
    JOHANNA. *(As* MARY *bends her head, weeping
        softly)*
Who would find fault with a child
For fetching water to the beggars
On the steps of the temple?
Or giving fruit from his father's trees
To the half-caste men of Samaria
Passing this way with their flocks,
Going to Capernaum, unable to buy bread
Of the true Jews?
Or for carrying little flowers from the hills
Into the house of the desert woman who lies
Dying of her sins, though the priests
Have warned us the very boards of her threshold
Are accursed? . . . Not I.
    MARIEMME.
Nor I.
At the same time,
Even children must be taught it is not meet
To break bread with the dogs of the road; and I—
With my own eyes—
Have seen him give food to the lepers,
And sit down by the roadside with them,
Eating and drinking as though it were a great honor
Instead of a danger and a wrong.
I know that my uncle thinks
This fondness for low company
A bad sign, Mary.
    JOHANNA.
And if those who wasted three whole days
Away from their work and their homes,
Searching the city with you,
Have been vexed by the child's waywardness,
You cannot think it strange or unlikely
That they wonder
Because he is never punished
As other children are punished
For the trouble he has caused.
    MARY. *(Lifting her head; speaking in a level voice,
        at last)*
My son has been punished
For this trouble he has caused.

My son has often been punished
For trouble he has caused me.
    JOHANNA. *(Doubtfully)*
That is not the belief in the village;
It is said among the women
Who gossip at the fountain
That never once
Has your hand been lifted, or Joseph's,
To strike at your son.
    MARY.
That is true.
My hand, or Joseph's,
Has never been lifted against him.
    MARIEMME.
Then how have you punished him, Mary?
    MARY.
He has looked into my heart
And seen that I was not pleased with him;
He has sought my eyes
And they have remained averted from him;
He has spoken softly at my side
And my lips have not answered him;
He has kissed my hand
And I have drawn it away from his lips;
He has leaned his head against my side
And I have not put my hand upon it;
He has not heard me sing or speak
Since he answered me unkindly
When I cried out to him, reproaching him,
When we found him in the temple.
    JOHANNA.
You found him *in the temple*!
That, I had not been told.
    MARIEMME.
Nor I; they said
You had told no one where you found him.
    MARY. *(Her eyes fixed on the mystery; steadily)*
In the temple;
Where we had gone
Not to search for him
But to pray for him
And to buy animals
To offer as sacrifices
For his return.
We had asked the Roman soldiers
Who keep watch in the Tower of Antonia
Over all that is done in the courts of the temple and
   in the city
If they had seen a child

Wandering alone.
They had not seen him, they said;
But they were kind and did not laugh
As they laugh in Jerusalem
At those out of Galilee;
They do not esteem, there, those who are come
From the little town of Nazareth up to the large city.
But in the temple,
Under a far portico
Where even the eyes of Rome
Could not fall,
In a circle of gray heads—
Where the gray-bearded doctors
Sit in the seats of the mighty —
From a long distance
I saw shining
A child's hair, all golden and flying;
And I saw his face,
Stained bright with the swift breathing
Of the thoughts within him, lifted
Flowerlike in that gray circle;
And heard his voice
Trembling with his thoughts, and eager—
His young sweet voice, lifted
Against those old voices
Like high music flowing
Into soft thunder. . . . And my knees
Bent under me, and I fell, sobbing,
In my joy and my pride.
But Joseph
Caught me up, and hurried me
To where they were sitting—
Those learned doctors,
With him in their midst,
Asking them questions and replying,
As if he were one of themselves,
One of those wise great men of the temple, and not
Just a little boy, twelve years old, and my son!
    JOHANNA. *(Awkwardly, deeply impressed)*
It was a great honor, certainly,
To have such great men
Take notice of him
And converse with him.
    MARIEMME.
That is true.
    (Quietly)
I will tell my uncle.
    MARY. *(Sharply)*
Tell no one—no one!

There are many things
In my heart hidden—
Which I have told none.
There are many sayings
Which he has said,
Which I keep in my heart,
And share with none;
For none would believe;
Or if they believed would not understand.
He himself, often,
Divining the wonder
In some simple words
Which have come from his lips,
Or in some simple thing
He has touched with strangeness—
Such as the swift blooming
Of seeds he has planted,
Or the sudden peace
Of the roughened sea
When he has gone out with the fishermen
To cast their nets—
Has bade me again and again:
"Tell it not."
There is a secrecy about good works
He cherishes more than praise.

    MARIEMME.
Still, my uncle would keep secret
This story of him in the temple,
If I told him, and asked it.

    MARY.
No, no. . . . Be still.
Let it be known, if ever,
From those whom he talked with in the temple;
Even so, others—our neighbors and kinsmen—
Will think it unseemly
That a child should venture
To speak at all among the elders.

    MARIEMME. (After an instant)
Perhaps that is true.
I will not speak of it.
But even though they found the boy remark-
    able,
It does not change the fact
That he had run away,
And had been lost to you
Three days;
And should have been for that
More sternly punished
Than he has been or will be.

    ELIZABETH. (Softly)
Speak not to her of punishment;
I heard her cry out, reproaching him,
Saying:
"Son—why hast thou dealt thus with us? Behold,
Thy father and I have sought thee,
Sorrowing." . . . I heard her say it—
The first words of reproach
Ever I heard to him from her—
And heard his answer,
Saying——

    MARY.
Say not! Be still.
My words were for my son, only.

    ELIZABETH.
But having heard you answer him,
May I not say
That, when he saw you troubled,
The light went from his face,
And he, too,
Sorrowed, and has been
Silent and very sorrowful
For his fault since?

    MARY.
That is true. There lies between us
A hurt which punishes both;
His heart is sore;
And mine is very sore
That him I reproached
When on my knees
I should have cried my thanks to heaven
For having thus found him—
For having borne him!

    JOHANNA.
No, no! Be not unwise,
Speak not so passionately
Of what was said, and well said,
And which you could not but have said
At such a moment.

    MARY. (As if she had not heard)
Ah—but
I cried out as I cried out,
Because I had fallen and lain
Where my knees gave way,
Before Joseph lifted and guided me
To where I had seen him, far off, standing—
And I was distraught still
With my fears for him;
But had he come there

Where I had fallen,
And bent above me,
I should have had no words;
Only glad tears;
The sharp words came
Because the tears could not;
Not there—
Before the doctors of the law.

ELIZABETH.
Mary, Mary ——

MARY. (In a different voice; decisively)
But be not afraid—
I shall not relent
Until he has won from me
Forgiveness
For all which has vexed me,
And vexed others.

(A little girl has come into the room, and stands
near MARIEMME, crying. MARY turns with some
relief from her own thoughts, and takes notice
of her)

Martha, my child,
What is it?
Why are you crying?
Has anyone hurt you?
Come, tell me,
Tell me.

(She bends toward the child, opening her arms;
but MARTHA continues to sob)

MARIEMME. (Sternly)
Hush, hush! No more of this noise!

(Then to the others, as MARY yearns toward the
child, who remains apart, trying to subdue her
grief)

Her kitten is dead;
And her brothers and playmates
Are burying it. Hush, Martha; or go home.

MARTHA. (Lifting her face)
And leave my kitten
For others to bury?

MARIEMME.
Yes; stop crying,
Or we will go home
And leave your kitten
For the other children to bury.

MARTHA. (With childish defiance)
I will not go home!
And I will not let them bury my kitten!

(MARIEMME rises and goes toward her)

Other children
May speak so to their parents,
But not you to me!
Will you be quiet
And obey me, or not?

(There is an instant's pause, while MARTHA con-
trols her sobbing. MARIEMME speaks again in
the stern, firm voice of a kind parent who feels
herself in the right)

There; that is better.
Did you not promise
That if your father
Left your kitten
To be buried in a box on the hillside
Instead of taking it with the offal
And throwing it into the sea,
That you would stop crying
And be sensible,
Like a big girl, like your big brothers?

MARTHA. (Whispering)
Yes, mother.

MARIEMME.
And you have not kept that promise, have you?

MARTHA.
No, mother.

MARIEMME.
Well, then—keep it now,
Or you shall be punished.

JOHANNA. (Kindly)
I will give you another kitten, Martha,
A beautiful kitten, Martha,
The color of sea sand, with eyes
The color of the clear blue sea itself;
But its pointed ears,
And its soft feet,
And its damp blunt nose,
And its short little tail, like a sheep's,
Are as dark as shadows;
And it looks so wise
You do not wonder because foolish people
In the great desert where it came from
Pray to cats instead of to God.

MARTHA. (Stubbornly)
I want my own kitten.
I loved her.

MARIEMME. (Impatiently)
We will go home!

MARTHA. (Passionately)
No, no!

[110]

MARIEMME.
Then say, "I thank you for the new kitten,"
If you want to go back to your brothers and your
friends.
  MARTHA. *(With quivering lips, to* JOHANNA*)*
I thank you
For the new kitten ——
    (She halts)
  MARY. *(Kindly)*
She shall have some figs—
The very first figs of the year;
Look ——
    (She fetches a plate of figs from the table)
You shall have all these,
To take to the other children
For a feast!
  MARIEMME.
You like figs, don't you?
And your kitten's funeral
Will be very grand,
With a feast to end it.
You would like that, wouldn't you?
  MARTHA.
Yes, mother.
  MARIEMME.
Then hold your tunic, so—
    (She loops up the child's tunic)
So I can fill it;
But you must walk carefully,
Because if you fall
You will crush the soft figs,
And the cloth will be soiled;
Do not run; but first
Say, "Thank you for the beautiful fruit,
Madam Mary."
  MARTHA. *(Meekly, making a careful curtsy)*
Thank you for the beautiful fruit,
Madam Mary.
  MARIEMME.
And kiss me.
    (MARTHA averts her face)
  MARIEMME. *(Insistently, sternly)*
I said, *kiss me.*
  MARY. *(Unhappily, in a low voice)*
Let her go.
  MARIEMME.
No! Martha ——
    *(MARTHA lifts her miserable eyes, and kisses her
    mother on each cheek)*

MARIEMME. *(Well pleased)*
There—
My little girl is a good girl
Again; and her mother loves her
Again. . . . Now you may go.
  MARY. *(From the doorway)*
I do not see my son among the others.
Martha—
    *(MARTHA pauses on the doorstep, as MARY con-
    tinues)*
Was he not with you?
  MARTHA.
No, madam;
He has not played with us
All day.
  MARY. *(In a strained voice)*
His father bade him
Play near the house, and not go
Beyond the brook, out of my sight.
Have you heard nothing of him at all?
  MARTHA.
James said that he saw him going
Up into the high pasture alone;
He called to him,
But he did not answer.
    (MARY's lips tighten)
  MARIEMME. *(To MARTHA)*
Well, you and your brothers
Are not to go where you cannot hear me
When I call.
We must start home presently.
  MARTHA.
And leave my kitten!
  MARIEMME. *(Checking the tears which are about
    to fall again)*
Sh-h! Be careful! Or— There! That is better.
    *(The child controls herself, not daring to speak;
    and after an instant, with her head lifted
    bravely, goes out the door and disappears from
    the vista beyond)*
  MARIEMME. *(Complacently)*
That is the way
One must manage a child, Mary;
It would be unkind
To let her give way to her sorrow.
One must be firm but unangered;
One must command, but be gentle,
As our mother was with her children;
For why is our very stature

Greater than a child's if our wisdom
Is not greater than his,
And so must prevail
Over the ignorance, and the hardheartedness,
And the stubborn wills of childhood?
Look!
Martha is turning, and smiling now, and waving her
    hand,
    (She points proudly through the open window,
    as she continues)
Making her peace, showing
I have conquered.
    MARY. *(Quietly)*
That is well.
    (But even as MARIEMME *is watching her child*
    her eyes flash with annoyance, for again there is
    the sound of sobs)
    MARIEMME.
Listen!
    (She moves toward the door, angrily; but MARY
    stops her)
    MARY.
Let her be. She has done her best
To obey you and command her sorrow.
Do not call her back; not now,
But listen, and say,
When you have heard
What I shall tell you, if my son were your son,
Or yours, Johanna,
Or yours, cousin,
You would think still
Your wisdom greater,
As your stature is greater,
Than his.
    (For an instant she reflects; then continues, first
    in a voice which reasons with itself and then
    with a surge of feeling which leaps into pure
    ecstasy and travail)
Twelve years now,
Always with some wonder
And always with uneasiness,
But often with a stirring of hope
Like the stirring of a fresh wind
Out of the mysterious sea,
I have looked on my son.
I wish to deal wisely with him.
But I may be only a foolish mother,
And my foolish dreams and my visions
May be sent not from the Lord but from the evil one

To make me proud among women.
If I am vain, if I am deluded,
Persuade me, for his sake, his sweet sake,
Persuade me. . . . And I will bid his teachers
Show him such harshness
As they deem wise for his correction;
I will tell my husband
No longer to hold his hand,
Because of my fancies,
When the boy does not his bidding;
I will myself learn from you, Mariemme,
To bend my child to my own will,
And bend never again myself to his. . . .
But. . . .
The prophets—
    (Very solemnly)
Have told us over and over
Of one who should be born of a maiden
In Bethlehem of Judea,
Who should be a Governor
To rule Israel, to lead Israel
Out of her long bondage, and make
Her mighty among the nations;
He, this one, the prophets have told us,
Shall sit upon the right hand to God
With the prophets of all ages;
He shall be God's messenger on earth;
He shall rule nations for God;
He shall do God's work, and share in His eternal glory
As a son in the house of his father.
So— Listen—
I saw angels; doubt me, doubt that I saw angels,
But doubt not that there was a voice in my soul
Saying— But no matter.
    (She pauses, her secret too dear for revelation,
    then continues with more reserve)
It matters only that a voice spoke,
And as my eyes see each of you this day,
That day my eyes saw plainly a great angel
Saying
That I should bear a son; saying more
Of which I will not speak; for I shall speak
Not of myself now—not of my visions even, but of
    him.
You have heard, I think,
Of the three wise men who came
Out of the unknown East, following a star
To the stable,
That night when I lay on the straw

In the stall of an ox,
With my son, new-born, at my breast.
And there, saying
"All hail to our King," they knelt,
And while the kind cattle with their great eyes
Looked on, laid gifts fit for kings only,
Before a babe cradled in a humble manger!
>   (*She pauses, then moves swiftly to a chest cov-
>   ered by a worn rug; continuing*)
Here are those gifts. Look! See for yourselves.
>   (*Even old* ELIZABETH *rises, and in the moment's
>   silence which follows, the three women look
>   with awe at the three gold vessels which they
>   see when* MARY *unlocks the chest and opens it*)
>   MARY. (*Presently, out of the pause*)
In this plain chest, you see the rich treasures—
Frankincense and myrrh and gold—
Brought by the three.
But do not speak of it, for fear of thieves.
I keep them so, for him; untouched and safe.
>   (*She closes the chest, locks it, covers it again
>   with the rug, and continues with deep feeling*)
In those first years, those years in Egypt,
Where we were sent by dreams, I used to see,
Plainly, a light running with the first running
Of my young child's feet in the shadows
Of our tent. . . . And from the distance
When he came toward me a light came running,
      dancing
Before him; day dawning in a vale
Was not so fair as his approach. I have not seen that
      light
Again, alas, since those first years,
In that strange country.
>   JOHANNA. (*In a tone of disappointment, having
>   expected more*)
And is this all?
>   MARIEMME.
And for these reasons, only,
You believe your son different
From others?
>   MARY. (*Humbly*)
It seems in telling, I know,
Little reason enough for assurance
Such as mine. . . . But was it not remarkable
I saw the angel?
Was it not singular
Those wise men came with such rich gifts;
And God, in dreams, sent us into the land

Of the Egyptians, and later called us hence?
And that, at times, I saw the light?
>   JOHANNA. (*Dryly*)
Not so remarkable as that your cousin bore
In her old age a son; she too beheld an angel.
>   MARY. (*Wearily, her glance resting for a second on
>   ELIZABETH*)
I know, I know.
>   (*Then, after an instant, with the wistful obsti-
>   nacy of one who must believe*)
But not only
These things have I found marvelous,
Which in the telling seem little,
But also many a thing which he has said,
And which I have kept in my heart, unforgotten—
Which indeed, once heard from a child's lips,
None could forget. . . .
"*Do any gather grapes of thorns,*" he asked once;
"*Or figs of thistles?*" . . . "Why, no, my son," I
      answered;
"Why ask such questions?" . . .
"Then," said he,
"*By their good fruits you know good trees.*"
It seemed a simple thing to say, and yet a strange
      thing
For him to ponder on, and so I waited;
"*Mother,*" he said at last,
"*It is the same with us as with the trees.*"
>   JOHANNA.
What did he mean by that?
>   MARY.
I think that it is plain; as with the trees,
By our fruit shall men know us. . . .
Again,
Staring at lilies growing wild and golden
In a green field, he touched my arm and said—
Pointing—"*They do not toil or spin,
As you do, mother, yet King Solomon
In all his glory surely was not as these.*"
>   MARIEMME.
What did he mean by that?
>   MARY.
I understood; he meant that as it was God's will
That the idle lilies should be lovely,
It is by will of His that we are what we are—
And go in humble garments or silken robes,
Spinning or toiling not—it does not matter.
>   JOHANNA.
I grant you it is not often that young children

Speak thus; but I think, Mary,
That you have taken his carelessly dropped words
And given them deep meanings of your own.

ELIZABETH.

And not wise meanings, Mary—if you think
God clothes us as He does the flowers and hills and
    valleys.
God lets us live, and gives us time and weather
And the green fruitful earth; but by his work
Each man must build his house,
And feed and clothe himself.

MARY.

My son thinks otherwise.

MARIEMME. (With a short laugh)

Oh, Mary! As if that mattered!

MARY. (Unsmiling)

"If I should ask for bread, mother," he said, once—
"You would not put a stone into my hand."

MARIEMME. (Gaily)

And that means what?

MARY.

That God, the father of men, is not less
In kindness and His great riches than I;
If we but ask of Him shall we receive.

JOHANNA.

Child, child, such nonsense for an honest woman!
A nomad from the desert, doing no work
But living from day to day upon his wits
Might talk so of his heathen gods!

MARY. (Not heeding her, continuing)

"Heaven is God's throne,
The earth His footstool, and Jerusalem
The city of the great King,"
He said, as we paused on a hilltop, looking down
A week ago upon Jerusalem. . . .
It was his first sight of a city,
And all that day he talked of cities.
"A city set upon a hill cannot be hid," he said.
    (Then, looking up and seeing them half doubt-
    ful, half bored)
And but one other thing
I shall repeat to you:
An old man with his face twisted
Rode past us on the way, with his two sons;
Their faces, too,
Wore a wild look of hate. . . . And somewhat later
We came upon the three beside a brook
Where they had paused for food;
They told a tale

Of an old feud which they had ridden forth to end
Within the week in blood. They would not wait
To rest; they rode ahead, and so it happened
Again we overtook them, but this time
They fed with their dead flesh the desert vultures;
And with them lay, just dying too,
Three others, the three whom they had sought.
And my son said, standing above the old man's half-
    plucked corpse,
Speaking, it seemed to me, to all the world,
Though there was none beside him but myself—
And it was not to me he spoke—
"Love your enemies, as yourself," he said.

JOHANNA. (Interrupting)

As if that could be done! It is a good thing
None heard him but yourself; or they would tell
Some evil spirit had filled the boy with thoughts
Deplorable, and nearly lunatic.

MARY. (Continuing)

"Bless them," he said, "that curse you!
    (Her voice rises as she speaks)
Do good to them that hate you.
And pray for them which despitefully use you—
For God's sun rises on the evil and the good,
And His rain falleth on the just and on the unjust."
    (Then, her voice dropping)
And that I think beautiful! That, I think,
Comes from some wisdom greater than his own.
That, I think, might have been said
By some great ruler, or prophet. I am proud of that!

MARIEMME.

But why? What does it mean?

MARY.

Do you not see?
If God deprive not some of sun and rain,
How dare we visit on those whom He afflicts not
Our little hate? Rather let our love—
Like His—be like to sun and rain
And cause some good thing to grow up in place of
    hate.

MARIEMME. (Primly)

But this is not according to the teachings
Of the synagogue.

MARY.

You do not believe ——

JOHANNA, ELIZABETH and MARIEMME. (Speaking
    together, one kindly, one impatiently, one re-
    gretfully, shaking their heads)

No. . . . No.

MARY.

Then ——

(Lifting her eyes as if to find God above her;
her exaltation gone, but not all hope)

A sign! A sign, O God!

That I may know and, knowing, may see clearly

What Thou wouldst have me do!

Whether my son is indeed *Thy* son,

Or my reason clouded concerning him

By the arrogance of my love for him

And the proud dreams I have wrought for him

Out of my hope, out of my faith!

The dreams are passing; the hope is passing;

I have no arrogance now—

And my faith is but as a reed

Which will stand only in the world's winds

If it be Thy will to strengthen it, Lord!

(She hides her face in her hands)

THE WOMEN. *(Softly to one another)*

Sh-h. . . . Let us leave her.

She is overwrought. . . .

The worry of those three days has confused her. . . .

Come away.

MARTHA'S VOICE. *(Calling loudly, joyously)*

Mother! Mother! Look—look!

(MARTHA, followed by her brothers and several
other children, comes tumbling into the room)

MARIEMME.

Children, children, what is it?

What has happened?

MARTHA.

My kitten, mother! Look!

Jesus came and saw me crying—

And he spoke to my kitten—

And it was alive again!

(She holds her kitten for them all to see; MARY
looks on, and a light comes into her eyes; the
kitten arches itself on MARTHA's shoulder)

MARIEMME. *(Impatiently)*

What is this?

JOHANNA.

What are you saying, child?

ELIZABETH.

Is this true?

THE CHILDREN. *(In turn)*

Yes, yes; it is true!

Jesus came—

And spoke to it—

As we were about to nail down the lid of the box—

And it suddenly leaped up ——

MARTHA.

Into my arms! And lives!

MARIEMME. *(After an instant)*

It's plain, it was not dead.

MARTHA.

It was! It was! Jesus made it live!

MARIEMME.

Sh-h—you must not say such things!

They are wrong.

MARTHA.

But they are true!

My kitten *was* dead—

Everyone said it was dead!

THE CHILDREN. *(Gravely)*

It was dead ——

MARTHA.

It was cold and hard

Since yesterday;

Father told me it was dead

And should be thrown

Into the sea.

MARY. *(Softly, yearningly, suddenly)*

Where is my son?

MARTHA.

He said you were not pleased with him;

He said you would not want to see him;

He said he would go back, up into the hills.

MARY. *(Going to the door and calling)*

Son. . . . Son!

(Then radiantly)

He hears me. . . . He is coming.

(Again she calls, her arms open. A light runs to-
ward her, transforming her, as she stands in the
doorway, calling softly, happily)

Jesus . . . darling!

(The others draw together, suddenly, a little
afraid)

Curtain

3. THE CARPENTER

HIS YOUTH

John Oxenham

But all too soon the much-loved father died,
And on his youth full early fell the care
Of her whose life was all bound up in him—
His sweet, young, saintly mother—and for her
No labour was too great, no toil too long.

His trade was humble, but he gave to it
Such pride of high endeavour that his skill
Won fame beyond his borders, and men came
From far to buy his plows that never turned
Poor furrows; and still more his perfect yokes;
So smoothly rounded these, so deftly shaped,
That no sleek neck was ever galled by them,—
So easy, so well-fitting, that they made
All burdens light; and dumb beasts everywhere
Thanked him who wrought so thoughtfully for them,
And got through twice the work they did before.—
But goads he could not bring his hand to make.

All that he did was always of his best;
To get perfection he would meet the dawn
And toil till daylight faded in the west.
Then in the dark he still went smoothing on,
With cunning fingers touched to tenderness,
Till not one burr or wrinkle in the wood
Remained. For, as he worked, he ever thought
Of that dumb brother who, somewhere, somewhen,
Would wear his yoke and maybe think of him.

When from the inner room his mother called,
"My son, the supper waits," He would reply,—
"I come!"—and straight would come, and with him
    bring
The heavy yoke he'd promised for next day

But had not yet wrought fully to his mind.
And, as he ate, he would go smoothing on
Till his deft fingers found in it content.

So his fame spread, because his smallest work
Was ever ripest product of his skill;—
And all men honoured him.

And, ever, as he worked, his mind ran deep
On life and death, and all that lies between.
His eager heart was stored with goodly things,
For all he saw, and heard, and read became
A very part of him, touched with his fire,
And radiant with the jewels of his thought.

His soul ranged wide and ever loftily,
But life's complexities and man's small care
For his true welfare weighed on him at times,
And clouded him with sorrow.
                              Yet he was
By nature joyous, since he lived so near
To Nature's heart and so could meet each ill,
Like Nature's self, with brave and hopeful cheer,
That drew the sting, dropped balm into the wound,
And healed its bitterness.

But, as he grew,
There burned within him such a pure white flame
Of love, and truth, and right 'twixt man and man,
That to his comrades he was friend of friends;
But to all evil—a devouring fire.
Full neighbourly he was; in counsel wise
Beyond his years, quick to appreciate
Life's humours as its ills, and gifted with
A rare direct simplicity of speech
All gemmed with stories perfect to the point.
So that men loved to listen to his talk,
And lingered in his workshop while he wrought.

His face was winning in its gladsomeness;
The children crowded round him as he toiled,
Begging for stories; and when business pressed,
He set them working, to their great delight,—
Clearing his shavings, sorting out his nails,
Helping the carpenter, and claiming toll
Of longer stories when his work was done;
While in and out the small birds flew, and chirped
Their love for him because he loved them so.

His strong calm eyes looked through the outer masks
Of men and things, and saw what dwelt within,
And whither it was tending, up or down.
None upon whom that clear gaze dwelt but knew
Its strange compelling power. It seemed as though
Their very souls lay bare unto his sight,
And none forgot that wondrous look of his.
Evil shrank from it as from lightning flame,
But to his loved ones it was like the joy
Of well-springs in a dark and thirsty land.

At eventide when his full work was done,
And thought and hope travailled within his soul,
He would at times climb up the dark hillside
And sit and think, in solemn commune there
With that, within him and without, which spoke
With ever-growing urgency of God,—
Of all God meant, to him and all mankind,
But more, far more, to him than to the rest.

And, as he sat, the birds and little beasts
Would creep up close and sit and watch him there,
With eyes like tiny stars, and bated breaths,
For they in him found sweet companionship,
And he found good and God in everything.

And up and down the dusty way
    The village folk would often wend;
And on the bench, beside Him, lay
    Their broken things for Him to mend.

The maiden with the doll she broke,
    The woman with the broken chair,
The man with broken plough, or yoke,
    Said, "Can you mend it, Carpenter?"

And each received the thing he sought,
    In yoke, or plough, or chair, or doll;
The broken thing which each had brought
    Returned again a perfect whole.

So, up the hill the long years through,
    With heavy step and wistful eye,
The burdened souls their way pursue,
    Uttering each the plaintive cry:

"O Carpenter of Nazareth,
    This heart, that's broken past repair,
This life, that's shattered nigh to death,
    Oh, can You mend them, Carpenter?"

And by His kind and ready hand,
    His own sweet life is woven through
Our broken lives, until they stand
    A New Creation—"all things new."

"The shattered idols of my heart,
    Desire, ambition, hope, and faith,
Mould Thou into the perfect part,
    O Carpenter of Nazareth!"

THE CARPENTER
OF NAZARETH

George Blair

In Nazareth, the narrow road,
    That tires the feet and steals the breath,
Passes the place where once abode
    The Carpenter of Nazareth.

CARPENTER

Isabel Fiske Conant

To the kind, the tall Carpenter
Planing the long boards,
The tree-hearts whispered
Songs without words.

The eucalyptus sang to Him
Never to His loss.
The cypress stretched its bared beams
To be shaped like a cross.

The gentle oleander
And all the many-leaved,
Scattered bloom of shavings
Round Him lest He grieved—
The trees' sap stirred again
To give Him glad awe
As not to any other
That cleaved them with a saw.

He did not truly hurt them,
And they understood
And worshiped Him, the Builder
Of the earth and the wood.
The children flocked around Him,
Little boys and little girls,
Laughing at the shavings,
Turning them to curls.

Sometimes an old man
Sat and watched by Him,
His voice very gentle,
And his eyes growing dim.
Sometimes a woman,
Blue-robed and grave,
Bread, milk, and honey,
Smiling, to Him gave.

To the kind, the tall Carpenter
Planing new boards,
The tree-souls whispered
Music without words.

THE CARPENTER

G. A. Studdert-Kennedy

I wonder what He charged for chairs at Nazareth.
And did men try to beat Him down
And boast about it in the town—
"I bought it cheap for half-a-crown
From that mad Carpenter?"

And did they promise and not pay,
Put it off to another day;
O, did they break His heart that way,
My Lord, the Carpenter?

I wonder did He have bad debts,
And did He know my fears and frets?
The gospel writer here forgets
To tell about the Carpenter.

But that's just what I want to know.
Ah! Christ in glory, here below
Men cheat and lie to one another so;
It's hard to be a carpenter.

THE NAZARETH SHOP

Robert McIntyre

I wish I had been His apprentice, to see Him each
   morning at seven,
As He tossed His gray tunic far from Him, the Mas-
   ter of earth and of heaven.
When He lifted the lid of His work chest and opened
   His carpenter's kit
And looked at His chisels and augers, and took the
   bright tools out of it
While He gazed at the rising sun tinting the dew on
   the opening flowers
And smiled as He thought of His Father, whose love
   floods this planet of ours,
When He fastened His apron about Him, and put on
   His working-man's cap,
And grasped the smooth hasp of the hammer, to give
   the bent woodwork a tap,
Saying, "Lad, let me finish this ox yoke. The farmer
   must put in his crop."
O, I wish I had been His apprentice and worked in
   the Nazareth shop!

Some wish they had been on Mount Tabor, to
   hearken unto His high speech
When the quick and the dead were beside Him, He
   holding communion with each.
Some wish they had heard the soft accents that
   stilled the wee children's alarms,

When He won the sweet babes from their mothers
   and folded them fast in His arms.
Some wish they had stood by the Jordan when holy
   John greeted Him there
And seen the white dove of the Spirit fly down o'er
   the path of His prayer.
Some wish they had seen the Redeemer when into
   the basin He poured
The water, and, girt with a towel, the servant of all
   was the Lord.
But for me, if I had the choosing, O this would them
   all overtop,
To work all day steady beside Him, of old in the
   Nazareth shop.

These heavenly wonders would fright me, I cannot
   approach to them yet.
But, O, to have seen Him, when toiling, His forehead all jeweled with sweat,
To hear Him say softly, "My helper, now bring me
   the level and rule."
To hear Him bend over and teach me the use of the
   artisan's tool.
To hear Him say, "This is a sheep gate, to keep in
   the wandering flock,"
Or, "This is stout oaken house sill. I hope it will rest
   on a rock."
And sometimes His mother might bring us our meal
   in the midsummer heat,
Outspread it so simply before us, and bid us sit down
   and eat.
Then with both of us silent before Him, the blessed
   Messiah would stop
To say grace, and a tremulous glory would fill the
   Nazareth shop.

A STRANGER IN SCYTHOPOLIS

Katharine Lee Bates

Scythopolis, the Biblical Bethshan, was a Greek city in
the heart of Palestine. Here the youthful Jesus might well
have visited and viewed Hellenic civilization at first
hand. This poem by Katharine Lee Bates is a "just suppose" speculation based upon this possibility.

Eager he wandered the streets of Scythopolis,
A Hebrew youth, with the dust of twoscore miles
Staining his sandals, dark eyes dancing with bliss
Of beauty—arches and pillars and peristyles,
Porticos, domes and many an edifice
Noble in line and color. And ever the passers-by
   turned.
And spake with him till their hearts within them
   burned.

Simple his words, sounded with rustic burr
Of the Galilean, but he was himself the Word
Of God's own joy, and each leaf-crowned reveler
Moved on to a music in heart he had not heard
Since, a child, he ran with the wind. The sophister,
Even the cynic whose sneers had beaten on life like
   whips,
Marveled to find sweet laughter on their lips.

Beggars that crouched in the streets of Scythopolis,
Lean hands plucking at togas that swept them by,
Let pass his scrip too humble for avarice,
But it fed them with fruits as in limitless supply,
Figs, dates, olives, that thrilled the paralysis
From spirit and nerve till, arising, the happy lame
   walked free,
Till the bewildered blind cried out, "I see!"

Before a sculptured Diana in Parian
Marble the prentice carpenter drew quick breath
Of rapture. From her litter a courtesan
Beheld him standing like one that worshipeth,
And cowered back on her perfumed pillows, wan,
Smit by the silver shaft of chastity. Over him flew
Doves like a halo of wings against the blue.

Why were forbidden the streets of Scythopolis,
Wondered the young Nazarene as he lingered in
   them.
Were not Beauty and Mirth the angels of this
City more splendid than holy Jerusalem?
He knew by the Voice within him that not amiss
Had he done that day in seeking the glories of
   Roman and Greek,
Though he knew not yet that to him should the
   Gentiles seek.

THE YOUNG CARPENTER

Winifred Kirkland

What was to come of the fact that Jesus at twelve turned away from the holy, learned city of Jerusalem and went back to live for eighteen unrecorded years in a humdrum, ignorant little country town? Was he to find any adventure there worth the seething energy of his brain and of his heart?

Jesus of Nazareth at eighteen, is it possible to picture him? To see him we may employ all the step-by-step discoveries we have tried to make of him from babyhood to twelve years old, and in addition we cannot help using our later discoveries of him as a grown-up man. Day in, day out, the Nazareth people went past the door of the carpenter shop, paying little more attention to Jesus within than people pay to him to-day. If anybody in Nazareth had really noticed their carpenter, surely some item from these unknown years would somehow have floated down to us. Yet perhaps there were a few persons there who did look at the young Jesus with curiosity, trying to guess what was going on back of those clear eyes, just as we have been trying to guess. If you and I had stopped opposite a door always open to anyone what might we have seen?

There would have been first the dusty, dusky interior of an Oriental carpenter shop. There is a shaft of light from the doorway and in it we may pick out tools, homemade saw and auger and plane, so rude that we wonder at the skill that can produce with them yokes and boards and plows so smooth and so well-shaped. The young carpenter is perhaps singing at his work, for he loves work, loves all kinds of making. And he is alone, master of the shop now. They have begun to call him "our carpenter," even though he is still only eighteen. All his movements are vigorous and flowing and sure. He has girded up his tunic. His arms and feet and close-curled head are bare. His dark cheeks have a touch of red as if he had brought the hilltop with him into the closeness of the shop.

While his hands never cease from their quick, capable activity, his face is strangely intent as you watch him when he is alone. Sometimes thoughts go kindling across it, sometimes it is as still and grave as if carved out of marble. His eyes, ordinarily clear as brook water, at times turn as black and impenetrable as midnight. Sometimes Jesus' eyes seem to gaze farther off than anyone could measure. Then suddenly he spies you looking in at him, and he smiles that flashing, twinkling smile of his, as if he saw right into you, and yet liked you just the same.

Since that first wondering visit to Jerusalem things have happened that must deeply have influenced Jesus' developing mind. Three times every year he has gone back to Jerusalem for the three great yearly festivals. He must have become accustomed now to all the marvels of the Temple. Does he feel by this time that those yearly journeys are really necessary for a true approach to God? What ideas have already been forming in Jesus' brain in his later teens that in his first thirties he should be heard to say that a man's body is the temple of God, and that it makes little difference in what place you worship, because "God is a Spirit: and they that worship him must worship in spirit"?

Just across the hills Jesus has witnessed the rebuilding of Sepphoris, that city which his shocked childish eyes had seen burning. Proud new buildings now stand where the pitiful crosses of punishment once rose. Surely the glad thought must have come to Jesus that new and better building may always follow destruction. The teaching that he later gave the world is full of this hope.

Since that grave moment with the rabbis in the Temple, Jesus has had experience of grief. Perhaps he was always glad he went home with Joseph then, and kept all the loneliness of old age away from the man he called father, and himself received all the store of Joseph's wisdom into his own life so that he was able to carry on, strong and joyous afterward.

His biographers tell us not one word about Jesus from that scene in the Temple at twelve to the scene of his being baptized at thirty in the river Jordan. From Jesus' very first appearance in public, he is revealed as a most extraordinary man, although up to this moment he has been only an obscure, unnoticed village carpenter. As we study his words and his actions from this point on, Jesus seems to have such a knowledge of people and such a knowledge of God as no other man in history has ever had. Where did he learn such an insight into men and such a vision of God? There is only one answer. He must have learned it all in humble Nazareth.

Without his family or friends ever dreaming of

what was going on in his mind, Jesus, right there at home, came to know people and came to understand God in all that amazing intimacy he later showed. Jesus as a boy must have had such a ready, keen, and adventurous brain and heart that he was able to perceive more accurately than any man has ever perceived all the possibilities of a little up-country town. For Jesus nothing ever appeared humdrum. Quietly and all alone, he set to work to discover his neighbors, his God, and himself.

We can imagine that in these years when Jesus was growing up he was learning how to live at peace with himself, for as a child he had been often shaken by changing moods. The day-by-day routine of carpentry has steadied him. The words of the prophets learned by heart in school still sing in his soul, but they have now fallen into tune with the swishing of his plane and the beating of his hammer.

Jesus at eighteen is a practical young workman, supporting a widowed mother, and assisting a host of younger brothers and sisters. He still at times thinks about that glorious figure of his childhood's fancy, Messiah, but the young man Jesus, being no daydreamer, often forgets that great Helper-to-come because he is so busy helping people himself, his neighbors right there in Nazareth. He has his hands and his heart full trying to get food for starving people, and clothes for the destitute, welcoming the stranger in the town, going to see the sick, and making visits to the jail. Those were harsh days of history, even in Nazareth, and Jesus, poor and hard-working as he was himself, poured himself out in pity for those still poorer.

Sometimes those he tried to help hated him for it, resented his efforts and refused his advice. It hurt, of course, to have them feel like that toward him, but, while still young, Jesus must have learned his own cure for his own sensitiveness. "Father," he would say, for he had become quite accustomed to talking to God in silence, "they don't mean it. Forgive them. They don't really know what they're saying or doing."

In those unnoticed years in the Nazareth workshop Jesus passed from boyhood into his sublime manhood. How did he accomplish his magnificent growth? It could only have been by taking risks, for that is the only way anyone ever does grow. Now, far adventures were impossible for Jesus, though the distant glinting sea and the white highroads nearer by must have beckoned to his spirit. He was needed at home, he must remain year by year in a little town. The only adventure open to him was in Nazareth. He chose the adventure of loving everybody he knew, whatever the cost to himself. It was his tremendous friendliness that had frightened his mother when he was still a tiny child. Perhaps she saw that it would be just like Jesus some day to love a Judas.

In those silent years of his development in Nazareth Jesus was not only growing into the greatest lover of humankind that ever lived, but he was also growing to be the greatest lover of God that humankind itself has ever brought forth. While it is hard enough for us to guess how Jesus ever climbed to his heights of human love, it is still harder for us modern men and women to guess how he ever climbed to the heights of his love for God. We are very proud of being scientific in these days, and the science taught us from our babyhood does not, we think, allow much time for praying or talking to that unseen far-off God whom Jesus thought of as his close, personal Father. A boy of the present is ready to spend his life in searching out some secret of science. In just the same way the youthful Jesus, taught from babyhood the mystery of God, was ready to spend his life in searching out the secret ways of his Father.

Just as Jesus, watching his neighbors in Nazareth, came to believe that the only way really to understand people is first to love them, so also did he come to believe that the only way really to know God is first to love Him, however shadowy and strange and distant He may seem. Clearly Jesus in little Nazareth was learning how to live and grow by taking risks, for surely there is no greater risk than loving people—they may hurt you. And it is as great a risk to love God, for He may sometimes seem to fail you. Jesus, boy and man, grew by choosing always these two roads of risk, and yet as you read about him he never seems sorry for the choice he made while still a boy in Nazareth.

Jesus of Nazareth—baby and child and boy and youth—to try to discover him as he really was in a far-off hill town in a far-off century, has meant for some of us a burning desire always to go on trying to discover him more and more as, in manhood, he went up and down dark old Palestine in his blazing, brief career.

DEPARTURE FROM NAZARETH *

Edwin McNeill Poteat

Nazareth of Galilee was like many another small village in the great cleft of the Jordan Valley. It had no distinction to boast except that within a radius of forty furlongs most of the joinery throughout the countryside was done in its shops or by its residents. Carpenter booths flanked both sides of the principal street that twisted indecisively from north to south, and all day long the industrious whisper of plane and saw issued from their dim interiors. It was a subdued symphony, more pleasant, the villagers said, than the sharp percussions of the brass workers in Cana, five miles down the valley, and gave rise to the proverb current among the simple folk: the kettle, shaped by a hammer, dies before the stool, fashioned by a caress. Such village wisdom, compressed into homely and easily remembered words, comprised no little of the moral instruction that the elders committed to the lads apprenticed to the trade.

Up from the main street, toward the western limit of the low-roofed dwellings was the house of Joseph of the tribe of David. Mary, daughter of the tribe of David, widowed for fourteen years, lived with her family of four, three sons and one daughter. Their house was near the open fields, and easy of access to herdsmen and tillers of the soil, and often, during the day, oxen were to be seen outside the mud wall, waiting for repairs to clevis or shaft, or for the fitting of a new yoke; and an occasional shepherd might be seen testing the heft of a new crook, or sharpening a plow share blunted in the rocky soil of the hillside. The house faced the East, and across the court, the shop, through its very wide door,

---

* The title used here is the Editor's.

allowed the amplitude of the western sunlight to lengthen the working day, and a low gate at the south end of the yard afforded entrance and exit to both man and beast. Above it, cut in a wooden slab that swung from a wrought-iron arm, the end of which was bent like a shepherd's crook, one read in neatly cut characters: JOSEPH SON OF JACOB FAMILY OF DAVID.

Since the death of Joseph, Jesus had managed the affairs of the shop, and taught the trade to the three younger sons, James, Simon and Judah. Throughout the countryside the reputation of the sons of Joseph had spread, and their fame rested on two specialties; they made the strongest and lightest yoke that was to be found anywhere, said to have been the invention of the eldest son; and he, furthermore, enjoyed a repute unique among the carpenters of the town as being more expert in repair work than them all. No broken tool, no article of furniture, no shattered staff or yoke but could be restored by him to a condition said to be better even than before the damage occurred. For this reason one end of the shop was most of the time cluttered up with unassorted articles in various states of delapidation, and the other end filled with orderly rows of similar articles so exquisitely repaired that the point of breakage was difficult to discover.

One evening, long after the set of sun a shepherd knocked on the gate and when admitted, exhibited his crook, broken sadly in half. He had struck at a viper, he said, on his way back to the fold. It had been his father's crook and he believed it to have a strange potency which he could not explain, but which made its possible loss all but irreparable. Could the carpenter fix it before the morrow? Judah, for it was he who had answered the knock, showed the broken staff to his elder brother and repeated the shepherd's melancholy tale. Jesus picked up a wick that burned indifferently inside the house, and protecting it with a cupped hand, crossed the yard to the shop. The shepherd followed him, and watched silently while with practiced skill he sawed the broken ends, smoothed them with a crude file, and joined them expertly with a dowel pin.

"You work swiftly and easily, sir," he said appreciatively. "Why may I ask, do you make so much of repair work and, unlike the men of your craft along the street, so little of articles made new for common use?"

The carpenter vigorously rubbed dark wax over the fresh crack until it was all but invisible in the dim light. "It is easier to make, than to repair," he answered pleasantly. He took the crook by the lower end and struck the ground sharply with the bent elbow. It vibrated with a solid, resilient sound. "And there be few who know the joy of bringing back beauty or strength that has been lost by abuse or carelessness." He handed the stick to the shepherd who tested the repaired break under his bent knee.

"It is stronger than before," he ventured. "What can I do to repay your trouble?"

"Your thanks and your recollection," Jesus answered. And then: "Your sheep drop their lambs in the spring, but they cannot mend the broken leg or repair the wound the thorn bush makes. God has made men according to his own pleasure but in giving his sons the will either to serve him or to flee from him, he cannot repair the evil they do themselves. And who will repair the broken hearts? Are they not few who care? Those that are whole need not a physician, but alas for those who are sick and find no aid." He followed the shepherd to the gate and opened it. The man was no less bewildered by the carpenter's strange talk than by his refusal to ask compensation for his work. He tried to thank him as the gate closed between them in the darkness, and as he made his way down the alleyway, he could be heard thumping the ground with his crook. Jesus stood for a moment and looked up at a cluster of bright stars, and then walked slowly across the yard, and sat down on the doorsill by Judah. There was a long interval of silence. The light still burned in the shop. Judah got up to go and fetch it, but a draft of cool night air snuffed it suddenly when he was but halfway back to the house. He muttered irritatedly as he stumbled against a yoke beam in the dark.

"How long," he asked finally, "do you think the thanks of shepherds for repairs to their broken crooks will keep this family in bread?" There was annoyance in his tone and it was clear that his question was the resumption of a dispute begun earlier in the evening. "To one responsible for a family such methods may bring good to the soul, but it feeds no bodies." He waited for a reply, but there was none. "Our mother wonders and grieves deeply," he went on, "but she will not complain for love of you. 'Tis

well to consider lilies and birds, but not when one hungers for oil and flour."

Jesus stood up. His full height looked immensely tall in the darkness. He looked up at the cluster of burning stars again, and stepped out into the yard. "They that are sick . . ." He started to speak quietly but was interrupted tartly by his brother.

"They that are sick, they! What about us who are hungry?"

Jesus moved toward the gate and drew the bar so gently it made no sound, and as he stepped through he breathed deeply of the darkness. Above the village, a short mile from the house, the summit of the ridge smouldered black against the sky. He was careful to make no sound as he closed the gate behind him, and his footsteps, as he turned into a familiar path that led to the crest where he would spend the night in prayer, were only heard by his bewildered and unhappy brother.

He was hardly out of earshot before Judah was in the house again. In the little bedroom of his widowed mother he found Anna his sister. She was talking with Mary. Simon and James had not returned from the market place whither they were accustomed to go after the day's work was done.

"He has gone to the hilltop again," Judah announced bitterly. "It was his answer to my question."

"What question?" Mary asked.

"I asked him again how long we are to live on the thanks he exacts as price for the work we do. The villagers think that business throngs our doors and our shop is full of work, and they predict that we will grow rich and buy out the trade. Little they know that we . . ."

"But do you not fit yokes, and after the Feast of Tabernacles will you not go to work on the magistrate's new house?"

"Aye, but it fetches only enough for meager food and patches on old raiment."

"We have enough," she answered gently, "while we have him."

Judah bit his lip to restrain his anger. "Our father Joseph . . ."

"Your father Joseph was a godly man," she said in rebuke.

He bowed in deference to her words, but his heart was dark with anger and disappointment. Her love for her first-born exceeded that she felt for the others, and such was the proper thing with all pious mothers in Israel. But it was the blindness of her devotion that enraged the younger sons. She listened to his words as though the voice of God spoke in them. Only one thing disturbed the deep of her contentment. Four years previously her older daughter Rebecca had gone to Dimnah as the bride of Joel, son of Elah, who worked about the perfume vats of Magdala. She had borne him two daughters and they filled Mary's cup of joy to overflowing when they came to spend a Sabbath or the new moon at home. But Anna, grown swart and lovely at seventeen, was unwed and the fortunes of the family had so declined that the possible dower for her marriage would bring nothing better than a shepherd or an apprentice to a brass shop. And often she talked with her mother, and wept through the long still hours of the night. The House of Joseph, it was no mean name. Was it not of the lineage of David? Why had it fallen on such ill circumstances that a comely child should fail to have supplied for her a marriage of distinction and comfort? And neighbor tongues wagged in trying endlessly to explain why so busy a family seemed so niggardly toward its lovely daughter. So when Anna wept in her mother's arms, Mary sought betimes to console her by saying that so long as she was unwed, her heart would not be pierced by the sword that always hangs low above the woman who brings a man child to birth.

The soft, bright edge of day had hardly pushed over the eastern ridge when the gate to the House of Joseph opened quietly and a tall figure bent slightly as he entered. His step was elastic and his countenance was as bright as if for the moment he had captured all the radiance of the dawn in his face. Nothing about his manner bespoke an all-night vigil on the mountaintop. He crossed the yard and listened at the door. No one seemed yet to be astir. He went into the shop. On a shelf was a toy he had whittled on in odd hours, a tiny yoke of oxen, hitched to a plow. He blew the dust off it, and put it on the bench as he brushed aside the debris of the previous day's work with his foot. He looked lovingly about the shop—at its dusty walls and shelves, and the little piles of sawdust that he loved to run through his stout fingers. Then he picked up the toy and recrossed the yard to his mother's door. She called his name softly, and he entered her room, and seated himself beside her on the bed. She stroked his face fondly, and noted the tiny wooden oxen in his hand.

"My time is come," he said suddenly. She clutched tightly at her heart and then breathed deeply as if in resignation to a destiny she had long known she could not escape.

"My time is come," he said again, his eyes lighted with an unearthly fire. "My Father is moving the hearts of the sons of men. Down in the valley John gathers to him those who need repair, whose hearts are broken with folly, whose bodies are broken with sin. They come from Jerusalem, and from Judea to be baptized, confessing their sins."

He paused and Mary leaned toward him. A look of desperate inquiry burned in her eyes. He stood up and gripped her shoulders at arms' length with his powerful hands, and then held her fiercely against him long and breathlessly. It was the moment of farewell she had dreamed and dreaded, but no word was given her to speak.

At length he said, picking up the little toy again, "I shall stop for a fig and curd at Dimnah. The babes will like this; for several days I have been making it for them." He smiled reflectively, and for a moment the austere mood seemed to drop from him. And then with a tenderness his mother was never to forget, he put his arm about her and led her to the door. He raised his hand and pointed down the valley. It was gold and blue in the early light. They walked slowly through the gate and stopped. Once again he pointed down the valley, but neither spoke. Her eyes were bright with tears as he kissed her forehead. Then down the alleyway he strode with strong, confident steps, and as he turned the corner that would lose him from her sight, she raised her hand weakly. He returned her salute boldly and then was gone, never again to be known as the son of Mary, but henceforth to be called the Son of Man.

PART THREE

Legends

The inconceivable loveliness of Christ!

HARRIET BEECHER STOWE

1. LEGENDS OF INFANCY AND CHILDHOOD

THE CHERRY-TREE CAROL

Anonymous

Joseph was an old man,
    and an old man was he,
And he married Mary,
    the Queen of Galilee.

When Joseph was married,
    and Mary home had brought,
Mary proved with child,
    and Joseph knew it not.

Joseph and Mary walked
    through a garden gay,
Where the cherries they grew
    upon every tree.

O then bespoke Mary,
    with words both meek and mild:
"O gather me cherries, Joseph,
    they run so in my mind."

And then replied Joseph,
    with words so unkind:
"Let him gather thee cherries
    that got thee with child."

O then bespoke our Saviour,
    all in his mother's womb:
"Bow down, good cherry-tree,
    to my mother's hand."

The uppermost sprig
    bowed down to Mary's knee:

"Thus you may see, Joseph,
    these cherries are for me."

"O eat your cherries, Mary,
    O eat your cherries now;
O eat your cherries, Mary,
    that grow upon the bough."

As Joseph was a walking,
    he heard an angel sing:
"This night shall be born
    our heavenly king.

"He neither shall be born
    In housen nor in hall,
Nor in the place of Paradise,
    but in an ox's stall.

"He neither shall be clothed
    in purple nor in pall,
But all in fair linen,
    as were babies all.

"He neither shall be rocked
    in silver nor in gold,
But in a wooden cradle,
    that rocks on the mould.

"He neither shall be christened
    in white wine nor red,
But with fair spring water,
    with which we were christened."

Then Mary took her young son,
and set him on her knee:
"I pray thee now, dear child,
tell how this world shall be."

"O I shall be as dead, mother,
as the stones in the wall;
O the stones in the street mother,
shall mourn for me all.

"And upon a Wednesday
my vow I will make,
And upon Good Friday
my death I will take.

"Upon Easter-day, mother,
my rising shall be;
O the sun and the moon
Shall uprise with me.

"The people shall rejoice,
and the birds they shall sing,
To see the uprising
of the heavenly king."

THE CARNAL AND THE CRANE

Anonymous

As I passed by a river side,
And there as I did reign,
In argument I chanced to hear
A Carnal and a Crane.

The Carnal said unto the Crane,
If all the world should turn,
Before we had the Father,
But now we have the Son!

"From whence does the Son come,
From where and from what place?"
He said, In a manger,
Between an ox and ass.

"I pray thee," said the Carnal,
"Tell me before thou go,

Was not the mother of Jesus
Conceived by the Holy Ghost?"

She was the purest virgin,
And the cleanest from sin;
She was the handmaid of our Lord
And mother of our king.

"Where is the golden cradle
That Christ was rocked in?
Where are the silken sheets
That Jesus was wrapt in?"

A manger was the cradle
That Christ was rocked in:
The provender the asses left
So sweetly he slept on.

There was a star in the east land,
So bright it did appear,
Into King Herod's chamber,
And where King Herod were.

The Wise Men soon espied it,
And told the king on high
A princely babe was born that night
No king could e'er destroy.

"If this be true," King Herod said,
"As thou tellest unto me,
This roasted cock that lies in the dish
Shall crow full fences three."

The cock soon freshly feathered was,
By the work of God's own hand,
And then three fences crowed he,
In the dish where he did stand.

"Rise up, rise up, you merry men all,
See that you ready be;
All children under two years old
Now slain they all shall be."

Then Jesus, ah, and Joseph,
And Mary, that was so pure,
They travelled into Egypt,
As you shall find it sure.

And when they came to Egypt's land,
Amongst those fierce wild beasts,
Mary, she being weary,
Must needs sit down to rest.

"Come sit thee down," says Jesus,
  "Come sit thee down by me,
And thou shalt see how these wild beasts
  Do come and worship me."

First came the lovely lion,
  Which Jesus's grace did bring,
And of the wild beasts in the field
  The lion shall be king.

We'll choose our virtuous princes
  Of birth and high degree,
In every sundry nation,
  Whereer we come and see.

Then Jesus, ah, and Joseph,
  And Mary, that was unknown,
They travelled by a husbandman,
  Just while his seed was sown.

"God speed thee, man," said Jesus,
  "Go fetch thy ox and wain,
And carry home thy corn again
  Which thou this day hast sown."

The husbandman fell on his knees,
  Even upon his face:
"Long time hast thou been looked for,
  But now thou art come at last.

"And I myself do now believe
  Thy name is Jesus called;
Redeemer of mankind thou art,
  Though undeserving all."

"The truth, man, thou hast spoken,
  Of it thou mayst be sure,
For I must lose my precious blood
  For thee and thousands more.

"If any one should come this way,
  And enquire for me alone,
Tell them that Jesus passed by
  As thou thy seed did sow."

After that there came King Herod,
  With his train so furiously,
Enquiring of the husbandman
  Whether Jesus passed by.

"Why, the truth it must be spoke,
  And the truth it must be known;
For Jesus passed by this way
  When my seed was sown.

"But now I have it reapen,
  And some laid on my wain,
Ready to fetch and carry
  Into my barn again."

"Turn back," says the captain,
  "Your labor and mine's in vain;
It's full three quarters of a year
  Since he his seed has sown."

So Herod was deceived,
  By the work of God's own hand,
And further he proceeded
  Into the Holy Land.

There's thousands of children young
  Which for his sake did die;
Do not forbid the little ones,
  And do not them deny.

The truth now I have spoken,
  And the truth now I have shown;
Even the Blessed Virgin
  She's now brought forth a son.

ST. STEPHEN WAS A CLERK

Anonymous

Saint Stephen was a clerk in King Herod's hall,
And servèd him of bread and cloth, as ever king befall.

Stephen out of kitchen came with boar's head in his hand,
He saw a star that was fair and bright over Bethlehem stand.

He cast adown the boar's head and went into the hall:
"I forsake thee, King Herod, and thy workës all.

"I forsake thee, King Herod, and thy workës all;
There is a child in Bethlehem born is better than
    we all."

"What aileth thee, Stephen, what is thee befall?
Lacketh thee either meat or drink in King Herod's
    hall?"

"Lacketh me neither meat nor drink in King Herod's
    hall,
There is a child in Bethlehem born is better than
    we all."

"What aileth thee, Stephen, art thou mad, or thou
    ginnest to brede?
Lacketh thee either gold or fee or any richë weed?"

"Lacketh me neither gold nor fee, nor no richë weed,
There is a child in Bethlehem born shall help us at
    our need."

"That is all so sooth, Stephen, all so sooth ywis,
As this capon crow it shall, that lieth here in my
    dish."

That word was not so soonë said, that word in that
    hall,
The capon crew, *Christus natus est,* among the lordës
    all.

"Riseth up my tormentors, by twos and all by one,
And leadeth Stephen out of this town, and stoneth
    him with stone."

Took they then Stephen and stoned him in the way,
Therefore is his even on Christës own day.

THE BEASTS OF THE FIELDS

Jules Lemaitre

Old Sephora lived in the village of Bethlehem.
She made her living from a herd of goats and a
little orchard planted with fig trees.

As a young girl she had been servant for a priest
so that she was more knowing in matters of religion
than persons of her station usually are.

Returned to the village, married, several times a
mother, she had lost her husband and her children.
And then, though helping men according to her
means, the greatest part of her sympathy she poured
out on animals. She protected birds and mice; she
gathered in abandoned dogs and distressed cats;
and her little house was crowded with all these
humble guests.

She loved animals, not only because they are innocent, because they give their hearts to those who
love them, and because their trust is overwhelming,
but because she was swayed by a sense of justice.

She did not understand why those who could not
be wicked should suffer, nor how they could violate
a rule of which they knew nothing.

She could explain better or worse the suffering of
mankind. Taught by the priest, she did not believe
that everything ended in the sleepy peace of *scheol,*
nor that the Messiah when he should appear was
merely to establish the earthly kingdom of Israel.
The "Kingdom of God" would be the reign of
justice beyond the tomb. It was perfectly clear that
in the unknown world all suffering would deserve
expiation. Unmerited and purposeless suffering (like
that of little children or certain unfortunates who
had sinned only a little) would seem no more than
a bad dream and would be rewarded by a happiness
at least to an equal degree.

But what of the beasts that suffer? Those who
slowly die of cruel diseases—as men do—and raise
their pleading eyes to you? Dogs to whom affection
is never shown, or those who love their masters and
waste away from loneliness? Horses, whose long days
are nothing but heaving efforts, and weariness of
bleeding under blows, whose rest, even in the darkness of narrow stalls, is so mournful? Captive beasts
devoured by homesickness behind the bars of cages?
All those poor beasts whose life is a hopeless agony,
deprived even of a voice to utter what they endure,
a voice with which to curse? What end does their
suffering serve? What reward can they expect?

Sephora was a very simple old woman; but because she was sincerely hungry for justice, she often
turned over these questions in her mind; and the
thought of unexplained grief, obscured for her the
beauty of the day and the exquisite colors of the hills
of Judea.

When her neighbors came to tell her, "The Messiah is born; an angel proclaimed Him to us last night; He is in a stable with His mother only a quarter of a league from here; and we have worshipped Him," old Sephora replied:

"We shall see."

For she had an idea.

That evening, after having cared for her goats, fed her other beasts, and patted all of them, she made her way toward the miraculous stable.

In the enchantment of the blue night, the plain, the rocks, the trees, and even the blades of grass seemed motionless with joy. One would have said that the whole earth slept deliciously. But old Sephora did not forget that even at that moment unjust nature was doing wrongs that no future could right; she could not put away from her thoughts the fact that at that very moment, throughout the vast world, sick persons who were not wicked were sweating with anguish in their burning beds; travelers were being killed along the roads; men were being tortured by other men; mothers were weeping over their little dead babies; and animals were suffering terribly without knowing why.

Before her she saw a light, gentle but yet so alive that it paled the light of the moon. This glow spread from the stable huddled in a fissure of the rocks and supported by pillars of stone.

Near the entrance some camels slept on their bent knees in the midst of a pile of chased and colored vases, baskets of fruit, thick carpets unrolled, and open caskets in which jewels sparkled dazzlingly.

"Now, what's all this?" asked the old woman.

"The Kings are here," a man replied.

"Kings?" said Sephora, frowning.

She went into the stable, saw the infant Jesus in the manger between Mary and Joseph, the three Magi, shepherds, and laborers with their wives, their sons, and their daughters, and in a corner an ass and an ox.

"Let us see," she said.

The three Kings advanced to the Child, and the shepherds politely stepped back before them. But the Child made a sign to the shepherds to draw near.

Old Sephora did not stir.

The Child placed his little hand first upon the heads of the wives and the daughters because they are better and suffer the more, then upon the heads of the men and the boys.

And Mary spoke to them.

"Be patient; He loves you and has come to suffer with you."

Then the white King believed his turn had come. But the Child with a gentle gesture called the black King, then the yellow King.

The black King, with hair curled close and shining with oil, and smiling with all his teeth, offered to the New-born necklaces of bones of fish, varicolored pebbles, dates, and cocoanuts.

Mary spoke to him.

"You are not bad, but you do not know. Try to picture what you would be if you were not King in your country. Eat no more men, and beat no more of your subjects."

The yellow King, with slanting eyes, offered pieces of gilt embroidered with dragons, Chinese vases on which rays of the moon seemed marked in the enamel, a sphere of ivory curiously marked to represent the heavens with the planets and all the animals of creation, and sacks of tea gathered from selected bushes in the best season.

And Mary spoke to him.

"No longer hide yourself from your people. Believe no longer that all wisdom belongs to you and your race. And take care of those who have only mouldy rice to eat."

The white King in military uniform offered the Child delicate silver-ware, chiselled and inlaid weapons, statuettes carved in the form of beautiful women, and purple cases containing the writings of a sage named Plato.

And Mary spoke to him.

"Make no more unjust wars. Beware of pleasures that harden the heart. Proclaim equitable laws, and know that it is the concern of you and of all others that no one in your kingdom shall be badly treated."

And after the shepherds and the laborers, the Child blessed the Kings, in the order in which He had summoned them.

Old Sephora was thinking.

"This order is sensible. The Child began with those who need His coming most. He makes it plain that He is careful to deal with justice, that He will re-establish its reign in both this world and the other. His mother, also, talked well. Nevertheless, He doesn't think of everything. What will He do for the animals?"

But Mary understood her thoughts. She turned to her Son and the Child turned toward the ass and the ox.

The donkey, skinny and mangy, the ox, fat enough but sad, drew near to the manger and sniffed at Jesus.

The Child placed one hand on the nose of the ox while with His other hand He gently pressed one of the ears of the ass.

And the ox seemed to smile; and from the eyes of the ass dropped two tears to lose themselves in his thick hair.

At the same time one of the camels outside quietly entered the stable and stretched his trusting head toward the Child.

Old Sephora understood what all this meant:—there is also a paradise for suffering animals.

And then in her turn she stepped toward the Child.

THE VIRGIN OF THE ANGELS

Jules Lemaitre

During the eight days that she passed in the stable at Bethlehem Mary did not suffer very much. Shepherds brought cheeses, fruits, bread, and firewood. Their wives and daughters cared for the child and gave to Mary the attentions needed by a new mother. Then the Magi left behind their gifts of carpets, precious stuffs, jewels, and vases of gold.

At the end of the week when she was able to walk Mary wanted to return to her home in Nazareth. Some shepherds volunteered to escort her, but she said to them:

"I don't want you to leave your flocks and fields for us. My son will direct us."

"But," said Joseph, "shall we leave behind the gifts of the Magi?"

"Yes," said Mary, "since we can't carry them away with us."

"But they're worth a great deal of silver," said Joseph.

"So much the better," said Mary.

And she distributed the gifts of the Magi among the shepherds.

"But," persisted Joseph, "can't we keep just a few for ourselves?"

"What should we do with them?" replied Mary. "We have a greater treasure."

It was hot on the journey. Mary carried the child in her arms; Joseph carried a basket filled with a little linen and scanty provisions. Toward noon they halted, fatigued, at the margin of a wood.

Immediately from behind the trees appeared a band of tiny angels. They were chubby youngsters, pink and round-faced. On their backs were little wings which helped them to fly when they wished and which at other times made their movements easy and light. They were skilful and vigorous beyond anything their tender age and delicate figures would lead one to believe.

They offered to the travelers a jar of fresh water and fruit which they had gathered no one knew where.

When the holy family resumed their journey the angels followed. They relieved Joseph of his basket, and Joseph allowed them to carry it. But Mary would not let them have the child.

When night fell the angels arranged beds of moss beneath a wide sycamore and all through the night they watched over the slumber of Jesus.

So Mary returned to her home in Nazareth. It was a white house with a flat roof in a populous narrow way. There was a little covered terrace where Joseph had his workshop.

The angels did not leave them but continued to make themselves useful in a thousand ways. When the child cried, one of them gently rocked him; others made music upon tiny harps for him; or when it was necessary changed his wrappings with the wave of a hand. When Mary awoke in the mornings she found her chamber swept. After every meal they speedily carried out the dishes and bowls, ran to wash them at the near-by fountain, and ranged them in the cupboard. When the Virgin went to the washhouse they carried the package of linen, divided it among them, joyously pounded the wet garments, dried them on the stones, and carried the bundle home. And if Mary in spinning her distaff grew drowsy from the great heat, they finished her task without waking her.

They displayed no less care of Joseph. They handed him his tools, arranged them after the work was finished, carried away the chips and shavings, and kept the shop in irreproachable order.

But, too well served by the angels and having almost nothing to do, Mary became bored.

Because she felt bored, she prayed at first; but while she prayed, she reflected.

One morning as she was getting up she saw the angels sweeping her chamber. She snatched the broom and threatened to chase them out. They scattered. But after dinner at noon, as they started to clear the table she gave one a smart rap on his fingers and this put all of them to flight. They returned shortly. When she began to spin an angel tried to take her spindle. She brandished it like a weapon and chased the intruder to the door of Joseph's shop. An hour later as she was seated beside the child sewing she spied two angels who had slipped under the cradle and were slyly rocking it. She rose, turned them out of the room and slammed the door so violently that one of the angels was caught by the tip of a wing. He uttered a little cry. Mary released him, but she said:

"So much the worse for you. That will teach you to meddle in what doesn't concern you. Tell your companions and don't let me see any of you again!"

"But," said Joseph, "why do you drive these little creatures away? They help us a great deal."

"That's just the reason," Mary replied.

"I don't understand," Joseph continued. "Since your son is the Messiah, it's perfectly natural that he should be served by angels, and that his mother should profit by it."

"Oh!" said Mary, "here are words with no meaning. Don't you know that the Messiah has come into the world to suffer with men and first of all to endure all the ills natural to babies? And all these sufferings, I should be able to relieve as much as is in me, since I'm his mother. But I don't want anybody else to take care of these matters. Don't other mothers care for their own children? What a coward I should be if I avoided my share of a mother's trials. Besides, I'm sure my baby would rather be tended by me than by those winged brats. And I know that I shall be more closely associated with his redeeming spirit if as other women I suffer from accepting completely his human condition. Yes, I wish to be the only one to

dress my son, the only one to rock him to sleep, the only one to keep my house, the only one to use my distaff, the only one to go to the washhouse. And as these humble tasks are almost a joy, they will bring no great merit to me, I'm sure; but I should be blamed if I let angels do them for me. Do you understand?"

"I think I do, my dear girl. . . . But must I also give up the little services the angels perform for me?"

"Evidently, my friend."

"Well, I thought that being the husband of the mother of the Messiah would give me the right to some slight advantages. But you must be right: for you are more intelligent and wiser than I am, although you're only fifteen years old and I'm past sixty."

Now, the next night, as the infant Jesus cried and refused to go to sleep, suddenly there was heard in the street a delicately soothing melody.

Mary opened the casement and saw by the light of the moon, standing against the wall of the house, all the angels playing on their tiny harps.

"You again?" she called to them. "Suppose my baby doesn't want to go to sleep? Suppose it pleases him to cry and suffer with his teeth? Isn't his mother with him, eh? Clear out, now, or I'll get angry!"

On the morrow they did not reappear during the entire day. But the day after Mary saw them in the courtyard huddled together under the fig-tree, timid, shame-faced, and weeping silently.

"My little angels," she said to them, "I may seem severe to you because you are too young to understand. But listen now! Old Sephora who lives across the way is paralyzed. A little further along is good Rachel with twelve children—and a hard time in rearing them. And you will find in Nazareth enough other unfortunate women. Well, then, you should help them to keep house, to wash clothes, to tend their babies. Since you desire to please my son, that's the best way to succeed."

And noticing their little noses wrinkled with chagrin, she added:

"And when he is bigger, perhaps I'll let you play with him. But first, do what I've just told you."

And that year all the poor women and the sick of Nazareth were aided and all the little babies rocked by these invisible servants (for only Mary and Joseph could see the angels); and none of the sucking infants cried at all, except the baby Jesus who wished to suffer for them.

THE FLIGHT INTO EGYPT

Selma Lagerlöf

Far away in one of the Eastern deserts many, many years ago grew a palm tree, which was both exceedingly old and exceedingly tall.

All who passed through the desert had to stop and gaze at it, for it was much larger than other palms; and they used to say of it, that some day it would certainly be taller than the obelisks and pyramids.

Where the huge palm tree stood in its solitude and looked out over the desert, it saw something one day which made its mighty leaf-crown sway back and forth on its slender trunk with astonishment. Over by the desert borders walked two human beings. They were still at the distance at which camels appear to be as tiny as moths; but they were certainly two human beings—two who were strangers in the desert; for the palm knew the desert-folk. They were a man and a woman who had neither guide nor pack-camels; neither tent nor water-sack.

"Verily," said the palm to itself, "these two have come hither only to meet certain death."

The palm cast a quick, apprehensive glance around.

"It surprises me," it said, "that the lions are not already out to hunt this prey, but I do not see a single one astir; nor do I see any of the desert robbers, but they'll probably soon come."

"A seven-fold death awaits these travelers," thought the palm. "The lions will devour them, thirst will parch them, the sand-storm will bury them, robbers will trap them, sunstroke will blight them, and fear will destroy them."

And the palm tried to think of something else. The fate of these people made it sad at heart.

But on the whole desert plain, which lay spread out beneath the palm, there was nothing which it had not known and looked upon these thousand years. Nothing in particular could arrest its attention. Again it had to think of the two wanderers.

"By the drought and the storm!" said the palm, calling upon Life's most dangerous enemies. "What is that that the woman carries on her arm? I believe these fools also bring a little child with them!"

The palm, who was far-sighted—as the old usually are,—actually saw aright. The woman bore on her arm a child, that leaned against her shoulder and slept.

"The child hasn't even sufficient clothing on," said the palm. "I see that the mother has tucked up her skirt and thrown it over the child. She must have snatched him from his bed in great haste and rushed off with him. I understand now: these people are runaways.

"But they are fools, nevertheless," continued the palm. "Unless an angel protects them, they would have done better to have let their enemies do their worst, than to venture into this wilderness.

"I can imagine how the whole thing came about. The man stood at his work; the child slept in his crib; the woman had gone out to fetch water. When she was a few steps from the door, she saw enemies coming. She rushed back to the house, snatched up her child, and fled.

"Since then, they have been fleeing for several days. It is very certain that they have not rested a moment. Yes, everything has happened in this way, but still I say that unless an angel protects them—

"They are so frightened that, as yet, they feel neither fatigue nor suffering. But I see their thirst by the strange gleam in their eyes. Surely I ought to know a thirsty person's face!"

And when the palm began to think of thirst, a shudder passed through its tall trunk, and the long leaves' numberless lobes rolled up, as though they had been held over a fire.

"Were I a human being," it said, "I should never venture into the desert. He is pretty brave who dares come here without having roots that reach down to the never-dying water veins. Here it can be dangerous even for palms; yea, even for a palm such as I.

"If I could counsel them, I should beg them to turn back. Their enemies could never be as cruel toward them as the desert. Perhaps they think it easy to live in the desert! But I know that, now and then, even I have found it hard to keep alive. I recollect one time in my youth when a hurricane threw a whole mountain of sand over me. I came near choking. If I could have died that would have been my last moment."

The palm continued to think aloud, as the aged and solitary habitually do.

"I hear a wondrously beautiful melody rush through my leaves," it said. "All the lobes on my leaves are quivering. I know not what it is that takes possession of me at the sight of these poor strangers. But this unfortunate woman is so beautiful! She carries me back, in memory, to the most wonderful thing that I ever experienced."

And while the leaves continued to move in a soft melody, the palm was reminded how once, very long ago, two illustrious personages had visited the oasis. They were the Queen of Sheba and Solomon the Wise. The beautiful Queen was to return to her own country; the King had accompanied her on the journey, and now they were going to part. "In remembrance of this hour," said the Queen then, "I now plant a date seed in the earth, and I wish that from it shall spring a palm which shall grow and live until a King shall arise in Judea, greater than Solomon." And when she had said this, she planted the seed in the earth and watered it with her tears.

"How does it happen that I am thinking of this just to-day?" said the palm. "Can this woman be so beautiful that she reminds me of the most glorious of queens, of her by whose word I have lived and flourished until this day?

"I hear my leaves rustle louder and louder," said the palm, "and it sounds as melancholy as a dirge. It is as though they prophesied that someone would soon leave this life. It is well to know that it does not apply to me, since I can not die."

The palm assumed that the death-rustle in its leaves must apply to the two lone wanderers. It is certain that they too believed that their last hour was nearing. One saw it from their expression as they walked past the skeleton of a camel which lay in their path. One saw it from the glances they cast back at a pair of passing vultures. It couldn't be otherwise; they must perish!

They had caught sight of the palm and oasis and hastened thither to find water. But when they arrived at last, they collapsed from despair, for the well was dry. The woman, worn out, laid the child down and seated herself beside the well-curb, and wept. The man flung himself down beside her and beat upon the dry earth with his fists. The palm heard how they talked with each other about their inevitable death. It also gleaned from their conversation that King Herod had ordered the slaughter of all male children from two to three years old, be-

cause he feared that the long-looked-for King of the Jews had been born.

"It rustles louder and louder in my leaves," said the palm. "These poor fugitives will soon see their last moment."

It perceived also that they dreaded the desert. The man said it would have been better if they had stayed at home and fought with the soldiers, than to fly hither. He said that they would have met an easier death.

"God will help us," said the woman.

"We are alone among beasts of prey and serpents," said the man. "We have no food and no water. How should God be able to help us?" In despair he rent his garments and pressed his face against the dry earth. He was hopeless—like a man with a death-wound in his heart.

The woman sat erect, with her hands clasped over her knees. But the looks she cast toward the desert spoke of a hopelessness beyond bounds.

The palm heard the melancholy rustle in its leaves growing louder and louder. The woman must have heard it also, for she turned her gaze upward toward the palm-crown. And instantly she involuntarily raised her arms.

"Oh, dates, dates!" she cried. There was such intense agony in her voice that the old palm wished itself no taller than a broom and that the dates were as easy to reach as the buds on a brier bush. It probably knew that its crown was full of date clusters, but how should a human being reach such a height?

The man had already seen how beyond all reach the date clusters hung. He did not even raise his head. He begged his wife not to long for the impossible.

But the child, who had toddled about by himself and played with sticks and straws, had heard the mother's outcry.

Of course the little one could not imagine that his mother should not get everything she wished for. The instant she said dates, he began to stare at the tree. He pondered and pondered how he should bring down the dates. His forehead was almost drawn into wrinkles under the golden curls. At last a smile stole over his face. He had found the way. He went up to the palm and stroked it with his little hand, and said, in a sweet, childish voice:

"Palm, bend thee! Palm, bend thee!"

But what was that, what was that? The palm leaves rustled as if a hurricane had passed through them, and up and down the long trunk traveled shudder upon shudder. And the tree felt that the little one was its superior. It could not resist him.

And it bowed its long trunk before the child, as people bow before princes. In a great bow it bent itself towards the ground, and finally it came down so far that the big crown with the trembling leaves swept the desert sand.

The child appeared to be neither frightened nor surprised; with a joyous cry he loosened cluster after cluster from the old palm's crown. When he had plucked enough dates, and the tree still lay on the ground, the child came back again and caressed it and said, in the gentlest voice:

"Palm, raise thee! Palm, raise thee!"

Slowly and reverently the big tree raised itself on its slender trunk, while the leaves played like harps.

"Now I know for whom they are playing the death melody," said the palm to itself when it stood erect once more. "It is not for any of these people."

The man and the woman sank upon their knees and thanked God.

"Thou hast seen our agony and removed it. Thou art the Powerful One who bendest the palm-trunk like a reed. What enemy should we fear when Thy strength protects us?"

The next time a caravan passed through the desert, the travelers saw that the great palm's leaf-crown had withered.

"How can this be?" said a traveler. "This palm was not to die before it had seen a King greater than Solomon."

"Mayhap it hath seen him," answered another of the desert travelers.

THE FLIGHT INTO EGYPT

Thornton Wilder

From time to time there are auctions of the fittings that made up the old Dime Museums, and at such an auction you should be able to pick up a revolving cyclorama of the Holy Land and Egypt, which is the scenery for this piece. Turn down the gas-lights, for it is night in Palestine, and introduce a lady and a child on a donkey. They are accompanied by an old man on foot. The Donkey's name is HEPZIBAH.

HEPZIBAH. [*For the tenth time.*] I'm tired.

OUR LADY. I know, I know.

HEPZIBAH. I'm willing to carry you as far and as fast as I can, but within reason.

ST. JOSEPH. If you didn't talk so much you'd have more strength for the journey.

HEPZIBAH. It's not my lungs that are tired, it's my legs. When I talk I don't notice how tired I am.

OUR LADY. Do as you think best, Hepzibah, but do keep moving. I can still hear Herod's soldiers behind us.

[*Noise of ironmongery in the wings, right.*]

HEPZIBAH. Well, I'm doing my best.

[*Silence. The Tigris passes on the cyclorama.*] We must talk or I'll have to halt. We talked over the Romans and the whole political situation, and I must say again that I and every thinking person can only view such a situation with alarm, with real alarm. We talked over the village, and I don't think there's anything more to say about that. Did I remember to tell you that Issachar's daughter's engagement had been broken?

OUR LADY. Yes.

HEPZIBAH. Well, there's always ideas. I hope I can say honestly that I am at home in ideas of all sorts. For instance, back in the yard I'm the leader of a group. Among the girls. Very interesting religious discussions, I can tell you. Very helpful.

ST. JOSEPH. [*As some more iron is heard falling in Judea; the Euphrates passes.*] Can't you hurry a bit?

HEPZIBAH. I always say to the girls: Girls, even in faith we are supposed to use our reason. No one is intended to swallow hook, line and sinker, as the saying is. Now take these children that Herod is killing. Why were they born, since they must die so soon? Can any one answer that? Or put it another way: Why is the little boy in your arms being saved while the others must perish?

ST. JOSEPH. Is it necessary to stop?

HEPZIBAH. I was stopping for emphasis.—Mind you, it's not that I doubt. Honest discussion does not imply doubt necessarily.—What was that noise?

OUR LADY. I beg of you to make all the haste you can. The noise you hear is that of Herod's soldiers.

My child will be slain while you argue about Faith. I beg of you, Hepzibah, to save him while you can.

HEPZIBAH. I assure you I'm doing the best I can, and I think I'm moving along smartly. I didn't mean that noise, anyway; it was a noise ahead. Of course, your child is dearer to you than others, but *theologically speaking*, there's no possible reason why you should escape safely into Egypt while the others should be put to the sword as the Authorized Version has it. When the Messiah comes these things will be made clear, but until then I intend to exercise my reasoning faculty. My theory is this. . . .

OUR LADY. Hepzibah, we shall really have to beat you if you stop so often. Hepzibah, don't you remember me? Don't you remember how you fell on your knees in the stable? Don't you remember my child?

HEPZIBAH. What? What! Of course!

OUR LADY. Yes, Hepzibah.

HEPZIBAH. Let me stop just a moment and look around. No, I don't dare to stop. Why didn't I recognize you before! Really, my lady, you should have spoken more sharply to me. I didn't know I could run like this; it's a pleasure. Lord, what a donkey I was to be arguing about reason while my Lord was in danger.

[*A pyramid flies by.*]

Do you see the lights of the town yet? That's the Sphinx at the right, madam, yes, 3655 B.C. Well, well, it's a queer world where the survival of the Lord is dependent upon donkeys, but so it is. Why didn't you tell me before, my lady?

ST. JOSEPH. We thought you could carry us forward on your own merit.

HEPZIBAH. Oh, forgive me, madam; forgive me, sir. You don't hear any more soldiers now, I warrant you. Please don't direct me so far—excuse me—to the right, madam. That's the Nile, and there are crocodiles. My lady, may I ask one question now that we're safe?

OUR LADY. Yes, Hepzibah.

HEPZIBAH. It's this matter of faith and reason, madam. I'd love to carry back to our group of girls whatever you might say about it. . . .

OUR LADY. Dear Hepzibah, perhaps some day. For the present just do as I do and bear your master on.

[*More pyramids fly by; Memnon sings; the Nile moves dreamily past, and the inn is reached.*]

THE WINDFLOWERS
AND THE SAGE

Laura Spencer Portor

While Mary and the Christ-Child
  Fled from King Herod and death,
The patient ass that carried them
  Stumbled and failed for breath.

Where curved the steep hill downward,
  Mary's heart stood still to see
That Herod's soldiers, sword in hand,
  Came riding bloodily.

"Oh, holy little Son!" she cried,
  "How hide thy tenderness?"
Then saw she, growing by the road,
  Windflowers in lovely dress.

"Oh, windflowers, lovely windflowers!
  Be good and open wide
Your tender leaves and blossoms that
  My Lord therein may hide!"

But lest they spoil their loveliness
  The windflowers answered "Nay!"
Then Mary turned with pleading
  Where by the dusty way

A humble sage-bush blossomed,
  Who, when the same request
Was made of her, bent humbly down
  And opened her sweet breast;

And spread her leaves so widely kind,
  So reverently deep,
The little Lord might shelter find,
  And hide Him there, and sleep.

Then the most blest of women
  Bowed low, and blessed it there;
Since when the humble sage-brush breathes
  Sweet fragrance on the air.

THE JOYOUS MIRACLE

Frank Norris

Mervius had come to old Jerome's stone-built farm-house, across the huge meadow where some half-dozen of the neighbouring villagers pastured their stock in common. Old Jerome had received a certain letter, which was a copy of another letter, which in turn was a copy of another letter, and so on and so on, nobody could tell how far. Mervius would copy this letter and take it back to his village, where it would be copied again and again and yet again, and copies would be made of these copies, till the whole countryside would know the contents of that letter pretty well by heart. It was in this way, indeed, that these people made their literature. They would hand down the precious documents to their children, and that letter's contents would become folklore, become so well known that it would be repeated orally. It would be a legend, a mythos; perhaps, by and by, after a long time, it might gain credence and become even history.

But in that particular part of the country this famous letter was doubly important, because it had been written by a man whom some of the peasants and labourers and small farmers knew. "I knew him," said old Jerome, when Mervius had come in and the two had sat down on either side of the oak table in the brick-paved kitchen. Mervius—he was past seventy himself—slipped off his huge wooden sabots and let his feet rest on the warm bricks near the fireplace, for the meadow grass had been cold.

"Yes, I knew him," said Jerome. "He took the name of Peter afterwards. He was a fisherman, and used to seine fish over in the big lake where the vineyards are. He used to come here twice a week and sell me fish. He was a good fisherman. Then the carpenter's son set the whole country by the ears, and he went away with him. I missed his fish. Mondays and Wednesdays he came, and his fish were always fresh. They don't get such fish nowadays."

"I'll take the letter you have," said Mervius, "the copy, that is—and my wife will transcribe it; I—I am too old, and my eyes are bad. This carpenter's son, now—and you say, he set the people by the ears. It is a strange story."

Old Jerome put his chin in the air. "He was the son of a carpenter, nothing else. We all know his peo-ple; you did, and I. His father built the bin where I store my corn, and some stalls in my brother's barn in the next village. The son was a dreamer; anyone could have told you he would have perished in the end. The people were tired of him, a mild lunatic. That was all."

Mervius did not answer directly. "I have read this letter," he said, "this fisherman's letter. The man who looks after my sheep lent me a copy. Peter was not always with the man, the carpenter's son. One thing he has left out—one thing that I saw."

"That *you* saw!" exclaimed old Jerome.

Mervius nodded.

"I saw this man once."

"The carpenter's son?"

"Yes, once, and I saw him smile. You notice this letter never makes record of him smiling."

"I know."

"I saw him smile."

"As how?"

Mervius wrapped his lean old arms under the folds of his blouse and, resting his elbows on his knees, looked into the fire. Jerome's crow paced gravely in at the door and perched on his master's knee. Jerome fed him bits of cheese dipped in wine.

"It was a long time ago," said Mervius; "I was a lad. I remember I and my cousin Joanna—she was a little girl of seven then—used to run out to the cow stables early of cold mornings and stand in the fodder on the floor of the stalls to warm our feet. I had heard my father tell of this man, this carpenter's son. Did you ever hear," he added, turning to old Jerome, "did you ever hear—when you were a boy—hear the older people speak of the 'White Night'? At midnight it grew suddenly light, as though the sun had risen out of season. In fact there *was* a sun, or star—something. The chickens all came down from their roosts, the oxen lowed, the cocks crew, as though at daybreak. It was light for hours. Then toward four o'clock the light faded again. It happened in midwinter. Yes, they called it the 'White Night.' It was strange. You know the followers of this man claim that he was born on that night. My father knew some shepherds who told a strange story . . . however.

"For the children of our village—that is to say, my little cousin Joanna, my brother Simon, the potter's little son Septimus, a lad named Joseph, whose father was the olive presser of the district, and my self—the village bleach green was the playground.

"This bleach green was a great meadow by the brook, on the other side of my father's sheepfolds. It belonged to the fuller of the village. After weaving, the women used to bring here their webs of cloth to be whitened. Many a time I have seen the great squares and lengths of cloth covering the meadow, till you would have said the snow had fallen.

"It was like that on a holiday, when the five of us children were at our play along the banks of the little brook. Across the brook was the road that led to the city, and back of us the bleach green was one shimmer of white, great spreads and drifts of white cloth, billowing and rippling like shallow pools of milk, as the breeze stirred under them. They were weighted down at the corners with huge, round stones. It was a pretty sight. I have never forgotten that bleach green.

"I remember that day we had found a bank of clay, and the potter's son, Septimus, showed us how to model the stuff into pots and drinking vessels, and afterwards even into the form of animals: dogs, fishes, and the lame cow that belonged to the widow at the end of the village. Simon made a wonderful beast that he assured us was a lion, with twigs for legs, while I and Septimus patted and pinched our lump of clay to look like the great he-pig that had eaten a litter of puppies the week past—a horror that was yet the talk of all the village.

"Joanna—she was younger than all the rest of us—was fashioning little birds, clumsy, dauby little lumps of wet clay without much form. She was very proud of them, and set them in a row upon a stick, and called for us to look at them. As boys will, we made fun of her and her little clumsy clay birds, because she was a girl, and Simon, my brother, said:

"'Hoh, those aren't like birds at all. More like bullfrogs. *I'll* show you.'

"He and the rest of us took to making all manner of birds—pigeons, hawks, chickens, and the like. Septimus, the potter's son, executed a veritable masterpiece, a sort of peacock with tail spread, which was very like, and which he swore he would take to his father's kiln to have baked. We all exclaimed over this marvel, and gathered about Septimus, praising him and his handiwork, and poor little Joanna and her foolish dauby lumps were forgotten. Then, of course, we all made peacocks, and set them in a row,

and compared them with each other's. Joanna sat apart looking at us through her tears and trying to pretend that she did not care for clay peacocks, that the ridicule of a handful of empty-headed boys did not hurt her, and that her stupid little birds were quite as brave as ours. Then she said, by and by, timid-like and half to herself, 'I think my birds are pretty, too.'

"'Hoh,' says Septimus, 'look at Joanna's bullfrogs! Hoh! You are only a girl. What do you know? You don't know *anything*. I think you had better go home. We don't like to play with girls.'

"She was too brave to let us see her cry, but she got up, and was just about going home across the bleach green—in the green aisles between the webs of cloth—when Simon said to me and to the others:

"'Look, quick, Mervius, here comes that man that father spoke about, the carpenter's son who has made such a stir.' And he pointed across the brook, down the road that runs from the city over toward the lake, the same lake where you say this Peter used to fish. Joanna stopped and looked where he pointed; so did we all. I saw the man, the carpenter's son, whom Simon meant, and knew at once that it was he."

Old Jerome interrupted: "You had never seen him before. How did you know it was he?"

Mervius shook his head. "It was he. How could *I* tell? I don't know. I knew it was he."

"What did he look like?" asked Jerome, interested.

Mervius paused. There was a silence. Jerome's crow looked at the bright coals of the fire, his head on one side.

"Not at all extraordinary," said Mervius at length. "His face was that of a peasant, sun-browned, touched, perhaps, with a certain calmness. That was all. A face that was neither sad nor glad, calm merely, and not unusually or especially pleasing. He was dressed as you and I are now—as a peasant—and his hands were those of a worker. Only his head was bare."

"Did he wear his beard?"

"No, that was afterward. He was younger when I saw him, about twenty-one maybe, and his face was smooth. There was nothing extraordinary about the man."

"Yet you knew it was he."

"Yes," admitted Mervius, nodding his head. "Yes, I knew it was he. He came up slowly along the road near the brook where we children were sitting. He walked as any traveller along those roads might, not thoughtful or abstracted, but minding his steps and looking here and there about the country. The prettier things, I noted, seemed to attract him, and I particularly remember his stopping to look at a cherry tree in full bloom and smelling at its blossoms. Once, too, he stopped and thrust out of the way a twig that had fallen across a little ant heap. When he had come opposite us, he noticed us all standing there and looking at him quietly from across the brook, and he came down and stood on the other bank and asked us for a drink. There was a cup in an old bucket not far away that was kept there for those who worked on the bleach green. I ran to fetch it, and when I had come back he, the carpenter's son, had crossed the brook and was sitting on the bank, and all the children were about him. He had little Joanna on his knee, and she had forgotten to cry. He drank out of the cup I gave him, and fell to asking us about what we had been doing. Then we all cried out together and showed him our famous array of clay peacocks."

"And you were that familiar with him?" said old Jerome.

"He seemed like another child to us," answered Mervius. "We were all about him, on his shoulders, on his knees, in his arms, and Joanna in his lap—she had forgotten to cry.

"'See, see my birds,' she said. I tell you she had her arms around his neck. 'See, they said they were not pretty. They are pretty, aren't they, quite as pretty as theirs?'

"'Prettier, prettier,' he said. 'Look now.' He set our little clay birds before him in a row. First mine, then Simon's, then those of Joseph and Septimus, then one of little Joanna's shapeless little lumps. He looked at them, and at last touched the one Joanna had made with his finger-tip, then— Did you ever see, when corn is popping, how the grain swells, swells, swells, then bursts forth into whiteness? So it was then. No sooner had that little bird of Joanna, that clod of dust, that poor bit of common clay felt the touch of his finger than it awakened into life and became a live bird—and white, white as the sunshine, a beautiful little white bird that flew upward on the instant, with a tiny, glad note of song. We children shouted aloud, and Joanna danced and clapped her hands. And then it was that the carpenter's son

smiled. He looked at her as she looked up at that soaring white bird, and smiled, smiled, just once, and then fell calm again.

"He rose to go, but we hung about him and clamoured for him to stay.

"'No,' he said, as he kissed us all, 'I must go, go up to the city.' He crossed the brook and looked back at us.

"'Can't we go with you?' we cried to him. He shook his head.

"'Where I am going you cannot go. But,' he added, 'I am going to make a place for just such as you.'

"'And you'll come again?' we cried.

"'Yes, yes, I shall come again.'

"Then he went away, though often looking back and waving his hand at us. What we said after he had gone I don't know. How we felt I cannot express. Long time and in silence we stood there watching, until his figure vanished around a bend in the road. Then we turned and went home across the bleach green, through the green aisles between the webs of white cloth. We never told what had happened. That was just for ourselves alone. The same evening we heard of a great wonder that had been worked at a marriage in a town near by, water turned to wine, and a little later another, a man blind from his birth suddenly made to see. What did we care? He had not smiled upon those others, those people at the marriage, that crowd in the market-place. What did we care?"

Mervius stopped, and slipped his feet back into his sabots, and rose. He took the letter from Jerome and put it in the pocket of his blouse.

"And you saw that?"

Mervius nodded, but old Jerome shook his head in the manner of one who is not willing to be convinced.

"He was a dreamer with unspeakable pretensions. Why, his people were labouring folk in one of the villages beyond the lake. His father was a carpenter and built my corn bin. The son was a fanatic. His wits were turned."

"But this thing I saw," said Mervius at the door. "I saw it, who am speaking to you."

Jerome put his chin in the air.

". . . A dreamer. . . . We were well rid of him. . . . But I was sorry when Peter went away. . . . Mondays and Wednesdays he came, and his fish were always fresh."

2. LEGENDS OF THE PASSION

A BALLAD OF CHRISTMAS

Walter de la Mare

It was about the deep of night,
  And still was earth and sky,
When 'neath the moonlight dazzling bright,
  Three ghosts came riding by.

Beyond the sea, beyond the sea,
  Lie kingdoms for them all:
I wot their steeds trod wearily—
  The journey was not small.

By rock and desert, sand and stream,
  They footsore late did go:
Now like a sweet and blessed dream
  Their path was deep with snow.

Shining like hoar-frost rode they on,
  Three ghosts in earth's array;
It was about the hour when wan
  Night turns at hint of day.

Oh, but their hearts with woe distraught
  Hailed not the wane of night,
Only for Jesu still they sought
  To wash them clean and white.

For bloody was each hand, and dark
  With death each orbless eye;—
It was three traitors mute and stark
  Came riding silent by.

Silver their raiment and their spurs,
  And silver-shod their feet,
And silver-pale each face that stares
  Into the moonlight sweet.

And he upon the left that rose
  Was Pilate, Prince of Rome,
Whose journey once lay far abroad
  And now was nearing home.

And he upon the right that rode
  Herod of Salem sate,
Whose mantle dipped in children's blood
  Shone clear as Heaven's gate.

And he these twain betwixt that rode
  Was clad as white as wool,
Dyed in the Mercy of his God
  White was he crown to sole.

Throned mid a myriad saints in bliss
  Rise shall the Babe of Heaven
To shine on these three ghosts, I wis,
  Smit thro' with sorrows seven.

Babe of the Blessèd Trinity
  Shall smile their steeds to see:
Herod and Pilate riding by,
  And Judas one of three.

THE LEGEND
OF THE DOGWOOD TREE

Geraldine Farrar

The dogwood tree was once as broad
  And sturdy as the branching oak.
It grew in deepest forest green,
  And blossomed forth in waxen sheen,

More lordly than the shapely pine.
    The deer, the birds, all woodland things,
'Neath canopies so cool and wide
    Sought shelter there at eventide.

In strength and beauty years it grew,
    And only praise and glory knew—
Till on a day of dark despair
    Rude hands did outrage on it there.
From arching branches in cool shade,
    Two heavy beams were cut and laid,
Where crosswise, dark against the sky,
    Our blessed Lord must faint and die.

Then horror overcame the tree
    That, helpless, this its destiny should be!
In anguish deep, "Dear Lord," it cried,
    "Was it for this I grew in pride?"
And with a smile our Lord gave sign,
    E'en as His lips touched bitter wine:
"Dear tree, your pity thus for me,
    Shall ever bloom in memory!

"Though never more you touch the sky,
    You'll serve no cross whereon men die!
A slender sapling you shall sway,
    And to the world recall this day;
My cross in springtime men shall see;
    My crown of thorns will also be.
The whiteness of each petal rim
    The stain of blood and tears will dim.

"No cruel hand shall cut you down,
    And legend shall your beauty crown.
No garden ever quite so fair,
    Unless a dogwood blossoms there!"
And thus, a symbol of our Lord—
    His cross, His crown, His holy word—
Shall in this tree of beauty bright
    Forever fill the world with light.

ROBIN REDBREAST

John Banister Tabb

When Christ was taken from the rood,
    One thorn upon the ground,

Still moistened with the Precious Blood,
    An early robin found,
And wove it crosswise in his nest,
    Where, lo, it reddened all his breast.

PETER AND JOHN

Elinor Wylie

Twelve good friends
    Walked under the leaves,
Binding the ends
    Of the barley sheaves.

Peter and John
    Lay down to sleep
Pillowed upon
    A haymaker's heap.

John and Peter
    Lay down to dream.
The air was sweeter
    Than honey and cream.

Peter was bred
    In the salty cold:
His hair was red
    And his eyes were gold.

John had a mouth
    Like a wing bent down:
His brow was smooth
    And his eyes were brown.

Peter to slumber
    Sank like a stone,
Of all their number
    The bravest one.

John more slowly
    Composed himself,
Young and holy
    Among the Twelve.

John as he slept
    Cried out in grief,

Turned and wept
  On the golden leaf:

"Peter, Peter,
  Stretch me your hand
Across the glitter
  Of the harvest land!

"Peter, Peter,
  Give me a sign!
This was a bitter
  Dream of mine—

"Bitter as aloes
  It parched my tongue.
Upon the gallows
  My life was hung.

"Sharp it seemed
  As a bloody sword.
Peter, I dreamed
  I was Christ the Lord!"

Peter turned
  To holy Saint John:
His body burned
  In the falling sun.

In the falling sun
  He burned like flame:
"John, Saint John,
  I have dreamed the same!

"My bones were hung
  On an elder tree;
Bells were rung
  Over Galilee.

"A silver penny
  Sealed each of my eyes.
Many and many
  A Cock crew thrice."

When Peter's word
  Was spoken and done,
"Were you Christ the Lord
  In your dream?" said John.

"No," said the other,
  "That I was not.
I was our brother
  Iscariot."

THE FAIRY TREE

Temple Lane

All night around the Thorn Tree
  The little people play,
And men and women passing
  Will turn their heads away.

From break of dawn till moonrise
  Alone it stands on high,
With twisted sprigs for branches
  Across the winter sky.

They'll tell you dead men hung there,
  Its black and bitter fruit,
To guard the buried treasure
  Round which it twines its root.

They'll tell you Cromwell hung them:
  Sure that could never be!
He'd be in dread, like others,
  To touch the Fairy Tree.

But Katie Ryan saw there
  In some sweet dream she had,
The Blessed Son of Mary—
  And all His face was sad.

She dreamt she heard Him saying—
  "Why should they be afraid
When from a branch of Thorn Tree
  The crown I wore was made?"

O if your heart's a child-heart
  And if your eyes are clean,
You'll never fear the Thorn Tree
  That grows beyond Clogheen!

3. LEGENDS OF LATER YEARS AND OF TODAY

THE FIRST CHRISTMAS TREE

Eugene Field

Once upon a time the forest was in a great commotion. Early in the evening the wise old cedars had shaken their heads ominously and predicted strange things. They had lived in the forest many, many years; but never had they seen such marvellous sights as were to be seen now in the sky, and upon the hills, and in the distant village.

"Pray tell us what you see," pleaded a little vine; "we who are not as tall as you can behold none of these wonderful things. Describe them to us, that we may enjoy them with you."

"I am filled with such amazement," said one of the cedars, "that I can hardly speak. The whole sky seems to be aflame, and the stars appear to be dancing among the clouds; angels walk down from heaven to the earth, and enter the village or talk with the shepherds upon the hills."

The vine listened in mute astonishment. Such things never before had happened. The vine trembled with excitement. Its nearest neighbor was a tiny tree, so small it scarcely ever was noticed; yet it was a very beautiful little tree, and the vines and ferns and mosses and other humble residents of the forest loved it dearly.

"How I should like to see the angels!" sighed the little tree, "and how I should like to see the stars dancing among the clouds! It must be very beautiful."

As the vine and the little tree talked of these things, the cedars watched with increasing interest the wonderful scenes over and beyond the confines of the forest. Presently they thought they heard music, and they were not mistaken, for soon the whole air was full of the sweetest harmonies ever heard upon earth.

"What beautiful music!" cried the little tree. "I wonder whence it comes."

"The angels are singing," said a cedar; "for none but angels could make such sweet music."

"But the stars are singing, too," said another cedar; "yes, and the shepherds on the hills join in the song, and what a strangely glorious song it is!"

The trees listened to the singing, but they did not understand its meaning: it seemed to be an anthem, and it was of a Child that had been born; but further than this they did not understand. The strange and glorious song continued all the night; and all that night the angels walked to and fro, and the shepherd-folk talked with the angels, and the stars danced and carolled in high heaven. And it was nearly morning when the cedars cried out, "They are coming to the forest! the angels are coming to the forest!" And, surely enough, this was true. The vine and the little tree were very terrified, and they begged their older and stronger neighbors to protect them from harm. But the cedars were too busy with their own fears to pay any heed to the faint pleadings of the humble vine and the little tree. The angels came into the forest, singing the same glorious anthem about the Child, and the stars sang in chorus with them, until every part of the woods rang with echoes of that wondrous song. There was nothing in the appearance of this angel host to inspire fear; they were clad all in white, and there were crowns upon their fair heads, and golden harps in their hands; love, hope, charity, compassion, and joy beamed from their beautiful faces, and their presence seemed to fill the forest with a divine peace. The angels came through the forest to where the little tree stood, and gathering around it, they touched it with their hands, and kissed its little branches, and sang even more sweetly than before. And their song was about the Child, the Child, the Child that had been born. Then the stars came down from the skies and danced and hung upon the branches of the tree, and they, too, sang that song,— the song of the Child. And all the other trees and the vines and the ferns and the mosses beheld in wonder; nor could they understand why all these things were being done, and why this exceeding honor should be shown the little tree.

When the morning came the angels left the forest, —all but one angel, who remained behind and lingered near the little tree. Then a cedar asked: "Why do you tarry with us, holy angel?" And the angel answered: "I stay to guard this little tree, for it is sacred, and no harm shall come to it."

The little tree felt quite relieved by this assurance, and it held up its head more confidently than ever before. And how it thrived and grew, and waxed in strength and beauty! The cedars said they never had seen the like. The sun seemed to lavish its choicest rays upon the little tree, heaven dropped its sweetest dew upon it, and the winds never came to the forest that they did not forget their rude manners and linger to kiss the little tree and sing it their prettiest songs. No danger ever menaced it, no harm threatened; for the angel never slept,—through the day and through the night the angel watched the little tree and protected it from all evil. Oftentimes the trees talked with the angel; but of course they understood little of what he said, for he spoke always of the Child who was to become the Master; and always when thus he talked, he caressed the little tree, and stroked its branches and leaves, and moistened them with his tears. It all was so very strange that none in the forest could understand.

So the years passed, the angel watching his blooming charge. Sometimes the beasts strayed toward the little tree and threatened to devour its tender foliage; sometimes the woodman came with his axe, intent upon hewing down the straight and comely thing; sometimes the hot, consuming breath of drought swept from the south, and sought to blight the forest and all its verdure: the angel kept them from the little tree. Serene and beautiful it grew, until now it

was no longer a little tree, but the pride and glory of the forest.

One day the tree heard some one coming through the forest. Hitherto the angel had hastened to its side when men approached; but now the angel strode away and stood under the cedars yonder.

"Dear angel," cried the tree, "can you not hear the footsteps of some one approaching? Why do you leave me?"

"Have no fear," said the angel; "for He who comes is the Master."

The Master came to the tree and beheld it. He placed His hands upon its smooth trunk and branches, and the tree was thrilled with a strange and glorious delight. Then He stooped and kissed the tree, and then He turned and went away.

Many times after that the Master came to the forest, and when He came it always was to where the tree stood. Many times He rested beneath the tree and enjoyed the shade of its foliage, and listened to the music of the wind as it swept through the rustling leaves. Many times He slept there, and the tree watched over Him, and the forest was still, and all its voices were hushed. And the angel hovered near like a faithful sentinel.

Ever and anon men came with the Master to the forest, and sat with Him in the shade of the tree, and talked with Him of matters which the tree never could understand; only it heard that the talk was of love and charity and gentleness, and it saw that the Master was beloved and venerated by the others. It heard them tell of the Master's goodness and humility,—how He had healed the sick and raised the dead and bestowed inestimable blessings wherever He walked. And the tree loved the Master for His beauty and His goodness; and when He came to the forest it was full of joy, but when He came not it was sad. And the other trees of the forest joined in its happiness and its sorrow, for they, too, loved the Master. And the angel always hovered near.

The Master came one night alone into the forest, and His face was pale with anguish and wet with tears, and He fell upon His knees and prayed. The tree heard Him, and all the forest was still, as if it were standing in the presence of death. And when the morning came, lo! the angel had gone.

Then there was a great confusion in the forest. There was a sound of rude voices, and a clashing of swords and staves. Strange men appeared, uttering loud oaths and cruel threats, and the tree was filled with terror. It called aloud for the angel, but the angel came not.

"Alas," cried the vine, "they have come to destroy the tree, the pride and glory of the forest!"

The forest was sorely agitated, but it was in vain. The strange men plied their axes with cruel vigor, and the tree was hewn to the ground. Its beautiful branches were cut away and cast aside, and its soft, thick foliage was strewn to the tenderer mercies of the winds.

"They are killing me!" cried the tree; "why is not the angel here to protect me?"

But no one heard the piteous cry,—none but the other trees of the forest; and they wept, and the little vine wept too.

Then the cruel men dragged the despoiled and hewn tree from the forest, and the forest saw that beauteous thing no more.

But the night wind that swept down from the City of the Great King that night to ruffle the bosom of distant Galilee, tarried in the forest awhile to say that it had seen that day a cross upraised on Calvary, —the tree on which was stretched the body of the dying Master.

THE OCEAN CHRIST

Anatole France

That year many of the fishers of Saint-Valéry had been drowned at sea. Their bodies were found on the beach cast up by the waves with the wreckage of their boats; and for nine days, up the steep road leading to the church were to be seen coffins borne by hand and followed by widows, who were weeping beneath their great black-hooded cloaks, like women in the Bible.

Thus were the skipper Jean Lenoël and his son Désiré laid in the great nave, beneath the vaulted roof from which they had once hung a ship in full rigging as an offering to Our Lady. They were righteous men and God-fearing. Monsieur Guillaume Truphème, priest of Saint-Valéry, having

pronounced the Absolution, said in a tearful voice:

"Never were laid in consecrated ground there to await the judgment of God better men and better Christians than Jean Lenoël and his son Désiré."

And while barques and their skippers perished near the coast, in the high seas great vessels foundered. Not a day passed that the ocean did not bring in some flotsam of wreck. Now one morning some children who were steering a boat saw a figure lying on the sea. It was a figure of Jesus Christ, life-size, carved in wood, painted in natural colouring, and looking as if it were very old. The Good Lord was floating upon the sea with arms outstretched. The children towed the figure ashore and brought it up into Saint-Valéry. The head was encircled with the crown of thorns. The feet and hands were pierced. But the nails were missing as well as the cross. The arms were still outstretched ready for sacrifice and blessing, just as He appeared to Joseph of Arimathea and the holy women when they were burying him.

The children gave it to Monsieur le Curé Truphème, who said to them:

"This image of the Saviour is of ancient workmanship. He who made it must have died long ago. Although to-day in the shops of Amiens and Paris excellent statues are sold for a hundred francs and more, we must admit that the earlier sculptors were not without merit. But what delights me most is the thought that if Jesus Christ be thus come with open arms to Saint-Valéry, it is in order to bless the parish, which has been so cruelly tried, and in order to announce that he has compassion on the poor folk who go a-fishing at the risk of their lives. He is the God who walked upon the sea and blessed the nets of Cephas."

And Monsieur le Curé Truphème, having had the Christ placed in the church on the cloth of the high altar, went off to order from the carpenter Lemerre a beautiful cross in heart of oak.

When it was made, the Saviour was nailed to it with brand new nails, and it was erected in the nave above the churchwarden's pew.

Then it was noticed that His eyes were filled with mercy and seemed to glisten with tears of heavenly pity.

One of the churchwardens, who was present at the putting up of the crucifix, fancied he saw tears streaming down the divine face. The next morning when Monsieur le Curé with a choir-boy entered the church to say his mass, he was astonished to find the cross above the churchwarden's pew empty and the Christ lying upon the altar.

As soon as he had celebrated the divine sacrifice he had the carpenter called and asked him why he had taken the Christ down from his cross. But the carpenter replied that he had not touched it. Then, after having questioned the beadle and the sidesmen, Monsieur Truphème made certain that no one had entered the church since the crucifix had been placed over the churchwarden's pew.

Thereupon he felt that these things were miraculous, and he meditated upon them discreetly. The following Sunday in his exhortation he spoke of them to his parishioners, and he called upon them to contribute by their gifts to the erection of a new cross more beautiful than the first and more worthy to bear the Redeemer of the world.

The poor fishers of Saint-Valéry gave as much money as they could and the widows brought their wedding-rings. Wherefore Monsieur Truphème was able to go at once to Abbeville and to order a cross of ebony highly polished and surmounted by a scroll with the inscription I.N.R.I. in letters of gold. Two months later it was erected in the place of the former and the Christ was nailed to it between the lance and the sponge.

But Jesus left this cross as He had left the other; and as soon as night fell He went and stretched Himself upon the altar.

Monsieur le Curé, when he found Him there in the morning, fell on his knees and prayed for a long while. The fame of this miracle spread throughout the neighbourhood, and the ladies of Amiens made a collection for the Christ of Saint-Valéry. Monsieur Truphème received money and jewels from Paris, and the wife of the Minister of Marine, Madame Hyde de Neuville, sent him a heart of diamonds. Of all these treasures, in the space of two years, a goldsmith of La Rue St. Sulpice, fashioned a cross of gold and precious stones which was set up with great pomp in the church of Saint-Valéry on the second Sunday after Easter in the year 18—. But He who had not refused the cross of sorrow, fled from this cross of gold and again stretched Himself upon the white linen of the altar.

For fear of offending Him He was left there this time; and He had lain upon the altar for more than two years, when Pierre, son of Pierre Caillou, came to tell Monsieur le Curé Truphème that he had found the true cross of Our Lord on the beach.

Pierre was an innocent; and, because he had not sense enough to earn a livelihood, people gave him bread out of charity; he was liked because he never did any harm. But he wandered in his talk and no one listened to him.

Nevertheless Monsieur Truphème, who had never ceased meditating on the Ocean Christ, was struck by what the poor imbecile had just said. With the beadle and two sidesmen he went to the spot, where the child said he had seen a cross, and there he found two planks studded with nails, which had long been washed by the sea and which did indeed form a cross.

They were the remains of some old shipwreck. On one of these boards could still be read two letters painted in black, a J and an L; and there was no doubt that this was a fragment of Jean Lenoël's barque, he who with his son Désiré had been lost at sea five years before.

At the sight of this, the beadle and the sidesmen began to laugh at the innocent who had taken the broken planks of a boat for the cross of Jesus Christ. But Monsieur le Curé Truphème checked their merriment. He had meditated much and prayed long since the Ocean Christ had arrived among the fisherfolk, and the mystery of infinite charity began to dawn upon him. He knelt down upon the sand, repeated the prayer for the faithful departed, and then told the beadle and the sidesmen to carry the flotsam on their shoulders and to place it in the church. When this had been done he raised the Christ from the altar, placed it on the planks of the boat and himself nailed it to them, with the nails that the ocean had corroded.

By the priest's command, the very next day this cross took the place of the cross of gold and precious stones over the churchwarden's pew. The Ocean Christ has never left it. He has chosen to remain nailed to the planks on which men died invoking His name and that of His Mother. There, with parted lips, august and afflicted He seems to say:

"My cross is made of all men's woes, for I am in truth the God of the poor and the heavy-laden."

THE HOLY CROSS

Eugene Field

Whilst the noble Don Esclevador and his little band of venturesome followers explored the neighboring fastnesses in quest for gold, the Father Miguel tarried at the shrine which in sweet piety they had hewn out of the stubborn rock in that strangely desolate spot. Here, upon that serene August morning, the holy Father held communion with the saints, beseeching them, in all humility, to intercede with our beloved Mother for the safe guidance of the fugitive Cortes to his native shores, and for the divine protection of the little host, which, separated from the Spanish army, had wandered leagues to the northward, and had sought refuge in the noble mountains of an unknown land. The Father's devotions were, upon a sudden, interrupted by the approach of an aged man who toiled along the mountain-side path,—a man so aged and so bowed and so feeble that he seemed to have been brought down into that place, by means of some necromantic art, out of distant centuries. His face was yellow and wrinkled like ancient parchment, and a beard whiter than Samite streamed upon his breast, whilst about his withered body and shrunken legs hung faded raiment which the elements had corroded and the thorns had grievously rent. And as he toiled along, the aged man continually groaned, and continually wrung his palsied hands, as if a sorrow, no lighter than his years, afflicted him.

"In whose name comest thou?" demanded the Father Miguel, advancing a space toward the stranger, but not in threatening wise; whereat the aged man stopped in his course and lifted his eyebrows, and regarded the Father a goodly time, but he spake no word.

"In whose name comest thou?" repeated the priestly man. "Upon these mountains have we lifted up the cross of our blessed Lord in the name of our sovereign liege, and here have we set down a tabernacle to the glory of the Virgin and of her ever-blessed son, our Redeemer and thine,—whoso thou mayest be!"

"Who is thy king I know not," quoth the aged man, feebly; "but the shrine in yonder wall of rock I know; and by that symbol which I see therein, and by thy faith for which it stands, I conjure thee, as

thou lovest both, give me somewhat to eat and to drink, that betimes I may go upon my way again, for the journey before me is a long one."

These words spake the old man in tones of such exceeding sadness that the Father Miguel, touched by compassion, hastened to meet the wayfarer, and, with his arms about him, and with whisperings of sweet comfort, to conduct him to a resting-place. Coarse food in goodly plenty was at hand; and it happily fortuned, too, that there was a homely wine, made by Pietro del y Saguache himself, of the wild grapes in which a neighboring valley abounded. Of these things anon the old man partook, greedily but silently, and all that while he rolled his eyes upon the shrine; and then at last, struggling to his feet, he made as if to go upon his way.

"Nay," interposed the Father Miguel, kindly; "abide with us a season. Thou art an old man and sorely spent. Such as we have thou shalt have, and if thy soul be distressed, we shall pour upon it the healing balm of our blessed faith."

"Little knowest thou whereof thou speakest," quoth the old man, sadly. "There is no balm can avail me. I prithee let me go hence, ere knowing what manner of man I am thou hatest me and doest evil unto me." But as he said these words he fell back again even then into the seat where he had sat, and, as through fatigue, his hoary head drooped upon his bosom.

"Thou art ill!" cried the Father Miguel, hastening to his side. "Thou shalt go no farther this day! Give me thy staff,"—and he plucked it from him.

Then said the old man: "As I am now, so have I been these many hundred years. Thou hast heard tell of me,—canst thou not guess my name; canst thou not read my sorrow in my face and in my bosom? As thou art good and holy through thy faith in that symbol in yonder shrine, hearken to me, for I will tell thee of the wretch whom thou hast succored. Then, if it be thy will, give me thy curse and send me on my way."

Much marvelled the Father Miguel at these words, and he deemed the old man to be mad; but he made no answer. And presently the old man, bowing his head upon his hands, had to say in this wise:—

"Upon a time," he quoth, "I abided in the city of the Great King,—there was I born and there I abided. I was of good stature, and I asked favor of none. I was an artisan, and many came to my shop, and my cunning was sought of many,—for I was exceeding crafty in my trade; and so, therefore, speedily my pride begot an insolence that had respect to none at all. And once I heard a tumult in the street, as of the cries of men and boys commingled, and the clashing of arms and staves. Seeking to know the cause thereof, I saw that one was being driven to execution,—one that had said he was the Son of God and the King of the Jews, for which blasphemy and crime against our people he was to die upon the cross. Overcome by the weight of this cross, which he bore upon his shoulders, the victim tottered in the street and swayed this way and that, as though each moment he were like to fall, and he groaned in sore agony. Meanwhile about him pressed a multitude that with vast clamor railed at him and scoffed him and smote him, to whom he paid no heed; but in his agony his eyes were always uplifted to heaven, and his lips moved in prayer for them that so shamefully entreated him. And as he went his way to Calvary, it fortuned that he fell and lay beneath the cross right at my very door, whereupon, turning his eyes upon me as I stood over against him, he begged me that for a little moment I should bear up the weight of the cross whilst that he wiped the sweat from off his brow. But I was filled with hatred, and I spurned him with my foot, and I said to him: 'Move on, thou wretched criminal, move on. Pollute not my doorway with thy touch,—move on to death, I command thee!' This was the answer I gave to him, but no succor at all. Then he spake to me once again, and he said: 'Thou, too, shalt move on, O Jew! Thou shalt move on forever, but not to death!' And with these words he bore up the cross again and went upon his way to Calvary.

"Then of a sudden," quoth the old man, "a horror filled my breast, and a resistless terror possessed me. So was I accursed forevermore. A voice kept saying always to me: 'Move on, O Jew! move on forever!' From home, from kin, from country, from all I knew and loved I fled; nowhere could I tarry,—the nameless horror burned in my bosom, and I heard continually a voice crying unto me: 'Move on, O Jew! move on forever!' So, with the years, the centuries, the ages, I have fled before that cry and in that nameless horror; empires have risen and crumbled, races have been born and are extinct, mountains have been cast up and time hath levelled them,—still I do live and still I wander hither and thither

upon the face of the earth, and am an accursed thing. The gift of tongues is mine,—all men I know, yet mankind knows me not. Death meets me face to face, and passes me by; the sea devours all other prey, but will not hide me in its depths; wild beasts flee from me, and pestilences turn their consuming breaths elsewhere. On and on and on I go,—not to a home, nor to my people, nor to my grave, but evermore into the tortures of an eternity of sorrow. And evermore I feel the nameless horror burn within, whilst evermore I see the pleading eyes of him that bore the cross, and evermore I hear his voice crying: 'Move on, O Jew! move on forevermore!'"

"Thou art the Wandering Jew!" cried the Father Miguel.

"I am he," saith the aged man. "I marvel not that thou dost revolt against me, for thou standest in the shadow of that same cross which I have spurned, and thou art illumined with the love of him that went his way to Calvary. But I beseech thee bear with me until I have told thee all,—then drive me hence if thou art so minded."

"Speak on," quoth the Father Miguel.

Then said the Jew: "How came I here I scarcely know; the seasons are one to me, and one day but as another; for the span of my life, O priestly man! is eternity. This much know you: from a far country I embarked upon a ship,—I knew not whence 'twas bound, nor cared I. I obeyed the voice that bade me go. Anon a mighty tempest fell upon the ship and overwhelmed it. The cruel sea brought peace to all but me; a many days it tossed and buffeted me, then with a cry of exultation cast me at last upon a shore I had not seen before, a coast far, far westward whereon abides no human thing. But in that solitude still heard I from within the awful mandate that sent me journeying onward, 'Move on, O Jew! move on'; and into vast forests I plunged, and mighty plains I traversed; onward, onward, onward I went, with the nameless horror in my bosom, and—that cry, that awful cry! The rains beat upon me; the sun wrought pitilessly with me; the thickets tore my flesh; and the inhospitable shores bruised my weary feet,—yet onward I went, plucking what food I might from thorny bushes to stay my hunger, and allaying my feverish thirst at pools where reptiles crawled. Sometimes a monster beast stood in my pathway and threatened to devour me; then would I spread my two arms thus, and welcome death, crying: 'Rend thou this Jew in twain, O beast! strike thy kindly fangs deep into this heart,—be not afeard, for I shall make no battle with thee, nor any outcry whatsoever!' But, lo, the beast would cower before me and skulk away. So there is no death for me; the judgment spoken is irrevocable; my sin is unpardonable, and the voice will not be hushed!"

Thus and so much spake the Jew, bowing his hoary head upon his hands. Then was the Father Miguel vastly troubled; yet he recoiled not from the Jew,—nay, he took the old man by the hand and sought to soothe him.

"Thy sin was most heinous, O Jew!" quoth the Father; "but it falleth in our blessed faith to know that whoso repenteth of his sin, what it soever may be, the same shall surely be forgiven. Thy punishment hath already been severe, and God is merciful, for even as we are all his children, even so his tenderness to us is like unto the tenderness of a father unto his child—yea, and infinitely tenderer and sweeter, for who can estimate the love of our heavenly Father? Thou didst deny thy succor to the Nazarene when he besought it, yet so great compassion hath he that if thou but callest upon him he will forget thy wrong,—leastwise will pardon it. Therefore be thou persuaded by me, and tarry here this night, that in the presence of yonder symbol and the holy relics our prayers may go up with thine unto our blessed Mother and to the saints who haply shall intercede for thee in Paradise. Rest here, O sufferer, —rest thou here, and we shall presently give thee great comfort."

The Jew, well-nigh fainting with fatigue, being persuaded by the holy Father's gentle words, gave finally his consent unto this thing, and went anon unto the cave beyond the shrine, and entered thereinto, and lay upon a bed of skins and furs, and made as if to sleep. And when he slept his sleep was seemingly disturbed by visions, and he tossed as doth an one that sees full evil things, and in that sleep he muttered somewhat of a voice he seemed to hear, though round about there was no sound whatsoever, save only the soft music of the pine-trees on the mountain-side. Meanwhile in the shrine, hewn out of those rocks, did the Father Miguel bow before the sacred symbol of his faith and plead for mercy for that same Jew that slumbered anear. And when, as the deepening blue mantle of night fell upon the hilltops and obscured the valleys round about, Don

Esclevador and his sturdy men came clamoring along the mountain-side, the holy Father met them a way off and bade them have regard to the aged man that slept in yonder cave. But when he told them of that Jew and of his misery and of the secret causes thereof, out spake the noble Don Esclevador, full hotly,—

"By our sweet Christ," he cried, "shall we not offend our blessed faith and do most impiously in the Virgin's sight if we give this harbor and this succor unto so vile a sinner as this Jew that hath denied our dear Lord!"

Which words had like to wrought great evil with the Jew, for instantly the other men sprang forward as if to awaken the Jew and drive him forth into the night. But the Father Miguel stretched forth his hands and commanded them to do no evil unto the Jew, and so persuasively did he set forth the godliness and the sweetness of compassion that presently the whole company was moved with a gentle pity toward that Jew. Therefore it befell anon, when night came down from the skies and after they had feasted upon their homely food as was their wont, that they talked of the Jew, and thinking of their own hardships and misfortunes (whereof it is not now to speak), they had all the more compassion to that Jew, which spake them passing fair, I ween.

Now all this while lay the Jew upon the bed of skins and furs within the cave, and though he slept (for he was exceeding weary), he tossed continually from side to side, and spoke things in his sleep, as if his heart were sorely troubled, and as if in his dreams he beheld grievous things. And seeing the old man, and hearing his broken speech, the others moved softly hither and thither and made no noise soever lest they should awaken him. And many an one— yes, all that valiant company bowed down that night before the symbol in the shrine, and with sweet reverence called upon our blessed Virgin to plead in the cause of that wretched Jew. Then sleep came to all, and in dreams the noble Don Esclevador saw his sovereign liege, and kneeled before his throne, and heard his sovereign liege's gracious voice; in dreams the heartweary soldier sailed the blue waters of the Spanish main, and pressed his native shore, and beheld once again the lovelight in the dark eyes of her that awaited him; in dreams the mountain-pines were kissed of the singing winds, and murmured drowsily and tossed their arms as do little children that dream of their play; in dreams the

Jew swayed hither and thither, scourged by that nameless horror in his bosom, and seeing the pleading eyes of our dying Master, and hearing that awful mandate: "Move on, O Jew! move on forever!" So each slept and dreamed his dreams,—all slept but the Father Miguel, who alone throughout the night kneeled in the shrine and called unto the saints and unto our Mother Mary in prayer. And his supplication was for that Jew; and the mists fell upon that place and compassed it about, and it was as if the heavens had reached down their lips to kiss the holy shrine. And suddenly there came unto the Jew a quiet as of death, so that he tossed no more in his sleep and spake no word, but lay exceeding still, smiling in his sleep as one who sees his home in dreams, or his mother, or some other such beloved thing.

It came to pass that early in the morning the Jew came from the cavern to go upon his way, and the Father Miguel besought him to take with him a goodly loaf in his wallet as wise provision against hunger. But the Jew denied this, and then he said: "Last night while I slept methought I stood once more in the city of the Great King,—aye, in that very doorway where I stood, swart and lusty, when I spurned him that went his way to Calvary. In my bosom burned the terror as of old, and my soul was consumed of a mighty anguish. None of those that passed in that street knew me; centuries had ground to dust all my kin. 'O God!' I cried in agony, 'suffer my sin to be forgotten,—suffer me to sleep, to sleep forever beneath the burden of the cross I some time spurned!' As I spake these words there stood before me one in shining raiment, and lo! 'twas he who bore the cross to Calvary! His eyes that had pleaded to me on a time now fell compassionately upon me, and the voice that had commanded me move on forever, now broke full sweetly on my ears: 'Thou shalt go on no more, O Jew, but as thou hast asked, so shall it be, and thou shalt sleep forever beneath the cross.' Then fell I into a deep slumber, and, therefrom but just now awaking, I feel within me what peace bespeaketh pardon for my sin. This day am I ransomed; so suffer me to go my way, O holy man."

So went the Jew upon his way, not groaningly and in toilsomewise, as was his wont, but eagerly, as goeth one to meet his bride, or unto some sweet reward. And the Father Miguel stood long, looking after him and being sorely troubled in mind; for he knew not what interpretation he should make of all these things. And anon the Jew was lost to sight in the forest.

But once, a little space thereafter, while that José Conejos, the Castilian, clambered up the yonder mountain-side, he saw amid the grasses there the dead and withered body of an aged man, and thereupon forthwith made he such clamor that Don Esclevador hastened thither and saw it was the Jew; and since there was no sign that wild beasts had wrought evil with him, it was declared that the Jew had died of age and fatigue and sorrow, albeit on the wrinkled face there was a smile of peace that none had seen thereon while yet the Jew lived. And it was accounted to be a most wondrous thing that, whereas never before had flowers of that kind been seen in those mountains, there now bloomed all round about flowers of the dye of blood, which thing the noble Don Esclevador took full wisely to be a symbol of our dear Lord's most precious blood, whereby not only you and me but even the Jew shall be redeemed to Paradise.

Within the spot where they had found the Jew they buried him, and there he sleeps unto this very day. Above the grave the Father Miguel said a prayer; and the ground of that mountain they adjudged to be holy ground; but over the grave wherein lay the Jew they set up neither cross nor symbol of any kind, fearing to offend their holy faith.

But that very night, when that they were returned unto their camp half a league distant, there arose a mighty tempest, and there was such an upheaval and rending of the earth as only God's hand could make; and there was a crashing and a groaning as if the world were smitten in twain, and the winds fled through the valleys in dismay, and the trees of the forest shrieked in terror and fell upon their faces. Then in the morning when the tempest ceased and all the sky was calm and radiant they saw that an impassable chasm lay between them and that mountain-side wherein the Jew slept the sleep of death; that God had traced with his finger a mighty gulf about that holy ground which held the bones of the transgressor. Between heaven and earth hung that lonely grave, nor could any foot scale the precipice that guarded it; but one might see that the spot was beautiful with kindly mountain verdure and that flowers of blood-red dye bloomed in that lonely place.

This was the happening in a summer-time a many years ago; to the mellow grace of that summer succeeded the purple glory of the autumn, and then came on apace the hoary dignity of winter. But the earth hath its resurrection too, and anon came the beauteous spring-time with warmth and scents and new life. The brooks leapt forth once more from their hiding-places, the verdure awaked, and the trees put forth their foliage. Then from the awful mountain peaks the snow silently and slowly slipped to the valleys, and in divers natural channels went onward and ever downward to the southern sea, and now at last 'twas summer-time again and the mellow grace of August brooded over the earth. But in that yonder mountain-side had fallen a symbol never to be removed,—aye, upon that holy ground where slept the Jew was stretched a cross, a mighty cross of snow on which the sun never fell and which no breath of wind ever disturbed. Elsewhere was the tender warmth of verdure and the sacred passion of the blood-red flowers, but over that lonely grave was stretched the symbol of him that went his way to Calvary, and in that grave slept the Jew.

Mightily marvelled Don Esclevador and his warrior host at this thing; but the Father Miguel knew its meaning; for he was minded of that vision wherein it was foretold unto the Jew that, pardoned for his sin, he should sleep forever under the burden of the cross he spurned. All this the Father Miguel showed unto Don Esclevador and the others, and he said: "I deem that unto all ages this holy symbol shall bear witness of our dear Christ's mercy and compassion. Though we, O exiled brothers, sleep in this foreign land in graves which none shall know, upon that mountain height beyond shall stretch the eternal witness to our faith and to our Redeemer's love, minding all that look thereon, not of the pains and the punishments of the Jew, but of the exceeding mercy of our blessed Lord, and of the certain eternal peace that cometh through his love!"

How long ago these things whereof I speak befell, I shall not say. They never saw—that Spanish host—they never saw their native land, their sovereign liege, their loved ones' faces again; they sleep, and they are dust among those mighty mountains in the West. Where is the grave of the Father Miguel, or of Don Esclevador, or of any of the valiant Spanish exiles, it is not to tell; God only knoweth, and the saints: all sleep in the faith, and their reward is cer-

tain. But where sleepeth the Jew all may see and know; for on that awful mountain-side, in a spot inaccessible to man, lieth the holy cross of snow. The winds pass lightly over that solemn tomb, and never a sunbeam lingereth there. White and majestic it lies where God's hands have placed it, and its mighty arms stretch forth as in a benediction upon the fleeting dust beneath.

So shall it bide forever upon that mountain-side, and the memory of the Jew and of all else human shall fade away and be forgotten in the surpassing glory of the love and the compassion of him that bore the redeeming burden to Calvary.

THE TRAVELLING MAN
A MIRACLE PLAY
Lady Gregory

A MOTHER.
A CHILD.
A TRAVELLING MAN.

Scene: A cottage kitchen. A woman setting out a bowl and jug and board on the table for breadmaking.

CHILD. What is it you are going to make, mother?

MOTHER. I am going to make a grand cake with white flour. Seeds I will put in it. Maybe I'll make a little cake for yourself too. You can be baking it in the little pot while the big one will be baking in the big pot.

CHILD. It is a pity daddy to be away at the fair on a Samhain night.

MOTHER. I must make my feast all the same, for Samhain night is more to me than to any other one. It was on this night seven years I first came into this house.

CHILD. You will be taking down those plates from the dresser so, those plates with flowers on them, and be putting them on the table.

MOTHER. I will. I will set out the house to-day, and bring down the best delf, and put whatever thing is best on the table, because of the great thing that happened me seven years ago.

CHILD. What great thing was that?

MOTHER. I was after being driven out of the house where I was a serving girl. . . .

CHILD. Where was that house? Tell me about it.

MOTHER. (*Sitting down and pointing southward.*) It is over there I was living, in a farmer's house up on Slieve Echtge, near to Slieve na n-Or, the Golden Mountain.

CHILD. The Golden Mountain! That must be a grand place.

MOTHER. Not very grand indeed, but bare and cold enough at that time of the year. Anyway, I was driven out a Samhain day like this, because of some things that were said against me.

CHILD. What did you do then?

MOTHER. What had I to do but to go walking the bare bog road through the rough hills where there was no shelter to find, and the sharp wind going through me, and the red mud heavy on my shoes. I came to Kilbecanty. . . .

CHILD. I know Kilbecanty. That is where the woman in the shop gave me sweets out of a bottle.

MOTHER. So she might now, but that night her door was shut and all the doors were shut; and I saw through the windows the boys and the girls sitting round the hearth and playing their games, and I had no courage to ask for shelter. In dread I was they might think some shameful thing of me, and I going the road alone in the night-time.

CHILD. Did you come here after that?

MOTHER. I went on down the hill in the darkness, and with the dint of my trouble and the length of the road my strength failed me, and I had like to fall. So I did fall at the last, meeting with a heap of broken stones by the roadside.

CHILD. I hurt my knee one time I fell on the stones.

MOTHER. It was then the great thing happened. I saw a stranger coming towards me, a very tall man, the best I ever saw, bright and shining that you could see him through the darkness; and I knew him to be no common man.

CHILD. Who was he?

MOTHER. It is what I thought, that he was the King of the World.

CHILD. Had he a crown like a King?

MOTHER. If he had, it was made of the twigs of a bare blackthorn; but in his hand he had a green branch, that never grew on a tree of this world. He took me by the hand, and he led me over the stepping-stones outside to this door, and he bade me to go in and I would find good shelter. I was kneeling down to thank him, but he raised me up and he said, "I will come to see you some other time. And do not shut up your heart in the things I give you," he said, "but have a welcome before me."

CHILD. Did he go away then?

MOTHER. I saw him no more after that, but I did as he bade me. (*She stands up and goes to the door.*) I came in like this, and your father was sitting there by the hearth, a lonely man that was after losing his wife. He was alone and I was alone, and we married one another; and I never wanted since for shelter or safety. And a good wife I made him, and a good housekeeper.

CHILD. Will the King come again to the house?

MOTHER. I have his word for it he will come, but he did not come yet; it is often your father and myself looked out the door of a Samhain night, thinking to see him.

CHILD. I hope he won't come in the night time, and I asleep.

MOTHER. It is of him I do be thinking every year, and I setting out the house, and making a cake for the supper.

CHILD. What will he do when he comes in?

MOTHER. He will sit over there in the chair, and maybe he will taste a bit of the cake. I will call in all the neighbours; I will tell them he is here. They will not be keeping it in their mind against me then that I brought nothing, coming to the house. They will know I am before any of them, the time they know who it is has come to visit me. They will all kneel down and ask for his blessing. But the best blessing will be on the house he came to of himself.

CHILD. And are you going to make the cake now?

MOTHER. I must make it now indeed, or I will be late with it. I am late as it is; I was expecting one of the neighbours to bring me white flour from the town. I'll wait no longer, I'll go borrow it in some place. There will be a wedding in the stonecutter's house Thursday, it's likely there will be flour in the house.

CHILD. Let me go along with you.

MOTHER. It is best for you to stop here. Be a good child now, and don't be meddling with the things on the table. Sit down there by the hearth and break up those little sticks I am after bringing in. Make a little heap of them now before me, and we will make a good fire to bake the cake. See now how many will you break. Don't go out the door while I'm away, I would be in dread of you going near the river and it in flood. Behave yourself well now. Be counting the sticks as you break them. (*She goes out.*)

CHILD. (*Sitting down and breaking sticks across his knee.*) One—and two—O I can break this one into a great many, one, two, three, four.—This one is wet—I don't like a wet one—five, six—that is a great heap.—Let me try that great big one.—That is too hard.—I don't think mother could break that one.— Daddy could break it.

(*Half-door is opened and a travelling man comes in. He wears a ragged white flannel shirt, and mud-stained trousers. He is bareheaded and barefooted, and carries a little branch in his hand.*)

TRAVELLING MAN. (*Stooping over the child and taking the stick.*) Give it here to me and hold this.

(*He puts the branch in the child's hand while he takes the stick and breaks it.*)

CHILD. That is a good branch, apples on it and flowers. The tree at the mill has apples yet, but all the flowers are gone. Where did you get this branch?

TRAVELLING MAN. I got it in a garden a long way off.

CHILD. Where is the garden? Where do you come from?

TRAVELLING MAN. (*Pointing southward.*) I have come from beyond those hills.

CHILD. Is it from the Golden Mountain you are come? From Slieve na n-Or?

TRAVELLING MAN. That is where I come from surely, from the Golden Mountain. I would like to sit down and rest for a while.

CHILD. Sit down here beside me. We must not go near the table or touch anything, or mother will be angry. Mother is going to make a beautiful cake, a cake that will be fit for a King that might be coming in to our supper.

TRAVELLING MAN. I will set here with you on the floor. (*Sits down.*)

CHILD. Tell me now about the Golden Mountain.

TRAVELLING MAN. There is a garden in it, and there is a tree in the garden that has fruit and flowers at the one time.

CHILD. Like this branch?

TRAVELLING MAN. Just like that little branch.

CHILD. What other things are in the garden?

TRAVELLING MAN. There are birds of all colours that sing at every hour, the way the people will come to their prayers. And there is a high wall about the garden.

CHILD. What way can the people get through the wall?

TRAVELLING MAN. There are four gates in the wall: a gate of gold, and a gate of silver, and a gate of crystal, and a gate of white brass.

CHILD. (*Taking up the sticks.*) I will make a garden. I will make a wall with these sticks.

TRAVELLING MAN. This big stick will make the first wall.

(*They build a square wall with sticks.*)

CHILD. (*Taking up branch.*) I will put this in the middle. This is the tree. I will get something to make it stand up. (*Gets up and looks at dresser.*) I can't reach it, get up and give me that shining jug.

(*Travelling Man gets up and gives him the jug.*)

TRAVELLING MAN. Here it is for you.

CHILD. (*Puts it within the walls and sets the branch in it.*) Tell me something else that is in the garden.

TRAVELLING MAN. There are four wells of water in it, that are as clear as glass.

CHILD. Get me down those cups, those flowery cups, we will put them for wells. (*He hands them down.*) Now I will make the gates, give me those plates for gates, not those ugly ones, those nice ones at the top.

(*He takes them down and they put them on the four sides for gates. The Child gets up and looks at it.*)

TRAVELLING MAN. There now, it is finished.

CHILD. Is it as good as the other garden? How can we go to the Golden Mountain to see the other garden?

TRAVELLING MAN. We can ride to it.

CHILD. But we have no horse.

TRAVELLING MAN. This form will be our horse. (*He draws a form out of the corner, and sits down astride on it, putting the child before him.*) Now, off we go! (*Sings, the child repeating the refrain*)—

> Come ride and ride to the garden,
>   Come ride and ride with a will:
> For the flower comes with the fruit there
>   Beyond a hill and a hill.

Refrain

> Come ride and ride to the garden,
>   Come ride like the March wind;
> There's barley there, and water there,
>   And stabling to your mind.

TRAVELLING MAN. How did you like that ride, little horseman?

CHILD. Go on again! I want another ride!

TRAVELLING MAN (*sings*)—

> The Archangels stand in a row there
>   And all the garden bless,
> The Archangel Axel, Victor the angel
>   Work at the cider press.

Refrain

> Come ride and ride to the garden, &c.

CHILD. We will soon be at the Golden Mountain now. Ride again. Sing another song.

TRAVELLING MAN (*sings*)—

> O scent of the broken apples!
>   O shuffling of holy shoes!
> Beyond a hill and a hill there
>   In the land that no one knows.

Refrain

> Come ride and ride to the garden, &c.

CHILD. Now another ride.

TRAVELLING MAN. This will be the last. It will be a good ride.

(*The mother comes in. She stares for a second, then throws down her basket and snatches up the child.*)

MOTHER. Did ever anyone see the like of that! A common beggar, a travelling man off the roads, to be holding the child! To be leaving his ragged arms about him as if he was of his own sort! Get out of that, whoever you are, and quit this house or I'll call to some that will make you quit it.

CHILD. Do not send him out! He is not a bad man; he is a good man; he was playing horses with me. He has grand songs.

MOTHER. Let him get away out of this now, himself and his share of songs. Look at the way he has your bib destroyed that I was after washing in the morning!

CHILD. He was holding me on the horse. We were riding, I might have fallen. He held me.

MOTHER. I give you my word you are done now with riding horses. Let him go on his road. I have no time to be cleaning the place after the like of him.

CHILD. He is tired. Let him stop here till evening.

TRAVELLING MAN. Let me rest here for a while, I have been travelling a long way.

MOTHER. Where did you come from to-day?

TRAVELLING MAN. I came over Slieve Echtge from Slieve na n-Or. I had no house to stop in. I walked the long bog road, the wind was going through me, there was no shelter to be got, the red mud of the road was heavy on my feet. I got no welcome in the villages, and so I came on to this place, to the rising of the river at Ballylee.

MOTHER. It is best for you to go on to the town. It is not far for you to go. We will maybe have company coming in here. (*She pours out flour into a bowl and begins mixing.*)

TRAVELLING MAN. Will you give me a bit of that dough to bring with me? I have gone a long time fasting.

MOTHER. It is not often in the year I make bread like this. There are a few cold potatoes on the dresser, are they not good enough for you? There is many a one would be glad to get them.

TRAVELLING MAN. Whatever you will give me, I will take it.

MOTHER. (*Going to the dresser for the potatoes and looking at the shelves.*) What in the earthly world has happened all the delf? Where are the jugs gone and the plates? They were all in it when I went out a while ago.

CHILD. (*Hanging his head.*) We were making a garden with them. We were making that garden there in the corner.

MOTHER. Is that what you were doing after I bidding you to sit still and to keep yourself quiet? It is to tie you in the chair I will another time! My grand jugs! (*She picks them up and wipes them.*) My plates that I bought the first time I ever went marketing into Gort. The best in the shop they were. (*One slips from her hand and breaks.*) Look at that now, look what you are after doing. (*She gives a slap at the child.*)

TRAVELLING MAN. Do not blame the child. It was I myself took them down from the dresser.

MOTHER. (*Turning on him.*) It was you took them! What business had you doing that? It's the last time a tramp or a tinker or a rogue of the roads will have a chance of laying his hand on anything in this house. It is jailed you should be! What did you want touching the dresser at all? Is it looking you were for what you could bring away?

TRAVELLING MAN. (*Taking the child's hands.*) I would not refuse these hands that were held out for them. If it was for the four winds of the world he had asked, I would have put their bridles into these innocent hands.

MOTHER. (*Taking up the jug and throwing the branch on the floor.*) Get out of this! Get out of this I tell you! There is no shelter here for the like of you! Look at that mud on the floor! You are not fit to come into the house of any decent respectable person!

(*The room begins to darken.*)

TRAVELLING MAN. Indeed, I am more used to the roads than to the shelter of houses. It is often I have spent the night on the bare hills.

MOTHER. No wonder in that! (*She begins to sweep floor.*) Go out of this now to whatever company you are best used to, whatever they are. The worst of people it is likely they are, thieves and drunkards and shameless women.

TRAVELLING MAN. Maybe so. Drunkards and thieves and shameless women, stones that have fallen, that are trodden under foot, bodies that are spoiled with sores, bodies that are worn with fasting, minds that are broken with much sinning, the poor, the mad, the bad. . . .

MOTHER. Get out with you! Go back to your friends, I say!

TRAVELLING MAN. I will go. I will go back to the high road that is walked by the bare feet of the poor, by the innocent bare feet of children. I will go back to the rocks and the wind, to the cries of the trees in the storm! (*He goes out.*)

CHILD. He has forgotten his branch! (*Takes it and follows him.*)

MOTHER. (*Still sweeping.*) My good plates from the dresser, and dirty red mud on the floor, and the sticks all scattered in every place. (*Stoops to pick them up.*) Where is the child gone? (*Goes to door.*) I don't see him—he couldn't have gone to the river—it is getting dark—the bank is slippy. Come back! Come back! Where are you? (*Child runs in.*)

MOTHER. O where were you? I was in dread it was to the river you were gone, or into the river.

CHILD. I went after him. He is gone over the river.

MOTHER. He couldn't do that. He couldn't go through the flood.

CHILD. He did go over it. He was as if walking on the water. There was a light before his feet.

MOTHER. That could not be so. What put that thought in your mind?

CHILD. I called to him to come back for the branch, and he turned where he was in the river, and he bade me to bring it back, and to show it to yourself.

MOTHER. (*Taking the branch.*) There are fruit and flowers on it. It is a branch that is not of any earthly tree. (*Falls on her knees.*) He is gone, he is gone, and I never knew him! He was that stranger that gave me all! He is the King of the World!

A CHRISTMAS NIGHT

John Drinkwater

Christ for a dream was given from the dead
To walk one Christmas night on earth again,
Among the snow, among the Christmas bells.
He heard the hymns that are his praise: *Noël*,
And *Christ is Born*, and *Babe of Bethlehem*.
He saw the travelling crowds happy for home,
The gathering and the welcome, and the set
Feast and the gifts, because he once was born,
Because he once was steward of a word.
And so he thought, "The spirit has been kind;
So well the peoples might have fallen from me,
My way of life being difficult and spare.
It is beautiful that a dream in Galilee

Should prosper so. They crucified me once,
And now my name is spoken through the world,
And bells are rung for me and candles burnt.
They might have crucified my dream who used
My body ill; they might have spat on me
Always as in one hour on Golgotha" . . .
And the snow fell, and the last bell was still,
And the poor Christ again was with the dead.

❧

THE GOLDEN LEGEND

Don Marquis

Jesus had been going about New York for more than a year, and the rumors of his various quiet activities had come to the ears of certain persons who liked them none too well.

It was not the occasional miracles which he had been performing; the offensive and dangerous thing was the way in which he sometimes talked with people. These conversations frequently had the most disturbing results: people would listen to him, and then go and do the most extraordinary things without any respect at all for the established social order.

The miracles were nothing. To know that Jesus, or anyone else, is able to walk on the water, or cure hardened arteries, or restore to his pop-eyed family some poor simpleton who has fallen into a new subway excavation and broken his neck, is very interesting indeed; but it does not necessarily strike the overlords of our complicated society as over-whelmingly important.

A miracle is a miracle: there it is, and that's that; you can take it or leave it, believe in it or not; you can call it supernatural or supremely natural; in any event, it need have very little effect upon general human conduct.

There was a Gadarene swineherd one time who witnessed Jesus transfer a legion of devils from a maniac to a herd of swine. The hogs ran down a steep place to the sea and were destroyed. The swineherd was impressed for the moment, and afraid; but later he became angry. Here were 2,000

hogs gone, which he was supposed to be in charge of, and he was out of a job, and his reputation as a responsible swineherd ruined for life.

It was all very well for him to go about explaining that the hogs were destroyed through circumstances which were quite beyond his control. People either would not listen to him at all, or disbelieved his story when they heard it.

The more he thought about it, the angrier the swineherd became, and he later joined the mob in front of Pilate's palace and bellowed for the crucifixion of the Galilean prophet. He never had the slightest suspicion that there was an great truth involved in the matter; and, indeed, after nineteen hundred years, what great truth does emerge? The thought that it must be very unpleasant to be a devil, or to be possessed of devils, and that it is unlucky to be a hog, is one that humanity in general might very well be trusted to grasp without all the spectacular trimmings. The thing is picturesque, and there is about it the grotesque humor of folklore. And of course the picturesque and the humorous are always welcome; but the only thing that need be taken seriously is the act of kindness towards the man possessed of the devils. And it seems that the man might possibly have been relieved, as Jesus relieved so many others, without all this fuss.

But ethical ideas are different. They are loaded. They are always dangerous. Under the influence of an ethical idea any meek little rabbit of a Long Island commuter is apt to get off the eight fifty-seven train and run down to the Wall Street district and bite the fiercest financial bulldog there. There had been enough of that sort of thing going on in New York—enough of these attempts on the part of rabbits and guinea pigs to bite bulldogs and wolf-hounds—since Jesus had been coming to the city, to make the rulers of the metropolis uncomfortable. Something would have to be done about Jesus, or there might be a good deal more of it, with very far-reaching results.

Something would have to be done . . . but what? It was to consider this question that three or four dozen men prominent in the life of the city met one evening in a building in uptown New York. To be specific, they met in a large new church, which was being built in imitation of several important European churches—although no one was quite able to tell *which* particular European church it imitated.

It was commonly said to combine the best features of several of them.

There were politicians, bankers, commercial magnates, newspaper proprietors and editors, representatives of several Christian denominations, in the solemn assemblage—in short, the Best People of the community, the solid people, the people interested in seeing that the current system of civilized society should suffer no overthrow at the hands of idealistic radicals.

Several Jews were present, both Jewish religious leaders and men of affairs. It was notable from the beginning of the meeting that these were less forward in their demand that some drastic action be taken than were the Gentiles. The Jews were, in fact, worried and anxious; and seemed to have come less from any spontaneous interest in the proceedings than from the motive of proving that they were patriotic Americans, and conservative New Yorkers, concerned to give evidence of their solidarity with the best thought of the community.

One queer thing about the meeting was, that while all of those participating knew well enough that the man with whom they were concerned was really Jesus of Nazareth, they seldom referred to him by that appellation. They called him "Josephson," and "Joshua ben Josef," and several other names, as if they were willing to hide from themselves his identity; as if, indeed, an acknowledgment of his identity might go far, in itself, to weaken their case against him in their own minds.

"This Josephson," said one of his self-constituted judges, "is a charlatan. He claims to be a prophet of some sort; and to my mind this stamps him as blasphemous and sacrilegious."

This was a lie, for Jesus had made no claims whatever. He had just said what he had said, and done what he had done, and allowed people to draw their own conclusions.

"He is an anarchist," said another one, who had a prominent place in municipal affairs. "He was clubbed by the police down in Union Square the other day, and that proves that he is an anarchist. For if he hadn't been an anarchist, he wouldn't have been clubbed, would he?"

There were those present to whom this seemed irrefutable logic. And when the speaker went on to say that anarchy must be stamped out at any cost, he received a round of applause. "These people," he said, "if they don't like our American system of government, should go back where they came from."

A Jewish rabbi observed mildly that there had always been a certain amount of controversy as to just where Jesus came from. Perhaps nobody caught the rabbi's drift; at any rate, there was no comment on this.

A well-known radical, who was frequently described as a Philosophical Anarchist, got up and denied that Jesus was an anarchist; repudiated him, in effect. In the following two minutes he was also repudiated by a Communist, a Socialist, a Bolshevist sympathizer, a Holy Roller, a Theosophist, an International Banker, a Prohibitionist, and a Vegetarian. He was In Bad, in the current slang of the era; it was felt that something was going to happen to him, and they were shying away from him. Just a week or two previously, before public sentiment had begun to crystallize against him, all these people, and a good many more, had been eagerly claiming him as one of themselves, trying to gild their Causes with his fame.

"He isn't orthodox," said a Protestant minister who had been making himself conspicuous for years as a thundering Modernist.

"Orthodox—you make me laugh!" This was from a priest of the Greek Church. "I shouldn't say anything about Josephson's orthodoxy one way or the other, if I were you. As far as I can see, there's no one here at all, except myself, who can lay the slightest claim to being an Orthodox Christian."

A Roman Catholic priest who was present demurred to this, and the revival of a classic controversy was imminent, when another Jewish rabbi arose.

"Gentlemen," said he, "before we go any further with this inquiry, I should like to have one point cleared up. This man Josephson is a Jew. Whether he is what he is said in some quarters to be, Jesus of Nazareth, or a reincarnation of Jesus of Nazareth, he is still a Jew. For Jesus of Nazareth was one of our people——"

"What's the point you want cleared up, Doctor?" interrupted an impatient international banker.

"Just this," said the Rabbi. "Josephson is a Jew, and I want to know whether the animosity I discover against him in this meeting does not have a trace, a tinge, of racial antagonism—whether it is not, in fact, an anti-Semitic feeling."

Loud cries of "No! No!" from every part of the church answered the Rabbi.

A well-meaning liberal got up and said: "Rabbi, it is really an anti-Christian feeling."

Whether he said it satirically or sincerely, it was instantly felt that the utterance had not helped matters any, for there was an indignant chorus of "No! No!" once more; in which joined Roman Catholics, Episcopalians, and every variety of Protestant; the Protestants being the most vociferous, through sheer numerical strength, for they include, like a certain well-known brand of pickle, fifty-seven varieties.

The Christians, Roman Catholic and Protestant, made it evident that they were shocked and distressed by Josephson's imposture—by the claim, made for him, if he had not made it himself, that he was Jesus of Nazareth, back on earth once more.

Just at this moment Jesus himself came into the church. He was guarded—escorted, in fact, by two policemen. Twiller Van Durden followed along behind, at a discreet distance, because Twiller had been present at his arrest. Like another disciple, on a previous occasion, Twiller wanted to see what was going to happen to his friend, and whether it was possible for him to do anything about it himself.

One of the first persons Twiller saw in the church was his brother Walter, sitting proudly among the big business men. And then Twiller realized that something dreadful was probably going to happen. For Walter was stupid, and the men among whom he was seated were stupid; and dreadful things are just as apt to happen when stupid people control a situation as when definitely ill-natured people are in charge.

Jesus had been arrested in a restaurant on East Forty-fifth street, between Third Avenue and Lexington. It is a very pleasant place, with a big back yard, run by an Italian named Tony. Twiller was there having his dinner, and presently Jesus came in and sat down at the same table, and the two renewed a pleasant former acquaintance. The big kitchen of the place is also the dining room, and Tony and his wife and children cook the food on a range in the corner and carry it right to the plates of the patrons, hot and flavorous.

There was an Italian wedding party having dinner at the large central table, and when Jesus came in they had just been thrown into consternation by Tony's announcement that they could not have any red wine with their dinner. The pretty little dark-eyed bride, and more especially her parents, were aghast; they expostulated. A wedding party without wine? Who ever heard the like? It took the shine off the party; it made the wedding itself seem almost illegal.

There was no help for it, Tony explained. He simply did not dare to serve wine tonight. He had poured every ounce in the place down the sink an hour earlier. This was a few months before the repeal of the Eighteenth Amendment made drinking legal once more in America. Tony, it seemed, had been caught between two rival gangs of racketeers. The Blarney gang and the Spaghetti gang were making a fight for the lordship of the district in which his restaurant was located, and if he purchased supplies from one of them, the other would shoot up his place or turn him in to the cops.

Twiller regarded the wedding party and their disappointment with sympathy—happy, innocent people, with a native gayety of disposition, their humble festival was spoiled. While he was wondering if he couldn't find a way out for them, suddenly a way was found—or seemed to find itself, as if by magic.

The water in the glasses before them surprisingly became wine. There were no histrionic effects attendant upon this sudden change. Indeed—and it was the queerest part about the whole affair—nobody seemed to know that there had not been wine there all the time. The disappointment, the whole series of antecedent events, seemed to be wiped completely from their consciousness; a pleasant harmony prevailed, with no recollection of anything else before.

And when the police came, and found wine on the premises, actually being consumed, how was it that they had connected Josephson with its presence? Twiller, for the life of him, could not remember. There seemed to have been a sort of haze enveloping everything between the events at Tony's place, and the entrance of Jesus—or Josephson—into the church, and his arraignment before the solemn, deliberative body which sat there in judgment, eagerly awaiting some pretext for action against him.

"Josephson," said Walter Van Durden, "it seems you are a bootlegger!"

Jesus made no reply. Perhaps he knew perfectly well that Walter had had a couple of highballs himself before coming to the meeting. He said nothing to the effect that human laws are all nonsense when they get in the way of divine laws.

"Josephson," said an international banker, "you are an anarchist. Only the other day you said, down in Union Square, that it is as easy for a camel to pass through a needle's eye as for a Rich Man to enter the kingdom of Heaven."

Jesus said nothing; but Twiller Van Durden suddenly spoke up: "He said that a couple of thousand years ago; not down in Union Square the other day. But maybe you just heard about it the other day." Twiller had been reading the New Testament. He added: "In my estimation, it's just as true as it was two thousand years ago."

"Do you mean," said the international banker, "that the possession of great riches *always* connotes wickedness? Irrespective of how they were acquired or how they are used?"

Jesus said nothing. The assemblage seemed impressed for a moment. And then a tactless radical asked the international banker:

"Would you like to tell us, in detail, how yours were acquired and have been used?"

There was a moment of undignified levity in the church, and the international banker sat down without pressing the point.

"Josephson," said a Bishop, "you are an atheist."

"Josephson," said another man, "you are a blasphemer."

Jesus said nothing at all. And the charges went on . . . and on and on . . . the company gradually working themselves into a heat of rage with the vehemence of their own denunciation. Twiller judged that they were getting more and more angry, really with themselves, because they knew that the charges they were making were not true. They thought that they were angry with Josephson, and only later would they perceive that their hatred and ill-nature had been lacerating themselves.

But angrier and angrier they were getting. There was no doubt of it. Everyone in the church, except Jesus himself, shook and quivered with the agitation.

At the very crest of this wave of anger, a Jewish rabbi got up and said:

"Gentlemen—I think we Jews had better leave this meeting! We don't want to have any part in what is evidently going to happen to this man Josephson."

He looked around the room and gathered up the eyes of his fellow Jews present. Then he continued:

"This man came before one of our meetings a good many years ago, and what happened then did not turn out to be so fortunate for the Jewish people. It wasn't the Jewish people as a whole who got him crucified, but only a meeting of the best citizens. But the blame was put upon the whole Jewish people. And I know perfectly well what you are all getting ready to do now—you are going to do the same thing over again, and you're getting ready to blame it upon us Jews! Yes, it's going to be put onto the whole Jewish people again! Come—let's get away from here!"

And all the Jews present marched out in a compact little body.

There was a heavy silence for some moments, and then the charges and denunciations broke out again, with renewed vigor.

Finally, another hush fell; a strange hush. The editor of an important paper got up, after this silence had lasted for some time . . . got up slowly, as if he were somehow impelled to rise.

"Listen, gentlemen," he said, "what we are going to do is in everybody's mind, although none of us has phrased it yet.

"And none of us has phrased the real reason why we are going to do it, either.

"We might as well get some honesty behind this thing; come down to brass tacks with regard to our motive. All these charges of law violation, blasphemy, and sacrilege are nonsense, and we know they are.

"We want to get rid of this Josephson for one reason, and one reason only; and to my mind it is a sufficient reason in itself, and needs no lies nor apologies to bolster it up.

"We want to eliminate him because he is an idealist, and because he really means, sincerely and effectively, the application of the Christian ideal to our current society. And if we permit him to go on talking to people and convincing them, he will bring it about, too.

"There's this about idealism, and particularly about Christian idealism—some people are able to take it, undiluted, and practice it. But most people are not. They can go a certain way with it, and they can't go any farther; and the attempt to make hundred per cent Christian idealists out of them leads to all manner of distressing circumstances, embroils them with the facts of the universe as they feel and know them, and with the established order of human society. Humanity is not yet ready for a thorough-going Christian ethic. Something like a new species will have to be evolved. We are in an intermediate state, and we can't stand too much spirituality—at least, all the time. Prophets of an *absolute* idealism confuse us, and earn our enmity. We can't live with them, and we can't live in a state of society dominated by them. After all, we are largely flesh, and they are practically all spirit. It is our instinct to conform in action to a division which we find throughout the universe. We simply *aren't* all spirit, and we can't act as if we were; and if we try to act as if we were, it leads to a disintegration of what we *really* are. It tears us to pieces. We feel this absolute idealism, this absolute spirituality, as an enemy. This man said once, years ago, that he brought a sword into the world; and he did, and now he has come back here again to sharpen the sword. We've got to get rid of him, or go ourselves.

"There is the issue, squarely joined.

"Do you want the world to go on very much like it is going on now, as it always has gone on; or do you want it changed in accordance with the Christian ideal?

"For my part, I don't want it changed. I couldn't stand it if it were changed. The Christian ideas and ideals, if they were really put into practice, instead of being merely talked about, in churches and elsewhere, would burst the world asunder. Cover them up with any sort of talk or clever explication you like, attempt to explain them away if you will, the fact is that if they are really put into effect it means a revolution in every department of human life, an overturning of all our cherished institutions. Do we believe in these ideals enough to follow through with

them to the limit, to face all that their sincere practice connotes? I don't, for one!

"Let us be candid about it. If we eliminate this man, we do it because he is a sincere idealist, and not because he is any of the things we have called him tonight—because he is that, and we can't stand it. It's too perturbing. It's too dangerous to us."

He sat down. Jesus got up and spoke for the first time. He went to the end of the nave, where a statue of Christ on the cross faced the main body of the church. Directly opposite it, blazoned on the wall in prodigious gold lettering, were the words THE GREATEST OF THESE IS CHARITY.

He looked at the letters. He looked at the statue.

"Gentlemen," he said, "I am minded to save you a certain amount of trouble. At the same time, I cannot allow you to dodge your share of responsibility."

With these words, the Christ upon the cross was suddenly gone. An instant later, Jesus himself had taken its place; and an instant after that, he seemed to have turned to stone there. He backed up to it, with his arms spread wide, and crucified himself. It all happened so quickly and so strangely that most of those in the church thought that nothing whatever had happened.

But a good many persons who were familiar with the stone figure, which had been carved by a famous sculptor, began to see a look on the face of the statue which they had never noticed before—a faint smile, too good-natured to be really satirical, although partaking somewhat of the nature of satire, too. This element of satire, perhaps, having something to do with the fact that the eyes of the statue are fixed all day long upon the golden legend at the opposite end of the church: THE GREATEST OF THESE IS CHARITY.

PART FOUR

His Work on Earth

———

From the deep dark we cry out to a wisdom very far above our blunders, to a strength above our feebleness, and to a kindliness above our spites, our lewdness, and our busy hatreds.

JAMES BRANCH CABELL

1. BEGINNINGS OF . .
HIS MINISTRY

THE WILDERNESS

Caroline Hazard

Up from the Jordan straight His way He took
To that lone wilderness, where rocks are hurled,
And strewn, and piled—as if the ancient world
In strong convulsions seethed and writhed and shook,
Which heaved the valleys up, and sunk each brook,
And flung the molten rock like ribbons curled
In midst of gray around the mountains whirled:—
A grim land, of a fierce, forbidding look.
The wild beasts haunt its barren stony heights,
And wilder visions came to tempt Him there;
For forty days and forty weary nights,
Alone He faced His mortal self and sin,
Chaos without, and chaos reigned within,
Subdued and conquered by the might of prayer.

TEMPTED

Katharine Lee Bates

Into the wilderness
Straightway our Lord was driven of the Spirit;
Swept by that stress
Of rapture, sun and stars were but one shining
Till forty days had passed
And, Son of Man though Son of God, He hungered.

Why should He fast
With power to make stones bread; why fear, with
      succor
Of angels at His call;
Why fail, when all the world was to His Father
A golden ball,
One out of many, but a little present
For a beloved Son?

Ecstasy, faint with its own bliss, encountered
The scorpion
Of self, love's enemy. For love is holy
In loving; love is safe
Only in saving; love, despised, rejected,
The world's white waif,
Needs nothing that this earth can give of glory,
For love dwelleth in God.

So Christ's immortal rose above His mortal
And on it trod.

From PARADISE REGAINED

John Milton

"Thou hast said much here of 'Paradise Lost,' but what
hast thou to say of 'Paradise Found'?" Thus, according
to his own statement, Milton's Quaker friend, Thomas
Ellwood, after reading the great epic. How much if any

influence the query had upon Milton is questionable. But the great Puritan poet did go on to write a "short epic" upon the exclusive subject of Christ's redemption, finding his literary model in the Book of Job. Instead of the Crucifixion, he made the Temptation in the Wilderness his subject; here Christ successfully resisted the temptation of Satan to which Adam had succumbed. Two significant passages from *Paradise Regained* are given here.

BOOK III, *lines 250-443*

With that (such power was given him then), he took
The Son of God up to a mountain high.
It was a mountain at whose verdant feet
A spacious plain outstretched in circuit wide
Lay pleasant; from his side two rivers flowed,
The one winding, the other straight, and left between
Fair champaign, with less rivers intervened,
Then meeting joined their tribute to the sea.
Fertile of corn the glebe, of oil, and wine;
With herds the pasture thronged, with flocks the hills;
Huge cities and high-towered, that well might seem
The seats of mightiest monarchs; and so large
The prospect was that here and there was room
For barren desert, fountainless and dry.
To this high mountain-top the Tempter brought
Our Saviour, and new train of words began:—
"Well have we speeded, and o'er hill and dale,
Forest, and field, and flood, temples and towers,
Cut shorter many a league. Here thou behold'st
Assyria, and her empire's ancient bounds,
Araxes and the Caspian lake; thence on
As far as Indus east, Euphrates west,
And oft beyond; to south the Persian bay,
And, inaccessible, the Arabian drouth:
Here, Nineveh, of length within her wall
Several days' journey, built by Ninus old,
Of that first golden monarchy the seat,
And seat of Salmanassar, whose success
Israel in long captivity still mourns;
There Babylon, the wonder of all tongues,
As ancient, but rebuilt by him who twice
Judah and all thy father David's house
Led captive, and Jerusalem laid waste,
Till Cyrus set them free; Persepolis,
His city, there thou seest, and Bactra there;

Ecbatana her structure vast there shews,
And Hecatompylos her hundred gates;
There Susa by Choaspes, amber stream,
The drink of none but kings; of later fame,
Built by Emathian or by Parthian hands,
The great Seleucia, Nisibis, and there
Artaxata, Teredon, Ctesiphon,
Turning with easy eye, thou may'st behold.
All these the Parthian (now some ages past
By great Arsaces led, who founded first
That empire) under his dominion holds,
From the luxurious kings of Antioch won.
And just in time thou com'st to have a view
Of his great power; for now the Parthian king
In Ctesiphon hath gathered all his host
Against the Scythian, whose incursions wild
Have wasted Sogdiana; to her aid
He marches now in haste. See, though from far,
His thousands, in what martial equipage
They issue forth, steel bows and shafts their arms,
Of equal dread in flight or in pursuit—
All horsemen, in which fight they most excel;
See how in warlike muster they appear,
In rhombs, and wedges, and half-moons, and wings."
He looked, and saw what numbers numberless
The city gates outpoured, light-armèd troops
In coats of mail and military pride.
In mail their horses clad, yet fleet and strong,
Prauncing their riders bore, the flower and choice
Of many provinces from bound to bound—
From Arachosia, from Candaor east,
And Margiana, to the Hyrcanian cliffs
Of Caucasus, and dark Iberian dales;
From Atropatia, and the neighbouring plains
Of Adiabene, Media, and the south
Of Susiana, to Balsara's haven.
He saw them in their forms of battle ranged,
How quick they wheeled, and flying behind them shot
Sharp sleet of arrowy showers against the face
Of their pursuers, and overcame by flight;
The field all iron cast a gleaming brown.
Nor wanted clouds of foot, nor, on each horn,
Cuirassiers all in steel for standing fight,
Chariots, or elephants indorsed with towers
Of archers; nor of labouring pioneers
A multitude, with spades and axes armed,
To lay hills plain, fell woods, or valleys fill,
Or where plain was raise hill, or overlay

With bridges rivers proud, as with a yoke:
Mules after these, camels and dromedaries,
And waggons fraught with utensils of war.
Such forces met not, nor so wide a camp,
When Agrican, with all his northern powers,
Besieged Albracca, as romances tell,
The city of Gallaphrone, from thence to win
The fairest of her sex, Angelica,
His daughter, sought by many prowest knights,
Both Paynim and the peers of Charlemagne.
Such and so numerous was their chivalry;
At sight whereof the Fiend yet more presumed,
And to our Saviour thus his words renewed:—

"That thou may'st know I seek not to engage
Thy virtue, and not every way secure
On no slight grounds thy safety, hear and mark
To what end I have brought thee hither, and shew
All this fair sight. Thy kingdom, though foretold
By Prophet or by Angel, unless thou
Endeavour, as thy father David did,
Thou never shalt obtain: prediction still
In all things, and all men, supposes means;
Without means used, what it predicts revokes.
But say thou wert possessed of David's throne
By free consent of all, none opposite,
Samaritan or Jew; how couldst thou hope
Long to enjoy it quiet and secure
Between two such enclosing enemies,
Roman and Parthian? Therefore one of these
Thou must make sure thy own: the Parthian first,
By my advice, as nearer, and of late
Found able by invasion to annoy
Thy country, and captive lead away her kings,
Antigonus and old Hyrcanus, bound,
Maugre the Roman. It shall be my task
To render thee the Parthian at dispose,
Choose which thou wilt, by conquest or by league.
By him thou shalt regain, without him not
That which alone can truly reinstall thee
In David's royal seat, his true successor—
Deliverance of thy brethren, those Ten Tribes
Whose offspring in his territory yet serve
In Habor, and among the Medes dispersed:
Ten sons of Jacob, two of Joseph, lost
Thus long from Israel, serving, as of old
Their fathers in the land of Egypt served,
This offer sets before thee to deliver.
These if from servitude thou shalt restore
To their inheritance, then, nor till then,

Thou on the throne of David in full glory,
From Egypt to Euphrates and beyond,
Shalt reign, and Rome or Cæsar not need fear."
     To whom our Saviour answered thus, unmoved:—
"Much ostentation vain of fleshly arm
And fragile arms, much instrument of war,
Long in preparing, soon to nothing brought,
Before mine eyes thou hast set, and in my ear
Vented much policy, and projects deep
Of enemies, of aids, battles, and leagues,
Plausible to the world, to me worth naught.
Means I must use, thou say'st; prediction else
Will unpredict, and fail me of the throne!
My time, I told thee (and that time for thee
Were better farthest off), is not yet come.
When that comes, think not thou to find me slack
On my part aught endeavouring, or to need
Thy politic maxims, or that cumbersome
Luggage of war there shewn me—argument
Of human weakness rather than of strength.
My brethren, as thou call'st them, those Ten Tribes,
I must deliver, if I mean to reign
David's true heir, and his full sceptre sway
To just extent over all Israel's sons!
But whence to *thee* this zeal? Where was it then
For Israel, or for David, or his throne,
When thou stood'st up his tempter to the pride
Of numbering Israel—which cost the lives
Of threescore and ten thousand Israelites
By three days' pestilence? Such was thy zeal
To Israel then, the same that now to me.
As for those captive tribes, themselves were they
Who wrought their own captivity, fell off
From God to worship calves, the deities
Of Egypt, Baal next and Ashtaroth,
And all the idolatries of heathen round,
Besides their other worse than heathenish crimes;
Nor in the land of their captivity
Humbled themselves, or penitent besought
The God of their forefathers, but so died
Impenitent, and left a race behind
Like to themselves, distinguishable scarce
From Gentiles, but by circumcision vain,
And God with idols in their worship joined.
Should I of these the liberty regard,
Who, freed, as to their ancient patrimony,
Unhumbled, unrepentant, unreformed,
Headlong would follow, and to their gods perhaps
Of Bethel and of Dan? No; let them serve

Their enemies who serve idols with God.
Yet He at length, time to himself best known,
Remembering Abraham, by some wondrous call
May bring them back, repentant and sincere,
And at their passing cleave the Assyrian flood,
While to their native land with joy they haste,
As the Red Sea and Jordan once he cleft,
When to the Promised Land their fathers passed.
To his due time and providence I leave them."

So spake Israel's true King, and to the Fiend
Made answer meet, that made void all his wiles.
So fares it when with truth falsehood contends.

BOOK IV, *lines 499-639*

To whom the Fiend, now swoln with rage, re-
    plied:—
"Then hear, O Son of David, virgin-born!
For Son of God to me is yet in doubt.
Of the Messiah I have heard foretold
By all the Prophets; of thy birth, at length
Announced by Gabriel, with the first I knew,
And of the angelic song in Bethlehem field,
On thy birth-night, that sung thee Saviour born.
From that time seldom have I ceased to eye
Thy infancy, thy childhood, and thy youth,
Thy manhood last, though yet in private bred;
Till, at the ford of Jordan, whither all
Flocked to the Baptist, I among the rest
(Though not to be baptized), by voice from Heaven
Heard thee pronounced the Son of God beloved.
Thenceforth I thought thee worth my nearer view
And narrower scrutiny, that I might learn
In what degree or meaning thou art called
The Son of God, which bears no single sense.
The Son of God I also am, or was;
And, if I was, I am; relation stands:
All men are Sons of God; yet thee I thought
In some respect far higher so declared.
Therefore I watched thy footsteps from that hour,
And followed thee still on to this waste wild,
Where, by all best conjectures, I collect
Thou art to be my fatal enemy.
Good reason, then, if I beforehand seek
To understand my adversary, who
And what he is; his wisdom, power, intent;
By parle or composition, truce or league,
To win him, or win from him what I can.

And opportunity I here have had
To try thee, sift thee, and confess have found thee
Proof against all temptations, as a rock
Of adamant and as a centre, firm
To the utmost of mere man both wise and good,
Not more; for honours, riches, kingdoms, glory,
Have been before contemned, and may again.
Therefore, to know what more thou art than man,
Worth naming Son of God by voice from Heaven,
Another method I must now begin."

So saying, he caught him up, and, without wing
Of hippogrif, bore through the air sublime,
Over the wilderness and o'er the plain,
Till underneath them fair Jerusalem,
The Holy City, lifted high her towers,
And higher yet the glorious Temple reared
Her pile, far off appearing like a mount
Of alabaster, topt with golden spires:
There, on the highest pinnacle, he set
The Son of God, and added thus in scorn:—
"There stand, if thou wilt stand; to stand upright
Will ask thee skill. I to thy Father's house
Have brought thee, and highest placed: highest is
    best.
Now shew thy progeny; if not to stand,
Cast thyself down. Safely, if Son of God;
For it is written, 'He will give command
Concerning thee to his Angels; in their hands
They shall uplift thee, lest at any time
Thou chance to dash thy foot against a stone.'"

To whom thus Jesus: "Also it is written,
'Tempt not the Lord thy God.'" He said, and stood;
But Satan, smitten with amazement, fell.
As when Earth's son, Antæus (to compare
Small things with greatest), in Irassa strove
With Jove's Alcides, and, oft foiled, still rose,
Receiving from his mother Earth new strength,
Fresh from his fall, and fiercer grapple joined,
Throttled at length in the air expired and fell,
So, after many a foil, the Tempter proud,
Renewing fresh assaults, amidst his pride
Fell whence he stood to see his victor fall;
And, as that Theban monster that proposed
Her riddle, and him who solved it not devoured,
That once found out and solved, for grief and spite
Cast herself headlong from the Ismenian steep,
So, strook with dread and anguish, fell the Fiend,
And to his crew, that sat consulting, brought
Joyless triumphals of his hoped success,

Ruin, and desperation, and dismay,
Who durst so proudly tempt the Son of God.
So Satan fell; and straight a fiery globe
Of Angels on full sail of wing flew nigh,
Who on their plumy vans received Him soft
From his uneasy station, and upbore,
As on a floating couch, through the blithe air;
Then, in a flowery valley, set him down
On a green bank, and set before him spread
A table of celestial food, divine
Ambrosial fruits fetched from the Tree of Life,
And from the Fount of Life ambrosial drink,
That soon refreshed him wearied, and repaired
What hunger, if aught hunger, had impaired,
Or thirst; and, as he fed, Angelic quires
Sung heavenly anthems of his victory
Over temptation and the Tempter proud:—
    "True Image of the Father, whether throned
In the bosom of bliss, and light of light
Conceiving, or, remote from Heaven, enshrined
In fleshly tabernacle and human form,
Wandering the wilderness—whatever place,
Habit, or state, or motion, still expressing
The Son of God, with Godlike force endued
Against the attempter of thy Father's throne
And thief of Paradise! Him long of old
Thou didst debel, and down from Heaven cast
With all his army; now thou hast avenged
Supplanted Adam, and, by vanquishing
Temptation, hast regained lost Paradise,
And frustrated the conquest fraudulent.
He never more henceforth will dare set foot
In paradise to tempt; his snares are broke.
For, though that seat of earthly bliss be failed,
A fairer Paradise is founded now
For Adam and his chosen sons, whom thou,
A Saviour, art come down to reinstall;
Where they shall dwell secure, when time shall be,
Of tempter and temptation without fear.
But thou, Infernal Serpent! shalt not long
Rule in the clouds. Like an autumnal star,
Or lightning, thou shalt fall from Heaven, trod down
Under his feet. For proof, ere this thou feel'st
Thy wound (yet not thy last and deadliest wound)
By this repulse received, and hold'st in Hell
No triumph; in all her gates Abaddon rues
Thy bold attempt. Hereafter learn with awe
To dread the Son of God. He, all unarmed,
Shall chase thee, with the terror of his voice,

From thy demoniac holds, possession foul—
Thee and thy legions; yelling they shall fly,
And beg to hide them in a herd of swine,
Lest he command them down into the Deep,
Bound, and to torment sent before their time.
Hail, Son of the Most High, heir of both Worlds,
Queller of Satan! On thy glorious work
Now enter, and begin to save Mankind."
    Thus they the Son of God, our Saviour meek,
Sung victor, and, from heavenly feast refreshed,
Brought on his way with joy. He, unobserved,
Home to his mother's house private returned.

§

THE SACRED FIRE BURNS

Ivan Nazhivin

Ivan Nazhivin's novel, *According to Thomas,* is not an attempt to tell the Gospel-story from Thomas's point of view; cf., for example, William E. Barton's "The Gospel According to Judas Iscariot," p. 334 ff. Thomas was the "rationalist" among the Apostles, and Nazhivin's title is intended merely to indicate that he has tried to write the life of Jesus from a naturalistic standpoint. Whether that point of view be accepted or rejected, Nazhivin's Chapter VII, given below, presents a vivid picture of Jesus as he is conceived to have been early in his ministry. The title has been supplied by the editor from a phrase used by Nazhivin toward the end of the selection.

———

Every time that Jeshua came back to visit Galilee he had a feeling of relief, almost of happiness. Judæa, with its sun-scorched hills where life seemed withered and parched with suffering, lay behind him; and here he was surrounded by the dear hills of his childhood, clothed in magnificent woods, by the villages with their simple, hardworking population, by luxuriant gardens, vineyards and tinkling streams, birds and flowers. But in spite of the extraordinary richness of nature and the diligence of the inhabitants life here was far from being a Paradise. Taxation brought the people to the very limit of endurance: the Romans raised levies, the tetrarch Herod took enormous sums from them, the rulers of the

Temple demanded supplementary taxes, and the landlords skinned the peasantry. But nevertheless it was a great relief to come to Galilee, if only because here there were no haughty Sadducees, no Pharisees perpetually flying into raging passions, and no Romans with their heavy armor. A fair number of heathen of various types lived in Galilee: it was called the Galil-ha-Goim, the district or land of the peoples. And this created an atmosphere of relative tolerance and freedom. Here everyone was listened to willingly, and a narrow-minded Sopher, even if he knew the whole Torah by heart, enjoyed no special authority here. But the Galileans too liked noise and disputation; they were pious and extremely superstitious, and were treated with contempt by the intellectuals of Jerusalem whenever they made their appearance in the city for the great festivals. They were accustomed to hearing themselves called "Galilean blockheads" in Jerusalem, and their way of speaking caused endless ridicule.

Nazareth was then a small quiet town of some three or four thousand inhabitants. Its wretched clay-built houses, its tiny gardens, its silent barns, and its wine-presses hewn in the rocks, and the great storks' nests at the tops of hoary trees, made it seem more like a village than a town. Its inhabitants did not disdain either a beaker of wine or a good joke or a merry song, and for that reason the scribes looked down with contempt on this frivolous people: they would say with a sneer—"Can anything good come out of Nazareth?"

The women with their washtubs were gathered as usual round the well under the venerable plane-trees. Their faces were covered, as custom demanded, but light and warmth, and sometimes, too, mute invitation, lay in their beautiful dark eyes. Jeshua called a friendly greeting as he passed, and went on to his house, which stood peacefully blinking at the setting sun. The house lay hidden among fig trees and pear trees and clambering vines whose grapes were already filled with precious juice. Turtle doves were cooing in the leafy thickets.

In the cool shade within the modest little house only the barest necessaries were to be found: at the threshold, of course, the Mesuse was hung, with its extracts from the law; and inside the house little mats and carpets for sleeping lay spread on the floor. In one corner of the walls there were a few vessels and the indispensable corn-measure, which served both

as a measure for small articles of every kind and, in the evening, as a stand for the lamp. In another corner the hand-worked millstones, whose grinding noise so often broke the stillness of the little town, were lying at rest; and behind the millstones a hoe, spade, and broom were leaning against the wall. Two old leathern bottles, the larger filled with wine and the smaller with oil, completed the furniture. There was no chimney. In cold weather they would all gather round to warm themselves at the hearth in the middle of the room. Here and there on the walls crystals of saltpeter had formed—they called it "leprosy"—and the moist air was filled with an unpleasant odor; for when it was very cold the housewife, Miriam, would bring the young sheep and goats into the house for the night, as indeed all the peasants did; and an unpleasant odor remained as a reminder of their visit.

From the far side of the house, in the shadow of the trees, came the sound of planing. There one of the brothers was at work; but there was no sign of anyone else being at home. They all had to work away from the house. Jeshua, to refresh himself, began the necessary ablutions.

Joseph, the head of the family, had died a long time before. The mother, Miriam, was getting on in years; and all the sisters were already married. The brothers, like Jeshua, wandered about the country in a constant search for work. They were all building-workers of one kind or another. The mother had once, a long time before, urged Jeshua to marry and bring someone home to help her in the house; but he refused, and disappeared from home for a long period, during which his wanderings took him to Tyre, Sidon, and Cæsarea Philippi. And though the furthest points of his wanderings were only four or five easy days' journey from Nazareth, the rich country of the heathen seemed to everyone to be very far away and very strange.

"Shelom!"

His brother Jacob, working at the planing-bench, looked up; a reddish, almost withered beard framed his apathetic features.

"Shelom!" he answered morosely, without a smile. He always thought that Jeshua, the eldest of them, abused his position and did too little work.

They had hardly exchanged a dozen words when their mother, Miriam, came out from the barn. She was now thin and faded, and the only relics of her former beauty were her great black eyes, filled with sadness.

A wan smile lit up her face as she saw her son. She asked him about his affairs, what he was proposing to do, and how he was. They all three felt that they had really nothing to say to each other. Jeshua was a fragment that had been broken off; he lived in a world of his own, a world which seemed to the other members of the family to be not only inaccessible but even to some extent hostile. "Why do you look after other peoples' roofs? Wouldn't it be better for you to see whether your own roof needs repair?" This was how Jacob had once spoken, in order to express publicly his hostile attitude to Jeshua's activity.

Neighbors passed by and greeted Jeshua cheerfully over the low stone fence; many even stopped and exchanged a few words with him; but they too tended to regard him as a sheep that had broken away from the Nazareth flock. And when from time to time he spoke in their synagogue, they did not pay much attention to what he said—it would have been better if he had stuck to his own business; and now he wanted to teach them all. But people were talking about him, and so they called him "Rabbi"—sometimes in jest, but sometimes also in earnest.

After the humble meal, eaten in silence in the yard where everyone could see them, Jeshua went up to the roof, anticipating a delicious sleep after such a long journey. A cool and gentle breeze was blowing as it always did in Galilee. The stars shone over his head. In the distant mountains he could hear the howling of jackals. Bats were circling over the flat roofs and the dark gardens, whistling softly, disappearing into the darkness and then returning, passing swiftly hither and thither. Everything was still, peaceful and beautiful. . . .

But sleep would not come. His heart longed for Miriam; and then he would think of his quiet Engedi, which he had now left forever; while at the same time his soul was filled with thoughts which were constantly before his mind, thoughts which, it seemed to him, would yield a rich harvest. He thought of the days of his childhood in this white house, so simple, so dear, and so far away, so far away. . . . How easy and clear everything had seemed to him then.

He had been circumsized on the eighth day after his birth like all new-born boys, and had thereby been brought once and for all into the ranks of the chosen people of Adonai, who thought that they were destined to rule the world—the more scorching the calamities that befell them, the more ardent grew their dreams and hopes of unparalleled glory and power already close at hand.

When as yet he could hardly stammer his first few words, he had been taught his first prayer by the gentle, Godfearing Joseph, whom until quite recently he had regarded as his father. Then he had gone, with the other dirty and ragged children of Nazareth, to the Khazzawn for lessons. The children sat on the clay floor, and the Khazzawn, armed with a staff, kept strict control over them from the heights of his teacher's chair. The children fixed their eyes on the text of the law, and without knowing a single letter all simultaneously repeated the sacred words, swaying in unison. . . . And so they gradually made progress, until Jeshua in his twelfth year was already able to read, "Listen, O Israel" without a mistake. The scribes would say, "The temple can fall into ruin—so long as the children come to school!"—or "The breath of the children who come to school is the pillar on which the whole of society rests." But all of these sayings were merely beautiful flowers of speech; in reality education went no further than learning a few prayers and precepts from the law—nor could it be otherwise, for the teachers themselves hardly knew more than this. The only real schooling Jeshua had had, as was the case with every intelligent and thoughtful person, was from life itself. And it was in this school that he had built up his knowledge in the green quiet of Nazareth, in Jerusalem, which he had first visited on a pilgrimage in his twelfth year, in the synagogue, or by the gates of the city when he heard the heated disputes of his fellow citizens, in the wise speeches of the Sophers, of the scribes whom he tried to understand; and his soul had trembled at the prophetic writings of Isaiah, whose golden visions had enchanted him. Under the guidance of the ageing Joseph he had learned the trade of a carpenter, for Joseph knew that "the man who teaches his child no trade teaches him to rob." But later on his mind turned towards the search for truth, towards the life of which the prophets spoke so impressively, and he had secretly joined the rebels, those who were fighting for their people. With the rebels he had hidden at one time in the wild, marshy region of the Sea of Merom, and at another time in the mountain wildernesses of Galaad, whence they would emerge for their fierce attacks on the oppressors of their people. But in the end he had come to feel that though perhaps a part of the truth lay there, the whole truth itself was somewhere else. . . .

He fell asleep as the cocks crowed for the third time in the stillness of the night. But hardly had the East begun to redden beyond the mountains when Jeshua was up again, filled with a new readiness for life. And he felt an impulse now to take up the yoke of that peaceful hardworking life which he had led there as a child and which the Galileans around him were still living.

After he had prayed, he came down into the house. His mother was driving the donkey and the four goats to meet the shepherd. He removed the dung which had collected under the shelter, chopped firewood from some dry branches, and then discussed with Jacob the work that was in hand. They decided that Jeshua was to finish the stairs that had been ordered for the synagogue, while Jacob would go round to one of the neighbors to fix up a commission to build a barn. Jeshua turned back his sleeves, tied a string round his hair to prevent it from getting in his way while he was working, and then took up the saw, full of eagerness for work.

Those days of simple, quiet labor and nights of reflection, of exaltation, of struggle, passed without a break. He felt his loneliness in these thoughts of his; only his mother's cousins, the sons of Cleopas, seemed to like hearing him talk. But they lived in Magdala; and moreover, what attracted them was perhaps his protest against the prevailing injustice of the world—they may have had some spirit of revenge—rather than any dreams of brotherly love. Twice also—in their chance wanderings—they said he had been visited by disciples of Johanan, who had scattered after the arrest of their teacher. But they said little, and looked at him furtively now and then as if asking him something.

Uncertain rumors about the appearance of Jeshua had reached Johanan in prison, and he was impatiently awaiting further developments. Perhaps the young Galilean who had made such an extraordinary impression upon him might be that avenger and savior whom all awaited. But then, why was he still hesitating? The same question was on the lips of Johanan's disciples when they came to visit Jeshua

in Nazareth; but they were puzzled when they found him leading the life of a simple laborer: it did not quite seem to fit the picture of the hero for whom the people were waiting.

At his home, too, he was spiritually isolated. His firm determination to come forward among the people with the word of salvation was often weakened by anxious doubts. He could not yet see things quite clearly. The voice of the Tempter, as he called it, had not yet been silenced. If the people did not listen to the prophets—the voice suggested—what right have you to believe that they will follow you? He would answer: it will be necessary to explain everything more fully, still more convincingly, so that the word of salvation may be understood by all. Then everyone will comprehend it and obey its call. Even the most fearful sacrifice is not too great, if only this sacred purpose can be fulfilled! He thought of Johanan, languishing in the subterranean dungeons of Machærus. But even this was not so terrible. They could treat Johanan like this, because he was isolated. But when the leaven has leavened the whole lump, the foe will be powerless, and life will blossom forth like the flowers of paradise.

And again another line of thought would cross his mind—a line which from time to time he had found terrifying through its very novelty. Moses, the prophets, the scribes and the zealots of the type of Judas of Gamala, all fought and died for Judah. But were not all men equal? Even those of other faiths? Was not even his own faith different from the faith of the scribes of Jerusalem? And even the scribes: was not their faith now different from what it had been in the past? Were not their constant disputations and conflicts the best proof that, at bottom, they had no single truth, no uniform faith? Nothing could quench his own love for mankind in general, for all men; and if mankind were to be invited to partake of the divine food, all men—so he thought—must be invited.

What a thing it would be to achieve—to clear away all the evil obstacles dividing man from man, and to bring freedom not only to the Jews but to all men wandering in confusion: for every son of man is at the same time a son of God. It was his task to fuse all the different religions into a single unity, into the religion of the pure and loving heart; and above mankind, united in brotherhood, to set God as their only Lord, as their loving Father . . . this was the call he had received from God, whose voice he had heard within him sounding with such commanding force during the quiet, starry nights. And for this new wine he needed new bottles; for new wine is not put into old bottles. . . .

He felt the divine intoxication of this new wine, he felt the sacred fire burning within him, he heard the trumpets of the angels summoning him to battle. But how and where was he to begin? Who would listen to him, to an insignificant Galilean? And once more he would pore over the ancient Isaiah's words:

"The Lord alone shall be exalted in that day. For the day of the Lord of Hosts shall be upon every one that is proud and lofty, and upon every one that is lifted up; and he shall be brought low: and upon all the cedars of Lebanon, that are high and lifted up, and upon all the oaks of Bashan, and upon all the high mountains, and upon all the hills that are lifted up, and upon every high tower, and upon every fenced wall, and upon all the ships of Tarshish. . . . And the Lord alone shall be exalted in that day!"

These could not be mere empty words. . . .

"And the Spirit of the Lord shall rest upon him, the spirit of wisdom and understanding, the spirit of counsel and might, the spirit of knowledge and of the fear of the Lord; and shall make him of quick understanding in the fear of the Lord: and he shall not judge after the fear of his eyes, neither reprove after the hearing of his ears; but with righteousness shall he judge the poor, and reprove with equity for the meek of the earth and he shall smite the earth with the rod of his mouth, and with the breath of his lips shall he slay the wicked. And righteousness shall be the girdle of his loins, and faithfulness the girdle of his reins. The wolf also shall dwell with the lamb, and the leopard shall lie down with the kid; and the calf and the young lion and the fatling together; and a little child shall lead them. And the cow and the bear shall feed; their young ones shall lie down together: and the lion shall eat straw like the ox. And the suckling child shall play on the hole of the asp and the weaned child shall put his hand on the cockatrice's den. They shall not hurt nor destroy in all my holy mountain: for the earth shall be full of the knowledge of the Lord, as the waters cover the sea. . . ."

And now more frequently than in the past there would come into his mind those passages in the ancient writings which speak of the suffering and death of the one who was to make known the truth. There was particularly the well-known passage in Isaiah, where the prophet speaks—in mysterious words of sadness, which at the same time are filled with the promise of eternal happiness—of the "man of sorrows," the unknown, the despised and persecuted, the man, however, who through his fearlessly borne sufferings would win the right to set up the kingdom of truth and justice. This man is the servant of the eternal, the man who without fear will face destruction in order that he may bring happiness to men. . . .

"Are you coming to Simeon's wedding tomorrow?" his mother asked in a sleepy voice from the corner where she was sitting. "They say that you must come."

"I will come," Jeshua answered, tearing himself away from Isaiah. "It is a long time since I have seen them."

Simeon was the brother of the merry Isaac. Jeshua smiled as he thought of Isaac: and then again in the stillness of the night his parched lips sought the invisible chalice filled with the new wine. . . .

2. THE MYSTIC

ON THE ROAD

John Oxenham

For road-mates and companions he chose twelve,
—All, like himself, of homeliest degree,
All toilers with their hands for daily bread,
Who, at his word, left all and followed him.

He told them of The Kingdom and its laws,
And fired their souls with zeal for it and him.

He taught a new sweet simple rule of Right
'Twixt man and God, and so 'twixt man and man,—
That men should first love God and serve Him well,
Then love and serve their neighbours as themselves.

They loved him for his gentle manliness,
His forthright speech, his wondrous winning ways,
His wisdom, and his perfect fearlessness,
And for that something more they found in him
As in no other.

For through the mortal the immortal shone—
A radiant light which burned so bright within
That nought could hide it. Every word and look,
And a sweet graciousness in all he did,
Proclaimed him something measurelessly more
Than earth had ever seen in man before,
And with him virtue went and holy power.

But yet they did not fully apprehend,
And still looked to him as the promised one
Who should take off the burden of their yoke
And free the land from Rome.

Through all the land he journeyed, telling forth
The gracious message of God's love for man,—
That God's great heart was very sore for man,
Was hungering and thirsting after man,
As one whose dearly loved have gone astray,
As one whose children have deserted him.

The people heard him gladly, flocking round
To catch his words, still more to see his deeds,
The men all hopeful, and the women touched
By this new message and the messenger;
And everywhere the children drew to him
And found in him a sweet new comradeship.

Strange was his teaching, stranger still his deeds;—
He healed the sick and gave the blind their sight,
With his own hands cleansed lepers of their sores,
And raised the dead,—all in the name of God,
And for the love God's great heart held for them.

And they looked on in wonder and amaze,
And heard him for the wonders that he wrought.
And as they worked, and as they ate, they said,—
"This of a truth is he—the promised one,
Who shall take off the burden of our yoke
And set us free from Rome. For never man
In all the world spoke thus, nor did such deeds."

He spoke in glowing words of homely things
That were to them their very daily life,
And turned them to such fruitage that not one
Could e'er forget; they met them everywhere,
In field and fold, at home, and on the road,
Telling again the message that he brought.
And those he cured were there before their eyes,
Living memorials of God's love for man.

But, in the priestly places, fear of him
And his subversive teaching grew apace.
Envy and hatred, malice, all the powers
Of evil-vested interests were set
To stay the message and the messenger.

They poisoned with their venom every mind
They could wean from him with their subtle guile;—
He was a traitor to their ancient faiths—
A false Messiah, leading men astray.
He cast out devils with the Devil's help,—
He was a rebel against God and Rome,
And Rome would crush him with her heavy foot
And all who followed him.

They strove to trap him with insidious talk,
But all their craft he turned so that they fell
Into the pits they digged for him;—and all
The common folk hung on his words the more,
And would acclaim him King.

But he went calmly on his chosen way,
Healing the broken, balming all life's wounds
With rich outpouring of the grace of God,
Telling to all men everywhere the word
Of God's undying love for all mankind;—
Living and loving graciously, that men
Should see in him the mirror of God's love.

He rent the veils that hung 'twixt God and man,
And strove to open hearts long closed to Him,
That they might see Life whole, and share with Him
The joyousness of God's companionship.

ALONE INTO THE MOUNTAIN

Katharine Lee Bates

All day from that deep well of life within
Himself has He drawn healing for the press
Of folk, restoring strength, forgiving sin,
Quieting frenzy, comforting distress.
Shadows of evening fall, yet wildly still
They throng Him, touch Him, clutch His garment's
    hem,

Fall down and clasp His feet, cry on Him, till
The Master, spent, slips from the midst of them
And climbs the mountain for a cup of peace,
Taking a sheer and rugged track untrod
Save by a poor lost sheep with thorn-torn fleece
That follows on and hears Him talk with God.

JESUS PRAYING

LUKE 6:12

Hartley Coleridge

He sought the mountain and the loneliest height,
For He would meet his Father all alone,
And there, with many a tear and many a groan,
He strove in prayer throughout the long long night.
Why need He pray, who held by filial right,
O'er all the world alike of thought and sense,
The fulness of his Sire's omnipotence?
Why crave in prayer what was his own by might?
Vain is the question,—Christ was man in need,
And being man his duty was to pray.
The son of God confess'd the human need,
And doubtless ask'd a blessing every day.
Nor ceases yet for sinful man to plead,
Nor will, till heaven and earth shall pass away.

A BALLAD OF
TREES AND THE MASTER

Sidney Lanier

Into the woods my Master went,
Clean forspent, forspent.
Into the woods my Master came,
Forspent with love and shame.
But the olives they were not blind to Him,
The little gray leaves were kind to Him,
The thorn-tree had a mind to Him,
When into the woods He came.

Out of the woods my Master went,
And He was well content.
Out of the woods my Master came,
Content with love and shame.
When Death and Shame would woo Him last,
From under the trees they drew Him last:
'Twas on a tree they slew Him—last
When out of the woods He came.

THE MYSTICISM OF JESUS

Sheldon Cheney

When the Messiah came, saying that "The Kingdom of God is at hand," the Jews as well as the Gentiles rejected Him. It was inevitable that influential Romans should act against Him; for He affronted officialdom by refusing to acknowledge the Emperors as divine, and He affronted the populace by condemning immorality and violence. On the other hand, the Jews failed to recognize in Him their promised deliverer. He wielded no political power, and He threw back on each man the responsibility of his own deliverance, revealing only a "way."

That his religion was a mystical one doubtless confused many who heard Him speak. He preached the experiencibility of God, the bringing of the joys of Eternal Life into the mortal sphere, the fellowship of a sacred communion. He spoke not of the freedom the Jewish prophets had so long envisioned and foretold, "the day of recompense," the riches shared, the oppressors put down. He offered no leadership in military glory. His message was that of a contemplative who walked in the presence of God.

It was the members of the mystery brotherhoods who were prepared to understand Him. Whether these were Greek or Egyptian or Roman, they were trained to the philosophy that begins with belief in the Kingdom of God within you, in a Divine indwelling light.

The great gift Jesus brought from Judaism, as contrasted with Hellenism, was the conception of a Father-God. There was also the strain of mysticism from the Psalmists and the prophets. The Jews had

among them, moreover, certain groups of mystics who combined beliefs out of Judaism with others from foreign sources—Egyptian, Far Eastern, and, of course, Greek. The Essenes were the most famous sect within Palestine. They believed in One God, practical communism, and a moderate asceticism, were engaged in charitable works, and aimed at an ideal of holy living, contemplation, and Divine illumination. They believed in baptism, prophecy, the soul's immortality and resurrection, and the existence of angels. The Essene higher wisdom was carefully veiled from all but initiates.

The Essenes and the Neo-Pythagoreans, and the surviving members of the Orphic and Dionysian brotherhoods, would understand the message of Jesus because His life was essentially that of the self-abandoning mystic. The way of His own illumination, His self-identification with God, his retirement into solitary contemplation and prayer when mortal problems impended, and His casting away of self that a communion might be founded—this is all in the pattern of the seer exalting the Spirit and bringing down the Life of Transcendence, of the Eternal, to the world of material and time. His own years he made an example of the "new" life, the "saving" life, of the man possessed of God.

His ethical teachings, even, are those of the mystic "mad with the Spirit." Poverty, compassion, pacifism, forgiveness, humility of the self toward the Divine—are not these attributes implicit in the lives of seers from Lao-Tse and the Buddha Gautama to Saint Francis and Brother Lawrence?

It is hardly necessary to remind ourselves of the visions Jesus experienced—how "He saw the Spirit of God descending," and "Lo, a voice from Heaven saying, 'This is my beloved Son' "—or of the characteristic periods of withdrawal for intercourse with God, from which He went back strengthened to His ministry among men, or, after the Agony, to make the supreme mortal sacrifice. His very way of meeting the world was that of the extreme visionary. "Take no thought . . ." and "Resist not evil." There is too the injunction to lay up treasures in Heaven, "for where your treasure is, there will your heart be also." There is, indeed, in all literature no statement of the way of life of the mystic who has committed all to God that surpasses in rich suggestiveness the Sermon on the Mount.

But it is the deified life as a whole that so shines

forth as a model to all Christian mystics after, so that the phrase "the imitation of Christ" carries an import of perfect holiness, continuous communion with God, and the illumining of mortal environment with a joyous Heavenly light. This is the avatar in perfect example. This is the Son of God conscious in every mortal act of His Divine being and Divine responsibility.

Jesus did not escape, nor has any committed mystic altogether escaped, the dark night that precedes the day of Light. He experienced temptation and frustration and the disappointment that came with the inability of common men to grasp His message. He felt that He had failed of His mission—in life. But unfalteringly He persevered, selflessly, knowing that in death He would triumph. And, indeed, then the message was made clear to those who had faltered, denied. Upon the cross, as if to emphasize the humanness of his being, he cried out (if Mark is to be believed) in desperation of suffering. But the end is in glory: being disappears into Being, and the faithful ones see Him triumphant in the vision of the Ascension. Jesus wrote down, so far as is known, not one word. Nevertheless books of the sayings of Jesus were in common currency in the century during which Christianity took shape. From these and from personal recollection the several framers of the Gospels drew, and the wisdom of the Christ was given to the wider world.

"This is the Life Eternal, that they might know Thee . . ." is but one of the sayings that are essentially mystical. The words fix the basic metaphor by which He was to present His message of attainment. To know God, to live a life of consciousness of His presence, to feel oneself a citizen of His joyous Kingdom, is to partake of Life Eternal: such is the essential Christian revelation.

The figure He used most frequently in His preaching was that of the Kingdom. Before taking thought of things, "Seek ye first the Kingdom of God." And "I must preach the Kingdom of God to other cities also: for therefor am I sent." The Sermon on the Mount opens with an enumeration of those who shall be blessed, who shall "see God" and know "the Kingdom of Heaven." The parables oftenest begin with the words, "The Kingdom is like unto . . ." whether it be "like unto treasures hid in a field," or "like unto leaven," or "like unto a grain of mustard seed."

When the Disciples ask why He speaks to the multitude in parables, Jesus answers: "Because it is given unto you to know the mysteries of the Kingdom of Heaven, but to them it is not given." He thus touches upon a mystery of the secret life: that, though it is appointed for all, initiates only are ready for it. Its wisdom must be somewhat veiled. Yet it must be preached, even though the one preaching die for it.

Patiently, when He meets lack of comprehension, the Master explains that "The Kingdom of Heaven is within you." He is explicit: not here, not there, "but within you." The millions who pray daily, "Thy Kingdom come," are petitioning—if the words of Jesus signify—for entry into His Eternal Life, for inward union with God in the mystic's sense. It is within, not without, that a portal opens upon God's presence. The one who believes experiences a new birth, enters, "rests" in Him.

But at the time of the ministry of Jesus the road to that consummation has been obscured. The Christ's own preaching fails to reveal the way for numbers of men. Even the example of Divine living is not enough; they will not believe fully, passionately, until His mortal life is done, until the dénouement of a death-sacrifice makes clear the significance of his story.

Then the ones who are ready recognize that He has lived the life of the invisible in the visible. He has known the one Reality, has been conscious of the one Kingdom. He has brought down Divinity, as Son of Man and Son of God. He has interwoven the mortal with the Transcendent order. In the supreme act of surrender, the bodily crucifixion, the end of the sacrificial life is made clear: the final issue is ascension, joy.

Among the sayings of Jesus are a few that suggest practical steps by which other men may approach the road into the Kingdom. Among the parables and the metaphoric figures and the oblique references—hardly less indirect and cryptic than the body of literature concerning the Greek Mysteries—there are phrases and directions patently calling the believing ones to participation. "If any man will come after Me, let him deny himself, and take up his cross, and follow Me. . . . For what is a man profited if he shall gain the whole world, and lose his own soul?" And: "Except ye be converted, and become as little children, ye shall not enter into the Kingdom of Heaven."

Upon the nature of His own Sonship he is specific. Then: "Where two or three are gathered together in my name, there am I in the midst of them." At the Last Supper He specified the symbols, the sharing of bread and wine, that would witness his "covenant," that would mark the communion of those who had entered, through belief in Him, into the Kingdom.

Even in these sayings, nevertheless, the meanings are veiled. The "way," as indicated in "self-denial" and "conversion" and "communion," the mystic meaning of entry into the Kingdom, of His presence in the community of holy ones, of the nature of the bread and wine as His actual Being—all this was destined to remain a mystery in most men's minds until there came interpreters and builders of a church.

Fortunately the disciples of the Christ included in their number both vivid historians and men of mystic vision. It is the author of the Gospel of John especially who adds perfect visionary understanding and imaginative poetry to his account of the life and ministry of Jesus. Paul too, hostile and callous, and legalistic until he is accorded, unaccountably, an ecstatic revelation and is converted, takes up the work of interpreting, preaching, organizing. It is he who recognizes the significance alight under the mystery-words and, more than any other, sets Christianity in the mould of a Christ-fellowship. It is he who speaks of the attainment of the Kingdom as "putting on Christ." It is he who places peace and serenity of the spiritual life, through mystic attainment to the Presence, first among Christian aims.

3. THE HEALER

RELIGION AND DOCTRINE

John Hay

He stood before the Sanhedrim;
The scowling rabbis gazed at him;
He recked not of their praise or blame;
There was no fear, there was no shame
For one upon whose dazzled eyes
The whole world poured its vast surprise.
The open heaven was far too near,
His first day's light too sweet and clear,
To let him waste his new-gained ken
On the hate-clouded face of men.

But still they questioned, Who art thou?
What hast thou been? What art thou now?
Thou art not he who yesterday

Sat here and begged beside the way,
For he was blind.

　　　　And I am he;
For I was blind, but now I see.

He told the story o'er and o'er;
It was his full heart's only lore;
A prophet on the Sabbath day
Had touched his sightless eyes with clay,
And made him see, who had been blind.
Their words passed by him on the wind
Which raves and howls, but cannot shock
The hundred-fathom-rooted rock.

Their threats and fury all went wide;
They could not touch his Hebrew pride;
Their sneers at Jesus and his band,

Nameless and homeless in the land,
Their boasts of Moses and his Lord,
All could not change him by one word.

I know not what this man may be,
Sinner or saint; but as for me,
One thing I know, that I am he
Who once was blind, and now I see.

They were all doctors of renown,
The great men of a famous town,
With deep brows, wrinkled, broad and wise,
Beneath their wide phylacteries;
The wisdom of the East was theirs,
And honor crowned their silver hairs;
The man they jeered and laughed to scorn
Was unlearned, poor, and humbly born;

But he knew better far than they
What came to him that Sabbath day;
And what the Christ had done for him,
He knew, and not the Sanhedrim.

THE HEALING OF
THE DAUGHTER OF JAIRUS

Nathaniel Parker Willis

Freshly the cool breath of the coming eve
Stole through the lattice, and the dying girl
Felt it upon her forehead. She had lain
Since the hot noontide in a breathless trance—
Her thin pale fingers clasp'd within the hand
Of the heart-broken Ruler, and her breast,
Like the dead marble, white and motionless.
The shadow of a leaf lay on her lips,
And, as it stirr'd with the awakening wind,
The dark lids lifted from her languid eyes,
And her slight fingers moved, and heavily
She turn'd upon her pillow. He was there—
The same loved, tireless watcher, and she look'd
Into his face until her sight grew dim
With the fast-falling tears; and, with a sigh

Of tremulous weakness murmuring his name,
She gently drew his hand upon her lips,
And kiss'd it as she wept. The old man sunk
Upon his knees, and in the drapery
Of the rich curtains buried up his face;
And when the twilight fell, the silken folds
Stirr'd with his prayer, but the slight hand he held
Had ceased its pressure; and he could not hear,
In the dead utter silence, that a breath
Came through her nostrils; and her temples gave
To his nice touch no pulse; and at her mouth
He held the lightest curl that on her neck
Lay with a mocking beauty, and his gaze
Ached with its deathly stillness.

                    It was night—
And softly, o'er the Sea of Galilee,
Danced the breeze-ridden ripples to the shore,
Tipp'd with the silver sparkles of the moon.
The breaking waves play'd low upon the beach
Their constant music, but the air beside
Was still as starlight, and the Saviour's voice,
In its rich cadences unearthly sweet,
Seem'd like some just-born harmony in the air,
Waked by the power of wisdom. On a rock,
With the broad moonlight falling on his brow,
He stood, and taught the people. At his feet
Lay his small scrip, and pilgrim's scallop-shell,
And staff—for they had waited by the sea
Till he came o'er from Gadarene, and pray'd
For his wont teachings as he came to land,
His hair was parted meekly on his brow,
And the long curls from off his shoulders fell,
As he leaned forward earnestly, and still
The same calm cadence, passionless and deep—
And in his looks the same mild majesty—
And in his mien the sadness mixed with power—
Fill'd them with love and wonder. Suddenly,
As on his words entrancedly they hung,
The crowd divided, and among them stood
JAIRUS THE RULER. With his flowing robe
Gather'd in haste about his loins, he came
And fixed his eyes on Jesus. Closer drew
The twelve disciples to their Master's side;
And silently the people shrank away,
And left the haughty Ruler in the midst
Alone. A moment longer on the face
Of the meek Nazarene he kept his gaze,
And, as the twelve look'd on him, by the light

Of the clear moon they saw a glistening tear
Steal to his silver beard; and, drawing nigh
Unto the Saviour's feet, he took the hem
Of his coarse mantle, and with trembling hands
Press'd it upon his lips, and murmur'd low,
"Master! my daughter!"—

                   The same silvery light
That shone upon the lone rock by the sea,
Slept on the Ruler's lofty capitals,
As at the door he stood, and welcomed in
Jesus and his disciples. All was still.
The echoing vestibule gave back the slide
Of their loose sandals, and the arrowy beam
Of moonlight, slanting to the marble floor,
Lay like a spell of silence in the rooms,
As Jairus led them on. With hushing steps
He trod the winding stair; but ere he touch'd
The latchet, from within a whisper came,
"Trouble the Master not—for she is dead!"
And his faint hand fell nerveless at his side,
And his steps falter'd, and his broken voice
Choked in its utterance: but a gentle hand
Was laid upon his arm, and in his ear
The Saviour's voice sank thrillingly and low,
"She is not dead; but sleepeth."

                   They pass'd in.
The spice-lamps in the alabaster urns
Burn'd dimly, and the white and fragrant smoke
Curl'd indolently on the chamber walls.
The silken curtains slumber'd in their folds—
Not even a tassel stirring in the air—
And as the Saviour stood beside the bed,
And pray'd inaudibly, the Ruler heard
The quickening division of his breath
As he grew earnest inwardly. There came
A gradual brightness o'er his calm, sad face;
And, drawing nearer to the bed, he moved
The silken curtains silently apart,
And look'd upon the maiden.

                   Like a form
Of matchless sculpture in her sleep she lay—
The linen vesture folded on her breast,
And over it her white transparent hands,
The blood still rosy in their tapering nails.
A line of pearl ran through her parted lips,
And in her nostrils, spiritually thin,

The breathing curve was mockingly like life;
And round beneath the faintly tinted skin
Ran the light branches of the azure veins;
And on her cheek the jet lash overlay,
Matching the arches pencill'd on her brow.
Her hair had been unbound, and falling loose
Upon her pillow, hid her small round ears
In curls of glossy blackness, and about
Her polish'd neck, scarce touching it, they hung
Like airy shadows floating as they slept.
'Twas heavenly beautiful. The Saviour raised
Her hand from off her bosom, and spread out
The snowy fingers in his palm, and said,
"Maiden! Arise!"—and suddenly a flush
Shot o'er her forehead, and along her lips
And through her cheek the rallied colour ran;
And the still outline of her graceful form
Stirr'd in the linen vesture; and she clasp'd
The Saviour's hand, and, fixing her dark eyes
Full on his beaming countenance—AROSE!

THE LEPER

Nathaniel Parker Willis

"Room for the leper! Room!" and as he came
The cry passed on. "Room for the leper! Room!"
And aside they stood—
Matron, and child, and pitiless manhood—all
Who met him on his way—and let him pass.
And onward through the open gate he came,
A leper, with ashes on his brow,
Sackcloth about his loins, and on his lip
A covering—stepping painfully and slow,
And with difficult utterance, like one
Whose heart is with an iron nerve put down,
Crying, "Unclean! unclean!"
    For Helon was a leper!

Day was breaking,
When at the altar of the temple stood
The holy priest of God. The incense lamp
Burned with a struggling light, and a low chant

Swelled through the hollow arches of the roof,
Like an articulate wail; and there, alone,
Wasted to ghastly thinness, Helon knelt.
The echoes of the melancholy strain
Died in the distant aisles, and he rose up,
Struggling with weakness; and bowed his head
Unto the sprinkled ashes, and put off
His costly raiment for the leper's garb,
And with the sackcloth round him, and his lip
Hid in the loathsome covering, stood still,
    Waiting to hear his doom:—

"Depart! depart, O child
Of Israel from the temple of thy God!
For he has smote thee with his chastening rod,
And to the desert wild,
From all thou lovest, away thy feet must flee,
That from thy plague his people may be free.

"Depart! and come not near
The busy mart, the crowded city more;
Nor set thy foot a human threshold o'er;
    And stay thou not to hear
Voices that call thee in the way, and fly
From all who in the wilderness pass by.

"Wet not thy burning lip
In streams that to a human dwelling glide;
Nor rest thee where the covert fountains hide;
    Nor kneel thee down to dip
The water where the pilgrim bends to drink,
By desert well, or river's grassy brink.

"And pass thou not between
The weary traveller and the cooling breeze;
And lie not down to sleep beneath the trees
    Where human tracks are seen.
Nor milk the goat that browseth on the plain,
Nor pluck the standing corn, or yellow grain.

"And now, depart! and when
Thy heart is heavy, and thine eyes are dim,
Lift up thy prayer beseechingly to Him
    Who, from the tribes of men,
Selected thee to feel His chastening rod:—
Depart, O leper, and forget not God!"

And he went forth,—alone! Not one, of all
The many whom he loved, nor she whose name

Was woven in the fibres of his heart,
Breaking within him now, to come and speak
Comfort unto him. Yea, he went his way,
Sick and heart-broken and alone,—to die!
For God had cursed the leper!

               It was noon,
And Helon knelt beside a stagnant pool
In the lone wilderness, and bathed his brow,
Hot with the burning leprosy, and touched
The loathsome water to his fevered lips,
Praying he might be so blessed,—to die!
Footsteps approached, and, with no strength to flee,
He drew the covering closer on his lip,
Crying, "Unclean! unclean!" and, in the folds
Of the coarse sackcloth, shrouding up his face,
He fell upon the earth till they should pass
Nearer the stranger came, and bending o'er
The leper's prostrate form, pronounced his name,
"Helon! Arise!" The voice was like the master-tone
Of a rich instrument,—most strangely sweet;
And the dull pulses of disease awoke,
And for a moment beat beneath the hot
And leprous scales with a restoring thrill.
"Helon, Arise!" And he forgot his curse,
And rose, and stood before him. Love and awe
Mingled in the regard of Helon's eye
As he beheld the stranger. He was not
In costly raiment clad, nor on his brow
The symbol of a princely lineage wore;
No followers at his back, nor in his hand
Buckler, sword, or spear; yet in his mien
Command sat throned serene, and, if he smiled,
A kingly condescension graced his lips,
The lion would have crouched to in his lair.
His garb was simple, and his sandals worn;
His statue modelled with a perfect grace;
His countenance the impress of a God,
Touched with the open innocence of a child;
His eye was blue and calm, as is the sky
In the serenest noon; his hair unshorn
Fell to his shoulders; and his curling beard
The fullness of perfected manhood bore.
He looked on Helon earnestly awhile,
As if his heart was moved, and, stooping down,
He took a little water in his hand
And laid it on his brow and said, "Be clean!"
And lo! the scales fell from him, and his blood
Coursed with delicious coolness through his veins,
And his dry palms grew moist, and on his brow

The dewy softness of an infant stole.
His leprosy was cleansed, and he fell down
Prostrate at Jesus' feet and worshipped him.

THE TEN LEPERS

Katharine Tynan

"And one of them . . . turned back . . ."

Not white and shining like an ardent flame,
  Not like thy mother and the saints in bliss,
But white from head to foot I bear my blame,
  White as the leper is.

Unclean! unclean! But thou canst make me clean:
  Yet if thou clean'st me, Lord, see that I be
Like that one grateful leper of the ten
  Who ran back praising thee.

But if I must forget, take back thy word;
  Be I unclean again but not ingrate.
Before I shall forget thee, keep me, Lord,
  A sick man at thy gate.

THE TEN LEPERS
IN THE WILDERNESS

Manuel Komroff

The long journey led him through that wild rocky wilderness, the black and sorrowful valley between the lands of Galilee and Samaria. Here in the shadow of a great jagged rock he rested.

Toward the west he could see the gentle slopes of Mount Carmel and toward the east, far off, he could see the green in the valley of the Jordan. But close about the briers grew finger-long thorns and the rocks presented weird shapes. Even the stones in the path beneath his feet were hard as flint and sharp as cinders. Great red lava rocks towered skyward and resembled giant warriors petrified in their march across this burning valley.

The air was still; not an insect, not a bird and no rivulet broke the silence. The stillness seemed deep as death. And here in this quiet and in the purple shadow of a great rock, he looked out into the desolate and hopeless valley.

Suddenly he heard the sharp snap of dried branches and the crunch of sandals on the hard stone. He looked about but saw nothing.

A voice which seemed to come from above him cried out: "Unclean!" It was a cry filled with terror.

He looked up and there, almost directly over him on top of the great rock, stood an old man in rags. His twisted figure, supported by a staff, was silhouetted against the clear sky.

"Unclean!" he repeated. "Tarry not here. We are outcasts and this valley of rocks belongs to us."

When he had spoken these words he stepped back and was gone from sight; but as the stranger did not move, he soon returned to the edge of the great rock.

"Go!" he cried. "We will share our sorrows with no man, or beast, or devil. Go! Go! Our bread is only stones. For water we have tears. The green leaves of our orchards are thorns." Then he raised his white arms and holding his staff aloft, cried: "And our blood has turned to milk. We are outcasts! Go!"

"Praise the good Lord in Heaven. He watches over all men."

"The good Lord in Heaven," cried the old man, again raising his deathly white arms, "has brought this upon us. We are forbidden to enter any town or village. The priests have driven us out. The floor of our house is a ground of cinders and the roof is the open sky: a sky that burns by day and chills by night. A place of worship has been denied us and our voices will not join in singing praises to the one who has driven us into this wilderness. Not toads or even adders could live among these rocks. The one you would have us praise is not here either."

"Where man is, there is the Lord also."

"Go!" the old man cried. "What we have here we will share with no one. The thorns, the cinders, the burning heat, the rocks, all that you see belongs to us. And our sorrows and wretchedness are also our own. Go, stranger! We will divide with no one."

"I ask nothing. But I am ready to give."

"You have nothing that I can see. Or perhaps your pity will drag out a coin or two. Then leave the coins and go in peace. We are unclean."

"How many are you?"

"Four are men; two are women; two are boys and two are girls. Altogether we are ten."

"Gather them all before me and let me speak to them."

"Stranger!" called the old man in anger. "You want us to expose our shame. Is it not enough? This!" He waved his arm over the arid wilderness. "This—our orchard of wretchedness! This, our reward from the Lord you praise. Go! And may your feet never wander into this hollow again. And if you do not go at once we will gather about you as children about their teacher. And we will embrace you with a clasp of hate. And here you will remain as one of us. One more who is unclean! So go at once while you are free."

"I am not afraid"

When the old man heard this he let out a coarse laugh. "The devil himself would not dare touch us. Heroes are born for armies, not for the wilderness!" He laughed again. Then his face grew grave and he held up his staff with a threatening gesture. "What you would not do willingly you will do soon enough. We will see."

He disappeared. Soon voices and strange noises were heard.

From places dug out under rocks, secret grottoes of this wilderness, the unclean outcasts emerged. Their faces, arms and legs were startling. Their parchment-white skin seemed drawn taut over weary bones. They came forward slowly. Their curious large eyes gazed hard at the stranger. They were certain that the sheer horror of their faces would drive him off. But he did not move.

The old man with the staff who had spoken before from the top of the great rock was now on the cinder ground, urging his outcasts forward. They were, as he had said, four men, two women, two boys and two girls. All together they were ten. The boys were a shade more than boys, though less than men. But the two girls were very young. These four children had been born in the wilderness and had never seen any other orchard but this one of rocks and thorns.

Closer and closer they came until they stood in a half-circle a few paces before him. Again the old man urged him to go.

But he held out his hand and said: "Suffer little children, and forbid them not, to come unto me: for such is the kingdom of heaven."

The children seemed eager to go toward the stranger, but the old man held out his staff and barred their way.

"Then you are prepared to remain here with us?"

"For all things am I prepared."

"And you fear not?"

"I fear not."

"And you choose the life of an outcast of your own free will?"

"I choose those who suffer. They are my people."

The old man gazed hard at the stranger, then he sank to his knees and bowed his head.

"Forgive me," he said. "I did not understand. And even now I do not understand; but one thing I know. You come to us as a friend and not as an enemy. This wilderness is our home. But were it a valley green and rich we would still welcome you; for no one has yet come out of the world to speak with us. Only one thing. Do not ask us to praise the Lord. Would you have us thank Him for our wretchedness? For this!" He waved his arm to indicate the pitiful condition of his companions and he waved it further to point to the wilderness about them.

Then one of the women spoke up boldly. "He has forsaken us. He has turned a deaf ear to our prayers. Oh, Lord, what have we done to be punished so!"

And the second woman, with skin as white as that pillar of salt that was once Lot's wife, spoke: "I have wept and I have prayed. Now I am hardened. The Lord is an evil Lord. He seeks vengeance. He destroys the good, the innocent. He gives riches to the vulgar. He gives life and health to evil ones. And He brings white leprosy to us who have lived modestly and blamelessly. Such human havoc the devil himself could not accomplish."

Then one of the four men spoke and said: "We do not need to pray. The beasts of the forests do not pray. The fish in the ocean do not pray. Foxes who live in holes do not pray. We are creatures lower than the beasts. So why should we pray?"

"The son of man hath not where to rest his head.

So has it always been and so will it always be." The stranger spoke these words as he sat in the purple shadow of the great rock. Ten outcasts stood before him.

"There are those," said one, "who live in palaces. And some in houses and others in huts. Even the oxen are given a shed for the night. But what have we?"

"I bring you life; that alone and nothing more. Suffer the little children to come unto me."

He held out his arms and the two young children ran toward him. He embraced them and stroked their heads. Suddenly the children burst into tears, but they did not leave his side.

"Are you afraid of me?" he asked in a soft and gentle voice.

"No," they said.

"Then why do you weep?"

They did not reply.

"Tell me why you are weeping," he asked again. Finally they dried their tears.

"I do not know," said one.

But the other looked into his face and said: "A strange feeling, almost frightening, came over me. It was as though a million needle points were rushing through my veins. And every toe and finger had inside it a little heart which was beating hard. And in my head, before my eyes, the heavens seemed to open. And your words were true. He who sits on the throne in heaven loves everyone, everyone. Even we who are poor and sick and have nothing: He loves even us. And I will pray to Him."

The child sank to her knees and clasped her hands in prayer. And as she prayed the blood seemed to return to her hands and face. And those who stood about looked on with wonder and astonishment.

"He loves you all," the stranger said. "And you who are poor and sick and have nothing: you are no longer poor and no longer sick, and the world that belongs to all people now also belongs to you. Go, show yourselves unto the priests and let them see that you have been cleansed."

All who were standing now sank to their knees and held their white arms up toward heaven. And slowly, very slowly, the red of life returned to their limbs and inch by inch crept upward, glowing, warm, throbbing, until it had reached the very tips of all their fingers. Twenty arms aglow with the red of life pointed toward heaven.

The women were the first to break the silence with shrill and exalted song. Then all joined in the singing and their voices resounded through the length and breadth of the wilderness.

When they had finished singing they rose and kissed each other and some danced about, so great was their joy. The children, who only a short time before came forward with weary and sick bodies, now ran with full vigor and chased each other in and out between the great rocks. Piercing happy voices filled the air.

The outcasts lost no time. So hateful was this wilderness to them that they prepared to leave at once. Each tied his few belongings together in a square of cloth and very soon they stood again before the stranger.

One of the women, whose face was now radiant, spoke: "You are the Master who has given us a new life. What would you have us do with this life?"

"Live the life that has been given you."

"And we who have been lost in this dark valley, how would you have us live now?"

"In peace and with love."

"That we will do willingly. But we who have been injured so much, so much, and carried a sorrow so great, are we really fit to return to our people? Can we be human again?"

"You who have suffered will understand those who are now suffering. So many tears have washed your hearts pure. Each man has a wilderness within him. Go, comfort those in need and remember the long dark years of your lives. Thy faith will make thee whole."

One by one they came and bowed before him and kissed the hem of his robe. And one by one they rose and walked away silently between the great rocks of the wilderness.

The ten lepers were now leaving the wilderness. The outcasts were returning home.

But the old man, the one who had stood over him on the great rock and waved his staff in the air, ran back and fell down at his feet.

"Forgive me," he pleaded. "I have done more than the others. It was I who forbade you to tarry. It was I who threatened you. And it was I who gathered the other nine together to frighten you away. Envy and hate were in my heart. Forgive me."

"You are forgiven. Go, join the rest and return to life."

The old man rose and cried: "Now we will live. Oh, how we will live!"

"With joy?" asked the stranger.

"With great joy. The fruits that have been denied us will taste very sweet indeed."

"And you will forget your dark days?"

"Yes. As soon as we can, we will forget."

"And you will forget that one passed here by chance and you were all healed and given back your life?"

"Master, I am ashamed. We will forget. Everything that we were and this great thing that you have done for us we will in time forget. It is not that our hearts are evil. But there is a blindness in the nature of man and gratitude melts with time."

"How long will you remember?"

"Perhaps a year, perhaps longer. Such is the nature of man. Oh, Master, I am ashamed! We are not worthy. Send a curse after us and let us return to our wretchedness."

"I have come to bring you life. Go. Hurry. Join the others and live once more. Forget or remember, it matters little. Only one thing matters. Believe and have faith."

He sat quietly in the shade of the jagged rock and watched the ten figures wind their long track across the valley.

THE SYRO-PHOENICIAN WOMAN

Anonymous

"It is not meet to take the children's bread, and cast it unto the dogs."
"Yet the dogs under the table eat of the children's crumbs."

Had Christ rebuffed me as he did that mother,
    I had been mortified so bitterly,
My smarting pride, all further speech to smother,
    Had filled my heart with such black ecstasy
    The miracle had ended differently—
    The fiend had left my child, but entered me.

Yet if I'm human, was she so much better?
    Or saw she something which the books omit—
Christ's eyes a-twinkle, as he spoke, that set her
    Though whelmed in trouble, catching at her wit?
    Did he not laugh, who owned her "saying" fit?
    And if he then blessed humour—cherish it.

THE WOMAN
WHO CAME BEHIND HIM
IN THE CROWD

George MacDonald

Near him she stole, rank after rank;
    She feared approach too loud;
She touched his garment's hem, and shrank,
    Back in the sheltering crowd.

A shame-faced gladness thrills her frame:
    Her twelve years' fainting prayer
Is heard at last! she is the same
    As other women there!

She hears his voice. He looks about,
    Ah! is it kind or good
To drag her secret sorrow out
    Before that multitude?

The eyes of men she dares not meet—
    On her they straight must fall!
Forward she sped, and at his feet
    Fell down, and told him all.

To the one refuge she hath flown,
    The Godhead's burning flame!
Of all earth's women she alone
    Hears there the tenderest name!

"Daughter," he said, "be of good cheer;
    Thy faith hath made thee whole:"
With plenteous love, not healing mere,
    He comforteth her soul.

THE DEMONIAC AND
THE SWINE

Anonymous

In general it is not wise to attempt a naturalistic explanation of the "miracles" recorded in the New Testament. The Gospel narratives are written in terms of a First Century supernaturalism which is as alien to our ways of thinking as is Nineteenth Century "rationalism." Not all the miracles are of a piece, however; there are some of which a naturalistic explanation may be acceptable; few will doubt that the Evangelists might easily have been prone to describe in terms of out-and-out supernaturalism a good many happenings which we ourselves might prefer to interpret differently.

In the case of the so-called "cursing" of the fig tree (Matthew 21:18-20 and Mark 11:12-14, 20-21) and in the case of the healing of the demoniac in the country of the Gadarenes (Matthew 8:28-34; Mark 5:1-20; Luke 8:26-36), the objections of the contemporary reader are less rationalistic than moral. The first story attributes both petulance and self-vaunting to Jesus; the second makes him tender of the demons but ruthless toward both the swine and their owners! It seems clear that in the first instance we have a nature parable which the Evangelists have seen fit to narrate in terms of a degraded nature-miracle, and that what really happened after the healing of the demoniac was something like what the anonymous author of *By An Unknown Disciple* has narrated here. The title of this selection has been supplied by the Editor.

Mark John was only a boy then, and what he wrote down he learnt from Peter. Peter was there, but he was hauling up the boats, and didn't know what had happened until he heard the shouts and saw the swine break away and rush down the hillside into the sea. He never saw the madman until all the swine were dead. How, then, did he know enough to tell Mark John? Well, of course, he heard the others talk. And then that was Peter's way. He was always sure that he knew everything until he did some hot-tempered, silly action, and then he was sure that he knew nothing. He would believe everything or nothing according to his temper towards the teller. He did not care for the labour of weighing facts to decide between false and true. You could never make Peter believe that even when people describe a thing as they think they saw it they may still speak falsehood. If a man told Peter that he had met a demon or a magician in the mountains Peter would be quite sure that it was a magician or a demon, unless the man who said he saw it was a Scribe or a Pharisee, and then Peter would say he was a liar.

Always Peter hated the explanations given by others. He never wanted to ask how things had happened. He felt so strongly that he was sure he knew and that other more subtle explanations smelt of the Scribes. Later he grew into somewhat of a tyrant, but always he was lovable.

Luke was not there. I do not know who told him. Yes, he was an educated man; but he was a physician, and he seldom saw beyond the things of the body. Witness the way he changed the Blessings. Peter never made such mistakes about the Message; to the end he loved the poor, but Luke wanted to keep them orderly.

Peter and Luke and Mark John—they are all dead now, and I can speak my mind. When they were here I often tried, but they did not want to listen. They liked their own way of seeing the miracle best, and, so, for the sake of peace and good-fellowship, I ceased to speak. If it were the truth, then one day it would prevail. So I kept silence. But you are waiting to know about the swine and the madman.

The dawn was breaking when we reached the land after that stormy passage across the lake, and I followed Jesus up the slope of the shore to the headlands. Peter and the other fishermen were busy hauling up the boats; some of the people who, like me, had been passengers, lay down to sleep, some followed us far behind in a little group. The light spread over the hills was purple and pink, and the stillness was broken only by the cheep of a sleepy bird.

I do not know if Jesus prayed as he walked, but I felt the stillness and the loneliness brought God near, and I followed in silence. When we reached the brow of the headland it was full daylight, and there, in the distance, was the herd of swine, slowly rooting its way towards us. The swineherds had turned aside to eat their morning meal, and, as they ate, pigs of all sizes and colours, of all ages and shapes, moved on alone, occupied only with filling their bellies. Here a small pig grunted in anger as he was pushed aside by a gaunt sow, whose barren dried-up teats touched the earth. There a great boar, with tusks pushed up under his lip, thrust himself out from the crowd with sidelong blows of his heavy head to seize the portion of some smaller pigs, who fled, squealing.

Jesus stood still to watch, and, as he watched, he smiled. When he spoke, it was to answer the question that had remained unspoken in my mind.

"No," he said, "why should we call them unclean? They are God's creatures, as we all are."

He turned as a man came forward out of the group that stood behind and said,

"Rabbi, it is not safe to be here. There are madmen amongst the tombs."

The man was urgent. Jesus looked him straight in the eyes, as if to measure him, and the man returned the look as straightly and went on speaking.

"They are possessed by demons. They tear their flesh—they can be heard screaming day and night. It is not safe to be here."

"How do you know they are possessed by demons?" asked Jesus.

"What else could it be?" said the man. "There are none that can master them. They are too fierce to be tamed."

"Has any man tried to tame them?" asked Jesus.

"Yes, Rabbi. They have been bound with chains and fetters. There was one that I saw. He plucked the fetters from him as a child might break a chain of field flowers. Then he ran, foaming, into the wilderness, and no man dare pass by that way now."

Jesus was silent. His eyes were bent on the ground, and, after a space, the man spoke again, and it was as if he made excuse.

"Rabbi, the demons make the man cut his flesh with stones; they tear his clothes to pieces. Men fear to touch him now. He goes naked."

Jesus lifted his eyes to the man's face.

"Have men tried only this way to tame him?" he asked.

"What other way is there, Rabbi?" asked the man.

"There is God's way," said Jesus. "Come. Let us try it," and he went towards the tombs. The man stepped back.

"Rabbi," he faltered. He turned to his companions, and fear seemed to seize upon them. Jesus stopped and looked back. His gaze went from man to man, and then his eyes fell upon me. It was as if a power passed from him to me, and immediately something inside me answered.

"Lead, and I follow," I said, and he went forward again. The others debated a while, and then, with hesitation and doubting, they, too, followed. The swineherds, who had drawn near to hear, joined themselves to the men, and left their pigs rooting and grunting.

It was not many cubit lengths to the tombs, but the others were far behind when we reached that desolation.

"Do men live here?" asked Jesus, as he looked at the abomination around us. I did not answer. I was watching for the madman. I think I caught sight of him at the moment that he first saw us, for, as I touched Jesus to point to his naked figure, he began to run towards us shrieking and bounding in the air. He had two sharp stones in his hands, and as he leapt he cut his flesh with them, and the blood ran down his naked limbs. The men behind us scattered and fled down the hillside; but Jesus stood still and waited.

I was about to step forward, thinking that the maniac would leap upon Jesus, when the miracle happened. For the man as if against his will stopped short. Then he opened his palms, and casting the sharp stones from him, he bowed himself to the ground before Jesus, and in a most piteous voice and with tears he cried:

"What do you want with me, O Son of the most high God? Do not say that you also have come here to torment me!"

"What is your name?" asked Jesus, and at the sound of his voice the man lifted up his head and answered bitterly,

"My name is Legion, for there are many possessing me."

"Why do you say you are possessed of demons?" said Jesus.

"I did not say it," answered the man. "It was they who said it when they loaded me with chains and tormented me in my agony. They will torture me again if they catch me," he cried, leaping to his feet as the men behind, seeing him quieted, came nearer.

Jesus turned and told the men to stand back. Then he put out his hand and touched the man.

"Be at peace!" he said. "There is none that will torment you now. You need no longer tear your clothes, or shriek, or cut your body with stones to frighten your torturers away."

The man fell on his face, and again bowed his head at the feet of Jesus.

"I was in fear," he said. "They were many, and I was one, and when the agony came upon me and they bound me with chains, I broke them like straws and fled. I was in fear."

"Fear is a foul spirit," said Jesus, "cast it out from you." And the man answered humbly:

"I will." And Jesus put his own cloak upon him and led him apart amongst the tombs to where he could wash the blood from his limbs.

It was then that the swineherds, who with the others devoured by curiosity had drawn near again, remembered their swine, and turning saw them on the edge of the cliff.

"See!" cried one to the other, "the swine are in danger. We shall lose some of them."

They ran warily, one to each end of the cliff (knowing the nature of swine and how they refuse to be driven save where they wish to go), meaning to get between the swine and the sea; but the other men being ignorant and unskilful, yet wishing to help, ran swiftly down the hillside in the face of the swine, who, seeing them come in haste, turned quickly and rushed in a mass towards the sea.

"Stand back!" shouted the swineherds. "You will drive them over the cliff." But it was too late. The swine had rushed one upon another, and the slope was steep, and in a moment they were swept over the edge of the cliff into the sea. The swineherds tore their hair when they saw the herd rush into the sea. They ran to the cliff edge and looked over to see where the swine were drowning in the deep water below.

"It is your fault," they cried to the man. "You rushed them down the hillside. We had but left them for a moment and, behold, they are all lost! What shall we tell our master? We cannot save them now. It is your fault." And they menaced the men. But the men answered back:

"How could we tell they would run like that? It was not our fault. We came to help you, and you say it was our fault." And the man who had spoken to Jesus about the madman cried out suddenly:

"It is the devils. They went into the swine. Did you not see how they left the madman? They talked with the Rabbi, and he gave permission for them to enter into the swine."

"But they were not his swine," cried the herds. "What right had he to drown our swine?"

"They were unclean beasts, and only fit for devils," cried the man. "It is not lawful to keep such beasts. Come, and ask for yourselves." And he brought the herds to where Jesus sat with the poor madman, now soothed and quiet, at his feet. And they told Jesus, and asked him if it were not true that the devils had entered into the swine out of the man; and he questioned them, and when they told how the pigs had rushed down the hillside when they had tried to drive them, he was sad, and said:

"They were afraid. It was the same devil that possessed this man." But the men did not understand.

"It must be so," said one swineherd to the other. "We will go and tell our master. How could we watch against demons? He will surely see that it was not our fault."

By this time a crowd had gathered from the boats and from the countryside, and they stood and watched Jesus and the madman as if they could not believe their eyes.

"Will any man give clothes to the naked?" Jesus asked them, and they ran to find clothes and brought food, which they put before the man. But all the time they were afraid, for the rumour had gone abroad that Jesus had sent the devils into the swine, and they feared the next thing. When the swineherds returned with their master, and he saw the madman sitting clothed, he, too, was afraid. And he talked with the crowd, and some of them came forward, and he asked if they might speak, and when Jesus gave them leave, they begged him to go away out of their country, for they had fear of him. And Jesus, looking at them, saw that it was true, for they trembled as they spoke, and he had compassion on them, and said that he would go, and he went down to the boats.

Peter was there, ready to put out, for he had heard the rumour, and knew the people were afraid. And the poor madman came too, and pressed upon Jesus that he might come with him, but Jesus refused him, and told him he must go home.

"You will be better at home," he said; "go to your own people and tell them of all God has done for you, and how he took pity on you," and he told the crowd that they were to care for him.

"They will do him no injury," Peter muttered, as

I helped him to push off. "They will be too much afraid that the devils will come back, and, perhaps, enter into their cattle this time. The Master was right to smite iniquity. It was well done to destroy those unclean beasts. It was sin to keep them."

But he said no word to Jesus, and he would not heed when I tried to tell what kind of devil it was that Jesus had sent out of the madman, and that had entered into the swine.

JOHN THE SIX

Josephine Johnson

I had come out that evening into the gray light of the locusts, hearing vaguely the old man's voice behind me saying his "Good night, Father Vallé" and the door closing, and had returned this greeting as always, but was still in that remote and exalted mood—as of one in whom flesh and spirit have wrangled, and the spirit, triumphant, sits with a smug and calm rejoicing. Still in me were the extreme peace and tranquillity of the words I had read and the silence of library rooms, high-shadowed and utterly voiceless. . . . *Plainness and clearness without shadow of stain. . . . Clearness divine.* . . . And the evening itself was like a wide hollow washed clean of dust.

I walked down past the convent and heard the pigeons moving and muttering quietly in the stone gutters. The blue seeds of the ivy hung in clusters and it was dark in the narrow garden where the nuns walked. It was always very soothing, very pleasant, to pass here, apart somehow from all noise and life. Under the aisle of elms the sisters drifted quietly, like black leaves along the path. Children stopped sometimes and tried to push their hard little skulls through the iron railings, and named the sisters in a loud whisper,—"Mary Bogardus . . . Mary Agnes . . . Mary Malthus . . . Sister Anna," —and clung like white whispering monkeys to the barred gate.

I had come on the children unexpectedly that night: four of them, shrill and clinging in the October dusk—three little girls and Shean Lynn, small and ugly as a little ape. The girls jumped down

and scattered giggling when they saw the priest, but Shean stared and hesitated. Over his shoulder dangled a bag of books and another on top, full of unsold magazines. He held one out and waved it in front of me, standing with a sort of timid defiance on the walk. "New edishun, awnly five cents," he mumbled. "Get your new edishun off of me, Father! All about—all about—" He stumbled and got red.

"All about the latest love suit and the penthouse widow and the broken heart," I finished for him, and took the stained magazine. I spoke vaguely, still in that remote and unruffled mood of peace, and held out my hand. Shean grinned and took it with hesitation.

We walked a few steps in silence, the child trying to pace solemnly, while his magazines thumped against his knees. He had on shoes, but one was bigger than the other, and he walked with a kind of shuffling hop.

We passed under the shadow of the church, and the windows were lighted for early service. A blue-gold stream came out across the pavement and Shean stared back at it over his shoulder. I asked if he went to church sometimes, and he shook his head, but made no comment.

We walked on a little way and then he cleared his throat like an old man. "I read the Saint John to myself," he said.

I was surprised, and stopped and looked down at him. "Saint John?" I repeated stupidly.

"John the Apostle," Shean said. He was a very homely and thin little boy with adenoids and bony cheeks, but his hands had a hard, determined grip, much older than his face.

I blundered down my mind, hunting in the apostle's story for what might have fascinated him in the brief record of suffering and resurrection. I thought how strange and incredible that Shean too might have found the amazing power of hope and belief, and that exaltation beyond understanding which is born of words. I thought of the manger scene, the preaching in the temple, and the austere dignity of Christ before Pilate. I thought of the glory of the Resurrection, the prophecy of the Second Coming, and I thought of Christ's words, *The meek shall inherit the earth.* I thought too of the fantastic glory of the Revelation, and I wondered if this might be what had brought the queer and excited light to his eyes; or, if not this, then what did he find in the story worth spelling out all the words with such labor and holding his pinched face over the page? Then I leaped to a sudden thought. "Is it where Christ says, *Suffer the little children to come unto me*—is that where you read the Saint John, Shean?"

Shean shook his head. "That ain't the part," he said. "I never read that part. I read all the time in John the Six. I turn where it talks about fish and bread. Where it says a boy come selling those loaves and two fish hooked on a string. And Christ feeds five thousand people off of that bread, and the two fish turns into a pile and spread out miles around." He waved his arms in a circle and gave a shuffling hop. "Were they baked or fried I don' know, but everybody ate till they almost puked, and still there was twelve basketfuls of the scraps left over. Twelve baskets left over and nobody wanted nothing! Boy, those fish must have been a sight! After Christ, I wouldn't have waited for nobody else to begin. I'd have eat as soon as *my* fish was done. I'd have wrop it aroun' with one of them buns and stuffed it in!"

From the way that his mouth moved, and the strange and retreated shining in his eyes, I knew that Shean was eating the fish and bread, and he clutched the invisible crumbs that spilled across his hands. Then he gave another excited shuffle and looked up at me. "That's a swell story, ain't it, Father?" he said.

"A swell story, Shean," I answered him.

He stooped and knotted the string again around his shoe, then jerked up, red and excited with a sudden thought. "Say, Father," he said, "what did they do with all them scraps? All them twelve bucket-loads left over? Say, maybe Christ made a big pudden out of all that bread! Boy, what a pudden *He'd* have made!"

All I could see of his face was two enormous eyes, and I could not answer.

THE SHEKEL
IN THE FISH'S MOUTH

Francis Quarles

What luck had Peter! For he took a fish
That stored his purse, as well as filled his dish.

THE FISHERS

Josephine Preston Peabody

Yea, we have toiled all night. All night
  We kept the boats, we cast the nets.
Nothing avails: the tides withhold,
  The Sea hears not, and God forgets.

Long ere the sunset, we took leave
  Of them at home whom want doth keep;
Now bitterness be all their bread
  And tears their drink, and death their sleep!

The gaunt moon stayed to look on us
  And marvel we abode so still.
Again we cast, again we drew
  The nets that naught but hope did fill.

And while the grasp of near Despair
  Did threaten nearer with the day,
Leagues out, the bounteous silver-sides
  Leaped through the sheltering waves, at play!

So, stricken with the cold that smites
  Death to a dying heart at morn,
We waited, thralls to hunger, such
  As the strong stars may laugh to scorn.

And while we strove, leagues out, afar,
  Returning tides,—with mighty hands
Full of the silver!—passed us by
  To cast it upon alien lands.

Against the surge of hope we stood
  And the waves laughed with victory;
Yet at our heart-strings, with the nets,
  Tugged the false promise of the sea.

So all the night-time we kept watch;
  And when the years of night were done,
Aflame with hunger, stared on us
  The fixed red eye of yonder sun.

Thou Wanderer from land to land,
  Say who Thou art that bids us strive
Once more against the eternal Sea
  That loves to take strong men alive.

Lo, we stood fast, and we endure:
    But trust not Thou the Sea we know,
Mighty of bounty and of hate,
    Slayer and friend, with ebb and flow.

Thou hast not measured strength as we
    Sea-faring men that toil. And yet—
Once more, once more—at Thy strange word,
    Master, we will let down the net!

THE YOUNG MAN OF NAIN *

Edwin McNeill Poteat

The village of Nain, long since lost in the dust of ancient Galilee, is still held in place in the memory of the years by the frail hands of a nameless widow and her son. Under the shadow of the proud summit of Mount Tabor, refreshed by the fertile and fragrant plain of Esdraelon, and beckoned toward the Great Sea by the white finger of Mount Carmel, the villagers of the simple town spent their indifferent days in shop, field and market, and came home at dusk to rest from their weariness in simple homes. Nain could boast no ancient episode such as gave fame to the neighbor town of Shunem. Jeremiah had once said boldly that the might of Jehovah advancing against the King of Egypt would be as Tabor and Carmel; but though Nain nestled nearest the base of the great mountain, she could claim little celebrity from the prophet's daring words. And so her people passed their lives undisturbed by great hopes, and undismayed by little fears, destined to pass out of time unknown save for the recollection of a casual visit hidden in a desultory record.

Except for one man, perhaps, though his name is also forgot. He was a teacher who nourished the ambition to become some day a great scribe. As a youth he had pored over the sacred books, his mind stirred to restlessness by the hopes and the disap-

* The title of this selection has been supplied by the Editor.

pointments of the prophets, and seeing in himself at times the fulfillment of the promises of Jehovah, and even, more recklessly, imagining himself as the agent of the great restitution.

But rewards for his diligence and his dreams came slowly. Teaching the village school was a dispiriting routine. Nothing was asked of him except that the law be laid upon the hearts of the children, and he soon found that when it was applied with too severe pressure, parents threateningly inquired if he was not too zealous for the forms of the ancient tradition, and whether he was trying to make prophets prematurely out of future shopkeepers and vinedressers. He had married in due time, and his bride dutifully shared his enthusiasms, but when their first and only son was born, her hands were filled with new and practical duties, while his head was agitated by new dreams. Thus for ten years life had moved on for them, his visions never dimmed, even by the dull indifference of those with whom he dared to share them, until, partly through a deeply born and long-suppressed anger he cried out one evening in remonstrance to the elders as they sat in the gate when the new moon called them to the solemn council.

He had been asked to make an explanation concerning the discipline in the village school. It was, they complained, too harsh. Moreover, the minds of the older lads were reported to be disturbed by notions that seemed new and dangerous, and were not according to the ancient law. The young teacher dared to ask the grave and threatening men wherein their knowledge of the law was superior to his, and to their angry retort that much of his teaching was nonsense out of his own perverse head, he replied with a passage from Jeremiah which long since he had found to be the solace and hope of his restless mind. "Behold the days will come, saith Jehovah, that I will make a new covenant with the house of Israel, and with the house of Judah: not according to the covenant that I made with their fathers that day I took them by the hand to bring them out of the land of Egypt; which my covenant they broke, although I was a husband unto them, saith Jehovah. But this is the covenant that I will make with the house of Israel after those days, saith Jehovah: I will put my law in their inward parts, and in their heart will I write it; and I shall be their God, and they shall be my people. And they shall teach no more every man his neighbor, saying, Know Jehovah; for they shall all know me, from the least of them to the greatest, saith Jehovah: for I will forgive their iniquity, and their sin will I remember no more." *

Despite the authentic sound of the words and the man's insistence that they were Jeremiah's, one of the elders sniffed contemptuously and observed that these were no times for new covenants. His fellows nodded in approval, and another added accusingly, "You show great fondness for those scriptures that encourage your idleness. What else can be the reason for your saying, 'They shall teach no more every man his neighbor'?"

"But it is the word of Jeremiah," answered the teacher, defensively.

"Aye, and what save a dungeon did he get for his folly?" the other answered hotly. "And mayhap you would prefer a dungeon to a schoolroom. You would find vermin there to listen to your tales. But while you sit in the seat of learning in our town, you will henceforth spare us your wisdom and instruct our sons in the ways of God." There was a grunt of unanimous assent to this speech, and the speaker beamed with surprise and delight at his own sudden clarification of the matter.

"But," the teacher continued testily, "I teach the way of God, did you but . . ."

Such an angry outbreak of rebuke greeted his attempt to justify himself that he was silenced by its clamor, and turning angrily from the council, he made his way home in the twilight, his heart heavy with disappointment and apprehension. His apprehensions were justified. It was not long reaching his ears that the elders were seeking a new scribe and had found in the village rabbi a strong supporter of their plan to make a change. The elders were shocked and not a little pleased to learn that teacher and rabbi had many times differed violently, and had the rabbi been anything but a cowardly little conformist, he long ago would have made an issue. His silence was due to his fear of the superior wisdom and zeal of the teacher; but when he found the elders suspicious of what was going on, he eagerly supplied them with much more incriminating material than the school children had hinted at. To the satisfaction of the elders it was established that their village school was under the control of a man who

---

* Jeremiah 31:31-34.

believed in an inner covenant that was perennially renewed in all questing hearts, a covenant which he claimed was more valid than Moses'. This was of course not only foolish, it was dangerous. What would become of the priesthood, the festivals, yes, and even the law itself if such things were allowed? And what about the temple in Jerusalem, and what of the nation? It was impossible to cure a madman of the vertigo of his own dizzy ideas, but that was no reason for putting him in charge of a school. Within a little less than a year, the young dreamer was accordingly relieved of his position. He thought there was a cruel delight sharpening the eyes of the chief of the elders as he came to deliver the official order that had already reached him by gossiping tongues. There were four of the older boys in the school who expressed their outrage and promised to come to him privately for instruction. His own son, still hardly more than a lad, warmed his heart by his loyalty, and, though it had to be rebuked, his childish rage against the old men deeply gratified his father.

The day the news came to him, he took a jug of water, some dried figs and a morsel of bread and climbed to the top of Mount Tabor alone. He stayed there, resting in the cleft of a great rock when the sun was hot, but he did not descend until long after the darkness had laid the towering mountain away to sleep, shrouded in a dark mist. But many times during the day, his eyes rested affectionately on the little village nestled so near its base, and he was surprised to note that the pity that stirred his heart was for its people, and not for himself.

The fortunes of the little family, always precarious, within a year became critical. The teacher held a few of the boys together for a while, but they afforded him no income, and pretty soon they found the odium that attached to his tutelage rather more than they could bear. For a few months after his dismissal he found groups of people in the village willing to listen to him as he expounded his novel ideas in the streets or on market days among the booths; but they soon wearied of his talk. Nevertheless he did not give up his dream, or abate his energy. A journey among nearby villages brought him momentary respite from the dull minds of his neighbors, and he was able to bring home to his family the meager hire his labors commanded. But he stayed only brief intervals at these places, and found that even the shortest stay was followed up by a report, quickly circulated, that he was mildly mad, and perhaps a dangerous person. "Is it nothing to you, all ye that pass by," he would cry as he stood at an intersection, quoting his favorite prophet, but fewer and fewer were those who stopped to heed his words. It was eight years later that he died. Sympathetic neighbors said he died of grief; those who had all along distrusted him gave glory to God for saving their generation from the pestilence of his ideas. His widow, faithful to him, and encouraging his ill-rewarded efforts when all others stood against him, mourned him long and devotedly, and on the day of his burial, in spite of the poverty of his obsequies and the blackness of the future, dedicated herself to tend the flame of his courage and idealism in their son, so that his dauntless piety would not die with his death.

Two years more lightened the burden of her grief by the realization with each passing day of the likeness of her growing son to his dead father. He looked like him, had that eager passion for learning, and the courage and persuasiveness in argument that the villagers, however they had deprecated it in his father, had never been able to forget. His mother, given to works of mercy among the needy, endeared herself by the simplicity and gentleness of her bearing, and there were many who, recalling the injustice of earlier years, sought in subtle ways to expiate it. There was much, indeed, to mitigate the loneliness of the days, and as she thought of the future, she saw her son, entering into the career his father had dreamed of, some day a great teacher perhaps, or even a great ruler among his people.

"Mother," the young man said to her as they finished their evening meal.

"Yes, my son."

"I wonder if the days are not soon to be fulfilled in which the sorrows of our people will be ended. Listen to these words of Jeremiah." He unrolled a scroll and, laying his hands down flat on its surface, read: "In those days they shall say no more, the fathers have eaten sour grapes and the children's teeth are set on edge. But everyone shall die for his own iniquity: every man that eateth sour grapes, his teeth shall be set on edge." *

---

* Jeremiah 31:29-30.

"But what says that word to us?" the mother asked.

"This: if we are not punished for the sins of our fathers, we will be rewarded for our own righteousness. Rome is not the penalty for the sin of any but ourselves. Had we a leader from among our people to stir us with a sense of our own moral obligations and promise us a destiny which our own deeds can win . . ." He was excited at the prospect, and as he lifted his hands to emphasize his words, the scroll furled itself with a shudder. He looked at it and laughed. "That's the way the mind of a Pharisee acts."

During the spring there were many times when his nimble mind picked up a word of wisdom from the ancient books, and lighted it with new understanding and promise, and ever the heart of his mother was glad, and the future brightened whenever she dared to anticipate it.

And then the portent of death invaded the little house again. One evening the young man complained of a throbbing agony underneath his heart, and all through the ominous night his mother tended him, brewing homely medicines, and cooling his burning forehead with wet napkins. But in the morning, as the top of Tabor picked up the first signal of the day and flashed it on to Carmel by the sea, the boy grew limp and silent, and his breathing as gentle as the utter motionlessness of death. His mother stood up and walked bravely to the door. The stillness of the dawn still pervaded the village. She would not rouse the neighbors; it was too late for help. She remembered the ancient story, endlessly told in Nain, of the widow of Shunem, the village less than a mile distant, and she wondered, for the moment, why in her day no prophets were abroad, prophets who could lay themselves upon a cold body and warm it back to life. When, she wondered, would Elijah come again?

She was surprised that so many shared her grief. She wished for the boy's father that he too might share the sympathy that they had denied him. And when, the next day, they carried her beloved dead through the Horse Gate on the east side of the village, she found herself thronged with mourners. Over and over in her mind the words of Jeremiah repeated themselves: "A voice is heard in Ramah, lamentation and bitter weeping, Rachel weeping for her children; she refuseth to be comforted because they are not." * She said to herself that she must not weep, that loyalty to the boy and his father demanded strong, silent grief. But in spite of the reminiscence and the resolution, she gave way to a convulsion of tears, leaning momentarily against the bier to support herself.

"Weep not." She heard a strange voice, firm, commanding, and infinitely tender. She looked through the mist of tears. A man was standing by the bier. He searched deftly among the grave clothes and put his hand firmly upon the young man's wrist. There was a convulsive shudder, and she heard the voice, firm, commanding and infinitely tender, say, "Young man, I say unto thee, Arise." The boy sat up, livid with the pallor of death, looked at his mother and smiled weakly, and then at the man who had touched him and said: ". . . dead bodies . . . ashes . . . all the fields . . . unto the Horse Gate toward the east . . . shall be holy unto Jehovah . . . nor thrown down forever." † When she reflected on it in later years she invariably remembered that she was neither terrified nor astonished at the restoration of the boy.

AN EPISTLE

CONTAINING THE STRANGE MEDICAL EXPERIENCE
OF KARSHISH, THE ARAB PHYSICIAN

Robert Browning

Karshish, the picker-up of learning's crumbs,
The not-incurious in God's handiwork—
This man's-flesh He hath admirably made,
Blown like a bubble, kneaded like a paste,
To coop up and keep down on earth a space
That puff of vapor from His mouth, man's soul—
To Abib, all-sagacious in our art,
Breeder in me of what poor skill I boast,
Like me inquisitive how pricks and cracks
Befall the flesh through too much stress and strain,
Whereby the wily vapor fain would slip

---

* Jeremiah 31 :15.
† Jeremiah 31 :40.

Back and rejoin its source before the term—
And aptest in contrivance (under God)
To baffle it by deftly stopping such—
The vagrant Scholar to his Sage at home
Sends greeting (health and knowledge, fame with
   peace)
Three samples of true snake-stone—rarer still,
One of the other sort, the melon-shaped
(But fitter, pounded fine, for charms than drugs);
And writeth now the twenty-second time.

My journeyings were brought to Jericho;
Thus I resume. Who studious in our art
Shall count a little labor unrepaid?
I have shed sweat enough, left flesh and bone
On many a flinty furlong of this land.
Also, the country-side is all on fire
With rumors of a marching hitherward;
Some say Vespasian cometh, some, his son.
A black lynx snarled and pricked a tufted ear;
Lust of my blood inflamed his yellow balls;
I cried and threw my staff and he was gone.
Twice have the robbers stripped and beaten me,
And once a town declared me for a spy;
But at the end, I reach Jerusalem,
Since this poor covert where I pass the night,
This Bethany, lies scarce the distance thence
A man with plague-sores at the third degree
Runs till he drops down dead. Thou laughest here!
'Sooth, it elates me, thus reposed and safe,
To void the stuffing of my travel-scrip
And share with thee whatever Jewry yields.
A viscid choler is observable
In tertians, I was nearly bold to say;
And falling-sickness hath a happier cure
Than our school wots of; there's a spider here
Weaves no web, watches on the ledge of tombs,
Sprinkled with mottles on an ash-gray back;
Take five and drop them . . . but who knows his
   mind,
The Syrian runagate I trust this to?
His service payeth me a sublimate
Blown up his nose to help the ailing eye.
Best wait; I reach Jerusalem at morn,
There set in order my experiences,
Gather what most deserves, and give thee all—
Or I might add, Judæa's gum-tragacanth
Scales off in purer flakes, shines clearer-grained,
Cracks 'twixt the pestle and the porphyry—

In fine, exceeds our produce. Scalp-disease
Confounds me, crossing so with leprosy—
Thou hadst admired one sort I gained at Zoar—
But zeal outruns discretion. Here I end.

Yet stay; my Syrian blinketh gratefully,
Protesteth his devotion is my price—
Suppose I write what harms not, though he steal?
I half resolve to tell thee, yet I blush,
What set me off a-writing first of all.
An itch I had, a sting to write, a tang!
For, be it this town's barrenness—or else—
The Man had something in the look of him—
His case has struck me far more than 'tis worth.
So, pardon if—lest presently I lose
In the great press of novelty at hand
The care and pains this somehow stole from me—
I bid thee take the thing while fresh in mind,
Almost in sight—for, wilt thou have the truth?
The very man is gone from me but now,
Whose ailment is the subject of discourse.
Thus then, and let thy better wit help all!
Of trance prolonged unduly some three days;
When, by the exhibition of some drug
Or spell, exorcization, stroke of art
Unknown to me and which 'twere well to know,
The evil thing out-breaking all at once
Left the man whole and sound of body indeed—
But, flinging (so to speak) life's gates too wide,
Making a clear house of it too suddenly,
The first conceit that entered might inscribe
Whatever it was minded on the wall
So plainly at that vantage, as it were,
(First come, first served) that nothing subsequent
Attaineth to erase those fancy-scrawls
The just-returned and new-established soul
Hath gotten now so thoroughly by heart
That henceforth she will read or these or none.
And first—the man's own firm conviction rests
That he was dead (in fact they buried him)
—That he was dead and then restored to life
By a Nazarene physician of his tribe:
—'Sayeth, the same bade "Rise," and he did rise.
"Such cases are diurnal," thou wilt cry.
Not so this figment!—not, that such a fume,
Instead of giving way to time and health,
Should eat itself into the life of life,
As saffron tingeth flesh, blood, bones and all!
For see, how he takes up the after-life.

The man—it is one Lazarus, a Jew,
Sanguine, proportioned, fifty years of age,
The body's habit wholly laudable,
As much, indeed, beyond the common health
As he were made and put aside to show.
Think, could we penetrate by any drug
And bathe the wearied soul and worried flesh,
And bring it clear and fair, by three days' sleep!
Whence has the man the balm that brightens all?
This grown man eyes the world now like a child.
Some elders of his tribe, I should premise,
Led in their friend, obedient as a sheep,
To bear my inquisition. While they spoke,
Now sharply, now with sorrow—told the case—
He listened not except I spoke to him,
But folded his two hands and let them talk,
Watching the flies that buzzed: and yet no fool.
And that's a sample how his years must go.
Look, if a beggar, in fixed middle-life,
Should find a treasure—can he use the same
With straitened habits and with tastes starved small,
And take at once to his impoverished brain
The sudden element that changes things,
That sets the undreamed-of rapture at his hand
And puts the cheap old joy in the scorned dust?
Is he not such an one as moves to mirth—
Warily parsimonious, when no need,
Wasteful as drunkenness at undue times?
All prudent counsel as to what befits
The golden mean, is lost on such an one;
The man's fantastic will is the man's law.
So here—we call the treasure knowledge, say,
Increased beyond the fleshly faculty—
Heaven opened to a soul while yet on earth,
Earth forced on a soul's use while seeing heaven;
The man is witless of the size, the sum,
The value in proportion of all things,
Or whether it be little or be much.
Discourse to him of prodigious armaments
Assembled to besiege his city now,
And of the passing of a mule with gourds—
'Tis one! Then take it on the other side,
Speak of some trifling fact—he will gaze rapt
With stupor at its very littleness
(Far as I see), as if in that indeed
He caught prodigious import, whole results;
And so will turn to us the bystanders
In ever the same stupor (note this point)
That we too see not with his opened eyes.

Wonder and doubt come wrongly into play,
Preposterously, at cross purposes.
Should his child sicken unto death—why, look
For scarce abatement of his cheerfulness,
Or pretermission of the daily craft!
While a word, gesture, glance from that same child
At play or in the school or laid asleep
Will startle him to an agony of fear,
Exasperation, just as like. Demand
The reason why—"'Tis but a word," object—
"A gesture"—he regards thee as our lord
Who lived there in the pyramid alone,
Looked at us (dost thou mind?) when, being young,
We both would unadvisedly recite
Some charm's beginning, from that book of his,
Able to bid the sun throb wide and burst
All into stars, as suns grown old are wont.
Thou and the child have each a veil alike
Thrown o'er your heads, from under which ye both
Stretch your blind hands and trifle with a match
Over a mine of Greek fire, did ye know!
He holds on firmly to some thread of life
(It is the life to lead perforcedly)
Which runs across some vast distracting orb
Of glory on either side that meager thread,
Which, conscious of, he must not enter yet—
The spiritual life around the earthly life.
The law of that is known to him as this,
His heart and brain move there, his feet stay here.
So is the man perplexed with impulses
Sudden to start off crosswise, not straight on,
Proclaiming what is right and wrong across,
And not along, this black thread through the blaze—
"It should be" balked by "here it cannot be."
And oft the man's soul springs into his face
As if he saw again and heard again
His sage that bade him "Rise" and he did rise.
Something, a word, a tick o' the blood within
Admonishes; then back he sinks at once
To ashes, who was very fire before,
In sedulous recurrence to his trade
Whereby he earneth him the daily bread;
And studiously the humbler for that pride,
Professedly the faultier that he knows
God's secret, while he holds the thread of life.
Indeed the especial marking of the man
Is prone submission to the heavenly will—
Seeing it, what it is, and why it is.
'Sayeth, he will wait patient to the last

For that same death which must restore his being
To equilibrium, body loosening soul
Divorced even now by premature full growth;
He will live, nay, it pleaseth him to live
So long as God please, and just how God please.
He even seeketh not to please God more
(Which meaneth, otherwise) than as God please.
Hence, I perceive not he affects to preach
The doctrine of his sect whate'er it be,
Make proselytes as madmen thirst to do;
How can he give his neighbor the real ground,
His own conviction? Ardent as he is—
Call his great truth a lie, why, still the old
"Be it as God please" reassureth him.
I probed the sore as thy disciple should.
"How, beast," said I, "this stolid carelessness
Sufficeth thee, when Rome is on her march
To stamp out like a little spark thy town,
Thy tribe, thy crazy tale, and thee at once?"
He merely looked with his large eyes on me.
The man is apathetic, you deduce?
Contrariwise, he loves both old and young,
Able and weak, affects the very brutes
And birds—how say I? flowers of the field—
As a wise workman recognizes tools
In a master's workshop, loving what they make.
Thus is the man as harmless as a lamb;
Only impatient, let him do his best,
At ignorance and carelessness and sin—
An indignation which is promptly curbed:
As when in certain travel I have feigned
To be an ignoramus in our art
According to some preconceived design,
And happed to hear the land's practitioners,
Steeped in conceit sublimed by ignorance,
Prattle fantastically on disease,
Its cause and cure—and I must hold my peace!

  Thou wilt object—Why have I not ere this
Sought out the sage himself, the Nazarene
Who wrought this cure, inquiring at the source,
Conferring with the frankness that befits?
Alas! it grieveth me, the learned leech
Perished in a tumult many years ago,
Accused—our learning's fate—of wizardry,
Rebellion, to the setting up a rule
And creed prodigious as described to me.
His death, which happened when the earthquake
    fell

(Prefiguring, as soon appeared, the loss
To occult learning in our lord the sage
Who lived there in the pyramid alone),
Was wrought by the mad people—that's their wont!
On vain recourse, as I conjecture it,
To his tried virtue, for miraculous help—
How could he stop the earthquake? That's their way!
The other imputations must be lies;
But take one, though I loathe to give it thee,
In mere respect for any good man's fame.
(And after all, our patient Lazarus
Is stark mad; should we count on what he says?
Perhaps not; though in writing to a leech
'Tis well to keep back nothing of a case.)
This man so cured regards the curer, then,
As—God forgive me! who but God himself,
Creator and sustainer of the world,
That came and dwelt in flesh on it awhile!
—'Sayeth that such an one was born and lived,
Taught, healed the sick, broke bread at his own
    house,
Then died, with Lazarus by, for aught I know,
And yet was . . . what I said nor choose repeat,
And must have so avouched himself, in fact,
In hearing of this very Lazarus,
Who saith—but why all this of what he saith?
Why write of trivial matters, things of price
Calling at every moment for remark?
I noticed on the margin of a pool
Blue-flowering borage, the Aleppo sort,
Aboundeth, very nitrous. It is strange!

Thy pardon for this long and tedious case,
Which, now that I review it, needs must seem
Unduly dwelt on, prolixly set forth!
Nor I myself discern in what is writ
Good cause for the peculiar interest
And awe indeed this man has touched me with.
Perhaps the journey's end, the weariness
Had wrought upon me first. I met him thus:
I crossed a ridge of short sharp broken hills
Like an old lion's cheek teeth. Out there came
A moon made like a face with certain spots
Multiform, manifold, and menacing;
Then a wind rose behind me. So we met
In this old sleepy town at unaware,
The man and I. I send thee what is writ.
Regard it as a chance, a matter risked
To this ambiguous Syrian—he may lose,
Or steal, or give it thee with equal good.
Jerusalem's repose shall make amends
For time this letter wastes, thy time and mine;
Till when, once more thy pardon and farewell!

The very God! think, Abib; dost thou think?
So, the All-Great, were the All-Loving too—
So, through the thunder comes a human voice
Saying, "O heart I made, a heart beats here!
Face, my hands fashioned, see it in myself!
Thou hast no power nor mayst conceive of mine,
But love I gave thee, with myself to love,
And thou must love me who have died for thee!"
The madman saith He said so; it is strange.

4. THE MASTER AND THE CHILDREN

BIBLE STORIES

Lizette Woodworth Reese

The room was low and small and kind;
  And in its cupboard old,
The shells were set out to my mind;
  The cups I loved, with rims of gold.

Then, with that good gift which she had,
  My mother showed at will,
David, the ruddy Syrian lad,
  With his few sheep upon a hill;

A shop down a rude country street,
  The chips strewn on the floor,
And faintly keen across the heat;
  The simple kinsfolk at the door;

Mary amid the homely din,
  As slim as violet;
The little Jesus just within,
  About His father's business set.

My mother rose, and then I knew,
  As she stood smiling there,
Her gown was of that gentle blue
  Which she had made the Virgin wear.

How far the very chairs were grown!
  The gilt rose on each back,
Into a Syrian rose was blown,
  And not our humble gold and black.

That week long, in our acres old,
  Lad David did I see;

From out our cups with rims of gold,
  The little Jesus supped with me.

THE SHEPHERD'S MADRIGAL

Geraldine Farrar

Come, little children, gather round,
  As on my flute I play.
A wondrous tale I would unfold
  Upon this Christmas day.

Once, long ago, the Holy Babe
  Came on this troubled earth.
Since then all children praise His name,
  And chant His glorious birth.

The Heavens sang, the stars were bright,
  The air was clear and mild,
As gentle Mary, proud and sweet,
  Looked on her sleeping child.

Uncrowned, He lay upon her breast,
  Yet none the less a King:
The humble manger was His throne,
  Let glad Hosannas ring!

The angel voices filled the sky,
  And echoed to far lands,
And all the glory of the world
  Was in His tiny hands.

So, children, at this Christmastide,
  Keep vigil, good and true;
The Holy Child in Bethlehem
  His birthday shares with you.

THE CHRIST-CHILD

Laura Spencer Portor

Oh, Brother Christ, come play with me,
And you shall share my Christmas tree!

Oh, Little Brother Christ, you may
Have all these gifts of mine, today,

And what you will, you may take home,
If you will come—if you will come.

And so the Little Christ-Child came,
To him who called upon his name.

The guttering Christmas candles' light
Flickered and flared across the night.

Above, the glorious heavens were starred,
But past them came the Little Lord.

The tinsel star, the gilded ball,
The broken toy,—He loved them all;—

And overhead, the Angel train
Waited the Christ-Child all in vain.

A CHRIST-CROSS RHYME

Robert Stephen Hawker

Christ, His Cross shall be my speed!
Teach me, Father John, to read:
That in Church on Holy Day
I may chant the Psalm and pray.

Let me learn that I may know
What the shining windows show:
Where the lovely Lady stands,
With that bright Child in her hands.

Teach me the letters A B C
Till that I shall able be
Signs to know and words to frame
And to spell sweet Jesus' Name.

Then, dear Master, will I look
Day and night in that fair book
Where the tales of Saints are told
With their pictures all in gold.

Teach me, Father John, to say
Vesper-verse and Matin-lay:
So when I to God shall plead,
Christ, His Cross shall be my speed!

THE BOY WHO SAW JESUS

Edward Wagenknecht

I

Andrew was a little Jewish boy who lived, very many years ago, in Palestine, in a small city called Tiberias, which was on the west shore of the Sea of Galilee. He lived with his father, Reuben, who was a fisherman, and two older brothers, Joseph and Judas. They made their home in a little, flat-roofed, one-room house.

Perhaps if his mother had lived, Andrew might have been a happy little boy, but she had died while he was so small that he could just barely remember her.

Andrew and his father and his brothers were very poor, but that was not what made the little boy unhappy. Everybody was poor in Tiberias. At least, everybody that Andrew knew. Andrew had never known anything but poverty; it did not occur to him to ask for anything else. He was unhappy because he was lonely. The world was such a vast, unfriendly place. Nobody in it seemed to understand him much better than his father or his brothers did. And they did not understand him at all.

Reuben, the father, did not wish to be unkind. He was a man who worked hard himself, from morning until night, and he expected everybody else to work also. As soon as his sons were old enough they were trained to help him when he went out fishing in his little boat. It was hard work to pull up the nets—even when you had not taken very much—and Reuben had need of all the hands he could get.

Reuben did not expect Andrew to work as hard as Joseph and Judas worked, for they were older and stronger than he was. But he did expect him to show some interest and to do his part.

You are not to suppose that Andrew was a bad boy. Joseph and Judas were disobedient sometimes, or got into mischief, but he never did. He always seemed willing to go out with the boat whenever his father told him to do so. But it was easy to see that his heart was not in his work. Even when his hands were working, his mind would be off somewhere wool-gathering, far away. When things quieted down he would go off by himself and sit quietly in a corner of the boat, and as likely as not when Reuben wanted him he might have to call three or four times before the boy gave any sign that he had heard. To a man who had never done anything except catch fish—and who had never wished to do anything except catch fish—to a father who believed that unless his son learned how to catch fish he would probably starve to death after he grew up, all this was very annoying.

Andrew kept much to himself. He loved to wander alone, across the fields or along the seashore. If, when he returned, you asked him where he had been or what he had done, he never seemed to have anything he could tell you.

That which satisfied his father and his brothers was not enough for him: he was looking for something more.

At first Reuben had been very patient with the lad. For one thing, he felt sorry for him, deprived so early of a mother's care. Leah had dearly loved her youngest child, and Reuben loved him too, for her sake if not for his own. There had been something of the dreamer about her also.

"It will pass," said Reuben to himself. "He is still very young. His mother's milk is not yet out of him."

Again he would say: "He is not a bad boy. He is only a little slow. When he gets older he will take hold of things, as Joseph and Judas do."

But it did not seem to be working out that way. Andrew was nine now; only three years more, and he must be ready to take his place in the congregation of Israel. And he seemed only to grow more dreamy, and—as far as Reuben could see—more useless as time went on. The fisherman was shocked one day when he realized for the first time that he almost hated his child. Small-minded, ignorant people always hate what they cannot understand, and Reuben was both ignorant and small-minded, though he was a good man according to his lights. He knew that Andrew had something inside him that he did not have himself, something that he never could have, not if he were to live a hundred years. He resented the boy's superiority to himself, resented it even while he refused to acknowledge it.

Reuben hated himself because he hated his son. And because he hated himself, he only hated his son the more. He did not actually mistreat the boy, but he rarely spoke to him nowadays except when he ordered him to get to work.

Andrew suffered silently under such treatment, for he was the kind of boy who greatly needs to have love about him. He did not love his father and his brothers—as he had loved his mother, or even as he loved the birds and the little lambs—for they had never given him a chance. But he would have loved them if the chance had come, for he was terribly lonely with nobody but the lambs and the birds to talk to.

II

It was just about this time that Andrew began to hear about a wonderful man who was coming to be talked about around the Sea of Galilee. His name was Joshua, or, as the Greeks had it, Jesus, and his father had been a carpenter in the inland city of Nazareth.

Jesus himself had been brought up to the carpenter's trade, and had worked at the bench until he was about thirty years old. But now he had given it up for good. He spent all his time going about the country helping people.

Nobody knew where this Jesus of Nazareth had got his strange power. He was not even a learned man, and everybody knew there had been nothing remarkable about his family.

At Capernaum he had done many wonderful things. He could heal sick people, it seemed, simply by placing his hands upon them, some of them people who had been sick a long time and had spent all their money on doctors without finding a bit of relief. Once they brought him into a room where a little girl had just died. "She is not dead," he said; "she is asleep." And they laughed at him. He said, "You must leave me alone with her for a time." So they did, and when they came back the little girl was sitting up in bed talking to Jesus. Nobody knew what he had done to her.

Even stranger stories than this were told of him. It was said that he had once walked on the water, as calmly, as confidently as men walk on dry land. It was said he had once fed a hungry crowd with five loaves and two little fishes.

The old men talked about these things wonderingly as they sat on their benches at the gates of the city in the evening when the day's work was done. Their wives and daughters talked about them too when they went to draw water from the well and carry it home in their goatskins. And always Andrew would listen quietly, with wide, shining eyes.

He did not care so much about the walking on the water. The healing of the sick he did like to hear about, for Andrew himself seemed to hurt, way deep down inside, whenever he knew that somebody around him was suffering. The walking on the water did not seem so very important. Some of the men said frankly that they did not believe such stories. Andrew did not go so far as that. If so wonderful a man as Jesus of Nazareth had appeared in the world, it seemed to Andrew quite a fitting thing that he should be able to walk upon the water if he wanted to. Andrew did not doubt for a moment that he might have done it. But it did not matter much whether he had done it or not. It was not because Jesus had walked on the water that Andrew loved him.

For he did love him. It had come to that. The little boy was in love with a man he had never seen.

He loved him most of all for the wonderful words he had spoken. He knew them only as they had been repeated to him—a scrap here, a fragment there, often sadly mangled in the telling. But it is impossible to spoil them, those matchless words, for those whose hearts are open to feel their beauty, as Andrew's was.

"Blessed are the pure in heart, for they shall see God."

"Blessed are the peace-makers, for they shall be called the children of God."

"Bless them that curse you; pray for them that despitefully use you."

"Ask, and it shall be given you; seek, and ye shall find; knock, and it shall be opened unto you."

It seemed to Andrew that this wise Teacher must know everything. He must know the answer to all the questions that were troubling Andrew's little mind, and to all the questions that all the other people in the world were asking too.

Then there were his stories. Andrew had never heard any stories that seemed to him quite so beautiful as the stories that Jesus told. There was the story of the young man who had left his father to go into a far country, where he led an evil life. When all his money was gone, and he was sick and hungry, he came back home. And instead of scolding him for what he had done, his father rushed out eagerly to meet him, and welcomed him home, and fed him and clothed him, and invited the neighbors in to make a great feast. "For," he said, "my son was dead and is alive again; he was lost and is found." And there was the story of the good Samaritan who found a Jew, his enemy, beaten by robbers and wounded upon the highway, and took him to an inn, and washed his wounds, and nursed him, and paid his own money to the innkeeper to look after him until he should return. "Take care of this Jew," he said, "and whatsoever thou spendest more, I, when I come back again, will repay thee."

If only Jesus of Nazareth would come to Tiberias! If only Andrew might see him, hear him speak, touch his hand! It seemed to him that he wanted that more than anything else in the world, more than always having enough to eat, more than having his father kind to him, more than anything!

III

At last, one day, the wonderful news came. Jesus was coming to Tiberias! He had left Capernaum and was working his way southward down the shore of the lake.

Andrew was almost beside himself with joy. If only he might see the Teacher, and talk to him, then everything else—he did not know how or why—would be all right.

And then a very terrible thing happened.

They were speaking of the Teacher one night at supper, now that his visit was drawing near, and Andrew put in a word which made them know how much he wanted to see Jesus.

He never spoke to his family of the things he felt most deeply, but he was so full of his longing to see Jesus that he just could not keep it to himself.

And Joseph and Judas laughed at him.

Laughed at him, laughed loud and scornfully. What did he think he was, they wanted to know, that the great Teacher could be bothered about him?

Reuben did not laugh. He never laughed. But he turned his black eyes on Andrew—they were stern and piercing under overhanging brows.

"When the Teacher comes," he said, "you will stay at home where you belong. It is bad enough that everybody in Tiberias should know I have a worthless son. I have no wish it should be made known through all Galilee."

A worthless son!

This was the most terrible thing Reuben had ever said to his child.

So Andrew wanted to see the Teacher and to talk to him! Joseph and Judas thought that very funny. They would never have dreamed of asking such a thing for themselves, nor could they have desired it. That their queer little brother could and did struck them as very comical indeed. It was much too good a joke to keep. They must tell their friends about it. And evidently everybody else thought it just as funny as they did. Wherever Andrew went it seemed to him that people were laughing at him.

The next few days were the worst he had ever lived through in his whole life. He felt he was without a friend in Tiberias. His father had definitely told him he was a worthless son; he had given up all hope of him. Worst of all was the doubt in his own heart. If everybody else thought he was wrong and silly, how could he possibly believe in himself?

Through it all he clung stubbornly to a single hope—the hope of seeing Jesus. That was all life held for him now. On it he staked everything. If he could not see the Teacher, it seemed to him that he must die.

IV

And then he came.

V

He came, one night at sunset, down the shore of the lake, on foot, with his chosen disciples about him, a poor man, poorly dressed, his robe covered with the dust of his journey.

The news spread quickly throughout Tiberias.

The cobbler immediately got his neighbors together, to carry his old, palsy-stricken mother down to the seashore so that she might be healed.

Mary and Rebecca, the two old sisters who lived alone together, went a bit reluctantly, having agreed that when the Teacher came they would let him settle a disagreement about some property which had embittered their home all winter.

And Reuben went too, fearfully and hopefully, to pray the Teacher to bless his nets, so that he might make a great catch when he went out to fish.

Many people went down to the seashore to meet Jesus as he came into Tiberias, but very few of them loved him. Nearly all of them wanted something.

When Andrew arrived, the Teacher was sitting on a stone by the seashore, talking quietly to those who had gathered about him. The boy had imagined him in a thousand different ways, each more wonderful than the last, but nothing that he had imagined was half so wonderful as what he saw. There was such strength and such loveliness in the Teacher's face that it seemed as if all the Beauty and all the Goodness in the world were centered there. His father's commands meant nothing to him now, nor did he care that he was making a fool of himself. He did what in all his brooding over the Teacher's coming he had never once dared to imagine himself doing; he rushed forward and cast himself at Jesus's feet, his arms around the Master's knees.

Not even Reuben had expected that. He was more angry than he had ever been in his life. It seemed to him indeed that he had good reason for anger. Now, indeed, his worthless son had disgraced him in the eyes of all men. How could the Teacher be expected to bless his nets after such a thing as this had happened?

He came forward quickly, and his respect for the

presence of Jesus could only just barely keep the harsh word on his lips from turning into an oath. He seized his son roughly by one arm and dragged him to his feet.

Jesus rose with the boy. He was not a very tall man, as height is measured in feet and inches, but it seemed just then as if he might be going to strike his head against the stars. It was not anger, for he was incapable of anger. He knew that when men do wrong it is either because they cannot see the light or because they lack the courage to follow it. But the hand that Reuben had raised to strike his son never descended.

"Suffer little children," he said (Reuben was never to forget his words), "suffer little children to come unto me, and forbid them not; for of such is the kingdom of God. Verily I say unto you, whosoever shall not receive the kingdom of God as a little child, shall in no wise enter therein."

"I thought . . ." began the embarrassed father, "I only meant . . ."

But Jesus continued, more sternly than before:

"Take heed that you despise not one of these little ones; for I say unto you that in heaven their angels do always behold the face of my Father which is in heaven."

What need is there that I should write any more? If you have followed my story thus far, you know how Andrew felt as the Master spoke these words quite as well as I could tell you. Much better, indeed; for you are a child yourself, and you know how children feel better than I do. From the depths he passed to the heights, to the loftiest heights he had ever known. Warmth, peace, and joy flowed into him.

He was always thereafter faithful to Jesus. He was too young to become one of his disciples, that day in Tiberias, though he would dearly have loved to do so, but in later years, after the Teacher had died, he was among the faithful who helped to carry on his work. His life, not so important as the world counts importance, was built into the very fabric of the Christian Church. Jesus won his heart, that day by the seashore, for time and for eternity. The Master vindicated the Boy, and the Boy gave the Master the opportunity to utter one of the most gracious sayings that ever fell from his lips.

5. MINISTRY TO WOMEN

MARY AND MARTHA

Francis Quarles

Martha with joy received her blessed Lord;
  Her Lord she welcomes, feasts, and entertains:
Mary sat silent; hears, but speaks no word;
  Martha takes all, and Mary takes no pains:
    Mary's to hear; to feast him Martha's care is;
    Now which is greater, Martha's love, or Mary's?

Martha is full of trouble, to prepare;
  Martha respects his good beyond her own:
Mary sits ill at ease, and takes no care;
  Mary desires to please herself, alone:
    The pleasure is Mary's; Martha's all the care is;
    Now which is greater, Martha's love, or Mary's?

'Tis true, our blessed Lord was Martha's guest;
  Mary was his, and in his feast delighted:
Now which hath greater reason to love best,

The bountiful inviter, or the invited?
   Sure, both loved well; but Mary was the debtor,
   And therefore should, in reason, love the better.

THE NEW LAW

William Blake

Jesus was sitting in Moses' chair.
They brought the trembling woman there.
Moses commands she be stoned to death.
What was the sound of Jesus' breath?
He laid his hand on Moses' law;
The ancient heavens, in silent awe,
Writ with curses from pole to pole,
All away began to roll.

WERE NOT
THE SINFUL MARY'S TEARS

Thomas Moore

Were not the sinful Mary's tears
   An offering worthy Heaven,
When o'er the faults of former years
   She wept—and was forgiven?

When bringing every balmy sweet
   Her day of luxury stored,
She o'er her Saviour's hallowed feet
   The precious perfume pour'd;

And wiped them with that golden hair
   Where once the diamonds shone:
Though now those gems of grief were there
   Which shine for God alone.

Were not those sweets, though humbly shed—
   That hair—those weeping eyes—
And the sunk heart that inly bled—
   Heaven's noblest sacrifice?

Thou that hast slept in error's sleep,
   Oh, wouldst thou wake in heaven,
Like Mary kneel, like Mary weep,
   "Love much," and be forgiven?

THE CONVERSION
OF MARY MAGDALENE *

Anonymous

The fascination which the courtesan exercises over the imagination of men has never been better illustrated than in the elaborate development of the legend of Mary Magdalene. There is nothing in the Gospels to indicate that she was ever a woman of bad character. She was healed by Jesus of "evil spirits and infirmities"—Mark says He cast seven demons out of her—which is about equivalent to saying in modern language that she was cured of mental disorders. Afterwards she, along with other women, ministered unto Jesus of her substance; on Easter morning she visited the sepulchre in the garden and saw the Risen Lord.

Tradition identifies her, quite unbiblically, with the woman who was a sinner and who anointed the feet of Jesus as He sat at meat in the house of Simon the Leper, and sometimes also with Mary the sister of Martha and Lazarus. The error is universal, and it is probably much too late in the day to do anything about it.

Certainly we need not allow any of these considerations to interfere with our enjoyment of such a lovely piece of pre-Raphaelite-like narrative as the Fourteenth Century Italian novel, *The Life of Saint Mary Magdalene,* from which a selection is given here.

For the Biblical data concerning Mary Magdalene, see the article on her in Hastings' *Dictionary of the Bible;* for her legend, cf. Edith Olivier's *Mary Magdalene* (Appleton, 1934).

And behold already she had begun to give a boundless love to Jesus Christ, who knowing what He would do in her soul, thus made one of these others answer her thought; and I think that he said: "See, though this Master is so good and works so many miracles, yet our elders accuse Him, saying that He eats with publicans and sinners, and that He forgives them their sins."

And Magdalen hearing this, gave her mind to listen well and to apprehend these words.

And another said: "And I tell you this: He called Matthew who was a usurer, and held his bank at such and such a place, and he left everything, and has become this Master's disciple, and is ever with Him."

And another began to tell of her who was taken in

---

* The title of this selection has been supplied by the Editor.

adultery, of the woman of Canaan, and of her of Samaria.

And the Magdalen hearing this, covered her face and began to weep.

And Mary Magdalen went away to her room, and locking the door, she threw herself down outstretched upon the ground with so great a cry, that it seemed as if her heart was broken, and she lamented, saying: "What have I done, and what has been my life, soiled and sunk in such evil, and full of so much misery, that even if there were no God, nor profit to the soul, yet ought I to cry and cry again to see myself thus debased and defamed in the sight of all who are good."

And she recalled too well all the things that she had ever done, weeping and lamenting for each one and for all, more than words can tell.

And the devils who molested her seeing this were all dismayed, saying: "What shall we do, for we have lost her?"

And they took counsel together and said: "We must no longer tempt her with sins as before, since we see that she is repenting them bitterly. But rather we must do thus: let us aggravate these sins in her sight, as greatly as we can; and then also let us do another thing: let us praise this Jesus for His great power, His virtue, and His rare excellence, so that she may not dare even think of desiring to go to Him; and if we can do this, she will despair, and then maybe it will be permitted to us to kill her; or if not, we will stimulate her to kill herself, and we cannot believe that thus she would be received of God; so many and such are the sins she has committed and made others commit."

O fools! to think yourselves wiser than He who created you!

And as Mary lay humiliated upon the ground, true contrition entered into her soul, and she repented, more than words can say, for the fault committed; and on the other side, and not from her own virtue, an unbounded love entered into her heart, which caused her to repent even more, and to be ashamed for the dishonor done to God and to all good people, and she spoke thus to herself: "See, if I went to hell it would be the fairest justice, and the most reasonable judgment that ever was; but the good God who created me in His own image will repair the dishonour I have done to Him, the evil life I have led, and the bad example I have given."

And at this she redoubled her bitter weeping.

And I think that Martha and Martilla went softly to the door of her room and listened to her sorrowful weeping, and sometimes she uttered a cry with such grievous sighs, that it seemed her heart was breaking. And the blessed Martha and Martilla returned to their room, with more gladness than could be told, and they thanked God with great reverence, and such love as none could estimate, and they said to each other: "Now we see that she is converted. Oh, what happiness we shall have together at last! Now what a miracle is this! This is a greater wonder than raising the dead. It seems that this blessed Master can do what He will, as if He were God."

Well, well, they said truly, for He was both God and man. However, I do not think that they understood this perfectly yet, but they were preparing themselves well for the comprehension thereof. And that night they could not sleep, but all the time they were praising God, and wondering how they might obtain the friendship of this blessed Master, and intimacy with Him. And, moreover, they were confident that such friendship would be brought about.

Now let us return to Mary Magdalen, who was in her room sorrowing for her sins. And the seven devils who had ever goaded her on, now, as they had agreed, magnified her sins, representing to her that her guilt was greater than words can say; and indeed it seemed so to her, and for a little she was stupefied at the thought of such and so many sins. And when they saw her thus overcome, they represented to her the mightiness of God, and the greatness of His virtues, that is, of His infinite power, wisdom, and goodness; and when they spoke of His goodness she uttered a great cry, saying: "Well do I discern that goodness, which has borne with me! How long ago might He not have sent me to hell, and still He has borne with me, that He might have mercy on me, waiting till I should repent me of my sins, till I should desire to do penance. And now I desire to do His will, according to the wisdom of this Master, whom He has sent on earth to heal me, body and soul; and it will seem to me a thousand years till I can throw myself at His feet. And if I thought I might find Him now, this night, I would go to seek Him, but I do not think that He desires it."

And when the devils perceived that the great light of faith had entered her soul, they marvelled much, and were aghast, scarcely knowing what more to say, since that by which they had thought to lead her to such iniquity, had surely led her to such good. But they took counsel once more, and spoke thus: "She says she will go to this Jesus, and if she goes, He will instantly cast us out from her, as He has already done to our companions, and we shall have no more power to urge her."

And they agreed to answer her in such and such a way, when she said in her heart: "Oh, good Messer Jesus, when shall I go forth to seek Thee! This night is longer than any I have ever known."

And the devils replied to her thoughts and said: "Art thou not ashamed to desire to go to Him? Now art thou not clothed in all the ugliness of sin? And know, one cannot discover that He has ever sinned, but is clean and pure as when His mother bore Him. And thou, corrupt and hateful to God and man, who art thou, that thou wouldst go to Him? Why, then! what impudence leads thee to Him? Wilt thou be bold enough to approach Him?"

And when this thought came to the Magdalen, she was abashed, and she perceived the ugliness of her sins; and the demons around her urged these words in many ways, seeing that she did not yet know what to reply. And while she was being thus molested, behold a divine light shone in her room, and said: "Mary, do not fear to go to Jesus, for He is the best and the most gentle Physician that has ever been seen in this world. And the greater and the viler the illness, so much the more the Physician, if he be good, stays beside him who is ill, and so much the more strives to heal him; for the greater the illness, the greater honour to the Physician. And this one heals quickly, so much the more to reveal His goodness; but thou must trust in Him."

And the Magdalen began to cry aloud, saying: "Thus will I do with all my faith and all my love; and I will place all my hope in Him as if I were ill, for I perceive and acknowledge that He is the supreme Physician for soul and body."

So then the devils were defeated upon this point, and they said to each other: "In this also we have gone from bad to worse. And thus He knows how to discomfit us, when He will." But still they looked out for somewhat more to say to her, and they brought this thought before her. "See, this Master desires poverty. His mother is poor, and it is His will that His disciples should all be poor, so much so, that they have sometimes gathered the ears of corn,

separating the grain with their hands, to eat it, for He wishes that they should possess nothing."

And this well-nigh overcame the Magdalen, for it was a new thought to her.

But immediately she was succoured, and she thought thus: "I will put myself entirely into the hands of this blessed Master, and He will take away from me this infirmity of soul, so that His will shall be my will. And all my delight and all my pleasure shall be to desire what will please Him. And, moreover, yesterday evening I understood that Zachary was so moved with gladness and consolation, when he received Him in his house, that he said to Him: 'Master, take all my goods and give them to the poor according to Thy will.' I think his soul was so full of happiness that he had no care for the outward things around him." And she said to herself: "This then is what thou hast to do; to go to Him as soon as thou art able, and put thyself in His hands, that He may work His will in thee without opposition. And blest indeed shall I be if He receives me!"

And the devil replied at once to her thoughts and said: "But perhaps He will not receive thee."

But she disregarded this answer, and took comfort, saying: "I will go to Him as the woman of Canaan went, with humility, importunity, and perseverance, that He may have mercy on me, for they have told me that He is benign and pitiful; so that I will go to Him whatever happens. And such is my desire to see Him, that if I were shut up, locked and bound in prison all day to-morrow, so that I could not go to seek Him, I think they would find me dead before the evening." And she said to herself: "Do not listen any longer to those thoughts that deter thee from what thou wouldst do. Cast them from thee, for it is right that thou shouldst do thus, through the goodness of God." And she began to say: "Alas! when will the day come that I may go to seek Him whom my soul desires! How long a night is this! Never have I seen one so long."

Well, well, she spoke truly.

And rising up with fervour she lit a lamp, and began to take ointments that she possessed, and she chose the most precious from amongst them, filling thereof an alabaster box, and prepared it to carry with her, all the while sighing and shedding tears. Then she went to the window and saw that day was breaking, and she was very, very glad, nor did she lie down to sleep as usual.

And Mary Magdalen waited no longer, but took her cloak and covered her face so as not to be recognized by all she met as usual, and she took the box under her cloak; and thus she went out very early all alone to seek Messer Jesus, the desire of her soul, who already loved her more than any can estimate. And she went to the Temple because they had told her that most of the time He was there, but she did not find Him, and she hurried hither and thither, and she could not find Him; she asked for Him, and none could tell her where He was, for Messer Jesus Christ did not wish her to find Him save at the Pharisee's house; and the more she sought Him, the more her longing grew, and compelled her ever on to look for Him.

Now it happened according to Christ's will, and they told Mary Magdalen that Messer Jesus had gone to eat in the house of Simon the Leper, where they had made a great banquet for Him, and that there were there many other Pharisees. But Mary paid no heed when they said that others were there besides the good Jesus, for she sought no other than Him. Nor do I think that she said: "Now how will this appear to others, and what will they say?" Neither: "It would not be meet to go into another's house, especially when they are feasting, and during a great banquet to weep where others are making merry." Or again: "Know that thou wilt be ill received, for thou art hateful in their sight and infamous in all the city."

No, no! the Magdalen thought none of these things; she had no other care but to find Christ, to receive mercy from Him, and to be reconciled with Him, for she loved Him more than herself, and above all other things that one can think of; and because of this all other care had left her; and the more she thought of Him the more she loved Him, and the more ardent was her longing.

So Mary Magdalen came to the house of the Pharisee, and, entering, she asked no word of any there, but went up the stairs; and the guests were already seated at the table. And when the Magdalen saw Him, she instantly recognized the good Jesus, and she went behind Him, and threw herself on the ground at His feet. And all who were there cast their glances on her with great surprise, but they said nothing to her, and did not send her away, for she was a great lady, according to the world, though we must admit she was of ill fame; and on

the other side, they thought that Jesus would chase her away, nor let such a woman touch Him, and they murmured in their hearts, saying that He did not recognize her.

Now let us return to Mary, who had taken the feet of Christ in her hands with great reverence, and she had no need to uncover them, for the Lord of all virtue went barefoot. And Mary Magdalen, kissing these feet, and weeping, washed them with her tears over and under, and dried them with her hair, and anointed them over and under with the precious ointment in that way which she thought would most benefit Him, first one foot and then the other; and Jesus was eating and let her do her will, and He delighted in that which she offered Him, while He cared nothing for all that was on the table. O Messer Jesus, who didst see the hearts and thoughts of others, Thou didst look into the hearts of these false Pharisees, who murmured against Thee, thinking that Thou hadst not the knowledge of a Prophet, who outwardly seemed religious and courteous, and made a great show of so being; and Mary Magdalen, who was at Thy feet, was hateful and displeasing to all virtuous people, and guilty through her past evil life, but the heart in her, as she wept at Thy feet, was made the dwelling-place of God; and she was in a state of grace, for God was in her, and she in Thee through Thy charity, and therefore her heart was more precious than all the treasures one can think of. And Thou, who art the true Judge, verily Thou couldst estimate that which our eyes seeing yet would not have known how to discern.

But, thou, Mary, wast speaking thus:

"Messer, my sins are such and so many that I could not count them, and my life is so hateful in mine own eyes that, while so close to Thy purity and touching Thy sweet feet, I have not the courage to remember it. But I know and believe that Thou knowest all things better than I could tell Thee, and therefore I ask nothing else but that Thou shouldst take away from me now and for ever and ever all that displeases Thee in me, and I know that Thou canst do this; and I ask this grace for love of Thy charity, and if Thou receivest and healest so great a sinner, it will be one of the greatest things Thou hast ever done."

And with this she wept so violently that I think her heart would have broken had not God strengthened her, for He reserved her for greater works, and

He hearkened to her words with great pleasure.

And Mary, weeping, again put up her hands, and said: "Oh, good Jesus, if I am not worthy to receive mercy from Thee, yet I ask from Thy kindness that which my heart desires. And I beseech Thee to give me grace through Thine infinite goodness that, having dishonoured Thee all my life, henceforth I can do Thee honour whilst Thou dost will that I should live, that I may do Thy will and never again mine own, and that Thou wilt give me grace to revenge on myself with true penitence the wrong I have done Thee."

And she said this with great fervour of heart, feeling that no vengeance could be enough to satisfy her, and to her mind all the pains in the world would be nothing in respect to her great fault.

And whilst she was thus at His feet, she heard Messer Jesus Christ speaking with Simon, as it is told in the Gospel; and she looked up to hear Him speak, for never before had she heard Him, and so sweet was the sound of His voice in her heart that well-nigh she swooned away. But she took comfort as she heard more distinctly, and she listened attentively to everything He said; but she was comforted only when she had heard all clearly, how He said that she had done well, and when she heard Him say: "Many sins are forgiven her, for she has loved much."

Oh, good Jesus, didst Thou say that the Magdalen had loved much? Yet this immensity of love was not great through length of time, for we know that she did not love Thee when she offended Thee. And therefore I think it was that boundless ocean of charity which is never so little but it overflows, and which is of rarer worth than all created things, whence she loved Thee and Thy love more than herself; and she grieved for the guilt of her sin towards Thee far more than for the evil consequences it might bring upon her. And her heart was sunk in humility and gratitude, and in such love that I think no brain could estimate it nor tongue tell it.

And this good Jesus turned towards her, who henceforth would no longer possess herself, and said: "Woman, thy faith hath made thee whole" (and I think it penetrated into her heart). "Thy petitions are granted, and thy desire shall be fulfilled." And He said: "Go in peace."

And then all the devils were cast out from her, and all the guilt of sin taken from her, and she was filled with the love of charity, and with greater gladness than I can tell. And she understood by this word that Jesus spoke, "Go in peace," that He wished her to go from Him.

And she turned again to those blessed feet, and kissed them, saying softly: "For all the things Thou hast ever done, and doest, and will do, I praise Thee and give Thee thanks, my Lord, as many as the stars in heaven, as many as the grains of sand in the sea, and in all the rivers of the world."

And once more lifting the hem of His garment, she pressed it to her face with devotion, and with bitter tears. And Messer Jesus willingly suffered all things from her, for He knew her soul. Oh, good Jesus, Thou didst no longer recall her past evil life; the love of charity had quenched all other things. Blessed be the desire of her heart in all eternity, for though in that hour she might not stay longer by His side, yet she bore Him with her in her heart, and for this reason she went in peace; for whoever is His, goes in peace.

From THE WOMAN OF SAMARIA

Edmond Rostand

This selection from Rostand's famous Biblical drama, which was written for Sarah Bernhardt, begins with Scene IV of Part I and runs to the beginning of Part II.

PETER. [*coming down*]
Curses upon this land; till plague devours
What grasshoppers refuse to eat thereof!
  JAMES. [*the same*]
Their crops be killed with hailstones from above,
And maggots at their roots, by heaven sent!
  ANDREW. [*the same*]
Their wives be barren, young men impotent.
O may they know all hunger and all thirst.
May enemies invade them as at first.
Where Sichar stands, let reeking ruins be!
  PETER.
Never again beneath an almond tree
Let one of them lie mumbling and at ease.

Curse rocks and fields and houses, crops and trees!
Curse all my eyes behold! Curse this whole area!
Curse root and stock and branch!

JESUS.
God bless Samaria. [*He comes down.*]

PETER.
What, Rabbi? But your rules for us began,
"Go not to gentiles nor Samaritan,
But to the wandering sheep of Israel."

ANDREW.
You hate these heathen.

JESUS.
    Nay, I love them well.

PETER.
But your words, Rabbi,—telling us to win
Israel's lost sheep?

JESUS.
I bade you to *begin*
With those, your brethren. For I know your heart.
Not finding room for all, I gave you part.
If I had said, "Love all my Father's sons,"
Ye too had been offended, little ones.
Ye groped, aye, bravely, on your shadowed way.
I might have blinded you with sudden day.
And could I feed your weakness on My wine,
So new, so strong? Nay, children, ye are mine,
But light must filter in, and I must spare
To give too much at first. But now, I dare.

ANDREW.
What, not to be a Jew, and yet to be . . .

JESUS.
Elisha healed the Syrian's leprosy.

PETER.
We've got to love them? Can it ever be?

JESUS.
You will love all men, having first loved Me.

PETER.
What is it you ask?

JESUS.
    Perfection, Simon! Oh,
It is no easy road on which ye go.
I bid you love your neighbors.

PETER.
      If we can.
Who is my neighbor, Lord?

JESUS.
A certain man
Went from Jerusalem to Jericho.
Robbers waylaid him, stripped his raiment off,

Wounded, and left him so.
The echoes seemed to scoff.
    He lay, half dead.
His wounds gaped sore and wide.
A priest came by. Seeing the ground so red,
He chose the other side.
A Levite came. He saw the dimming eye.
    He, too, passed by.
By the same road, came a Samaritan,
    He saw the man:
Filled with compassion, hastened to his side;
Poured oil and wine to stanch the wound so wide;
Lifted him gently, set him on his beast,
    And let him ride,
And lest his mule should stumble in the least,
    He walked beside.
He brought him to an inn, put him to bed,
    And when the dawn was red,
Said to the good man there,
    "Let him have every care
When I go hence.
    Here are two pence.
And what thou spendest more, will I repay."
And so this—heathen—went upon his way.
Which, think you, of these three,
Look in your hearts and see,—
Was, in God's sight
    A neighbor to this man,—
The priest, the Levite,
    The Samaritan?

PETER.
But, . . .

JESUS.
    Have ye understood?

JAMES.
      Yes, Lord.

JOHN [*to* JESUS, *leading him to the well-curb*]
      Come, rest.
The way was long and rough.

ANDREW.
      And sore oppressed,
They say, with robbers bands. They keep the pass;
One,—I forget his name,—

JESUS. [*gently*]
      'Tis Barrabas.

JOHN. [*kneeling beside him*]
You stopped yourself to ask that man the way,
When you were telling us,—speak on, we pray,—
The parable of him who sowed the grain.

JESUS. [*smiling*]
What must I tell you?
JOHN.
   None of it was plain.
JESUS.
I sow the seed.
 PETER. [*sitting at his feet*]
  The field . . .
JESUS.
   Is everywhere.
 ANDREW. [*seating himself as close to His feet as*
  he can]
The crop?
 JESUS.
  My children make the harvest fair.
 JAMES. [*the same*]
The other grain . . . ?
 JESUS.
   The wicked one has sown,
And while ye sleep, among you it is strown.
 BARTHOLOMEW.
The harvesters . . . ?
 JESUS.
   The angels, O my sheaves,
Will fill my Father's storehouse to the eaves.
 PETER.
I'll guard my field! Oh, I will never sleep!
 JESUS.
Thou wilt sleep, Simon. But this lesson keep
Well in your hearts; the husbandman forbears
To weed his field in haste, lest, gathering tares,
He kill the wheat, as oft the foolish do.
At harvest time he separates the two.
 NATHANIEL. [*with melancholy fervor*]
How good wheat smells, fresh taken from the mill!
I'm hungry.
 JESUS.
  Ask of heaven what you will.
The cloud could drop down manna honey-sweet.
 PETER.
You believe that?
 JESUS.
  Ask, Cephas.
 PETER.
   At my feet? . . .
 JESUS.
Yes.
 PETER.
  Manna for us?

JESUS.
  As fresh as dew in May.
 PETER.
But . . .
 JESUS.
  Pray.
 PETER.
   Still . . .
 JESUS.
    Pray . . .
 PETER.
     I . . .
 JESUS.
      Pray.
 PETER. [*without conviction*]
Kind Heaven, rain, from thy vast blue dome
The Hebrew's ancient food.
  [*After an interval*] It doesn't come.
 JESUS.
Because you prayed and doubted. That is death,
The life of every prayer is only faith.
Speak to its massy rock undoubtingly
And Mount Gerizim marches to the sea.
Go, ye of little faith, and buy your bread.
I will read here a book no eye hath read.
Go, James, Nathaniel, Peter, Judas, John . . .
  [*They go off.*]
 JESUS. [*to* PETER, *who lingers, altogether discom-*
  fited]
Simon, the angels who today look on,
Will feed your hunger with their wide-spread wings,
Assuage your thirst with harps of myriad strings.
By winds and harmonies the soul is fed,—
But now, beloved, go, . . . and buy your bread.
  [*The Disciples go off, some toward the town,*
  others toward the field. JESUS *is left alone.*]
 JESUS.
I am weary. Yes, but therefore was I born.
My hands are torn by many a wayside thorn;
My feet are blistered by the rocks they pressed,
But from my bruised body is exprest
Some wine of healing, as from trodden grapes,
In the winepress poured, the purple juice escapes.
From willing weariness some help will flow
To these, my brethren. While I walk below,
Each pang I bear has some result divine,
And I, O Father, conquer by this sign.
Now that I almost faint from weariness,
Thy love will send some token of success . . .

Straight fall the sunbeams. 'Tis the bright sixth hour.
A flute-like voice drifts like a breeze-tossed flower.
A woman comes from Sichem. Past the turn,
Hither she comes to draw. . . . The sun's rays burn.
[*He has sat down again on the well-curb.*]
So near she is that I can see her plain,
The silken girdle and the golden chain,
The veil enshadows, but hides not her grace,—
My Father's gift to all the Hebrew race.
I hear her silvern anklets softly ring.
Jacob, thy daughters, coming to this spring,
Always, advancing with unhurried tread,
Poising the jar on nobly lifted head,
Come, with grave smiles and half mysterious air;
Conforming to the graceful urns they bear,
Their bodies, slender vases; handle-wise
Their curved arms lifted to the brooding skies.
[*At this moment, the Samaritan woman appears
at the top of the hill, on the footpath.*]
Immortal splendour of this gesture free!
Always it seems most beautiful to Me,
This gesture every Hebrew woman learns,
Bearing to wayside wells the heavy urns,
For with that very gesture,—Ah, I know,—
A Hebrew maid came, thirty years ago,
The little, gentle handmaid of the Lord,
As yet untroubled by the wondrous word
That Gabriel bore her, in the Almighty's name.
So with her cruise my lovely Mother came.
This woman is a sinner. Carelessly,—
A vase that knows not the divinity
Her bare arms raised to Heaven yet dimly proves,—
She sings, while dreaming of unworthy loves.
PHOTINE. [*coming down the footpath*]

*O take ye the foxes that ravage the vines.
This love is a weight on the heart.
Bring me grapes, O my love . . . We will perish,
apart.
All gifts are my true lover's signs.
O take ye the foxes that ravage the vines.*

*At my lattice at eve he has spoken to me;
"Arise up, my fair one, and come, O my love.
The winter is past, clouds are lost in the sea;
'Tis the time, 'tis the time of the dove.*

*Then come, O my dear, to the meadows with me
And there I will show you a dove.*

*A fig tree drops sweetness and all is for thee.
Arise, O my fair one, my love.
The winter is past, clouds are drowned in the sea."*

JESUS.
A soul light as a wreath that withereth.
PHOTINE. [*She has reached the well, and, without
seeing JESUS, she fastens the amphora to the
windlass and slowly lets it down*]

*I slept. But sometimes when I sleep
My heart awakes with every breath.
"Open, my soul, my flower, I keep
Vigil for thee," my lover saith.*

*Oh, but I spake forbiddingly,
—Dear, well-known voice!—"Who makes such din?
My robe's cast off. It cannot be
Naked I cannot let you in."*

*My feet are bathed with mountain snow,
My feet are laved with perfumes sweet.
How can I come to open so,—
The black, black stone! My white, white feet!*

*How,—But I opened wide the door.
Against his might I am so weak!
Gone,—gone! I cannot find him more.
Nightlong for my lost love I seek.*

*'Gainst the locked door, in fierce despair
My hands beat, dropping down their myrrh.
I weep in my wild, roughened hair,
And tear the lips that dared demur.*

JESUS.
Not for a moment has she turned to Me.
PHOTINE.

Like a roe, like a hart, will my love ever flee?

JESUS.
Slowly the heavy jar begins to rise.
PHOTINE. [*Turning the heavy wooden windlass
that draws up the rope*]

*My well beloved—afar I roved—when dawn was
clear
A-seeking thee. Thou camest to me. And daylight
dies.
Yet in this night—a magic light—my need supplies.
I hold thee here.
Here in my eyes.*

Balsam and myrrh my senses stir. Lo, 'tis thy sighs.
Thy name, my lord, as ointment poured, is sweet to
    me;
Thy lightest word with honey stored, my almond
    tree,
    And thy clear eyes
    Holy heaven for me.

Like lute unstrung, like fruit wind-flung, my heart
    lies low,
Low at thy feet. Ah, lift it, sweet! and let me rest.
Spikenard and balm my bosom calm, so light you
    pressed.
    Ah, be a signet
    On my breast!

JESUS.
The water jar is looking glass for her.
PHOTINE.

Like a signet of brass, like a bundle of myrrh.

JESUS.
In the cool water, empty smiles she flashes,
Admires the dye upon her sweeping lashes,
Looks at her nails whereon a few drops fell,
—And the world's saviour waits beside the well!
    [PHOTINE *lifts her water jar and moves away*]
She is going—type of poor humanity
That almost finds the Way, but heedlessly
Chooses the by-path.
    [PHOTINE *goes up the footpath, humming her*
    broken song.]
        If I make no sign,
She too will go away. Yet all are mine—
    [PHOTINE *is nearly out of sight*]
O Woman,—I am athirst. The sun is very hot!
Give me to drink, I pray.
    PHOTINE.
        The Jews deal not,
—He is a Jew, this thirsty, wayworn man,—
With Sichemite or with Samaritan.
Little or large, all dealings they decline.
Our bread, they say, smells of the flesh of swine.
Honey from Sichem hives the Jews refuse;
They say it tastes of blood. My dripping cruise
Came from Samaria's tainted well but now.
A heathen bears it on her unclean brow.
You should refuse it, finding it to stink,
Instead of asking for . . .

JESUS.
        Give Me to drink!
PHOTINE.
Has your great thirst your teaching so refuted?
Know, Jew, that you would be the less polluted
Handling foul vermin, reptiles poisonous,
Than being succoured so by one of us.
    [*With quarrelsome volubility.*]
Stay till tomorrow. Either sit or stand.
I'll not let down my pitcher to my hand.
'Tis on my shoulder. There it will remain.
Ho, Eleazar, lacking gifts and train!
I'm not Rebecca, as you seem to think.
Be thirsty if you will. You shall not drink.
    [*Coming back a little way.*]
You see this water,—clear, so pure, so clear,
The cruise seems empty, though I filled it here,
So cool one sees the moisture on the cruise;
Silver and pearl this draught—which I refuse.
O Beggar, hear the thirst-provoking sound,
The tinkle, tinkle, in its depths profound,—
Light as a draught distilled of summer air!
No water is so cool, so clear, so fair.
Ah, well for you, the Law, be very sure,
Says that this purest water is impure!
JESUS.
Woman . . .
    PHOTINE.
        I'd rather pour it on the sod
Than give . . .
    JESUS.
        If you but knew the gift of God,
And Who brings light when in the dark you shrink--
And Who He is that says Give me to drink;
Who sitteth here upon the well's wide rim,
He would not ask of thee, but thou of Him.
PHOTINE.
You speak in riddles just to make me heed.
JESUS.
I would give living waters to they need.
PHOTINE.
Stranger, I listen, for I have no choice,
Some Influence masters me,—your eyes, your voice.
You speak of living waters. Yet you keep
Nothing to draw with, and the well is deep.
Whence hast thou then that water, wondrous Jew?
—It must be false and yet I think it true,—
Is there, in all the sources of Judea,
Water as limpid as this water here?

People an hour away come here to draw.
Our father Jacob built it, when he saw
The land athirst. Here drank his mighty sons,
Their wives, their servants, and their little ones.
Most famous of all famous springs and wells.
What is it this mysterious stranger tells?
Here Jacob's cattle ages since were fed,
Art greater then than Jacob?

JESUS.

Thou hast said.

PHOTINE.
In your cupped hands a little I will pour
Then you will see . . .

JESUS.

He thirsteth nevermore
Whom I have given to drink. With how much pain
You come to draw again and yet again,
But whoso drinks the living draught I give
Within himself shall welling fountains live,
And life eternal from those waters brim,
If he but drink the draught I bring to him.

PHOTINE.
What! For eternity to have no thirst?
A good thing to believe,—if one but durst.
Elijah's draught lasted a wondrous while
While he was in the desert. Ah, you smile?
Some learning to this woman you must grant,—
He went for forty days and did not want.
You've learned his secret in your wandering?
O Master, lead me to that hidden spring.
Show me this wonder, that your wanderings saw,
That I thirst not, nor hither come to draw.

JESUS.
Hearing, thou hearest not, nor givest heed
To any thirst but that of fleshly need.

PHOTINE.
Give me this water. Stranger, I implore,—
This living water, that I thirst no more.

JESUS.
Go call thy husband and return to Me.

PHOTINE.
My husband?

JESUS.

Go.

PHOTINE.
But I . . . but I

JESUS.

I see,
Thou art ashamed.

PHOTINE.
I have no husband.

JESUS.

Verily,
Thou saidest truly. Five men by that name
Were called, and thou wouldst call this sixth the
same.

PHOTINE.
Master . . .

JESUS.
Thou saidest truly, yea, and well.
Thou hast no husband, it is truth you tell.
That holy name thou hast no right to speak.

PHOTINE.
Master.

JESUS.
Five men have had thee. Didst thou seek
God's blessings, or the blessing of God's priest?
Troops of young friends and wholesome marriage
feast?
Torches? . . .

PHOTINE.

O Master.

JESUS.

Merry dulcimer,
Jests gay and tender; tremblings sweet, to stir
The myrtle crown set on thy drooping head? . . .

PHOTINE.
Lord, Lord! a prophet surely, who hast read . . .

JESUS.
Thou callest Me prophet since I know thy heart.
It is but part, and such a little part,
If thou wilt learn, of things that I can show.

PHOTINE.
O Master, canst thou tell?

JESUS.
What wouldst thou know?

PHOTINE.
'Tis then: You Jews our whole religion spurn
Because we worship here, and yet we learn
That your forefathers,—who are also ours,—
Worshipped here only. Have the heavenly powers
So changed? The priests and doctors understand.
We common folk, beset on either hand,
Wishing to kneel upon the holy mount,
Are told of two, that two high priests account
Holy,—yet each declares there is but one,
Ancient and chosen of God, beneath the sun.
"Pray on this mountain." "No, pray on the other,"

[213]

And so, we climb not neither one nor t'other. . . .
So, always in the valley I have trod. . . .
And . . . plucking flowers there . . . I forgot my
    God.

    JESUS.

Be of good comfort, for the hour is nigh
When all will worship God, both low and high,
Not at Gerizim, or Jerusalem.
In little Sichem, little Bethlehem,
Wherever any humble soul finds space
To speak to God. He dwells not in one place.
God is a Spirit. They who worship Him
Will never reach Him at the horizon's rim.
The Spirit goes where never foot has trod.
Nowhere, and Everywhere, man finds his God.

    PHOTINE.

I have lived far from God. I can receive
Only a little, but I do believe
Three things: the dead will some day come again;
Angels have visited this mortal plain,
And—fairest, surest hope beneath the sun,—
I wait the coming of the Promised One,
Await and love him, L'Ha-Schaab, Christ, Messiah!

    JESUS. [*lifting His eyes to heaven*]

The humblest, always! At my deep desire!
I thank Thee, Father!

        [*To* PHOTINE]

        What thinkest thou of Christ?

    PHOTINE.

That He will come.

    JESUS.

    And then?

    PHOTINE.

       Why that suffice...

He is coming.

    JESUS.

Coming . . . yes . . . What will He bring?

    PHOTINE.

I think He comes to teach us everything.

    JESUS.

Hear her, O Father

        Woman, have no fear.

Thou sayest the words that I have longed to hear.
Lift up thy head. Behold thy soul's Desire.
I—I that speak—am He. I am Messiah.

    PHOTINE. [*starts back, then, stammering, sinks
    to her knees*]

Thou! . . . I . . . Ha-Schaab! . . . Messiah! . . .
        Emanuel!

    JESUS.

Jesus.

    PHOTINE. [*on her knees*]

        Thou well-beloved.

    JESUS. [*watching her*]

           A hush of silence fell.

    PHOTINE. [*sings suddenly*]

*My well-beloved, long, long I roved, when dawn was
    clear,*
A-seeking Thee. Thou came to me. The old day dies.
Into my night, a magic Light my need supplies.
    I have Thee here,
    Before my eyes.

Balsam and myrrh my spirit stir. Lo, 'tis Thy sighs.
*Thy name, my Lord, as ointment poured, is balm
    to me,*
*Thy gentle word with perfume stored. Thou Myrtle
    tree.*
    Thy clear eyes
    Open Heaven for me.
My heart lies low;

        My God, what have I done?
For Him the same song, Oh, the very one!
Oh, sacrilege! The idle words and free!

    JESUS.

All words of love must speak at last of Me.
One must to Me the halting words address
To know the fullness of their tenderness.

    PHOTINE.

Master, adoring, I could but repeat
The words I knew. . . .

    JESUS.

       I know. The gift was sweet.
I have received it.

    PHOTINE.

        Oh, the old words came
With this new Love! Oh, shame!

    JESUS.

        Nay, feel no shame.
The love of Me comes always to a heart
Where lesser, human loves have had a part,
In the old lamp, a newer light discloses,
Makes fadeless garlands from life's fading roses:
Lo, I make all things new. Let none retard
Breaking the box of aloes or of nard.
The merchant sold it for its savour sweet,
But penitents expend it at my feet.

[*214*]

My feet are rested, where this gift is spread,
Wiped with the tresses of an humbled head.
Think not thy song is shameful in My eyes.
The soul that finds Me, in its first surprise,
Knows not its new song, though it stirs within.
Trembling, confused, rejoiced, it must begin
Some fragment of the song it learned elsewhere,
And, lo! the love-song has become a prayer!

PHOTINE.

"Who drinks the living water that I give
Shall never thirst." I thirst no more! I live, . . .
I'd weep upon Thy hands. Ah, thought too free!
How good He is! He holds them out to me! . . .
Lord, for the first time—O the very first,
I thirst no more, who was devoured with thirst!
I sought the broken cisterns every one.
I drank,—and thirsted ere the draught was done!
Sometimes I thought I loved. To love, I knew,
Would slake my thirst. That love was never true.
It left me parched and dry,—a tortured thing.
Someone would tell me of another spring.
Hope of new cisterns sunk in newer lands
Drove me, my empty pitcher in my hands.
Always I found the old, old, weary road,
Cattle that browsed or drew their heavy load,
The stunted olive trees along the way,
A sky of azure or a sky of gray;
With the old gesture, though my soul would tire,
I lowered the empty cruise of my desire;
Always I found the same deceitful thing,—
Roiled, brackish waters from a troubled spring.
From my hot lips the faithless pitcher fell.
Always my cruise was broken at the well!

JESUS.

What need, Photine, to tell Me? For I knew.

PHOTINE.

And now my soul seems bathed with morning dew.
Out of my shadows I have caught the gleam,
The rainbow arc above the living stream.
Gush, Spring of Love, and mount in jets of faith
And fall in drops of hope, dispelling death.
Sing, Living Water. Cast upon my soul
And all its dust, the flood that makes me whole!

JESUS.

Thou seekest new words for the new thoughts that
    rise,
But I rejoice to see thy tear-dimmed eyes.

PHOTINE.

My worthless words! My eyes not fit to see!

JESUS.

All tear-dimmed eyes are beautiful to me.
Strive not for words. I understand your tear.

PHOTINE.

O teach me.

JESUS.

For that cause, I waited here.
When my disciples come, who went to buy
Food in the village, leave me.

PHOTINE. [*with a gesture toward the cruise*]
                                 Master, I
Gave you no water,—Thou who givest Salvation!

JESUS.

I thirsted only for your salutation.

PHOTINE.

'Tis true. I offer water to the River.

JESUS.

I quench my thirst if I a soul deliver.

PHOTINE.

Here at Thy feet, I wait.

JESUS.

                         The air is blue.
Silence enfolds us. I will speak to you
Of My new Kingdom; how man grows divine;
The wheat and tares; the branches and the vine.

PHOTINE.

I listen.

JESUS.

          I will tell you of the seed;
The leavened meal; the pearl; and, if you heed,—

PHOTINE.

I listen!

JESUS.

          —I will teach you how to pray;
Tell of the flock left for one lamb astray,
Until the Shepherd found and brought it home.

PHOTINE.

I listen!

JESUS.

          How the King again will come;
Of roads, one safe and small, one wide and
    broad,
And of My Father.

PHOTINE.

                   O, I listen, Lord.

6. THE TEACHER

WHAT WENT YE OUT
FOR TO SEE?

Arthur Hugh Clough

Across the sea, along the shore,
In numbers more and ever more,
From lonely hut and busy town,
The valley through, the mountain down,
What was it ye went out to see,
Ye silly folk of Galilee?
The reed that in the wind doth shake?
The weed that washes in the lake?
The reeds that waver, the weeds that float?—
A young man preaching in a boat.

What was it you went out to hear
By sea and land, from far and near?
A teacher? Rather seek the feet
Of those who sit in Moses' seat.
Go humbly seek, and bow to them,
Far off in great Jerusalem.
From them that in her courts ye saw,
Her perfect doctors of the law,
What is it ye came here to note?—
A young man preaching in a boat.

A prophet! Boys and women weak!
  Declare, or cease to rave:
Whence is it he hath learned to speak?
  Say, who his doctrine gave?
A prophet? Prophet wherefore he
  Of all in Israel tribes?—
He teacheth with authority,
  And not as do the Scribes.

THE PRODIGAL SON

James Weldon Johnson

The greatest and most moving of the parables of Jesus is
here presented by Mr. Johnson as an old-time Negro
sermon in verse.

Young man—
Young man—
Your arm's too short to box with God.

But Jesus spake in a parable, and he said:
A certain man had two sons.
Jesus didn't give this man a name,
But his name is God Almighty.
And Jesus didn't call these sons by name,
But ev'ry young man,
Ev'rywhere,
Is one of these two sons.

And the younger son said to his father,
He said: Father, divide up the property,
And give me my portion now.
And the father with tears in his eyes said: Son,
Don't leave your father's house.
But the boy was stubborn in his head,
And haughty in his heart,
And he took his share of his father's goods,
And went into a far-off country.

There comes a time,
There comes a time
When ev'ry young man looks out from his father's
        house,
Longing for that far-off country.

And the young man journeyed on his way,
And he said to himself as he travelled along:
This sure is an easy road,
Nothing like the rough furrows behind my father's
    plow.

Young man—
Young man—
Smooth and easy is the road
That leads to hell and destruction.
Down grade all the way,
The further you travel, the faster you go.
No need to trudge and sweat and toil,
Just slip and slide and slip and slide
Till you bang up against hell's iron gate.

And the younger son kept travelling along,
Till at night-time he came to a city.
And the city was bright in the night-time like day,
The streets all crowded with people,
Brass bands and string bands a-playing,
And ev'rywhere the young man turned
There was singing and laughing and dancing.
And he stopped a passer-by and he said:
Tell me what city is this?
And the passer-by laughed and said: Don't you
    know?
This is Babylon, Babylon,
That great city of Babylon.
Come on, my friend, and go along with me.
And the young man joined the crowd.

Young man—
Young man—
You're never lonesome in Babylon.
You can always join a crowd in Babylon.
Young man—
Young man—
You can never be alone in Babylon,
Alone with your Jesus in Babylon.
You can never find a place, a lonesome place,
A lonesome place to go down on your knees,
And talk with your God, in Babylon.
You're always in a crowd in Babylon.

And the young man went with his new-found friend,
And bought himself some brand new clothes,
And he spent his days in the drinking dens,

Swallowing the fires of hell.
And he spent his nights in the gambling dens,
Throwing dice with the devil for his soul.
And he met up with the women of Babylon.
Oh, the women of Babylon!
Dressed in yellow and purple and scarlet,
Loaded with rings and earrings and bracelets,
Their lips like a honeycomb dripping with honey,
Perfumed and sweet-smelling like a jasmine flower;
And the jasmine smell of the Babylon women
Got in his nostrils and went to his head,
And he wasted his substance in riotous living,
In the evening, in the black and dark of night,
With the sweet-sinning women of Babylon.
And they stripped him of his money,
And they stripped him of his clothes,
And they left him broke and ragged
In the streets of Babylon.

Then the young man joined another crowd—
The beggars and lepers of Babylon.
And he went to feeding swine,
And he was hungrier than the hogs;
He got down on his belly in the mire and mud
And ate the husks with the hogs;
And not a hog was too low to turn up his nose
At the man in the mire of Babylon.

Then the young man came to himself—
He came to himself and said:
In my father's house are many mansions,
Ev'ry servant in his house has bread to eat,
Ev'ry servant in his house has a place to sleep;
I will arise and go to my father.

And his father saw him afar off,
And he ran up the road to meet him.
He put clean clothes upon his back,
And a golden chain around his neck,
He made a feast and killed the fatted calf,
And invited the neighbors in.

Oh-o-oh, sinner,
When you're mingling with the crowd in Babylon—
Drinking the wine of Babylon—
Running with the women of Babylon—
You forget about God, and you laugh at Death.
Today you've got the strength of a bull in your neck
And the strength of a bear in your arms,

But some o' these days, some o' these days,
You'll have a hand-to-hand struggle with bony
    Death,
And Death is bound to win.

Young man, come away from Babylon,
That hell-border city of Babylon.
Leave the dancing and gambling of Babylon,
The wine and whiskey of Babylon,
The hot-mouthed women of Babylon;
Fall down on your knees,
And say in your heart:
I will arise and go to my Father.

JESUS AS A STORY-TELLER

William Ellery Leonard

The stories of Jesus furnish bywords for conversation and literature; but their movement and color and passion are too seldom felt: they have been added to the conventionalities; hence their significance for the mind of Jesus may be overlooked. They bear witness to a teeming, creative brain. When Jesus walked by the lake or mountain, and the crowds gathered, and he began to speak to them in parables, where did he get his abundant supplies? —were they casual inventions of the moment?—had the artist before worked over them in secret?—what personal observation, experience, or folk-gossip or reading suggested this story or that?—did he bring them to their present perfection by successive retelling and remodeling, like the modern speaker with his favorite anecdotes?—with what tones, gestures, pauses, did the story-teller emphasize the pageantry of his fancy for his oriental hearers, those proverbial lovers of stories? To these things no man will ever reply. But answers are not always of chief moment. Often a question will do more to arouse thought than an answer—a realization that problems exist, a stimulation of curiosity, when we begin to understand because we begin to be properly astonished.

These stories came out of a teeming, creative brain that spoke to the living; and as such it is well to recognize their position in the written records of

the race, among the fables, allegories, and apologues that human ingenuity has wrought out to illustrate a point or to teach a lesson. Someone should write a book comparing in their art and purpose the stories of Jesus with the Old Testament parables (as that of the vineyard in Isaiah 5, elaborated by Jesus), and the Old Testament fables (those of vegetable life in Judges 9:8–15 and 2 Kings 14:9), with the parables of Buddha and the *Talmud*, with the fables of the *Hitopadesa* and Aesop, with the myths and parables of Plato, with the allegory of Hercules at the cross-roads of Prodicus, with the homely apologues of republican Rome, etc. His words begin to be examined by the Department of Comparative Religion; they still await examination by the Department of Comparative Literature.

If, on the one hand, the stories of Jesus are fresh creations, on the other hand as a type and method they have not only general analogies among other peoples, but closer parallels among his own people and in his own time than a Christian public unfamiliar with Rabbinical lore usually suspects.

But they concern us now only in the former aspect, as stories illustrating spiritual truths, as the manifest products of one mind, one artist, one creator. They belong to the world's "little masterpieces of fiction." Not only have they delighted the populace, but they have satisfied the severe standards of the Academicians. The clearness of outline and grace of form, so unlike anything in ancient Hebrew literature, is perhaps the most notable manifestation of that Hellenic quality in the mind of Jesus which we have already noted more than once. Jesus is perhaps the greatest artist the Jewish race has produced.

With wonderful economy of effort he sets his characters before us as living men and women. His device is not to describe, but to show them doing or speaking, whether it be the Good Samaritan binding up the wayfarer's wounds, or the shepherd coming home rejoicing with the lost sheep on his shoulder, or the woman sweeping her house, or the Unjust Steward with his account books, or Lazarus begging Father Abraham to dip a fingertip in water and cool his tongue. With the realistic exactness of one reporting an incident out of his own experience, he mentions now one, now another characteristic detail, such as only a poetic imagination would emphasize. With him it is not simply a grain of mustard seed, but a grain of mustard seed that a man took and cast into his garden, and it grew and became a tree and the birds of the heavens came and lodged in the branches thereof. Even in the brief mention of the woman making bread, he tells us she hid the leaven not simply in the meal, but in three measures of meal—and that makes the difference between a lay-figure and an actual housewife. It is just these apparently trivial touches that betray the born story-teller.

Again, his people are always represented as occupied with something interesting, something in which they are themselves vitally interested—whether it be buying land to make sure of a treasure buried there, or hunting for a lost sheep, or building a house, or guiding the plow—usually something that his peasant companions or groups of chance listeners would have found particularly interesting, as a part of their own world. Though Jesus tells the story of a king and his army, and of a rich merchant and his pearl, most of his inventions concern the homely activities of fisher, and vine-dresser, and shepherd, or the quiet familiar, if learned, professions of scribe and judge.

It is part of that homeliness that runs through so much of his imagery, and that doubtless character-ized his speech, noun, verb, and adjective, in the original Aramaic never to be restored.

Near to the folk also was his constant use of what our Latin grammar calls "direct discourse"—the lively dramatic method of the Scotch cotter or Irish politician, which is lost to the more elaborate syntax of polite society. He reports the householder, which went out at different hours of the day to hire more laborers into his vineyard, as in actual conversa-tion in the market-place; he does not tell us the Prodigal said he would arise and go to his father, but he lets us overhear the Prodigal's own spoken resolve.

Near to the folk, again, are his repetitions, like those familiar in Homer and in ballad poetry, found in the Gospel narratives about Jesus as well (e.g. Luke 19:31–34), and in all primitive recitals: as "Enter thou into the joy of thy Lord" in the parable of the Talents; and "I have sinned against heaven," etc. of the Prodigal Son; and "I pray thee have me excused," in the parable of the Invitations: each re-peated with the simple directness of an old folk tale.

His characters belong to the literature of the world, even with the more developed creations of so-called secular letters, with Thersites, Nestor,

Achilles, with Paolo and Francesca, the Canterbury Pilgrims, and Shakespeare's Theater.

The background is but lightly drawn, even in such a vivid scene as the Prodigal feeding the swine; or it is omitted altogether, where, however, the con-vincing reality of the actors suggests it so truly that we are surprised to find on rereading that our imaginations have supplied so much. Here again is seen the magic of the artist: it is not what his imagination does for us, so much as what it is able to make our imaginations do for ourselves, that dis-tinguishes from the dauber or poetaster, the painter or poet whom we love for making us so gloriously competent.

Hence the wearisome inanity of most efforts to fill in the parables by paraphrase. Yet our world—our customs, our tastes, the very look of our fields and houses and markets, our occidental sky itself—is so different that imagination, always making use of memory, may sometimes go astray; and a work of such wide and exact archaeological information, with such intelligent sympathy and such sweet quaintness of manner as *De Gelijkenissen van het Evangelie* of Dr. Koetsveld, hausvater, pastor, and scholar, is a delightful help and a welcome gift to any friend of Jesus: he brings back to us the world that was about Jesus, when the Poet of Galilee spoke to his villagers from boat or hillside; and to Jesus' allusions he gives for us something of the significance they had for his countrymen.

One might expect the realistic habit that adds so many little touches of accurate detail would have led him to locate, as is so common in folk-lore and legend, his stories in some appropriate place, feign-ing, for instance, that the sower went forth to sow in the fields back of Capernaum, or that the Prodigal wandered from a house in Nazareth to the rich Roman city on the coast, or that the virgins were the daughters of Cana; but he is thus definite only in the story of the man who was going down to Jericho. Moreover, his characters are unnamed, save the beggar on Abraham's bosom, who may have been named by the tradition after the Lazarus whom Jesus was reputed to have raised from the dead. And in this way his stories, with all their simple realism, ac-quire something of that remoteness and mystery characteristic of fairy tales, which usually tell of what happened somewhere, once upon a time, to some certain prince, or maiden, or forest child whose names we shall never know. The result is for us not unhappy: the literary instinct of men has long since devised from out the stories of Jesus signatures more significant and pretty than proper names: The Vineyard, The Prodigal Son, The Ten Virgins, The Talents, the Good Samaritan.

The character of his materials—the personages and incidents—and his manner of arranging and setting them forth offer beautiful evidence of Jesus' power to play upon the human heart. So many-sided and so elusive is his personality that his critic is constantly tempted to readjust the emphasis or alter the treatment of chapter and paragraph. Indeed, Jesus' power over the human heart is perhaps his power above all other powers as poet; and I can imagine a discussion of the Poet of Galilee which might be in effect but an analysis and exposition of this truth. Not that such a discussion would necessarily repudiate any of the ideas in these pages; but that it might set some of them in clearer relations and in a clearer light. It is certain at least that the power over the human heart he possessed as few even of the greatest artists who so far excelled him in complexity and ingenuity of form, and in quantity and variety of production.

But these stories exist not for themselves alone; like all great art, they have a meaning beyond themselves. Each exists for an idea; they all illustrate the ethical or religious principles that fired the imagination of the Poet of Galilee; and, despite certain tendencies in modern criticism and art, it must never be forgotten that the love of goodness and the love of God have been through the ages and will still be in the ages to come among the passions and themes of the creative mind.

The fitness of the stories as illustrations is quite independent of their excellence as narrative compositions.

They are a part of the glowing concreteness of a poet's thinking; but in this they are sometimes misunderstood. The parable of the Sower (with one or two others) is really an allegory, where each element in the story is symbolic of an element in the thought of the speaker; "it gives us," says Menzies, "under a thin disguise the experience of Jesus as a preacher"; though the correspondences are confused in the explanation which the Evangelists make Jesus give privately to his disciples.

But this is not their usual character. They are similes. In some this is formally obvious: "The Kingdom of Heaven is *like* a woman," etc.; "Everyone therefore which heareth these words of mine and doeth them, *shall be likened* unto a wise man, which built his house upon the rock," etc. But even the longest, The Prodigal Son, is, in relation to the thought illustrated, a simile. The point of comparison is that God forgives a repentant soul as a human father a son. The vivid details—the patrimony, the wandering to the far country, the swine, the fatted calf, the ring and the robe—but complete and vitalize the picture; they have not more symbolic meaning than the details of a Homeric simile. In either poet there is but one point of comparison; in either case the poet makes the comparison interesting and effective by dwelling on the independent characteristics of the material which furnishes the illustration.

Thus Jesus is not to be held responsible for the morality of people in these stories: neither for the harshness of the king that bade the man who owed him ten thousand talents to be sold with his wife, and his children, and all he had; nor for the injustice of the householder who gave the laborers of the eleventh hour as good a wage as those who had borne the scorching heat of the day; nor for the thrift of the gleeful, sly fellow that found a treasure hid in a field and bought the field without letting the man who sold it know why. In the same way he is not always careful of literary probability, as possibly in the story of a certain king which made a marriage feast for his sons, though the more intimately we acquaint ourselves with Jesus, the more we appreciate how his utterances abound in accurate knowledge of the customs and ways of his folk and times. What he chiefly desires is that these stories furnish him with a point to his purpose.

And Jesus, leaving the moral to take hold as it might, was loath to tag his parables with elucidations. He had too much literary taste: as artist he loved the eloquence of suppression, silence, stopping short. He had too much cleverness: he knew human nature too well; he knew the greater force of a point when the listener can catch it for himself; and though the quick-witted Pharisees and their kind seem to have got his drift easily enough, he was, as we read, chagrined at the obtuseness of his disciples in wanting glosses, and would have been chagrined at those glosses which, as seems likely, the Apostolic age was afterwards prone to put into his mouth.

Moreover, he was too adroit: simple parabolic teaching "enabled him to avoid harsh contradictions of the hopes cherished by his countrymen, and to insinuate into their minds his own spiritual views," * without unduly antagonizing.

But certainly he desired to be understood. Apparently the Apostolic age, wondering why not more of those who heard Jesus were converted, sought an explanation in the fact that he spoke in parables, so that, in the bitter words of Isaiah,

> Seeing, they may not see;
> And hearing, they may not understand.

This contradicts the nature of Jesus: he no more intended to hide his thought under a mystification than he advised hiding a lamp under a bushel.

These observations have touched on the parables, first, simply as inventions of a unique story-telling gift, and, second, as concrete symbols of spiritual ideas, according to the familiar function of the poet as discoverer of analogies between matter and spirit. A third aspect of their poetry concerns the quality of those ideas themselves; but any analysis of the underlying truths of the parables must be left until the years make me wiser for the task. It seems indubitable that no other body of poetry so slight in quantity ever contained teachings of equal loftiness and equal scope.

THE HUMOR OF JESUS

William Ellery Leonard

Certain conventions of Christianity have made its founder the gloomiest visage in history; and Nietzsche, looking upon that Christ, upbraided him that he never laughed: neither Christian nor Iconoclast has dealt here with the real Jesus. The Indignant, the Man of Sorrows, having the humanity of universal humanity, was the Humorist too. Indeed such a nature, so responsive, so subtle, so rich in emotions, in imagination, in understanding of his

fellow-men would have been an anomaly had it marked and felt only the tragedy, never the comedy, of the incongruous. But we need not altogether theorize: a few of the jests are on record.

According to the first chapter of the earliest gospel, Jesus founded his little order with a jest: after some brief addresses, presumably in the synagogues, which having no regular minister were free on the sabbath to any speaker in Israel wise in the Scriptures, Jesus was passing one day along by the Sea of Galilee; and he saw Simon and Andrew, the brother of Simon, casting a net into the sea, for they were fishers. And Jesus said unto them, "Come ye after me, and I will make you to become fishers of men." Socrates once playfully used a similar figure: "I am not altogether unversed in the art of catching men," but without the pun which gives point to the former.

The homely hyperboles so habitual with him, as in "If ye have faith as a grain of mustard seed," may have more than once been accompanied by a smile, the difference after all between the meaning and the humble symbol having a happy quaintness.

His fancy indulged at times in grotesque exaggerations, which need but to be pictured by us as they were by his original auditors to be recognized at once. The picture of a busybody with a stick of timber in his eye, solicitous for the sight of a neighbor with a fleck of dust in his, is itself ludicrous, and doubly as a type of the fault-finding hypocrite; thus, also, punctiliously to strain out the gnat before drinking a cup of wine, only thereafter to swallow a camel, is ludicrous, and doubly as a type of the punctiliousness and inconsistency of religious formalists. Are not these exactly paralleled in kind by the famous

> Parturiunt montes, nascitur ridiculus mus *

where the picture is also grotesque exaggeration, introduced in the same way to typify a human frailty. We smile at this line in Horace; but who ever smiled at those lines of Jesus? I think the Galilean peasants did.

It was Jesus, too, who conceived the desperate anxiety of self-interest in terms of the short man trying by worrying about it to add a cubit to his stature —the humor of which was remarked by Beecher; and we remember the comparison of the difficulty

---

* Menzies, The Earliest Gospel, p. 116.

* "The mountains are in labor and bring forth an absurd little mouse."

of the rich man, worming his way into heaven, with the easier feat of the camel, squeezing, legs, hump, and all, through the eye of a needle.

Thus the Jester could riot in wild and grotesque whimsies; but perhaps oftener to his mood was the delicate humor of a gentle realism: the children in the market-place at their games of mock funerals and weddings, chiding their comrades for not doing their mimic roles as agreed; the disgruntled house-holder roused in the night by an importunate neighbor come after bread for his guest, and constrained to open the door at last because the man kept up such a merciless knocking; the judge who yielded to the widow, not because he feared God or regarded man, but simply to get rid of her continual coming; the recipients of an unwelcome invitation who straightway began to make conventional excuses, especially the much-married man who could not remain away from his wife—how genially he handled such themes! Here, too, the humor is not only in the picture, but in the application.

Moreover, he was alert to get the humor out of a situation in actual life, as exemplified by the story of the new wine in old bottles, told at the chief Pharisee's table at the expense of the listeners, where he "pricked the bubble of their assumed superiority."

And may not the Knower of men have smiled as he saw the connoisseur drink the old wine and smack his lips and say, "That is good"? May he not have smiled at the simple shepherd and the women who, finding their lost possessions, gleefully called in their neighbors to gossip about it all?—or at the unseemly haste of the guests when he marked how they chose out the chief seats?—or at Martha, cumbered about much serving, who would enlist the Master against her sister, apparently idling at his feet? May not a sense of humor have reinforced his appreciation of the zeal of the little Zacchaeus with whom he decided to take lodgings? Was there not grim humor as well as bitter rebuke in his comment on those who think they shall be heard for their much speaking, and on those who disfigure their faces to be seen of men to fast? No man could look through human nature, as Jesus looked through it, without smiling sometimes in very truth.

Humor is as old as speech. Laughter rings round the world. And even Galilee had its mirth; and even we can hear it.

The above paragraph suggests two related subjects: the adroitness of Jesus in turning any situation, even the most trying to the advantage of himself or his cause . . . ; and the irony of Jesus. . . .

I mean an irony quite like that of Socrates, where superiority, conscious of its own, plays the part of inferiority; where knowledge pretends the ignorance, where wisdom pretends the folly, where purity pretends the impurity of the other party to the conversation, who is meanwhile complacently unaware of the situation until the real master chose by a deft stroke to reveal it. As Socrates pretended to humble himself before the Sophists, politicians, and smart set of Athens, so Jesus before the Scribes and Pharisees of Palestine.

This irony seasons, and will explain, many of his sayings: "They who are whole have no need of a physician," i.e., you Pharisees whose lives are such models of ethical and religious propriety, I can do you no spiritual good; but possibly [in a changed tone] with all your wisdom there is something for you in the old word, "I desire mercy and not sacrifice." The difficult parable of the Unjust Steward is certainly ironical.

Ironical, too, is his habit of clinching an argument, or of concluding a story with a question, the answer to which is perfectly obvious: "Doth not each of you on the sabbath loose his ox or his ass from the stall and lead him away to the watering?" "Whether of the twain did the will of his father?" "Which of them therefore will love him most?"

At times his irony becomes bitter sarcasm, as in Luke 13: 31ff.: "It cannot be that a prophet perish outside of Jerusalem," i.e., as a prophet I have a just claim to be murdered in the Holy City which from old has murdered the prophets; so Herod that fox—sly old villain though he is—won't have the pleasure of doing with me as with John.

In the story of Lazarus is a grim humor, happily compared by Paulsen with that of a mediaeval Dance of Death, a grotesque, ironic politeness in Abraham's nonchalant conversation with the poor fellow in Hell, reminding one of those gruesome old pictures, where Death invites the rich and great, who have fared so well at the table of life, now to come and have a dance with him.

The attitude of Jesus toward earthly riches and power is ironical in that he affects to take seriously the point of view of those who take these things so seriously, as in answering the question, "Is it lawful to give tribute to Caesar?"—itself introduced by the Pharisees and the Herodians with an impertinent irony not lost on the quick comprehension of Jesus. "Bring me a denarius that I may see it," he replied. And they brought it. "Whose is this image and super-scription?" [As if he did not know!] And they say unto him, "Caesar's." And Jesus said unto them, "Render unto Caesar the things that are Caesar's [i.e., you enjoy Rome's civic protection, and use her coin, and should not object to taxation] and unto God"—here abandoning all pretense of concern for such matters, and dismissing them with eloquent speed—"and unto God the things that are God's."

He saw the irony in the rich man's care of his possessions, which are not only of no positive value, but actual hindrances to getting the real values of life and the Kingdom of Heaven. "The ground of a certain rich man," so runs one of his stories—"brought forth plentifully, and he reasoned with himself, saying, 'What shall I do, because I have not where to bestow my fruits?' And he said, 'This will I do: I will pull down my barns and build greater; and there will I bestow my corn and my goods, and I will say to my soul, Soul, thou hast much goods laid up for many years; take thine ease, eat, drink, and be merry!' But God said unto him, 'Thou foolish one, this night is thy soul required of thee, and the things which thou hast prepared, whose shall they be?' So he that layeth up treasure for himself and is not rich toward God."

He saw the irony in his own end: in the Gardens of Gethsemane on the Mount of Olives, when the coming of the chief priests and the captains of the temple and the elders awoke the disciples sleeping for sorrow even as Jesus in sorrow had come from his prayer and was standing over them, he turned to his enemies; and to Judas he said, "Betrayest thou the Son of Man with a kiss?"—and to those who seized him, "Are ye come out as against a robber with swords and staves?"

And the bitter irony of it all must have filled his soul before the High Priest, who believed with fatuous ignorance that this man, the best of his race, must perish, lest the whole ancient order and all righteousness be undone; and before Pilate who, possessing the power of this world, was yet so powerless against the spiritual King of the Jews, to whom Jesus vouchsafed only the laconic "Thou sayest," as the irony of the situation compelled him to an irony

of attitude toward it. The bitter irony of it all must have filled his soul under the jeers and the scourging in the house of Caiaphas, under the crucifixion on the hill—until his broken spirit joined the defeated mortality of yesterday's twice ten thousand years with the despairing cry ,"My God, my God, why hast thou forsaken me!"

Indeed, the irony of Jesus has been succeeded by the irony of history: as Jesus mocked the sin, weakness, and folly of Time, so has Time in its sin, weakness, and folly mocked Jesus. It preferred Barabbas, the destroyer, to him, the redeemer; it crucified the most honest of men between two thieves. And thereafter it made the lover a tyrant; him who would suffer the little children to come unto his bosom it transformed into the fiend that whipped them into Hell; his spiritual institutions it parodied in the vast systems of the theologizing intellect; discipleship to him, which he said (or someone speaking in his spirit said) was in loving one another, it made dependent upon a metaphysical "credo quia absurdum." The Brother of Peace it made the source of one half and the excuse of the other half of the wars of the East and West and North and South; and the rejecter of all earthly goods, the contemner of all earthly magnificence, the way-faring preacher in sandals and girdle, it gave over to be represented and defended by Pontiff and Prince, clad in robes of cardinal and purple and dwelling in palaces of marble and gold.

JESUS EXPOUNDS HIS GOSPEL *

Ivan Nazhivin

After the Feast of Tabernacles Andreas persuaded his brother Simon to go with him to Capernaum. He had succeeded in alarming his brother by many dark hints of possible danger: he had suggested that the Rabbi was often overbold, that he came out too openly against the rulers of the temple. It would be

---

* The title of this selection has been supplied by the Editor.

THE STORY OF JESUS

better for them to have a look round at home and think things over. For without realizing where he was going a man might get involved in an evil business from which there was no way out. . . . Jacob the son of Zebediah and the red-haired Reuben had also left, but they had gone to spread the news of Johanan's execution among the people, to win new adherents and generally to make efforts to rally all possible support for Jeshua, whose veneration by the people they had seen with their own eyes. . . . On the other hand, Jeshua had been joined by two brothers from Gadarene, on the far side of the lake, who belonged to the band of rebels: Jonas, short, alert and good-natured, and Jehudiel, a sturdy and morose man with a sword slash across his face, whose only words were of revenge on all the enemies of the people. They carefully observed everything that was going on around Jeshua, as if they were expecting something to happen; from time to time they would disappear, and then turn up again. . . . The benevolent Thomas, too, would come to listen. Johanna also was always with the Rabbi, whose words had brought her under their spell. And there were many others who would be with the young Rabbi for a day or two and would then go away in doubt, giving place to other listeners of the same type. . . . And there came, too, from Magdala, the hunchback with the placid face.

One evening—it was already in the month of Marcheshvan—Jeshua at last made up his mind to visit Nicodemus, the member of the Sanhedrin. Nicodemus had often met him in the city and had always given him a very friendly greeting. The great house stood on the square over against the prætorium. It was magnificently furnished, but there was also a touch of neglect about everything in it, as there was about its master's clothing: it was clear that the owner of the house did not notice the gorgeous trappings and lived as it were in a world remote from them.

His workroom was piled up almost to the roof with every imaginable Hebrew and foreign work. Nicodemus had traveled a great deal: he had been in Athens and Rome, Egypt, Babylon, and Syria. He belonged to the party of the Pharisees, although his outlook was very far removed from that of the Pharisees. He was only a tireless seeker after truth. The Pharisees did not like him, on account of his free intercourse with foreigners; and the Sadducees also did not regard him as one of themselves, being suspicious of his leanings towards free thought. But nevertheless, against their will, they had to respect him as an intelligent man who had had wide experience. He was a member of the court department of the Sanhedrin, the so-called Beth-Din, the "house of justice." The authorities valued his knowledge of the law, and the people esteemed him for his generosity.

Jeshua responded to Nicodemus's hospitable welcome, and then glanced through some of the innumerable papyrus rolls without paying very close attention to them. After a while Nicodemus proposed to his guest that they should go up to the roof chamber, where they would be further from the servants and would be better able to converse in the darkness.

The night was still and warm, but overhead a gale seemed to be blowing. The clouds were driving swiftly across the stars, and the young moon was plunging through them. Sleep had already descended on the city. In the outlying parts, under the walls and in the gardens there was the incessant barking of dogs. The howling and barking of jackals from the Mount of Olives was faintly discernible. Only a few lights still burned in the dark city. . . .

They sat on a carpet, and for a long while were silent. Their hearts were peaceful and happy. But there was one subject, the most important subject, on which they wanted to talk. There was something which at one moment would light up their souls with the smile of spring, and then in the next moment would turn into thunder and lightning, or torture them with the madness of imperfect knowledge and a scorching thirst for the ultimate revelation.

"Yes, I have often heard you, Rabbi," Nicodemus at last broke the silence. "But I should like you to explain your doctrine to me fully, without reserve. . . ."

"Why should I hide anything from you?" Jeshua replied.

"You must not forget that I am a member of the Sanhedrin," Nicodemus answered with an ironical smile. "But I beg of you: trust me, and tell me everything. My soul too is yearning for truth. . . . In what does your doctrine consist?"

"I have no doctrine," Jeshua said. "I speak only what the Father puts into my heart. . . ."

"What Father?"

"God. . . ."

"You regard yourself as the son of God?"

"I think that all men are sons of God," Jeshua answered with conviction. "We all have one Father—God; we are all brothers, and the law which the Father has given us is one—love God and thy neighbor not only as thyself, but even more than thyself. . . ."

"And whom do you count as your neighbor?"

A warm light filled Jeshua's eyes: without intending it, Nicodemus had stirred his most secret thoughts, thoughts which he nurtured in his soul as a mother does the child in her womb.

"I would rather answer in a parable . . ." said Jeshua, after a moment's silence, and then he began, with a touch of solemnity: "A man was journeying from Jerusalem to Jericho, and he fell among thieves who stripped him of his raiment, and wounded him and departed, leaving him half dead. A priest came along, saw him and passed by. Then came a Levite, who also looked at him and passed by. A Samaritan who was passing looked at him and took pity on him, bound up his wounds, put him on his ass, and brought him to an inn, and took care of him. On the next day, before he departed, the Samaritan took out two denarii, gave them to the host of the inn and said to him: 'Take care of this wounded man, and if you have to spend more, I will pay it back to you on my return.' Which of these three do you think was the neighbor of that wounded man?"—and he turned to Nicodemus with shining eyes.

Nicodemus did not reply. He had a feeling of intense excitement: Jeshua had ventured to express something that lay deep in Nicodemus's soul. The mighty force of the new teaching which Jeshua had expounded there, under the stars which shone down on Jerusalem, could only be realized by those who knew the intense hatred cherished by the Jews against the heretical Samaritans, whom they regarded as "worse than the infidels." But Nicodemus had lived far too long among the Gentiles for him to nurture in his soul the fanatical Jewish hatred against people of other faiths. On his journeys he had made secret visits, without the knowledge of his compatriots, to the temples of Apollo, Dionysus, Hercules, Mithra, Adonis, Osiris, Isis and Hora, Baal and Astarte. He could not believe that the acropolis in Athens was empty and that the divinity dwelt only in the temple of Jerusalem. He even had a secret

leaning towards the religion of Mithra, which at that period was spreading more and more among the peoples of the Mediterranean. And this strange unusual man, with his simple and somewhat comic Galilean style of speech, this uneducated carpenter had suddenly expressed with remarkable clarity the secret thoughts which Nicodemus was hiding in his soul. . . . Nicodemus was moved, and could say nothing. Jeshua understood his silence, and a feeling of sympathy rose in his heart. . . .

"Have you lived much among the heathen?" Nicodemus asked at last.

"Yes, there are a good many of them among us in Galilee," Jeshua answered. "And I have also worked with the heathen in Tiberias, by our lake, in Tyre and in Sidon. . . . Everywhere men are men. . . ." he added quietly.

To Nicodemus this was something wonderful and magnificent. According to the law an uncircumcised man not only could not belong to God's people, but even his touch was defiling. It was not lawful to use wood from trees belonging to an infidel, or to light a fire with it. Even the bread baked with such a fire was proscribed. Nothing might be sold to a heathen which he might use for sacrifice to his disgusting idols. The hatred of the heathen was always increasing, and finally developed to such an extent that a proclamation was issued: "The Jew who kills a foreigner will not be delivered over by the Sanhedrin for execution, for the foreigner is not the neighbor of the Jew." And there is another passage: "If a foreigner falls into the sea, a Jew must not save him, for although it is written in the law—'thou shalt not defile thyself with thy neighbor's blood,' an infidel is not thy neighbor." The main reasons for the Jewish loathing and disgust for the foreigners was firstly that they were not circumcised, secondly that they ate swine-flesh, thirdly that they did not observe the Sabbath, and fourthly, that they presumed to represent the divinity in images—in a word, that they were audacious enough to live and think differently from the Jews.

"They are all men," Jeshua continued. "Their beliefs are various, it is true, but even Israel has not always had the same faith. The brazen snake in the wilderness and many idols of every kind in the highest places; Astarte and Baal. . . . The prophets in their time cast not a few of these gods into the Kidron. And now how do we stand? The Sadducees have their faith, the Pharisees theirs, and the Essenes yet another. . . ."

"The faiths of man are extremely varied," Nicodemus replied thoughtfully. "I remember once in Rome being present at a night service of the worshipers of Mithra. It was in winter, on the very day when the sun turns again towards summer, and all were waiting expectantly in pious prayer. Just at midnight priests carrying torches came out of the holy place and cried in joyous voices: Ἡ παεθένος τέτοκεν, αὔξει Οῶς'—which in our language signifies 'the virgin has given birth! The light has come!' And then all the faithful lighted their lamps and joyfully sang a holy song. . . . I saw also something of the same kind in Egypt: in the old temple at Denderah the whole starry sky is represented on one of the walls, and on it the goddess Isis with the little Hora in her arms. The Egyptians call her Queen of Heaven, Mother of God, Star of the Sea. . . . But," he stopped himself, noticing that Jeshua was showing signs of impatience, "I will not tire you with details. . . . But consider what I have found in all this multiplicity of faiths. Mithra was born of a chaste virgin. In the course of his life he had twelve pupils, and went with them from one end of the earth to the other, teaching and bringing light to men. Then he died, was buried, and rose again. And the faithful celebrate this resurrection even to this day. . . . They call him the Savior, and often represent him in the form of a lamb."

"I don't understand any of all that," Jeshua said gloomily.

"But just a moment . . ." Nicodemus rejoined. "That is the Mithra faith. But I saw just the same in Egypt. Among them arose Osiris, the Redeemer, who brought peace to men not by force of arms but by mercy and music. He too was betrayed and killed, and rose again. And in Abydos I was myself present at a feast in honor of the Redeemer, where the priests carried his coffin round among the faithful, while they cried triumphantly, 'Osiris has risen! Osiris has truly risen!' In Alphaka, too, in northern Syria, between Biblos and Baalbek, there is a cavern which has been famous since ancient times, a temple of Astarte, and near by a wooded gorge from which flows the river Adonis. I was told that Adonis or Tammuz was similarly born of a virgin, that he taught men goodness, that he was killed and rose again. Each autumn his death is mourned by the

Syrian women—it is noted by the prophet Ezekiel, chapter viii, verse 14—and each spring they celebrate his resurrection. And in Phrygia Attis also was born of a virgin; he met the same fate as the others, and men honor him and his glory with just the same piety. Among the Romans it is Hercules, miraculously begotten by a God, who brought much good to men, died, rose again, and went up to Heaven. Among the Greeks it is Zeus, who visited Semele, daughter of Cadmus king of Thebes, in a thundercloud, and she bore Dionysus the Redeemer. The disciples of the Greek teacher Pythagoras regarded him as an incarnation of God; it is said of Plato, another of the wise men among the Greeks, that his mother Periktiona conceived him of the God Apollo. . . . And in faraway India it was Krishna who was born in a cavern of the virgin Devaki. A bright star announced his birth to men. The enemies of the new-born child sought to destroy him, but as they could not find him the kings of those countries ordered all new-born children to be slain. But Krishna escaped death, wandered over the earth, and performed many miracles. He awaked people from the dead, healed lepers, the deaf and the blind, and protected the poor and the oppressed. And then his enemies killed him, some say with a bow-shot, while others maintain that he was crucified. Then he went down into hell for the redemption of sinners, and rising again, he ascended into heaven before the eyes of an immense multitude. The faithful say that on the last day of the world he will come to judge the living and the dead. . . . And so I have been thinking: as such Saviors appear in every part of the earth, are they not everywhere one and the same? . . . And perhaps it is true that all of this has been handed down by the ancients and that by the Savior is meant simply the sun, which . . ."

Jeshua suddenly rose.

"And you believe all this?" he asked, his voice trembling.

Nicodemus spread out his arms.

"We may want to believe it or not," he said gently, "but when we see that whole peoples believe it, it makes us think! And one thing is especially curious: they use different names and quarrel with each other, but when you look more closely into the matter, you find that it is all about one. . . ."

"Yes, about one . . ." Jeshua rejoined with warmth. "Everywhere the One! The chaste virgin, the crucifixion: some give it one name, some another, and they dispute among themselves. . . . And yet it is only words! . . . Perhaps it must be so," he interrupted himself. "I myself am so weak as sometimes to dispute about words, but always it is only words, dross, pretexts for the great divisions between men. . . . I know of nothing more terrible for men than this confusion of their thought. You ask me, wherein my faith lies. My faith is, above all, that I want to take from men these children's rattles, and free the truth from dross of any kind. . . ."

"But wherein lies truth?"

"Truth? Truth is: Love the Lord thy God with all thine heart and with all thy mind and with all thy might," Jeshua said in solemn tones, "and thy neighbor as thyself, and more than thyself, if that is possible. That is the whole law and the prophets, and there is not an iota more to be added, as the scribes are doing now: they are trying to add a second, a third, and a hundredth word, so that a fence rises around the law and there is so much enmity and bloodshed. In heaven is God, and on earth there are men, our brothers. Their one law is the voice of their heart. None of the rest is necessary—the chaste virgin, the legends, the fruitless sophistries which only cause dissension."

The air itself seemed to tremble at the vehemence with which Jeshua said this. But the sleeping city lay silent and dark, with the grim mass of the Antonia tower on one side and on the other the three-storied stone building of the temple with its golden roof. And opposite, across the square, the pillars of the prætorium showed white in the darkness. The last lights were extinguished, one after the other. . . .

THE TEACHING OF JESUS

J. Middleton Murry

The central conception of Jesus as teacher is the conception of the Kingdom of God. At all times he conceived the Kingdom of God under two aspects: objectively, as a mysterious condition of existence which was to descend upon the universal world—the actual reign of God—and, subjectively, as a condition of existence to be achieved by the individual within himself. The relation between these two conditions was simple. The man who achieved the new condition within himself would be, and knew that he would be, a partaker of the new condition when it overtook the universe.

The establishment of the objective condition in the universe, which we call, for mere distinction's sake, the Reign of God, was not a new idea in the Jewish religion. On the contrary, it was an old one; and it was one of the most living religious ideas of the pious Jew when Jesus began his ministry. Sometimes the Reign of God was understood materially, as a triumph of Israel, with God for their King, over all the nations of the earth; sometimes with a high degree of spirituality, as in the belief (not held by Paul alone) that the Jews were the chosen nation only in the sense that they had received "the oracles of God." Thus their partaking of the Reign of God depended upon their obedience to those oracles. Obviously such a conception was capable of a profound spiritual significance, and in the mind of the highly spiritual Jew the triumph of Israel over the nations might well become little less than the ultimate union of the world under the immediate sovereignty of God.

Between the world as it was and the Reign of God, clearly a gulf was fixed. The religious imagination of the Jew was busy, in the years immediately before the birth of Christ, in striving to bridge the gulf; to fill it, so to speak, with a picture of the mighty transition. The picture thus created was eschatology, the science of the last things. It had no firm outlines, it was still in actual process of creation when Jesus appeared. Jesus himself was to give it a transcendent form. So that, to a certain but very limited extent, those are right who would regard Jesus as the great eschatological prophet. He was that, indeed, but that was the less important part of him.

Though the outlines of the picture of last things were vague and variable, certain things in it were fixed; above all, the coming of a supernatural figure called Messiah, and the judgment of the world by him. This judgment was essential, for only those who had by their lives deserved the reward could be partakers of the Reign of God; the others must be swept away. Again, the general belief was agreed that a forerunner would come to announce the advent of Messiah, and that this forerunner would be Elijah.

All this Jesus, as prophet, accepted: these were to him the conditions of the objective manifestation of the Reign of God. As a teacher, he was not greatly concerned with them; as prophet and as Messiah-to-be, he was. As teacher, he was above all concerned with the attainment by the individual man of the subjective Kingdom of God. If this were achieved, the Last Things could take care of themselves: the members of the Kingdom of God could be *sure* of partaking of the Reign of God. Indubitably Jesus believed, when he began his ministry, that the Reign of God was imminent. But the prime importance to him of that impending cosmic revolution was that it made unspeakably urgent the achievement of the Kingdom of God within the individual that he might partake of the Reign of God. It was a call upon him to change his mind and soul.

Much and grievous misunderstanding of Jesus' teaching has been caused by rendering Jesus' call for a change of mind and soul as a call for "repentance." "Repentance" is ultimately a Pauline conception, which depends for its force upon an extreme consciousness of sin. The word, and above all the consciousness behind the word, has no real place in Jesus' thought or teaching, which was profoundly different and quite differently profound from Paul's. It was of another and a higher order.

The achievement of the Kingdom of God in the individual was for Jesus supereminently a natural process. It was a passing beyond the condition of strain and effort. There were, for him, three stages in the life of man: the unconscious life of the child, the conscious life of the man, and the new life of the member of the Kingdom. In the unconscious life of the child there was spontaneity and wholeness; in the conscious life of the man there was inhibition and division; in the new life of the member of the Kingdom, there was spontaneity and wholeness once more. Jesus taught, in the fullest sense of the word, the necessity and possibility of rebirth, not in the narrow and sectarian meaning, but with a new positiveness. The Pauline conception of unsleeping war between the soul and the body would have been abhorrent to him. Wholeness and spontaneity— these were the marks of the member of the Kingdom.

This is the meaning of his singular insistence that children are by nature and birthright members of the Kingdom, and therefore examples of the change that must overtake men; and unless the attainment of the Kingdom within the individual can be conceived as the entry into a new condition of wholeness, wherein after a period of separation knowing and being are once more at one, the significance of Jesus' teaching cannot be apprehended. "To do the will of God," for instance, meant for Jesus something very different from what is generally understood by the words. For Jesus, the will of the reborn man was *identical* with the will of God. There was no effort: it was no question of keeping commandments. "The Sabbath was made for man, not man for the Sabbath, therefore man is lord also of the Sabbath." The keeping of commandments, even of the two commandments which for Jesus comprehended the whole of the Law, was not so much insufficient as irrelevant. The member of the Kingdom did the will of God because he embodied the will of God.

The crucial reference for the teaching of "the mystery of the Kingdom of God" is the fourth chapter of Mark. If it be accepted that Mark's gospel is based upon the reminiscences of Peter, the fundamental importance of that chapter, in itself obvious, is immeasurably enhanced. There is singularly little of Jesus' teaching in Mark's Gospel; and the significance of the one chapter that is wholly devoted to it is increased accordingly. We may conclude that Peter believed that the real essence of Jesus' message was contained therein.

The immediately striking features of the chapter are, first, that the parables in it are wholly concerned with the sowing and growing of seed, and, second, that these parables are accompanied by some of the hardest of all Jesus' sayings. After speaking the parable of the Sower to the crowd at large, and ending with the almost esoteric formula: "He that can understand, let him understand," Jesus was asked for an explanation. He gave it, and the explanation, unlike other explanations of parables in the Gospels, is palpably authentic. But Jesus was plainly disappointed with the failure of his disciples to comprehend the first of his parables of the mystery of the Kingdom. "You do not understand this parable! How then will you understand the rest of the parables?" And, again, after giving his explanation, he said:

"Is a lamp brought to be put under a basket or a bed? Is it not to be put on a lamp-stand?

"For there is nothing hidden except to be revealed; nor is anything mysterious except to be made plain.

"He that can understand, let him understand."

That is to say—surely the meaning is unmistakable—that if Jesus spoke mysteriously, it was because he could do no other. In his strange parables, his mysterious words, was a light, an aid to direct comprehension; and in them he used his light as a light should be used, not to make things dark, but to make them clear. He went on:

"Take care what you understand. For with the measure with which you measure, it shall be measured to you again, and more added. For to him that hath, it shall be given: and from him that hath not shall be taken away even that which he hath."

It is clear that the two sayings, of which one is indeed hard, express, with the parallelism of Hebrew poetry, the same meaning; it is also clear that the saying: "With what measure you measure, it shall be measured to you again, and more added," whatever may be its application in other and later contexts, has here, in its original place, nothing to do with conduct. Jesus is not telling his disciples to take care what they do, but to take care what they hear; he is saying that in proportion to their understanding of his words they shall be recompensed, but not equally—more shall be given to them as a free gift. Likewise the saying: "To him that hath, it shall be given; and from him that hath not it shall be taken, even that which he hath," applies not to money, but to the same thing, namely understanding. These two grim sayings—and they are grim—have precisely the same meaning. If a man have a spark of understanding, it will be made a flame: if he have no spark, he is condemned forever to darkness.

But understanding of *what*? That is clear: the understanding of "the mystery of the Kingdom of God," which he sought to make clear in his parables of sowing and of seed. And the parables precisely fit the dark sayings. There is the sower who went forth to sow, and some of his seed fell on good ground and brought forth some *thirty, some sixty, some an hundredfold*. . . . "To him that hath, it shall be *given* . . . with the measure wherewith you measure it, it shall be measured to you again, and *more added*." There is a natural, yet miraculous growth in the soul of him who is able to receive the word. Again, "The Kingdom of God is as when a man casts seed on the earth, and sleeps by night and wakes by day, and the seed sprouts and shoots up—*he knows not how*. . . . *Of itself* the earth bears fruit, first the green leaf, then the ear, then the full corn in the ear." Let but the seed be given its earth in the human soul, and the growth follows, inevitable, incommensurable, by no act of the man. Again, the Kingdom is like a grain of mustard seed, the smallest seed of all, yet it leaps up and becomes a tree which birds may roost in.

It is not really possible to mistake Jesus' meaning: he is speaking of the human soul and the knowledge of the mystery of the Kingdom of God. If a man can understand a little, he will understand all—swiftly, but naturally. No arduous intellectual effort is necessary, nor will it avail him. Given the gleam of understanding, full comprehension follows, not of the man himself. It happens: without the gleam nothing happens at all.

But *what* is the mystery? That Jesus himself could not expound. It was a true mystery, and he called it by that name. But the mystery of the Kingdom of God is the mystery of the Fatherhood of God—the vast and loving indifference of the Creator. To know this mystery a rebirth of the individual man is necessary: rebirth and knowledge go hand in hand. This knowledge is therefore either meaningless or true; but if a man understands, the understanding is wonderful. Suddenly he catches a glimpse, and it shines "like a treasure hid in a field which when a man finds he goes joyfully and sells all that he has to buy that field."

In Jesus' teaching the rebirth of the individual man was a birth into a knowledge of God as Father. Apart from this rebirth, God could not be known; to know him was to know him as Father. Therefore, to assert or deny the fatherhood of God, without experience of this rebirth, is to utter empty words. Only those who have become God's sons can know him as Father. This is the real meaning of the famous sentence: "No man knoweth the Son but the Father, nor the Father save the Son." It is probable, and it has been supposed in the previous narrative, that these words were spoken at a moment when Jesus had realized that his teaching of rebirth had been rejected, and he had no choice but to believe himself the only actual son of God; but it is certain that the knowledge of God as Father which he claimed for himself was unique only by bitter accident. He taught that potentially all men were God's sons in precisely the same sense as he: the tragedy was that they refused to realize their potentialities.

To be reborn was to know God as Father with the same immediate knowledge that Jesus had achieved. But what was it—to know God as Father? Unfortunately, unless a man has felt in himself the need, and touched in himself the experience of rebirth, it is impossible to convey to him even an inkling of the content of this knowledge, concerning which Jesus himself spoke the inexorable sentence: "To him that hath, it shall be given, and from him that hath not shall be taken away that which he hath." But, although there was in Jesus' experience of God a quality peculiar to himself, an ineffable sweetness of personal reunion, which directly derived from the personal quality of Jesus himself, the *kind* of the experience was not unique: it can be paralleled exactly from the experience of great saints and great poets. Fundamentally, it was an act of profound obeisance to the apprehended wonder and beauty of the universe—a sudden and forever incontrovertible seeing that all things have their place and purpose in a great harmony. This is the meaning of Jesus' words:

"Love your enemies, and pray for them that do you harm. That thus ye may be sons of your Father: for he makes his sun to rise upon good men and bad, and his rain to fall upon the just and the unjust."

The utterance is crucial, for it reveals that to know the Father is to know, and to be filled with love for, the power which makes no distinction between good men and bad, just and unjust. That power which created the ineffable harmony of good and evil in the world created it with the surpassing love of the great Demiurge: and those who can for a moment see the universe with the Father's eyes must love it with *his* love.

It is manifest that a command to show love of the kind enjoined by Jesus in that saying cannot be obeyed, except by the reborn man. In order to be sons of the Father, men must know the Father; in order to love like the Father, they must know how the Father loves; in order to be perfect like the Father, they must know how the Father is perfect. Jesus' teaching of conduct is therefore in the main an enunciation of the spontaneous acts of the reborn man. When he sought to reduce it into the form of commandments, it was comprised in two simple ones which, being commands to love, are impossible to obey. No man can love either God or his neighbor

by taking thought; nor is love an end in itself to be pursued. Indeed, it cannot be pursued without falsity. And again, it is utterly impossible to separate loving one's neighbor from its first source, in loving God; until you can love your neighbor with God's love, you cannot really love him; until you know God you cannot know what his love is. The loving of men which can exist apart from the knowing of God is not love, as Jesus meant it, at all. The man who knows God knows immediately that he must forgive his enemies; and the man who does not know immediately that he must not resist evil, does not know God.

Of this order is most of Jesus' teaching of conduct: it is a *description* of the spontaneous and necessary acts of the man reborn into membership of the Kingdom and knowledge of the Fatherhood of God. Men were to be reborn into a new condition of being in which they naturally did the will of God; as one thus reborn, Jesus spoke and performed the will of God. If we conceive rebirth as the creation of a living and unbroken unity between the member of the Kingdom and God himself, we can distinguish two kinds in Jesus' teaching of conduct: he enjoined not only acts which were the fruit of this union between man and God, but also acts which should remove obstacles to this union. He declared what men did when they were reborn; and declared also what men must do if they desired to be reborn.

To the latter kind belongs his unmistakable teaching concerning possessions, which can indeed be mistaken only by those whose chief concern is not to expound, but to make palatable Jesus' teaching. He again and again demanded the complete abandonment of all possessions: not because of any evil inherent in money as such, but because wealth was a mighty obstacle in the way of union with God. It is the fashion among commentators to speak of the injunction to absolute poverty as "the Ebionite heresy." But who declared the Ebionites heretical? Not Jesus.

Nevertheless, it would be foreign to the spirit of Jesus' teaching to press the injunction to poverty in isolation. Not the possession of wealth so much as the attachment to wealth was what he denounced. "You cannot *serve* God and Mammon." And Jesus believed that the possession of wealth almost inevitably involved attachment to it, and consequently an inability to receive and respond to the teaching of the Kingdom. In the parable of the Sower the "deceit of riches" is represented as among the influences most hostile to an understanding of the mystery of the Kingdom.

But wealth is but one form of attachment to the unregenerate life. Jesus no less peremptorily enjoined the dissolution of far more precious attachments, the abandonment of home and family. And it would be dishonest to mitigate the injunction. Jesus evidently believed that a complete severance from all attachments whatsoever was a necessary preliminary of complete rebirth. We know he had chosen this path himself, and we know the result that was obtained thereby; we may understand, therefore, that Jesus' teaching of this necessity is extreme. He demands that, in order to prepare the way for the union of complete suffusion by God, a man should "hate his father and his mother, aye, and even his own life"; he demands, if need should be, even physical mutilation. "If thine eye is an obstacle, pluck it out and cast it from thee. . . ."

But it is all-important to realize that this ruthless rejection of all attachments is simply a means to the great end—the preparation of the good soil into which the mystery of the Kingdom may be received, and the swift and sudden growth into the knowledge that God is Father and men his sons. There is an ascetic side to Jesus' teaching; but this asceticism is as it were the preliminary technique of attainment. The goal once attained, the element of self-constraint immediately disappears; as Jesus fasted in the Wilderness, but never again. A new, rich spontaneity of life is achieved: the living water wells upward from the depths and flows gaily through the new-born man; in this newness of life attachments are not refused, the condition of attachment becomes simply impossible. The reborn son of God moves with an utter freedom through the worldly life. He does not need to hold himself aloof from it. No tension of the will nor rigor of denial is required of him. He is become simply incapable of attachments, because he is become wholly the living and conscious instrument of God's will. God has gained a new organ of expression, therefore his mere living is secured to him by God, and mere living—the maintenance of his physical body as the perfect organ of God's will—is all that he needs or desires.

"Do not go seeking for food and drink, and do not worry. It is the pagans of the world who set their minds on these. But your Father knows that you need them. Seek for his Kingdom, and these things shall be given you also."

The famous passage to which these words are the conclusion—"Take no thought for the morrow, what ye shall eat and what ye shall drink"—has in it not the faintest tinge of ascetic rigor. It is a description of the life of an achieved member of the Kingdom, not a command to abnegation as a means of entering it. The asceticism of Jesus' teaching applies only to the period of preparation; the preparation past, and rebirth achieved, the asceticism also is past, and the care-free life begins. For the new-born son the essentials of life are provided by God: he becomes one with the birds of the air and the lilies of the field. He sups joyfully with tax-gatherers and sinners, he gladly receives the harlot's perfume and loves the gift for "a thing of beauty"; he is to the eye of ascetic rigor "a gluttonous man and a winebibber." He lives, to outward seeming, at all adventure; he absolutely rejects all rules and ordinances; he fasts or feasts at his own sweet will, which is the sweet will of God. The member of the Kingdom is *an absolutely free man*, because he is absolutely obedient to God's will; and it is possible for him to be thus absolutely obedient because, by the preliminary abandonment of all attachments, he has made himself perfectly responsive to the voice of God.

Forgiveness, love, non-resistance to evil—these follow as the night the day in the new condition. The secret of it is that "You must be perfect as your Father in heaven is perfect." Man becomes one with God: just as God makes his sun rise on the evil man and the good, so the son of God loves the evil man and the good alike. He sees, as with God's own eyes, that these things must be so and not otherwise, and that evil will never be overcome save by the goodness which knows that evil has its own perfect right to existence. The goodness which denies evil, and rules directly to destroy it, is not goodness at all, for it is not in accordance with that perfection of God which has created evil and good alike. The perfect tolerance of God must be achieved by man.

Therein we touch the secret center of Jesus' profoundest teaching: it is no less than that man must *be* God. It is the highest and the truest wisdom ever taught to men; and of the man who lived it is no mystery that his followers should have come to believe that he was God made man. There was nothing else for them to believe. And even to-day there are only two things that can be believed about Jesus by those who can see the facts at all. Either Jesus was God made man, or he was man made God. It is easier and less exacting to believe the former: but the latter is the truth.

Perhaps it is unnecessary to say more concerning Jesus' teaching of the subjective attainment of the Kingdom of God. The teaching is, and was avowed by Jesus himself to be, either self-evident or incomprehensible. But it is necessary to insist that there was from the beginning a vital connection between the subjective attainment of the Kingdom, and the objective establishment of the Reign of God. The imminence of the Reign of God is everywhere presupposed in Jesus' teaching. The attainment of the subjective Kingdom carried with it the certainty of sharing in the objective Reign. The single phrase, the Kingdom of God, was used by Jesus in both meanings: and those are wholly wrong who would interpret it rigidly in one sense or the other. The meaning of the phrase is always apparent from the context. What is evident is that the profound originality of Jesus' teaching lies in his subjective teaching.

For, as we have said, the belief in the imminence of the objective Reign of God was by no means new in Jewish religion. John the Baptist had proclaimed it, and Jesus had followed him. Jesus had, so to speak, inherited from John the certainty that God's judgment was near at hand. Into the form of this inherited certainty he poured a new knowledge, of the nature of God and his judgment, and of the means by which a man could make himself secure of God's judgment. Thus, inevitably, the nature of the Reign of God was completely changed from what it had been to John the Baptist: it was changed from the transcendental theocracy established through the stern and awful judgment of God's Messiah into the blessed company of reborn and reunited sons of God. The Judgment was indeed still to come, but men had now, if they would but hear the glad tidings, a means of knowing beyond all doubt that they would be received in joy by a loving Father.

Therefore Jesus could truly say that John the Baptist had no part in the Kingdom of God: he did not know what it was.

"Verily, I tell you: among men born of women there has not arisen a greater than John the Baptist. But the least in the Kingdom of God is greater than he."

And a yet subtler and more profound distinction was to follow.

"From the days of John the Baptist until now the Kingdom of God suffers violence, and violent men snatch it to themselves. For all the Prophets and the Law prophesied until John. And if you can receive it, this is Elijah that was to come. He that hath ears let him hear!"

With the reference to John as the forerunner of himself, now become Messiah-to-be, which dates the saying as belonging to the time at Cæsarea Philippi, we are not now concerned. But the "violence" that was being done to the Kingdom of God from the days of John until the moment of Jesus' speaking, was the violence done to it by Jesus and those who understood his teaching. By achieving the Kingdom within themselves, they compelled the coming of the Reign. This may appear a violent argument; but, of course, it is not an *argument*. The attainment of union with God, as of a son with a Father, was in itself the guaranty that this condition was on the brink of perpetuation. The true disciple of Jesus, as it were, tasted already the joys of the eternal Kingdom, and with them the certainty that its establishment forever was but a matter of days. Thus, the member of the Kingdom, who comprehended the mystery of the Kingdom, compelled its coming. John the Baptist could only wait for it.

Therefore John belonged to the old order, the past dispensation; he was reckoned with the Law and the Prophets. For all his greatness, Jesus reckoned him as making one in the essential with the Pharisees who asked when the Kingdom would come, to whom he declared:

"The Kingdom of God will not come by watching for it; nor will men say, 'Here it is!' or 'There it is.' For, behold, the Kingdom of God is within you."

That did not mean, at all, for Jesus, that the Kingdom of God was only within men, purely subjective; but that the objective event could only be brought to pass by the subjective attainment.

Because Jesus' teaching of the Kingdom was thus rooted in subjectivity it has an eternal validity. No earthly disappointment can touch it. The Kingdom of God which has not come is the Kingdom which comes by watching; it will never come. The only

Kingdom of God which can come is that which Jesus taught; and if in the fullness of time it comes indeed, it will have come precisely as he taught that it would come, by the sacred "violence" which men will have done to it, and to themselves.

This was Jesus' only *teaching* of the Kingdom. It belongs to his ministry before Cæsarea Philippi: after Cæsarea Philippi he spoke differently concerning it, because he was then no longer a teacher, but the chosen Judge of humankind. He had found that men would not listen to his teaching, or, if they would listen, could not understand. They would not, they could not, by their own attainment, compel the Kingdom to come. There was nothing for it: Jesus alone, unaided, uncomprehended, would pluck down the Kingdom for them. He had waited for the Messiah in vain; now he would *be* Messiah, and men's Judge. No more sublime purpose has been conceived by the human mind than that which Jesus conceived when he made the Messiah—himself; and he not only conceived this purpose, but followed and endured it to the end. And if we need to seek for motives of this supreme dedication of himself, we shall find the deepest in his title and his words in the sentence, "The Son of Man came not to be served, but to serve, and to give his life a ransom for many." What men would not and could not receive from him as teacher, he would force upon them by becoming God's Messiah.

It could not be done. He was not God's Messiah, and at the last he knew it. But that a teacher of wisdom should have had the loving courage of that attempt to fathom and forestall the inscrutable purposes of God is an event in the history of mankind which even to-day has scarcely begun its full work upon the minds and souls of men. That final, deliberate act of sublime imagination and lonely heroism, absolutely differentiates the teaching of Jesus from that of other profound teachers of mankind. The teaching of Jesus is not his teaching only; it is his life and death.

Nevertheless, to understand it, we must keep distinct Jesus the teacher and Jesus the Saviour; we must remember always that it was only because of men's blindness of soul and hardness of heart that Jesus became the Saviour. And if we insist on regarding him as the Saviour, we become like the Pharisees who expected salvation as an external event. True, Jesus tried to give it thus to men who could not take it otherwise: but he knew at the last, as he had known at the beginning, that it could not be given save "to him that hath."

Nor can the conception of Jesus as Saviour and the teaching of Jesus ever be truly reconciled, for Jesus taught that the member of the Kingdom entered into an immediate relation to God. Therefore the idea that this relation should be mediated strikes at the very heart of his teaching. That Jesus himself did verily lay down his life to mediate it, that he did in fact succeed, in another way than any he had dreamed, in mediating it, does not affect the truth that he chose this path as a counsel of despair—a sublime *pis-aller*. To put the matter simply, to one who does veritably acknowledge the truth of Jesus' teaching, Jesus cannot be more than fellow-son or brother. Greatest of brothers, first of sons, no doubt: but the moment he becomes different in nature from fellow-son or brother, what he taught as teacher is denied.

And it is not possible to understand the teaching of Jesus and to deny it. To understand it is to accept it: it is either meaningless or true. It is, essentially, an *obvious* teaching. But obvious only to those who have in them a gleam of knowledge of the condition of life which it promises and from which it springs. "To him that hath it shall be given; and from him that hath not it shall be taken away, even that which he hath" is really a definition of the nature of the knowledge which Jesus taught. It is a knowledge which can be apprehended only through a change in the learner's being. To understand the teaching of the Kingdom, a man must already be of the Kingdom.

Futile, therefore, to attempt to expound the teaching of Jesus in detail. All that may be done is to indicate, as we have tried to do, the living center from which alone it can be apprehended in the spontaneous beauty of its truth. If a single word must be found to describe his teaching, it shall be this word "spontaneous." Indeed, if the significance of this word "spontaneous," applied to a fully conscious human being, be understood, the teaching itself is understood. It is a teaching of a profound and final human wisdom; therefore it is spontaneous; for spontaneity is the consummation of wisdom.

In other words, Jesus' teaching is, and is eternal because it is, a teaching of life. Life cannot be taught, it can only be lived and known. Those alone understand the teaching of Jesus who know that it is not teaching at all, but simply the living utterance of one who had achieved rebirth into a new condition of life. Its purpose is to create this new life in others, and in those who have ears to hear it new life is immediately born. Whether Jesus himself spoke, or the author of the fourth Gospel imagined them, the secret of Jesus' teaching is in the words, "I came that ye might have life, and have it more abundantly." The teaching of Jesus is a gay teaching, as all teaching of life must be. Good news, indeed: a promise of infinite riches: "Seek ye first the Kingdom of Heaven, and all these things shall be added unto you."

JESUS
AS THE PHARISEES SAW HIM

Edmond Fleg

M. Fleg has written the story of Jesus from the point of view of the Wandering Jew. The chapter reprinted here gives a good idea of how the Nazarene, in full career, may have been regarded by the Pharisees.

———————

The inn was filling up. Crowds arrived from Judæa and Idumæa, from the borders of Tyre and Sidon, from Decapolis, and other countries from beyond the Jordan. You can imagine how the inn-keepers put up their prices! They even had to turn people away!

One morning, Baruch and Reuben carried me out of the town on my litter in the direction from which we had come. Were they taking me home? I raged helplessly.

But Aunt Sephora, who was following with my uncle, said softly:

"You are going to see him."

Could it be true? Now I understood why the road was almost impassable. There were crowds in front of me, crowds behind me—all were moving towards him.

"Whom will he heal?"

We halted in the plain, a little beyond the peak near the Seven Springs—you know it, don't you?

I could not see a single blade of grass; wherever I looked there were bodies—upright, seated, recumbent—wedged closely together. Beside me, a figure shook with palsy; a little way off, I caught sight of a face that was a running mass of sores.

"I wonder how many paralytics there are," I thought.

To my left, a voice repeated the miracle of the water changed into wine at the wedding-feast at Cana. There was a murmur of prayers and, at intervals, a hideous outcry that sounded as though a thousand dogs had howled in unison.

"A man possessed by devils," explained Aunt Sephora.

Suddenly, there were ripples of excitement in the throng.

"They are coming! They are coming!"

"Up there! On the mountain!"

"Five of them are coming the other way! Now they have met! Let us climb up to them!"

"No, he wishes to be alone with the Twelve!"

"Look, they are sitting in a semi-circle as though they were at school!"

"He is going to speak to them! He is speaking to them!"

I could see nothing: nothing but backs, heads, uplifted arms that blotted out the mountain and the sky. . . .

Now the multitude was on the move again. My litter jolted up the path. We were drawing near! I was drawing near! . . . But how far I had still to go!

"Do you hear his voice?"

I could not hear a sound!

Another day, my litter was set down on the shore between two blind men who were guided by dogs.

Fingers pointed to a sail that glided over the sea. It came closer, grew larger as it approached, and was hauled down; as the ship neared land, the anchor was dropped.

To left and right of me, from the slopes behind me, there was a burst of acclamation. Someone stood on the deck, with the sun behind him. I could not distinguish his face, I could only see a figure that spoke. How sweetly the words were borne to me across the water! They fell on my listening ears as though they had been uttered for me alone!

"Blessed be ye poor, for yours is the Kingdom of

God! Blessed are the meek, for they shall inherit the earth! Blessed are ye that hunger now, for ye shall be filled! Blessed are ye that weep now, for ye shall laugh! Blessed are the merciful, for they shall find mercy! Blessed are the peace-makers, for they shall see God! . . ."

As I listened, I was filled with an ecstasy of wonder!

Blessed art thou! . . . Every fibre in my body quivered with the realisation of the falseness of all I had hitherto felt and believed. . . .

Because thou dost suffer, thou art blessed! . . . Everything whirled before my eyes. . . . Would the mountains flow like rivers? Would the sea arise like a mountain?

The others, they had never suffered—they were the unblessed! . . . Was everything reversed? Had white become black? Black become white? Was grief joy—joy grief? . . .

Blessed art thou . . . for thine is the Kingdom of Heaven! . . . The Kingdom of Heaven for me? For me who knew nothing, had nothing? Was it *because* I had nothing, *because* I was nothing, that I would be given the sum of joy, be joy incarnate? . . .

I listened to much more that was lovely that day; for he said: "Unto him that smiteth thee on one cheek, offer also the other," and: "Him that taketh away thy coat, forbid him not to take thy cloak also." He told us to love and forgive our enemies, set forth countless precepts that he must already have set forth, and which I was to hear again and again—for he never feared to repeat his counsels. As I listened, I was filled with such tenderness as I had never yet known.

"Has the Kingdom come?" I thought. "No—if the Kingdom had come, I should arise and walk! . . . When will he say to me: 'Take up thy bed, and walk'?"

The sail had once again been hoisted, the anchor weighed. Smaller and smaller grew the ship as it glided over the waves into the sun. . . .

That night, there were debates and discussions in the courtyard of the inn. In those blessed days, the Jews had not yet reached the point of splitting hairs in four, but they already split them into three!

Amongst the rest, was a Scribe called Doeg, a former pupil of Schammai, whom my uncle had known in Jerusalem when he himself was being taught by Hillel. This Scribe was muttering in a corner.

"He speaks eloquently, I admit," he contended. "But are they his own words? 'The meek shall inherit the earth' comes from the Psalms. 'Comfort to all that mourn' was promised in Isaiah. 'Love thy neighbour as thyself' comes from Moses, and Ben Sirach said: 'Forgive and ye shall be forgiven.'"

But Uncle Simeon replied thoughtfully:

"What matter if these things have already been said? He says them differently. It seemed to me that I had never heard them before. . . ."

There was a good deal of truth in my Uncle Simeon's words. Since then, I myself have compared the passages—one has to have some interest to occupy one's time during twenty centuries! I have read the parallels drawn by your scholars in their miscellanies between our Jewish precepts and those of Jesus. A resemblance is apparent in all of them; even the words are sometimes identical. Yes—Rabbi Tarphon spoke of the mote in the eye, and the beam; Rabbi Eliezer set forth that *yes* is an oath, and *no* is an oath, that spiritual adultery is as bad as adultery in the flesh, and that the hand which gives must not be conscious of giving. And so on down to *Our Father*, the essence of Christianity from beginning to end, yet from end to beginning—Jewish! . . . But in our writings, in the Old Testament, and the two Talmuds, the spirit of Christianity is sprinkled and diffused like the salt in the sea; whereas, in their Gospels it is condensed and compressed like the salicylic acid in aspirins. Moreover, the Christianity of the Gospels has a proprietary name—the name *Jesus!* . . .

"Granted that he says the same things differently," replied the Scribe. "But does he say them any better? To begin with, he does not even know his subject matter! Where, for instance, did he find in our writings: 'Thou shalt hate thine enemy'? It is nowhere written! And 'An eye for an eye, a tooth for a tooth!' Surely he must know that restitution has already taken the place of retaliation, and will take its place for ever!"

"Yes," answered my Uncle Simeon indulgently. "I noticed several discrepancies in his reasoning and quotations, but we must overlook them. He was not taught, as we were, by a Hillel or a Schammai! He taught himself, and will yet learn. We must give him time!"

"He is untaught—agreed," said Doeg. "Yet he presumes to teach a greater justice! Does not that of the Pharisees, yours, mine, suffice him? Do you remember that in his discourse from the ship—a discourse which he has already given, and to which, thanks to God's mercy, he does not give vent every day!—he said: 'Ye have heard that it was said by them of old time: Thou shalt not kill, and whosoever shall kill shall be in danger of the judgment; but I say unto you that whosoever is angry with his brother without a cause shall be in danger of the judgment, and whosoever shall say to his brother: *Raca!* shall be in danger of the Sanhedrin; but whosoever shall say: Thou fool! shall merit the punishment of *Gehinnom* * and hell-fire!' . . . It seems that a moment of anger is as great a sin as murder; that he who spews forth an insult is damned! Is this his greater justice?"

"He is still young, and has all the ardour of youth," responded my uncle mildly. "Even if he does exaggerate, our prophets fell into the same fault. He speaks both as a prophet and a rabbi. Hence your bewilderment—it is long since a prophet arose in our midst."

"Prophets—we have no need of prophets!" said the Scribe. "The wise men, the rabbis, have taken their place, and surpassed them! It lies with us to see that the Torah is observed!"

"But," timidly put in my cousin Reuben the Essene, "perhaps it is because the Kingdom is at hand that the Master exacts more than the Torah from the Torah!"

"Then why does he reiterate: 'Come unto me all ye that labour and are heavy-laden; my yoke is easy, and my burden is light'?" thrust back Doeg.

"Light!" exclaimed Baruch the Zealot. "Is it a light burden to labour for the Romans, or to go two miles if they compel us to go one? Let us help our enemies, pray for our enemies, love our enemies, by all means—only, who are these enemies? If they are my own personal enemies who have harmed none but me, I fully and freely forgive them; the Torah commands me to bring back my enemy's ox or his ass when they go astray, and so much the more to help him himself. Whether he be Jew or Gentile, I will love him if I can; the Torah commands me to love *all living creatures.* But as for the enemy of

Israel (who is the enemy of God since God chose Israel, and Israel alone chose Him), must I love him for the simple reason that the sun shines on the righteous and the unrighteous, and that it rains on the just and the unjust? Must I submit myself to the Romans? Must I bare my breast to them? Must I accept their yoke? Of what use is a Messiah to me if, under his sway, I have to serve the Romans instead of God?"

But Reuben objected gently:

"In the Kingdom of God, there will be no more Romans!"

Three days later, we waited for Jesus on the road which leads to Bethsaida . . . it is overgrown with brushwood now, but then it was a busy highway. The Jordan marked the boundary between the two tetrarchies, that of Herod Philip and that of Herod Antipas where we now found ourselves. As for the Romans who occupied Judæa and Jerusalem . . . but I need hardly give you a history lesson! . . . To be brief, as I lay in my litter I saw the customs-house where bundles were being opened, and beasts unloaded, and overheard the camel-drivers apply a thoroughly unflattering epithet to Levi, called Matthew, the customs official. Like every customs official of every age, he *rejoiced* in the most unsavoury reputation!

From the moment that Jesus appeared between two of his disciples, there was a frenzied scramble and a wild outburst of cries and entreaties. Women touched his robe and kissed it frantically. Halt, lame, hunchbacks and bandy-legged flung themselves at his feet, and licked the dust. The scrofulous exposed their scabs, the ulcerous their running sores; the blind fumbled in the air, and sought his eyes.

Suddenly a demoniac hurled them all aside, with a hideous howl. He jostled, scratched, and struck out with clenched fists, from which hung the rattling links of the chains he had snapped. He foamed at the mouth, his teeth chattered, and his knees knocked together with the sound of a hammer against an anvil. Beneath his tattered garment, shudders ripped up and down his body like waves on the sea.

"Let us alone," he shrieked. "What have we to do with thee, thou Jesus of Nazareth? Thou art come to destroy us! I know thee who thou art: the Holy One of God!"

* Hell.

But Jesus rebuked him, saying:

"Hold thy peace, and come out of him!"

The demoniac flung himself backward, bending his body like a bow till it touched the ground. A convulsion shook him from head to foot, and Something leapt from his mouth with a final howl.

Then he arose, fell on his knees, and with a voice that was the voice of angels—if there are angels—said:

"Blessed art thou, Jesus of Nazareth!"

This I saw with my own eyes, these eyes that now see you—I can see as clearly as though it were daylight by this moon. Hysteria! Suggestion! Hypnotism! I know that's what you are going to say. But can you tell me of any hypnotist who can work such wonders? I have been searching for twenty centuries, and haven't succeeded in finding him yet!

That evening, the same crowd wailed and implored before the house of Simon-Kephas—or Peter, if you prefer. There was talk of the latest miracles: the leper cleansed of his leprosy, the raising of the widow's son at Nain, and an even greater miracle— Jesus had said to Matthew, as he sat at the receipt of custom, "Follow me," and Matthew, the paid servant of the Romans, their tax-collector and publican, had followed him!

As I lay on my litter, I thought:

"How shall I ever draw near to the Rabbi through such a crowd, when even those with the full use of their limbs cannot draw near him? Shall I alone remain unhealed? Is my sin, the desire to understand, so great that I shall never reach him?"

And, as I had murmured to myself during so many sleepless nights, I now repeated once more:

"Arise! Take up thy bed and walk! . . . Arise! Take up thy bed and walk! . . ."

Suddenly I felt my litter sway. By the four cords that were fastened to it, it was being hoisted up above the heads of the crowd. Baruch, Reuben, and two others uncovered the roof where he stood. I could hear the voice of Jesus. Slowly, my litter was lowered until I lay at his feet.

"Be not afraid," he said. "Son, thy sins be forgiven thee. . . ."

Something, I knew not what, stirred softly in my bones. I was conscious of a warm tide that streamed through my veins—the warmth of my own blood. I felt the life-blood pulse through me.

"I am forgiven! . . . If I am forgiven, I shall be healed! . . ."

Power emanated from Jesus; it flowed towards me, filled me, flooded me. . . .

In a corner, voices were raised in complaint. Sternly, he said:

"Why reason ye these things in your hearts? Whether it is easier to say to the paralytic: 'Thy sin be forgiven thee,' or: 'Arise! Take up thy bed, and walk'? But that ye may know that the Son of Man has power on earth to forgive sins . . ."

He turned to me, and I heard him command:

"Arise! Take up thy bed, and walk!"

The power that flowed from him tugged softly at my arms and legs, whose rigidity relaxed; I felt it under my ribs, my back, my neck; it was raising me up!

"Arise! Take up thy bed, and walk!" I repeated. "Arise! Take up thy bed, and walk! . . ."

Suddenly, I was transformed into another being; I knew this other being was on his feet, knew that he was walking, moving away from the litter, knew he was coming back to lift it! And this other being was myself! It was I who stooped, raised the litter and bore it away! I was walking! I was walking! The power of Jesus was in every step I took! . . . But your Monsieur Couchoud affirms that this Jesus never existed! Think, Monsieur Fleg! This same Jesus said to me—to me myself whom you now see before you—"Arise!" And I arose! Yet your Arthur Drews, Bruno Bauers, Strausses and Robertsons have the audacity to tell me that he is a mere symbol, a legend, a fairy-story, a solar myth! They say this to *me* who could not walk, and who walked at a single word from him! Pah—don't talk to me of such persons, or I shall again be *paralysed*—with fury! . . .

Oh! If you had seen me when I returned to the inn with my litter on my shoulders! If you had seen my Aunt Sephora as she kissed me, wept over me, and embraced me! She, I assure you, did not take me to be a myth! Nor did my Uncle Simeon, nor my cousins, nor any of those who were gathered there.

Naturally, a discussion immediately arose—discussions are the breath of life! Doeg, Schammai's disciple, had begun again:

"Why has this man spoken blasphemies? Who can forgive sins but God alone?"

But Uncle Simeon, always inclined to leniency

through the teaching of Hillel, his master, and rendered still more indulgent by the miracle of my cure, exercised all his subtlety on behalf of Jesus:

"He did not say: 'I forgive thee thy sins.' He said: 'Thy sins be forgiven thee,' which is quite a different matter. If he knows that the Holy One, blessed be His name, has given him the power to heal at certain moments, he also knows that the Holy One has granted forgiveness. Wherefore, as Nathan announced it to David, he announces it to the sinner in the name of the Father."

"Are you comparing this blasphemer to a prophet?" exclaimed the disciple of Schammai. "May his bones be broken! A dog who allows men to call him the Son of God!"

"We are all the sons of God," replied Uncle Simeon.

"But the Son of Man! By what right does he call himself the Son of Man?"

"By the whole world's right! In good Hebrew, a son of the man . . ." (between ourselves, though, it would be better to translate it as *the son of man* —it would be more accurate and more lucid!) ". . . a son of man is a man, a poor man. Jesus is a son of man, I am a son of man, you are a son of man. . . ."

"But the Son of Man *who descended with the clouds of heaven, and came to the Ancient of days, and was given dominion and glory and power and a kingdom! The Son of Man whom all peoples will serve, whose dominion is an everlasting dominion, and whose kingdom will not be destroyed!* Is he a son of man, as we are; a poor man, as we are? Oh! I know your Jesus apes humility when he calls himself the *Son of Man*. He dare not—or, rather, he no longer dares—say openly what he means to say. But he hints, he implies, and allows us to hope that he is the Son of Man, above all other men, the Son of Man prophesied by Daniel, who will descend from Heaven, who is more than man, and who, more than all other men, is the Son of God! . . ."

Amongst the crowd was a proselyte, a Greek from Alexandria called Euphorbius, who now said quietly:

"Verily, the Jesus who performs such miracles is more than a son of man, more than a son of God— he is a god!"

"A god!" groaned Doeg. "I crossed the sea to convert you, and this is all you retain of my teaching! I have explained to you a hundred times that our God, the God of Israel, is the creator of heaven and earth, and that He is not manifest in wood, stone, bronze, or flesh and blood! I have told you a hundred times that He is neither here or there, but everywhere, invisible, infinite, eternal, and that, as the infinite can never be finite, He does not walk the earth in man's shape like your Zeus, Ares and Poseidon!"

Unmoved, the Greek replied:

"But if Zeus, Ares and Poseidon, lesser gods though they be, are yet powerful enough to assume any shape at will, why should not the God of Israel, that mighty God who created heaven and earth, make Himself small, if it seems good to Him, and take on the shape of man?"

At these words, Doeg could control himself no longer; he advanced on us with clenched fists, and shouted:

"Now you see to what a pitch he has led you— your *Son of God!*"

In short, the disciple of Schammai was mistrustful of the *Son of Man*, and being mistrustful of the *Son of Man*, was also mistrustful of his miracles.

But I had no mind to question and doubt him in the new joy of using my limbs. I came and went, strode up and down, and to and fro; I never paused, but walked tirelessly in the courtyard. . . . I little thought a time would come when I should long to stand still! . . .

THE ORIGINALITY OF JESUS

George A. Gordon

I

The Master of the Christian world has suffered much from two servants who are yet essential to enlightened religion—the metaphysical theologian and the historical critic. From the early days of Christianity till recent times, Jesus Christ, the Son of God, the second person in the Trinity, has figured in a metaphysical scheme of redemption. The historic person of the Prophet of Nazareth, the wealth and the glory of his humanity, have been sadly obscured. He has again and again faded from the friendship of the world; he has become dim and uncertain as a human reality in the fields of time; he has been largely lost as a teacher and guide; he has been known chiefly as the member of the God-head who had compassion upon a race gone into utter wreck and deserving only eternal damnation. The entire Calvinistic tradition tended more and more to count Jesus out. In my boyhood in Scotland he was a divine name, with a certain part to play in the drama of redemption; he was not a creative power in human life; he was not a sublime human reality. The Calvinistic tradition shows its logical issue in Carlyle. Nothing counts ultimately but the will of God. The Pilgrim theology, with all its high principles of faith,—the sovereignty of mind in the universe, the accountability of the soul to God, the great optimistic idea of redemption for sinful men, and the triumph, limited indeed, but real, of good over evil,—missed the superlative glory of the Master, his divine humanity. A metaphysic of the life of Jesus is a necessity; it should be, however, a limited necessity.

Our trouble to-day is from the other indispensable servant of enlightened religion—the historical critic. Read the Gospels, so he tells us, as one should any other book. True; but how should one read any other book worth reading? Apply the rules of historical criticism to Jesus as one would to Socrates. True again; but how should one apply the rules of historical criticism to Socrates? Shall one apply these rules to Socrates in such a way as to deny that he ever lived; in such a way as to show that, if he lived, he said nothing clearly ascertainable; that, if he spoke certain words, he spoke little of any great moment? That method of criticism would leave the mighty systems of Plato and Aristotle without historical antecedent. Criticism has here run a wild course; it has, however, settled down in the conviction that Socrates is the fountain-head of the wisdom of Greece about man and man's world.

To apply criticism to the Gospels in such a way as to give us no sure vision of Jesus at all, in such a way as to present him to us, if he did live, not as the originator of the mightiest of all religions, not as the supreme and supremely calm spiritual mind of the race, but as a well-meaning fanatic, as a totally mistaken and tragic figure, as one forever pushed aside in his wild apocalyptic dreams by the course of the world, can hardly be deemed satisfactory

either in method or result. To destroy the one and only adequate antecedent of historical Christianity is not criticism: it is an obvious and serious mistake.

It is true that the evils of criticism are to be cured by more criticism. Even in its utmost excesses criticism is like erysipelas, a self-limiting trouble. Anyone who is familiar with the criticism through which the Greek classics have passed in the last hundred years must be aware of this self-rectifying tendency in critical judgment. At one time, by certain scholars, about a dozen of the great body of writings usually attributed to Plato were allowed to be genuine; to-day critical opinion and tradition are practically agreed. More criticism, especially criticism of criticism, and the habit of discounting the idols of the historical critic's cave, will give, it is believed, a much saner result in this discipline than has lately prevailed.

There is another, and, in my judgment, a better way of approach to the Gospels than that used by the technical critic. After all, the New Testament is not the monopoly of the historical scholar. Services there are which none but he can render; services there are to this literature which others can render better than he. Studies on the outsides of things need to be supplemented by studies on the insides of things. The rabbinical scholar should not be too proud to listen now and then to the philosophic student of human wisdom. Indeed, the method of the philosophical mind should be the ally of the historical mind. The man who comes to the study of the teaching of Jesus from wide and profound acquaintance with the wisdom and the culture of the world is able to pronounce a judgment not lightly to be disregarded. John Stuart Mill, writing to Thomas Carlyle, says, "I have for years had the very same idea of Christ and the same unbounded reverence for him as now; it was because of this reverence that I sought a more perfect acquaintance with the records of his life; that indeed gave new life to the reverence, which in any case was becoming, or was closely allied with all that was becoming, a living principle in my character."

Books are symbols, their meaning cannot be found without sympathy. Learning is essential, yet all the learning in the world by itself cannot compass the secret of Jesus. Sympathy and imagination working in the interest of the hidden reality are indispensable. Learning alone can give the size and style of the cathedral window from the outside; learning alone can never give the vision of the window from the inside—its figure, color, wonder, and splendor. History, like the external world, like the universe, is a symbol, an offering to the soul of man by the way of his senses; without insight the meaning of the symbol is unattainable. Hidden in the Gospels is the creative mind, the original character of Jesus, and he is found there by thought.

Even among men of the highest genius there is no such thing as absolute originality. Consider for a moment one of the most original minds in the English tongue, Shakespeare. He did not invent the alphabet, the words, the syntax, the reality and power of the English language; or the English nation, its ways of thinking, its achievements, its character; or the comedy and the tragedy of human life. Shakespeare found these and a thousand other things of high moment, contributed by those who had gone before him. Yet Shakespeare is rightly regarded as a great original genius, in depth of mind, in comprehensiveness, in the richness and power of his comedy and tragedy, in the intimacy of his knowledge of life, in the unsurpassed grandeur of his dramatic presentations, especially in his portrayal of character. Shakespeare's originality is that of the mountain to the common earth; it is lifted to this unwonted elevation, to this outlook upon the world, to this vision of the naked heavens. In Shakespeare the common powers, insights, instincts, possessions of humanity are lifted to this dignity, this range of meaning, this majesty and mystery.

Jesus did not originate the Semitic dialect which was his native tongue, or the traditions of his race, their vast literature, their history, their character, their faith and hope. All these were the material furnished, ready. Yet he is in the sphere of the spirit original in the profoundest sense; he is original in himself, in his power to revive dead wisdom, to stamp with his character the unvalued truth, and put it in everlasting social circulation; he is original in depth of insight, in purity of vision, in the transcendence of his mind, the universality of his appeal.

II

In Jesus we find, in the highest degree, originality of character. This means something new, something of surpassing excellence, something of endless interest and influence. We know what originality of character means when applied to other great men. This kind of originality was evident in Lincoln: before him there was none like him; in his generation he was without a parallel; since his day no one has appeared of his type. He was something new, something excellent, something of enduring interest to all Americans. Probably no one would contest the assertion that Socrates was the human being of greatest originality in the race to which he belonged. Plato says, "He was like no one, either of the ancients or of the men of his own time"; he was a wonder in newness of type, in excellence, and in interest.

In the Old Testament there is no parallel to Jesus; among the prophets of Israel, among the great men whose name and character are recorded in that literature, there is no suggestion even of the unique personality of the Master. Among these great men, when the feeling is not merely tribal it is strictly national. The elevation of Israel's greatest men is the elevation of separation from the peoples of the world; their humanity is still limited, exclusive; man as man does not occupy the field of vision, does not influence the centres of feeling. The prophet's only hope is that the Gentile may become an Israelite by adoption. In the greatest of these ancient men there is nothing of the intrinsic and free humanity of Jesus; their character is an old-world character. The highest ideal of the Old Testament is that of the suffering servant of Jehovah, and this ideal touches Jesus only at one point of his character, his vicarious goodness. The Lord's Prayer is not a tribal or national prayer; the humanity of man is the ground of appeal to the Eternal humanity: "Our Father who art in heaven."

In the New Testament there is no one like Jesus. This is all the more remarkable because to his disciples Jesus became at once an object of passionate love and admiration. Stephen imitates the Lord's prayer upon the cross: "Father, forgive them; for they know not what they do," in the noble words, "Lord, lay not this sin to their charge"; and yet no one would think of likening the character of Stephen to the character of Jesus. Among the apostles there is no one to whom in vision, composure, dignity, disengagedness from the non-essential in religion, Jesus is not a decided contrast. When we come to the most ardent of the early disciples of Jesus, and his greatest apostle, Paul, we meet more of contrast than of resemblance. John Stuart Mill is completely right when he says that Paul's "character and idiosyncrasies were of a totally different sort."

The original character of Jesus is the moral side of his genius; that aspect confines our attention at this point. It is something free, and inevitable; silent as the movement of the earth, and sure; its strength is without tumult, without hesitation; and in it there are no fears, no divisions of heart; unity, certainty, sovereignty are its notes. The Gospels bear witness to one without predecessor and without successor, whose originality of character is declared in the paradoxical but luminous words of one of the greatest New Testament writers, as "without father, without mother, without genealogy, having neither beginning of days nor end of life"—a new type of human being, to which the coming world is to be conformed.

I cannot forget the impression made upon me in going from my first absorbing visit in Egypt to Palestine. Palestine was ancient, too; it was a part of that ancient world in which Egypt was supreme, for power and for length of years. Palestine, however, contained Jesus; and for the first time in my feeling was reflected the fact that Jesus was a modern man, the first, the original, the creative modern man. In him the spirit of man broke from the solemn melancholy of Egypt, the high exclusiveness of Israel, and the sovereign aristocracy of Greece, into the vision of the intrinsic dignity and measureless worth of man as man. The world has been sadly unfaithful to that vision, yet the vision itself has never altogether faded from our distracted life; today it abides in strength, and the person who was its original representative is still its authentic and incomparable type.

III

The next step in our discussion concerns the originality of the message of Jesus. Two views are current here and in conflict. One view is that Jesus was a pious and patriotic Jew, whose programme was essentially that of John the Baptist, national repentance and righteousness followed by national salvation, that is, deliverance from the Roman domination. According to this view, the mind of Jesus is to be approached through the imaginative literature of the generation preceding his own, by the habits

of thought and the forms of belief of his time. It is held that the idea of the continuous development of the life of man on the earth was something foreign to the mind of Jesus; the idea of catastrophe, it is contended, was ever present to him. On the wreck of the world his Messianic kingdom was to be established. He was a good man, but completely mistaken; he was a pure spirit, but he knew not the way that the world was taking; he was a representative Jew in his piety, in his patriotism, in his message, and in it there was nothing essentially new.

Here serious questions press for an answer. Is it fair to attribute the world-view of Jewish imaginative literature to this great Master of all Christians? Is it just to construe the few world-view sentences of Jesus, not written by himself, written a generation after his death by those to whom these views were the colored medium through which they read all serious words upon man's destiny—is it just to put a meaning upon these sentences in clear contradiction of the sure central body of the teaching of the Master? Was Jesus entirely under the power of the spirit of the age? Was he in no way able to rise above the poor apocalyptic nonsense discredited by the course of history? In our analysis of the records of his ministry, are we to find nothing there that did not come from him? Is scientific criticism leading us, blindfolded, back to something like an infallible reporter, and an inerrant report, which shall infallibly discredit the Divine speaker? Is not Matthew Arnold near the truth when he presumes that, when Jesus is made to speak words that the course of the world has set aside, the words are more likely to have come from the disciple than from the Master? In reading the mind of the Master, after the lapse of a generation of years, may not the disciple have read his own mind into the mind of the Lord? May not the apocalyptic addresses in the Gospels be a misinterpretation, a confused version of the mind of Jesus, which he would have refused to accept as the truth? Was it not possible for Jesus to use, to a certain extent, the mythology of his age, as other great teachers have used the mythologies of their respective ages—reality to the many, but poetry to them? Would it be fair to interpret Socrates, Plato, and Aristotle as Polytheists because of the sanction they gave to the popular faith? May not the nationalization of the teaching of Jesus, so far as it exists, have been the work of his disciples? May not the genius of Jesus have been, what history has indeed found it to be, spiritual and universal?

The view that regards Jesus as the sovereign religious genius of our race enters its protest here. This view holds that, while Jesus was obliged to accommodate his mind, to some extent, to the idiom of his time, he yet in his central ideas completely transcended his time. According to this view, the mind of Jesus must be found in the records of his ministry by the most careful analysis; this analysis must be made more in the light of what his message came to mean to his greatest disciples, than in the light of the Jewish literature standing in the background; this analysis must take into account what is after all supreme in the teaching of Jesus—his conception of God, and his conception of man.

Jesus' criticism of the Law, in the Sermon on the Mount, is surely something new in depth and in inwardness; nor is there anything in the Prophets or Psalms so absolute as the moral teaching of Jesus in that discourse. There man's life, his world, is in the searchlight of the Infinite Perfection; the ideal of that life, of that world, is something that overawes the highest souls by its authority and splendor: "Ye therefore shall be perfect as your heavenly Father is perfect."

If it should be said that there are more than mere hints of this teaching in the noblest words in the Old Testament and beyond it, in the loftiest traditions of other races, it is still true that to the best wisdom of his people Jesus has given the highest form, and to the rarest insights of the great in other nations an expression that supersedes the original utterance. The best experience of the best souls, in Israel and beyond Israel, finds its completest utterance in the authentic teaching of Jesus. In a sense profoundly true, that highest experience lives and moves in our world to-day by the power of his utterance.

Jesus was perhaps the most misunderstood teacher in history. His genius in the things of the spirit, had it taken its own high way, would have left him with no contact with his time. He was obliged to use the phrase "Kingdom of God," and he could not prevent the construction of this phrase as meaning an earthly kingdom. His disciples, let it be frankly stated, were incapable of comprehending their Teacher and his message; they read that message in the light of their education, habits of thought, beliefs, hopes, world-views. In this way it has come to pass that the Teaching of Jesus has been here and there touched by the darkened minds of the pious and good men who conserved the tradition of his career.

In the words of John the Baptist about Jesus there is a guide to the Master's genius: "I indeed baptize you with water; he shall baptize you with the Holy Spirit." Another word, this time from Jesus himself, can mean only the inwardness of his Kingdom: "The Kingdom of heaven is within you." History is the authentic interpreter of creative ideas. Two generations after the death of Jesus, a great interpreter of his teaching had come to see the absolute spirituality of the Master's central idea: "My Kingdom is not of this world." And in between the earliest and the latest of the Gospels stands the great interpretation of Jesus, in the Epistle to the Hebrews. Here Christianity has become, what it was essentially at the first and always, an Eternal reality, looking through ancient forms as through symbols, itself an Institute of the Spirit, in the life of the world and beyond time. So much history, as the great authentic interpreter of the message of Jesus, had achieved in elevating the mind of his leading disciples, in making it possible for them to apprehend the pure spirituality, the invisible and eternal reality of his Kingdom.

This process has gone ever onward. They have understood Jesus best who have had the largest share of his spirit, who have been able to bring the richness of a great religious experience to the interpretation of the life of his soul in God. The church of Christ has been from the beginning an institution of many and continuous blunders; yet in one respect it has been essentially clear in head and sound in heart: it has understood more and more deeply the Kingdom of God in the teaching of Jesus to be the reign of God in the minds and hearts of men; it has seen in that phrase a heavenly ideal hovering over all human society, seeking nothing for itself, and claiming nothing but to be the perfecting light and grace of human life. The church has thus seen the spirituality, the depth, and the wonder of the message of Jesus.

IV

Jesus' manner of teaching may be justly called original. In certain respects it resembles the manner of Socrates rather than that of any great recorded teacher in Israel. Socrates was, it is true, an educator rather than a teacher; yet the issue of his service to the mind was a great body of definite teaching. The Greek educator spoke his ideas, committing them to the minds of living men of uncommon power. He was an examiner of ideas, minds, methods of thought, and he was a searcher of the heart. His personality, his purpose, his dialectical method, his love of wisdom and his endless delight in the search for it, are behind the whole greater heritage of Greek philosophy, the original fountain of it, surely, and largely the directing genius of it.

In something of the same manner Jesus exercised his ministry. He was, first of all, a teacher of twelve men; his method was by conversation, a direct attack upon the mind, frequently by question and answer, often by the keenest dialectical encounter. "By what authority doest thou these things?" This question is flung at Jesus in the Temple by certain leaders of the people. Jesus replies. First answer this question: "The Baptism of John, whence was it? from heaven or from men?" These acute opponents of Jesus saw at once the logic of the question: they reasoned among themselves and said, "If we shall say from heaven, he will say, why then did ye not believe him; if we shall say from men, we fear the multitude, for all hold John as a prophet." They answered with safe agnosticism, "We know not." Jesus then rejoins, "Neither tell I you by what authority I do these things." There is Jesus' encounter with the politicians, and their crafty question, Is it lawful to give tribute to Cæsar or not? The wisdom and dialectical force of Jesus' answer have received universal recognition. Show me a penny. Whose is this image and superscription? Cæsar's. You are clearly under some sort of obligation to Cæsar. Render therefore unto Cæsar the things that are Cæsar's, and unto God the things that are God's.

To the dialectical genius of Jesus no less than to his divine humanity are due his defense of his interest in sinful men and women in his parables of the Lost Sheep, the Lost Coin, and the Lost Son. Here is the profoundest and widest wisdom in the possession of mankind, uttered in forms that for clear intelligibility and impressive beauty are matchless. There is no philosophy of human history like that contained in the Parable of the Lost Son. The vision of good, real and apparent, the sources of tragic mistake in confounding appearance and reality, the dis-

cipline of suffering, the awakening power of disillusionment, the illumination of experience, and the benignity of the Eternal Reality sovereign in all the courses of thought and life, are here depicted by a genius to whom man's intellect and heart are utterly transparent. There is hardly a phrase in this profound and wonderful Parable that does not compress within itself a world of meaning for mankind.

Another peculiarity of Jesus' manner as a teacher is his gift of characterization. It appears more or less in all his parables; it appears conspicuously in the parables just mentioned. The shepherd who seeks his lost sheep till he finds it, the woman who seeks her lost coin till she finds it, the father who seeks through all the courses of experiences his lost son, the Lost Son himself and the Elder Brother, are characters drawn with a master-hand, and they are in the imagination and feeling of the world forever. Still more striking, perhaps, is this power of characterization in the Parable of the Good Samaritan. It, too, springs from debate; after it was spoken, no reply was possible: it was conclusive and final.

The portrayal of character is rightly held to be the supreme example of poetic genius. In the Iliad there are immortal characters: Agamemnon, Achilles, and a score of others that cannot die. In the Odyssey we have another group: Odysseus the incarnation of intellect, as Achilles is the incarnation of physical prowess; Nausicaa, Penelope, Circe, and many others. These are extraordinary delineations of character, but large space is necessary for the full presentation of these groups of characters. The Clytemnestra of Æschylus is a wild and terrible woman; so is the Medea of Euripides; the Antigone of Sophocles is statuesque, full of loyalty, of piety, of tenderness, of strength. But in each case, to present in full length the character depicted requires a whole drama.

Shakespeare is justly regarded the greatest character poet of modern times. To the groups of characters that he has contributed to enrich human imagination and feeling, there is no modern parallel: Lear, Goneril, Regan, Cordelia, Kent; Hamlet, Ophelia, the guilty King and Queen; Othello, Desdemona, Iago; Imogen; Portia; and again, a hundred more; but Shakespeare requires room and time for the full display of these characters.

See what we find in this story that one can read in three or four minutes. A certain man was going down from Jerusalem to Jericho. The form of statement rouses at once the imagination. Who was he; in what home did he open his eyes; what was his early fortune, and how did he end his days? The impact upon the imagination is that of the supreme artist. The universal human being is introduced. A certain man went down from Jerusalem to Jericho—the typical man representing every man everywhere.

There are the robbers: one can see their hard faces silhouetted against the rock on the way down from Jerusalem to Jericho; one can see them, low-browed, dark-faced, with cruelty in their eyes, the plagues of society, the foes of mankind, the representatives of inhumanity all the world over, desperadoes, robbers by calling, murderers by vocation.

There are the priest and the Levite. With what complete mastery, in a few words, Jesus struck off those characters! They are in the memory and imagination of mankind wherever his Gospel has gone. They were not hypocrites: they were simply men who had separated religion from human service, piety from humanity, consecration to the Infinite in contempt of the need of mankind.

There was the good Samaritan, a compound of unconscious divinity and humanity; God was in his instincts, his kind was in his instincts, quickening his perceptions of human need and brotherhood, quickening his sympathies, moving his will to help. You see him with a face like the sunrise; again, he is known wherever the teaching of Jesus is known.

There was the innkeeper, a combination of kindliness and business; he is glad to welcome this man who had been unfortunate, glad to have a paying guest, and glad to be assured by the man who brought him that everything would be settled on business principles.

There was the lawyer, keen, subtle, a dialectician by profession, who had been victorious in a hundred encounters and who had perfect confidence in his power to "down" any man by asking questions which he himself could not answer. There was the great multitude hanging round in a circle, witnessing this duel of intellect between Jesus the Teacher and this acute antagonist. Lastly, there is the Master dominating all, silencing with a final silence his adversary, and towering majestic as the mountains of Judea over the whole scene.

One here recalls that marvel of painting, the "School of Athens," by Raphael, painted on a panel in the Vatican. The poetry of Greece, the science of Greece, the history of Greece, the philosophy of Greece, the whole history and the whole achievement of Greece are on that one panel; they are there in true perspective, in beautiful order, and the more one knows of the Greek and his art, his poetry, his philosophy, his genius, the more amazing is that panel. Such a panel is this parable which has painted on it all the typical forces that make up the seething tragic world of to-day. And yet one will meet people who say, "That little story? We knew that when we went to Sunday School." Yes, and you knew the Lord's Prayer, but do you now know what that prayer means for the universe and for mankind?

In the living wisdom of the world, it may be said, there is nothing to match the parabolic teaching of Jesus. In addition to the wealth of character created and depicted, the story is made to carry meanings of infinite moment; it sends the imagination to the depths of human need, to the heights of the Eternal Compassion, and this with ease incomparable, with a mastery to which there is no parallel in the influential wisdom of the world.

v

The most precious possession of mankind is the human experience won through the vision of great moral ideals, the eager pursuit of them, joy and sorrow in the service of them, life, love, death, and hope under their reign. For priceless value, nothing within the possession of human beings is to be compared to this. Here one finds in solution the moral nature of man, the moral world, and the moral universe in which man lives. Here is a body of thought, feeling, character, experience, fluid and vast as all the seas, and whose tide is the movement within it of the Eternal Spirit. We have here the spiritual wealth of mankind, in its ultimate source and character, as it lives in the heart of all races, as it moves in the soul of the greatest races, and as it has its being in the words spoken or written of the most gifted men.

The question of originality is finally one of insight and utterance in the superlative degree. How much of this precious experience of mankind has any single person, any school or group of persons, seen and wrought into the form of great influential speech? All our poets, all our philosophers, all our men of genius come at last to this judgment-seat. No writer will live, save in the mad sections of society, who is not a great representative of the highest human experience; no book will last that is not a vast coinage of the spiritual wealth of the world. The Greeks live, Homer, Pindar, Æschylus, Sophocles, Thucydides, Socrates, Plato, Aristotle, by their depth and sincerity, by their adequate fidelity to the best in some part of man's world; by the range, truth, and nobility of their utterance of the content of life as that content discovers itself in the great courses of human experience.

To this test all modern men of genius must come. Those who cannot meet the test, however they may shine for a day or a century, must pass. Dante is solitary, not because there is not a multitude of speakers, but because more and more it is recognized that his is the voice of the ten silent centuries. We are sure of Dante, Shakespeare, Milton, and a dozen or more others, who have felt the pulse of man, who have compassed much of his best life, and who have given it fresh, faithful, unforgettable expression.

Here Jesus stands supreme. In his brief career as a teacher, in the small compass of his utterance, he has been more comprehensive than any other recorded man of genius, of the deepest experience of the human soul, and he has given to that experience monumental forms of beauty and power. It is here that we find the highest witness of his originality, the final assurance of his ascendancy over the mind of the world. He best of all knows our human world; he best of all has seen its tragic grandeur; he is unequaled in reading and in rendering its mighty meanings; to his influence, in kind, in range, and in promise, there is no parallel among the sons of men. He is to-day the centre of the world's hope, as in a tragic sense he is the need and the blind desire of all nations. His religion is the sovereign version in history of the Kingdom of the Eternal Spirit as that Kingdom lives in the best life of the race. When men live *sub specie æternitatis,* they find in Jesus the only adequate utterance of their thoughts, feelings, purposes, and hopes. He more than all, he above all, is the prophet of the spiritual life of man in his pilgrimage through time.

VI

Jesus is indeed to be understood by his endowment and his environment. His endowment is clearly that of sovereign religious genius, and his environment is the Absolute Spirit. Jesus appeared in the world at a particular time; he came of a particular race; he was nurtured in the literature, traditions, beliefs, and hopes of his people. In all this he was a man of unique spiritual genius; and he is certainly no more to be understood through the limitations of inheritance and racial environment than other men of transcendent original power. The literature produced in Israel during the two hundred years preceding the birth of Jesus is, on the whole, eccentric and poor stuff; at its best, it is largely the hysteria of noble minds densely ignorant. Even the Book of Enoch, so highly prized by scholars, as giving the intellectual background of the age to which Jesus spoke, is in itself of inferior value, and when compared with the great prophets and psalmists of Israel, it is found upon a level greatly below theirs. In the Book of Enoch the soul of Abel offers and presses the prayer that the seed of his brother Cain shall be destroyed from the face of the earth, and annihilated among the seed of men. This Book of Enoch, not unfittingly here represented, is hardly a trustworthy guide to his mind whose prayer upon the cross was, "Father, forgive them; for they know not what they do." The truth is, the mind of Israel had become decadent; these books would merit the attention of no serious lover of reality, were it not for their antiquarian interest.

That the pure spiritual conceptions of Jesus could not shine in their own strength; that they must be presented in the idiom of the time in order to be understood even a little; that they were reported by men whom even the Master could not lift to his own level or free from the crude notions of the age; that his teaching lies embedded in this pervasive accommodation to modes of thought that meant one thing to the people, and another to him, and that his mind is to be reached, if at all, through sympathetic insight, should be clear to all.

Jesus is to be understood, not by his age, but by the Eternal God. His mind, his message, his character, his service to his people, and his hope for the world had their origin in God. At a level below him lie the best insights of his greatest predecessors in Israel; in an abyss below him lies the poor stuff by which many to-day try to understand him. If Jesus had been the product of his human environment, the world would never have heard of him, nor would that human environment ever have seen the light of day. There is little or nothing in it to detain the modern man.

If we are to have a great religion; if the universe is to be gathered into the Infinite Soul; if that Soul is to be apprehended through Fatherhood; if man is a spiritual person of permanent reality in the life of God; if the individual is not to be sacrificed to the social whole, and if the social whole is not to be sacrificed to the individual; if the fellowship of moral and accountable persons is the best world for the world of men, the religion of Jesus, originating in his own spirit, as that spirit lived and moved and had its being in the Eternal, is the religion for mankind. Historical antecedents, historical settings, may be interesting, may even shed light upon the pathway of our search; but it would seem to be unwise to seek in these the transcendent spiritual mind of Jesus. We should never think of explaining Plato, the philosophic "spectator of all time and all existence," by the mythologies and popular beliefs of the Greeks; and it seems hardly likely that scholars can long be content with the endeavor to find the origin of the deepest mind of Jesus save in the mind of God.

※

ESSENTIAL CHARACTER OF THE WORK OF JESUS

Ernest Renan

Renan's *Vie de Jésus* (1863) was the first modern biography of the Son of Man. The scandal occasioned by its publication has faded—it cost its author his chair in the Collège de France—and its scholarship has been superseded. But it still retains literary as well as historical importance; and its final chapter, in which the author sums up his impressions of the work of Jesus, can now be read with enjoyment by both believer and sceptic.

———

Jesus, it will be seen, limited his action entirely to the Jews. Although his sympathy for those despised by orthodoxy led him to admit pagans into the kingdom of God—although he had resided more than once in a pagan country, and once or twice we surprise him in kindly relations with unbelievers—it may be said that his life was passed entirely in the very restricted world in which he was born. He was never heard of in Greek or Roman countries; his name appears only in profane authors of a hundred years later, and then in an indirect manner, in connection with seditious movements provoked by his doctrine, or persecutions of which his disciples were the object. Even on Judaism, Jesus made no very durable impression. Philo, who died about the year 50, had not the slightest knowledge of him. Josephus, born in the year 37, and writing in the last years of the century, mentions his execution in a few lines, as an event of secondary importance, and in the enumeration of the sects of his time, he omits the Christians altogether. In the *Mishnah*, also, there is no trace of the new school; the passages in the two Gemaras in which the founder of Christianity is named, do not go further back than the fourth or fifth century. The essential work of Jesus was to create around him a circle of disciples, whom he inspired with boundless affection, and amongst whom he deposited the germ of his doctrine. To have made himself beloved, "to the degree that after his death they ceased not to love him," was the great work of Jesus, and that which most struck his contemporaries. His doctrine was so little dogmatic, that he never thought of writing it or of causing it to be written. Men did not become his disciples by believing this thing or that thing, but in being attached to his person and in loving him. A few sentences collected from memory, and especially the type of character he set forth, and the impression it had left, were what remained of him. Jesus was not a founder of dogmas, or a maker of creeds; he infused into the world a new spirit. The least Christian men were, on the one hand, the doctors of the Greek Church, who, beginning from the fourth century, entangled Christianity in a path of puerile metaphysical discussions, and, on the other, the scholastics of the Latin Middle Ages, who wished to draw from the Gospel the thousands of articles of a colossal system. To follow Jesus in expectation of the kingdom of God, was all that at first was implied by being Christian.

It will thus be understood how, by an exceptional destiny, pure Christianity still preserves, after eighteen centuries, the character of a universal and eternal religion. It is, in fact, because the religion of Jesus is in some respects the final religion. Produced by a perfectly spontaneous movement of souls, freed at its birth from all dogmatic restraint, having struggled three hundred years for liberty of conscience, Christianity, in spite of its failures, still reaps the results of its glorious origin. To renew itself, it has but to return to the Gospel. The kingdom of God, as we conceive it, differs notably from the supernatural apparition which the first Christians hoped to see appear in the clouds. But the sentiment introduced by Jesus into the world is indeed ours. His perfect idealism is the highest rule of the unblemished and virtuous life. He has created the heaven of pure souls, where is found what we ask for in vain on earth, the perfect nobility of the children of God, absolute purity, the total removal of the stains of the world; in fine, liberty, which society excludes as an impossibility, and which exists in all its amplitude only in the domain of thought. The great Master of those who take refuge in this ideal kingdom of God is still Jesus. He was the first to proclaim the royalty of the mind; the first to say, at least by his actions, "My kingdom is not of this world." The foundation of true religion is indeed his work: after him, all that remains is to develop it and render it fruitful.

"Christianity" has thus become almost a synonym of "religion." All that is done outside of this great and good Christian tradition is barren. Jesus gave religion to humanity, as Socrates gave it philosophy, and Aristotle science. There was philosophy before Socrates and science before Aristotle. Since Socrates and since Aristotle, philosophy and science have made immense progress; but all has been built upon the foundation which they laid. In the same way, before Jesus, religious thought had passed through many revolutions; since Jesus, it has made great conquests: but no one has improved, and no one will improve upon the essential principle Jesus has created; he has fixed forever the idea of pure worship. The religion of Jesus in this sense is not limited. The Church has had its epochs and its phases; it has shut itself up in creeds which are, or will be but temporary: but Jesus has founded the absolute religion, excluding nothing, and determining nothing unless it be the spirit. His creeds are not fixed dogmas, but images susceptible of indefinite interpretations. We should seek in vain for a theological proposition in the Gospel. All confessions of faith are travesties of the idea of Jesus, just as the scholasticism of the Middle Ages, in proclaiming Aristotle the sole master of a completed science, perverted the thought of Aristotle. Aristotle, if he had been present in the debates of the schools, would have repudiated this narrow doctrine; he would have been of the party of progressive science against the routine which shielded itself under his authority; he would have applauded his opponents. In the same way, if Jesus were to return among us, he would recognize as disciples, not those who pretend to enclose him entirely in a few catechismal phrases, but those who labor to carry on his work. The eternal glory, in all great things, is to have laid the first stone. It may be that in the "Physics," and in the "Meteorology" of modern times, we may not discover a word of the treatises of Aristotle which bear these titles; but Aristotle remains no less the founder of natural science. Whatever may be the transformations of dogma, Jesus will ever be the creator of the pure spirit of religion; the Sermon on the Mount will never be surpassed. Whatever revolution takes place will not prevent us attaching ourselves in religion to the grand intellectual and moral line at the head of which shines the name of Jesus. In this sense we are Christians, even when we separate ourselves on almost all points from the Christian tradition which has preceded us.

And this great foundation was indeed the personal work of Jesus. In order to make himself adored to this degree, he must have been adorable. Love is not enkindled except by an object worthy of it, and we should know nothing of Jesus, if it were not for the passion he inspired in those about him, which compels us still to affirm that he was great and pure. The faith, the enthusiasm, the constancy of the first Christian generation is not explicable, except by supposing at the origin of the whole movement, a man of surpassing greatness. At the sight of the marvellous creations of the ages of faith, two impressions equally fatal to good historical criticism arise in the mind. On the one hand we are led to think these creations too impersonal; we attribute to a collective action, that which has often been the work of one powerful will, and of one superior mind. On the other hand, we refuse to see men like ourselves in the authors of those extraordinary movements which have decided the fate of humanity. Let us have a larger idea of the powers which Nature conceals in her bosom. Our civilizations, governed by minute restrictions, cannot give us any idea of the power of man at periods in which the originality of each one had a freer field wherein to develop itself. Let us imagine a recluse dwelling in the mountains near our capitals, coming out from time to time in order to present himself at the palaces of sovereigns, compelling the sentinels to stand aside, and, with an imperious tone, announcing to kings the approach of revolutions of which he had been the promoter. The very idea provokes a smile. Such, however, was Elias; but Elias the Tishbite, in our days, would not be able to pass the gate of the Tuileries. The preaching of Jesus, and his free activity in Galilee, do not deviate less completely from the social conditions to which we are accustomed. Free from our polished conventionalities, exempt from the uniform education which refines us, but which so greatly dwarfs our individuality, these mighty souls carried a surprising energy into action. They appear to us like the giants of an heroic age, which could not have been real. Profound error! Those men were our brothers; they were of our stature, felt and thought as we do. But the breath of God was free in them; with us, it is restrained by the iron bonds of a mean society, and condemned to an irremediable mediocrity.

Let us place, then, the person of Jesus at the highest summit of human greatness. Let us not be misled by exaggerated doubts in the presence of a legend which keeps us always in a superhuman world. The life of Francis d'Assisi is also but a tissue of miracles. Has any one, however, doubted of the existence of Francis d'Assisi, and of the part played by him? Let us say no more that the glory of the foundation of Christianity belongs to the multitude of the first Christians, and not to him whom legend has deified. The inequality of men is much more marked in the East than with us. It is not rare to see arise there, in the midst of a general atmosphere of wickedness, characters whose greatness astonishes us. So far from Jesus having been created by his disciples, he appeared in everything as superior to his disciples. The latter, with the exception of St. Paul and St. John, were men without either invention or genius. St. Paul himself bears no comparison with Jesus, and as to St. John, I shall show hereafter, that the part he played, though very elevated in one sense, was far from being in all respects irreproachable. Hence the immense superiority of the Gospels

among the writings of the New Testament. Hence the painful fall we experience in passing from the history of Jesus to that of the apostles. The evangelists themselves, who have bequeathed us the image of Jesus, are so much beneath him of whom they speak, that they constantly disfigure him, from their inability to attain to his height. Their writings are full of errors and misconceptions. We feel in each line a discourse of divine beauty, transcribed by narrators who do not understand it, and who substitute their own ideas for those which they have only half understood. On the whole, the character of Jesus, far from having been embellished by his biographers, has been lowered by them. Criticism, in order to find what he was, needs to discard a series of misconceptions, arising from the inferiority of the disciples. These painted him as they understood him, and often in thinking to raise him, they have in reality lowered him.

I know that our modern ideas have been offended more than once in this legend, conceived by another race, under another sky, and in the midst of other social wants. There are virtues which, in some respects, are more conformable to our taste. The virtuous and gentle Marcus Aurelius, the humble and gentle Spinoza, not having believed in miracles, have been free from some errors that Jesus shared. Spinoza, in his profound obscurity, had an advantage which Jesus did not seek. By our extreme delicacy in the use of means of conviction, by our absolute sincerity and our disinterested love of the pure idea, we have founded—all we who have devoted our lives to science—a new ideal of morality. But the judgment of general history ought not to be restricted to considerations of personal merit. Marcus Aurelius and his noble teachers have had no permanent influence on the world. Marcus Aurelius left behind him delightful books, an execrable son, and a decaying nation. Jesus remains an inexhaustible principle of moral regeneration for humanity. Philosophy does not suffice for the multitude. They must have sanctity. An Apollonius of Tyana, with his miraculous legend, is necessarily more successful than a Socrates with his cold reason. "Socrates," it was said, "leaves men on the earth, Apollonius transports them to heaven; Socrates is but a sage, Apollonius is a god." Religion, so far, has not existed without a share of asceticism, of piety, and of the marvellous. When it was wished, after the Anto-

HIS WORK ON EARTH

nines, to make a religion of philosophy, it was requisite to transform the philosophers into saints, to write the "Edifying Life" of Pythagoras or Plotinus, to attribute to them a legend, virtues of abstinence, contemplation, and supernatural powers, without which neither credence nor authority were found in that age.

Preserve us, then, from mutilating history in order to satisfy our petty susceptibilities! Which of us, pygmies as we are, could do what the extravagant Francis d'Assisi, or the hysterical saint Theresa, has done? Let medicine have names to express these grand errors of human nature; let it maintain that genius is a disease of the brain; let it see, in a certain delicacy of morality, the commencement of consumption; let it class enthusiasm and love as nervous accidents—it matters little. The terms healthy and diseased are entirely relative. Who would not prefer to be diseased like Pascal, rather than healthy like the common herd? The narrow ideas which are spread in our times respecting madness, mislead our historical judgments in the most serious manner, in questions of this kind. A state in which a man says things of which he is not conscious, in which thought is produced without the summons and control of the will, exposes him to being confined as a lunatic. Formerly this was called prophecy and inspiration. The most beautiful things in the world are done in a state of fever; every great creation involves a breach of equilibrium, a violent state of the being which draws it forth.

We acknowledge, indeed, that Christianity is too complex to have been the work of a single man. In one sense, entire humanity has co-operated therein. There is no one so shut in, as not to receive some influence from without. The history of the human mind is full of strange coincidences, which cause very remote portions of the human species, without any communication with each other, to arrive at the same time at almost identical ideas and imaginations. In the thirteenth century, the Latins, the Greeks, the Syrians, the Jews, and the Mussulmans, adopted scholasticism, and very nearly the same scholasticism from York to Samarcand; in the fourteenth century every one in Italy, Persia, and India, yielded to the taste for mystical allegory; in the sixteenth, art was developed in a very similar manner in Italy, at Mount Athos, and at the court of the Great Moguls, without St. Thomas, Barhebræus, the Rabbis of Narbonne,

or the *Motécallémin* of Bagdad, having known each other, without Dante and Petrarch having seen any *sofi*, without any pupil of the schools of Perouse or of Florence having been at Delhi. We should say there are great moral influences running through the world like epidemics, without distinction of frontier and of race. The interchange of ideas in the human species does not take place only by books or by direct instruction. Jesus was ignorant of the very name of Buddha, of Zoroaster, and of Plato; he had read no Greek book, no Buddhist Sudra; nevertheless, there was in him more than one element, which, without his suspecting it, came from Buddhism, Parseeism, or from the Greek wisdom. All this was done through secret channels and by that kind of sympathy which exists among the various portions of humanity. The great man, on the one hand, receives everything from his age; on the other, he governs his age. To show that the religion founded by Jesus was the natural consequence of that which had gone before, does not diminish its excellence; but only proves that it had a reason for its existence, that it was legitimate, that is to say, conformable to the instinct and wants of the heart in a given age.

Is it more just to say that Jesus owes all to Judaism, and that his greatness is only that of the Jewish people? No one is more disposed than myself to place high this unique people, whose particular gift seems to have been to contain in its midst the extremes of good and evil. No doubt, Jesus proceeded from Judaism; but he proceeded from it as Socrates proceeded from the schools of the Sophists, as Luther proceeded from the Middle Ages, as Lamennais from Catholicism, as Rousseau from the eighteenth century. A man is of his age and his race even when he reacts against his age and his race. Far from Jesus having continued Judaism, he represents the rupture with the Jewish spirit. The general direction of Christianity after him does not permit the supposition that his idea in this respect could lead to any misunderstanding. The general march of Christianity has been to remove itself more and more from Judaism. It will become perfect in returning to Jesus, but certainly not in returning to Judaism. The great originality of the founder remains then undiminished; his glory admits no legitimate sharer.

Doubtless, circumstances much aided the success of this marvellous revolution; but circumstances only second that which is just and true. Each branch of the development of humanity has its privileged epoch, in which it attains perfection by a sort of spontaneous instinct, and without effort. No labor of reflection would succeed in producing afterward the masterpieces which Nature creates at those moments by inspired geniuses. That which the golden age of Greece was for arts and literature, the age of Jesus was for religion. Jewish society exhibited the most extraordinary moral and intellectual state which the human species has ever passed through. It was truly one of those divine hours in which the sublime is produced by combinations of a thousand hidden forces, in which great souls find a flood of admiration and sympathy to sustain them. The world, delivered from the very narrow tyranny of small municipal republics, enjoyed great liberty. Roman despotism did not make itself felt in a disastrous manner until much later, and it was, moreover, always less oppressive in those distant provinces than in the centre of the empire. Our petty preventive interferences (far more destructive than death to things of the spirit) did not exist. Jesus, during three years, could lead a life which, in our societies, would have brought him twenty times before the magistrates. Our laws upon the illegal exercise of medicine would alone have sufficed to cut short his career. The unbelieving dynasty of the Herods, on the other hand, occupied itself little with religious movements; under the Asmoneans, Jesus would probably have been arrested at his first step. An innovator, in such a state of society, only risked death, and death is a gain to those who labor for the future. Imagine Jesus reduced to bear the burden of his divinity until his sixtieth or seventieth year, losing his celestial fire, wearing out little by little under the burden of an unparalleled mission! Everything favors those who have a special destiny; they become glorious by a sort of invincible impulse and command of fate.

This sublime person, who each day still presides over the destiny of the world, we may call divine, not in the sense that Jesus has absorbed all the divine, or has been adequate to it (to employ an expression of the schoolmen), but in the sense that Jesus is the one who has caused his fellow-men to make the greatest step toward the divine. Mankind in its totality offers an assemblage of low beings, selfish, and superior to the animal only in that its selfishness is more reflective. From the midst of this uniform mediocrity, there are pillars that rise toward the sky, and bear witness to a nobler destiny. Jesus is the highest of these pillars which show to man whence he comes, and whither he ought to tend. In him was condensed all that is good and elevated in our nature. He was not sinless; he has conquered the same passions that we combat; no angel of God comforted him, except his good conscience; no Satan tempted him, except that which each one bears in his heart. In the same way that many of his great qualities are lost to us, through the fault of his disciples, it is also probable that many of his faults have been concealed. But never has any one so much as he made the interests of humanity predominate in his life over the littlenesses of self-love. Unreservedly devoted to his mission, he subordinated everything to it to such a degree that, toward the end of his life, the universe no longer existed for him. It was by this access of heroic will that he conquered heaven. There never was a man, Cakya-Mouni perhaps excepted, who has to this degree trampled under foot, family, the joys of this world, and all temporal care. Jesus only lived for his Father and the divine mission which he believed himself destined to fulfill.

As to us, eternal children, powerless as we are, we who labor without reaping, and who will never see the fruit of that which we have sown, let us bow before these demi-gods. They were able to do that which we cannot do: to create, to affirm, to act. Will great originality be born again, or will the world content itself henceforth by following the ways opened by the bold creators of the ancient ages? We know not. But whatever may be the unexpected phenomena of the future, Jesus will not be surpassed. His worship will constantly renew its youth, the tale of his life will cause ceaseless tears, his sufferings will soften the best hearts; all the ages will proclaim that, among the sons of men, there is none born who is greater than Jesus.

PART FIVE

The Social Gospel

═══════════

*There may be war between your country and my
country. Between you and me there will be
peace.*

TOYOHIKO KAGAWA,
TO AN AMERICAN AUDIENCE

1. RACE, CLASS, AND SOCIAL JUSTICE

THE SEARCH

James Russell Lowell

I went to seek for Christ,
  And Nature seemed so fair
That first the woods and fields my youth enticed,
And I was sure to find Him there:
  The temple I forsook,
  And to the solitude
Allegiance paid; but winter came and shook
  The crown and purple from my wood;
His snows, like desert sands, with scorchful drift,
  Besieged the columned aisle and palace gate;
My Thebes, cut deep with many a solemn rift,
  But epitaphed her own sepulchred state!
Then I remembered whom I went to seek,
And blessed blunt winter for his counsel bleak.

Back to the world I turned,
  For Christ, I said, is King;
So the cramped alley and the hut I spurned,
As far beneath His sojourning:
  Mid power and wealth I sought,
  But found no trace of Him,
And all the costly offerings I had brought
  With sudden rust and mould grew dim!
I found His tomb, indeed, where, by their laws,
  All must on stated days themselves imprison,
Mocking with bread a dead creed's grinning jaws,
  Witless how long the life had thence arisen;
Due sacrifice to this they set apart,
Prizing it more than Christ's own living heart.

So from my feet the dust
  Of the proud World I shook;
Then came dear Love and shared with me His
    crust.
And half my sorrow's burden took.
  After the World's soft bed,
  Its rich and dainty fare,
Like down seemed Love's coarse pillow to my head,
  His cheap food seemed as manna rare;
Fresh-trodden prints of bare and bleeding feet,
  Turned to the heedless city whence I came,
Hard by I saw, and springs of worship sweet
  Gushed from my cleft heart smitten by the
    same;
Love looked me in the face and spake no words,
But straight I knew those footprints were the
    Lord's.

I followed where they led,
  And in a hovel rude,
With naught to fence the weather from His head,
The King I sought for meekly stood;
  A naked, hungry child
  Clung round His gracious knee,
And a poor hunted slave looked up and smiled
  To bless the smile that set him free;
New miracles I saw His presence do—
  No more I knew the hovel bare and poor,

The gathered chips into a woodpile grew,
   The broken morsel swelled to goodly store;
I knelt and wept: my Christ no more I seek,
His throne is with the outcast and the weak.

From MILTON

William Blake

And did those feet in ancient time
   Walk upon England's mountains green?
And was the holy Lamb of God
   On England's pleasant pastures seen?

And did the Countenance Divine
   Shine forth upon our clouded hills?
And was Jerusalem builded here
   Among these dark Satanic Mills?

Bring me my bow of burning gold!
   Bring me my arrows of desire!
Bring me my spear! O clouds, unfold!
   Bring me my chariot of fire!

I will not cease from mental fight,
   Nor shall my sword sleep in my hand,
Till we have built Jerusalem
   In England's green and pleasant land.

COMRADE JESUS

Sarah N. Cleghorn

Thanks to St. Matthew who had been
At mass-meetings in Palestine,
We know whose side was spoken for
When Comrade Jesus had the floor.

"Where sore they toil and hard they lie,
Among the great unwashed dwell I;—
The tramp, the convict, I am he;
Cold-shoulder him; cold-shoulder me."

By Dives' door with thoughtful eye,
He did to-morrow prophesy;—
"The Kingdom's gate is low and small;
The rich can scarce wedge through at all."

"A dangerous man," said Caiaphas;
"An ignorant demagogue, alas!
Friend of low women, it is he
Slanders the upright Pharisee."

For law and order, it was plain,
For holy church, he must be slain.
The troops were there to awe the crowd
And violence was not allowed.

Their clumsy force with force to foil
His strong, clean hands He would not soil,
He saw their childishness quite plain
Between the lightnings of His pain.

Between the twilights of His end,
He made His fellow-felon friend;
With swollen tongue and blinding eyes
Invited him to Paradise.

Ah, let no local Him refuse!
Comrade Jesus hath paid His dues.
Whatever other be debarred
Comrade Jesus hath His red card.

AFRICA

Anonymous

I slept. I dreamed. I seemed to climb a hard, ascending track
And just behind me labored one whose face was
   black.
I pitied him, but hour by hour he gained upon my
   path.
He stood beside me, stood upright, and then I
   turned in wrath.
"Go back," I cried, "what right have you to stand
   beside me here?"

I paused, struck dumb with fear, for lo! the black
    man was not there—
But Christ stood in his place!
And oh! the pain, the pain, the pain that looked from
    that dear face.

SIMON THE CYRENIAN SPEAKS

Countee Cullen

He never spoke a word to me,
    And yet He called my name,
He never gave a sign to me,
    And yet I knew and came

At first I said, "I will not bear
    His cross upon my back;
He only seeks to place it there
    Because my skin is black."

But He was dying for a dream,
    And He was very weak,
And in His eyes there shone a gleam
    Men journey far to seek.

It was Himself my pity bought;
    I did for Christ alone
What all of Rome could not have wrought
    With bruise of lash or stone.

LITANY OF THE BLACK PEOPLE

Countee Cullen

Our flesh that was a battle-ground
Shows now the morning-break;
The ancient deities are downed
For Thy eternal sake.
Now that the past is left behind,

Fling wide Thy garment's hem,
That we stay one with Thee in mind,
O Christ of Bethlehem!

The thorny wreath may ridge our brow,
The spear may mar our side,
And on white wood from a scented bough
We may be crucified;
Yet no assault the old gods make
Upon our agony
Shall swerve our footsteps from the wake
Of Thine, toward Calvary.

And if we hunger now and thirst,
Grant our withholders may,
When heaven's constellations burst
Upon Thy crowning day,
Be fed by us,—and given to see
Thy mercy in our eyes,
When Bethlehem and Calvary
Are merged in Paradise.

O BLACK AND UNKNOWN BARDS

James Weldon Johnson

O black and unknown bards of long ago,
How came your lips to touch the sacred fire?
How, in your darkness, did you come to know
The power and beauty of the minstrel's lyre?
Who first from midst his bonds lifted his eyes?
Who first from out the still watch, lone and long,
Feeling the ancient faith of prophets rise
Within his dark-kept soul, burst into song?

Heart of what slave poured out such melody
As "Steal away to Jesus"? On its strains
His spirit must have nightly floated free,
Though still about his hands he felt its chains.
Who heard great "Jordan roll"? Whose starward eye
Saw chariot "swing low"? And who was he
That breathed that comforting, melodic sigh,
"Nobody knows de trouble I see"?

What merely living clod, what captive thing,
Could up toward God through all its darkness grope,
And find within its deadened heart to sing
These songs of sorrow, love and faith, and hope?
How did it catch that subtle undertone,
That note in music heard not with the ears?
How sound the elusive reed so seldom blown,
Which stirs the soul or melts the heart to tears?

Not that great German master, in his dream
Of harmonies that thundered amongst the stars
At the creation, ever heard a theme
Nobler than "Go down, Moses." Mark its bars,
How like a mighty trumpet-call they stir
The blood. Such are the notes that men have sung
Going to valorous deeds; such tones there were
That helped make history when Time was young.

There is a wide, wide wonder in it all,
That from degraded rest and servile toil
The fiery spirit of the seer should call
These simple children of the sun and soil.
O black slave singers, gone, forgot, unfamed,
You, you alone, of all the long, long line
Of those who've sung untaught, unknown, unnamed,
Have stretched out upward, seeking the divine.

You sang not deeds of heroes or of kings;
No chant of bloody war, nor exulting paean
Of arms-won triumphs; but your humble strings
You touched in chord with music empyrean.
You sang far better than you knew; the songs
That for your listeners' hungry hearts sufficed
Still live,—but more than this to you belongs:
You sang a race from wood and stone to Christ.

THE JEW TO JESUS

Florence Kiper Frank

O Man of my own people, I alone
Among these alien ones can know thy face,
I who have felt the kinship of thy race
Burn in me as I sit where they intone

Thy praises,—those who, striving to make known
A God for sacrifice, have missed the grace
Of thy sweet human meaning in its place,
Thou who art of our blood-bond and our own.

Are we not sharers of thy Passion? Yea,
In spirit-anguish closely by thy side
We have drained the bitter cup, and, tortured, felt
With thee the bruising of the heavy welt.
In every land is our Gethsemane.
A thousand times have we been crucified.

THE REFUGEE FROM JUDEA

A FANTASY

William Zukerman

What strange thoughts pass through one's mind while sitting alone on a cold night in front of an open hearth fire! The thin, blue flames leap up and wreathe around the dark, cold lumps of coal, as if engaged in some mysterious sacred dance to drive away chill, and resurrect the frozen dead with quick, fiery kisses. They invite one to fantastic day-dreaming; and in these days when humanity is not dreaming but acting out a horrible nightmare, the day-dreams of one man sitting before a hearth fire often intermingle with wisps of the universal nightmare that constantly float about in our consciousness; and together they form a strange dark tangle of fact and fancy, truth and lies, hope and despair, that settles heavily on the heart, and makes a man's thought toss about restlessly like a child in fever.

Yet the little dancing flames have also a curiously soothing effect on the troubled spirit. Or is it the soft, crackling voice of the fire? It is a quiet, rich, mellow voice, slow and unhurried, the voice of a kind, old Nanny who lulls frightened children to sleep by telling them a long, long tale of the triumph of good over evil, of the handsome Prince over the ugly witch.

"Once upon a time . . . ," the gentle voice begins. But—but suppose the story did *not* happen as the good Nanny used to tell it? Suppose virtue did *not* triumph? Courage did *not* win the day? Truth did *not* prevail? The forces of love did *not* rout the forces of hatred? Suppose the man who had set out in search of the Holy Grail came back empty-handed, tired, disillusioned, bored and indifferent to everything but a good meal and a warm bed? After all, is not this what usually happens in real life? Why, then, should it not happen also in man's dreams which he dreams for the soothing of his spirit? Why should his dreams be so distant from his reality? Perhaps, if the creations of his longing were nearer to his real life, his world might not be as dark as it is now?

Outside, the black night presses itself against the window like a lost soul in search of salvation. Out there, on the other side of the window, all is darkness and cold: a bitter wind, soaked through with rain, viciously bends the bare trees almost to the ground. But here, in this little room, all the meanness, the inexplicable cruelty and darkness which oppress the world so heavily, is barred out by a small attic window. Strange how the whole of that heavy power, which seems to crunch over life like a steamroller leaving men mangled beyond recognition, can be stopped by one small window-pane. Yet so it is. An entire universe is gathered into this small warm room, thickly populated with lilting little flames and leaping shadows that are able, in some mysterious manner, to pierce into the deep and devious caverns of thought and lead it to the surface.

"Suppose, in these days of nightmare and darkness," the thought insinuates itself softly, "some of the most beautiful stories which have sustained mankind for centuries were to be retold? Suppose they were retold more truthfully, nearer to reality, as the events they relate in all probability happened, and not as human imagination has embellished them? Would it not be more likely to bring to troubled spirits the comfort and peace they now lack? Would it not lull to sleep the many frightened children who find no rest? For what frightens children most in nightmares is that these are so different from the beautiful stories of love and valor with which they were lulled to sleep. Perhaps what we need is to make our day dreams more like reality, instead of continually flogging our poor nag of reality to reach the heights of our dreams?

"Suppose Jesus ran for his life on the night of Gethsemane instead of remaining in the Garden to pray and then die."

The voice of the fire is so soft it does not frighten thought, nor even startle it. "Suppose that, instead of accepting his Father's will, he had insisted on his own. Would not that have been the perfectly natural and human way? Would it not have been the sane, the practical, and in the long run even the best thing to do? Is not life sweet? Is not life the most precious gift received from our Father? Why should we give it up for something which may be nothing but a chimera? At best a thought, an idea, a vision? And even if this something is indeed the truth, is it more true than life itself? Jesus knew the great value of life. He taught its sacredness. What, then, would have been more natural than that he should wish to preserve it? All the accounts of the awful scene in the Garden testify that he thought of this possibility, that throughout the long terrible night of his passion he struggled with this temptation. Why should he not have yielded to it? How easy it would have been if, instead of remaining there to pray in an agony of sweating blood, he had taken with him Peter and the two sons of Zebedee and had escaped into the dark night and hidden in the hills of Galilee which they knew so much better than the Roman soldiers. A little later he might easily have slipped across the frontier into the neighboring Alexandria, and become a refugee in Egypt, instead of a martyr in Judea."

The fire on the hearth is now in full blaze. The hard, cold, black lumps of coal have yielded to the fiery embraces of the flames; have opened their hearts, and reveal to amazed eyes the buried treasures of centuries. What fantastic and unearthly beauty! Strange castles with towers and spires all burning in a glory the like of which can be seen only in the sky when the sun takes leave of the earth. The little fireplace is a throne of gold standing on a mountain of amber and rubies. The blue flames continue their sacred dance around the golden throne, writhing lithely in an ecstasy of passion. The crackle of the fire continues the tale.

"Alexandria of those days was a great and flourishing city, next to Athens the center of Greek culture. Its people were not as drunk with religion as were those of Judea, not as fanatical. Like all peoples under the influence of Greece, their spiritual interests were more philosophic than religious, and they were tolerant of unconventional thoughts and ideas. The city also had a rich and influential Jewish community; but it too was Greek rather than Judean in its outlook. The Alexandrian Jews were out of sympathy with the long-bearded fanatical priests of Jerusalem, even disliked them, and a victim of their persecution would have been given refuge, if not a warm welcome. Jesus would hardly have found any followers among them. For, in the first place, they were mostly well-to-do merchants and artisans to whom the idea of a kingdom of the poor would not have appealed. Secondly, they were under the influence of the rationalist philosopher Philo; and the simple truths of the Galilean refugee, which flowed from a source deeper than reason, would not have attracted their sophisticated minds. Above all, they had themselves too much contempt for Jews in general and Jews from Judea in particular to be influenced by anything that came from one of them, unless it was first accepted and praised by the Egyptians. But, in the old tradition of their race, they certainly would not have let the Galilean exile fall a financial burden on the non-Jews of Alexandria.

"There were, in fact, many other such refugees in Egypt then, and the rich Alexandrian Jews had in all probability formed a Refugee Committee to look after them. In that Committee, young Jesus, after being cross-examined by a number of supercilious young women and inspected by a still larger number of overbearing middle-aged and elderly men, would be sternly admonished not to attract too much attention to himself in the streets of Alexandria, not to speak Hebrew or Aramaic, and above all to emigrate as soon as possible to some distant part of the Roman Empire, like the newly discovered lands of the Teutons, the Gauls, the Angles, and other barbarians. Nevertheless, he would be given a meager subsidy to keep him from starvation in the meantime. As his physical needs were very small, he would have been satisfied.

"With time, indeed, he might even have begun to find followers: these would come, in the first instance, from the poorer Egyptians and the slaves of all nationalities who thronged the docks of Alexandria. For not all the people of Egypt in those days were under the influence of Greek rationalist philosophy. Still very strong in the masses were the traditions of old Egypt and the Orient; and there

was a longing in the air for a truth which the teaching neither of Philo nor of Aristotle could satisfy. At any rate, slaves and freemen who worked like slaves might have collected around the refugee from Judea. The ardor of his faith, the charm of his personality, his limpid simplicity, and the colorful contrast between his beautiful parables and the dry rationalism of the Greek philosophers, might well have increased his following. So a new sect would gradually be formed; it might find adherents not only in Alexandria and in the rest of Egypt, but also across the frontiers, in Greece, in Rome, even in Judea where it would come with the new irresistible prestige of the non-Jewish world, and hence would be eagerly accepted by those who had rejected it when first preached by an unknown Galilean Jew.

"The fame of the new teaching might also reach the ears of those practical and energetic people, present in all ages, whose business it is to materialize visions and to convert dreamers' dreams into practical propositions. It might have attracted a terrific fanatic and organizer like Paul of Tarsus, who would come to Alexandria to sit at the feet of the new teacher. With his coming, the new sect would be transformed beyond all recognition. The apostles, the dreamers, the doubters, the simple fishermen and dockers who first took up the new teaching, would be swept aside. Their place would be taken by sleek and fashionable preachers who knew everything and never had a doubt about anything. The teacher himself would lose all influence on the movement. He would become in his lifetime an almost legendary figure in whose name all the work of the preachers would be done.

"There would develop a feverish activity of organization and propaganda. A net of cells would be established. Contacts would be formed with governments, with important institutions, with men of wealth and influence. The word of God would be preached in a highly scientific manner according to the latest laws of psychology. It would penetrate into the most exclusive salons of Alexandrian society where the richly coiffured, painted and perfumed Egyptian ladies would speak daintily of the Kingdom of the Meek, and their young offspring would be among the most ardent admirers of the new teacher.

"After the Roman War in Judea and the destruction of the Temple, Jesus would return home, for his heart had always been in his native hills. There he would pick up the threads where he left them on the night of Gethsemane, now no longer as an obscure and persecuted preacher of the Galilean hills forever in danger of crucifixion, but as a famous exile who had returned to his native land and had been received with universal acclamation. He would begin to build his Kingdom of God on the very ruins of the destroyed Temple where the priests who had sought to have him crucified once ruled. He might even become a ruler himself, and his first act as ruler might be to strengthen the guard in the mountain passes of Galilee to prevent men under sentence of crucifixion from escaping to Egypt . . ."

At this moment the heart of the brightly burning coal suddenly caved in with a crash. In an instant all the fantastic castles, towers, spires, thrones of gold, mountains of rubies and emeralds lay in fiery fragments around the ruins. The sound of the crash interrupted the quiet flow of the story and startled the fire-gazer's thought into reality.

"Come to your senses!" whispered a frightened thought in his mind. "Do you realize what blasphemy you have just dreamed? Just think what the world would have lost if your horrible supposition were true! Lost not merely in goodness, in moral values, but in the grandeur of faith and in beauty. Think of the drabness of the life of a great portion of humanity without the somber grandeur of Calvary, without the austere beauty of the dark Cross standing out in sharp relief against a copper sky. Can you grasp the magnitude of the loss to the world of the suffering of this lonely, deserted and mocked man staggering up a dusty hill on a hot day, deliberately to lay down his life for his faith? Think of the millions oppressed, persecuted, tortured on the rack, who were enabled to live and to bear their pain and sorrow by the thought of his suffering, his loneliness, his anguish. Think of the millions who died on battle-fields, of the innumerable slaves in galleys and under the yoke, of the legions in prisons, concentration camps, torture chambers and execution places, of the poor, the hounded and driven, of the mocked and insulted, of all the hopeless and despairing who throughout nineteen centuries found solace in the thought of him who also was driven and tortured, mocked and insulted, and abandoned by all, even by his Father. Think, think, and be horrified into silence!"

A sudden hush did fall in the room, as if the gar-

rulous voice that was telling the tale was shamed by the outburst of outraged piety. For a moment the fireplace was dark, and it looked as if the tale was at an end. But the fire on the hearth was not extinguished; only dimmed by the caving-in of the coal; nor was the bitterness and defiance of the human imagination exhausted. Soon the fire resumes building its magic fairy-land with its streets of gold and houses of emeralds and rubies. And the fire-gazer's imagination, stirred again by this magic, rises in a new, hot and defiant rejoinder.

"For almost two thousand years," he begins, "men have died on battle-fields, in prisons, in concentration camps, by the hands of the executioner and on beds of pain, and many have indeed found solace in the thought of the suffering which the Son of Man willingly took upon himself. Almost two thousand years have passed since he shot up his life like a rocket into the dark sky to lighten humanity's night and to illumine the road for the suffering children of men. Yet now the darkness is thicker than ever, the end to the night is not in view, and the road to salvation has not yet been descried, still less followed. After two thousand years of pain and suffering immeasurable, of faith in his words which for pathos, depth and sincerity has no equal in the history of this world, his promise is no more fulfilled today than it was during his lifetime. Men still die in agony on the battle-fields, in prisons and concentration camps; they still groan under the yoke of slavery; they are still oppressed and down-trodden; they are still mocked, humiliated, spat upon and crucified, although he gave his life that all these things should be no more. Two thousand years of the preaching of the word of love, and the anguish of the night of Gethsemane still drags on; the shadow of Calvary has spread over the whole face of the world; humanity lies crushed under the cross; and the groans of the dying, the oppressed and humiliated go up to Heaven in such volume that they drown out every other sound in creation."

Now the shadows on the wall stood still as if they, too, were shocked by the fire-gazer's thoughts. Big, heavy, and warm, they no longer moved lithely and vivaciously as before, but bent their heads slowly like a group of hooded monks repeating in a whisper the dreadful blasphemy they had just heard. The man at the fire looked at them long and silently, as if he expected an answer from them. Failing to receive it, he suddenly turned upon them fiercely and spoke with great vehemence:

"Tell me, you who have served him all your lives, tell me, were the Son of Man to come down to the earth now, this very night, what would happen to him? Would he not be promptly clapped into a concentration camp, flogged, beaten, kicked, spat upon and crucified more surely and more brutally than in the days of Pilate? Would he not be subjected to greater indignities and humiliations? Would he not be driven off the Prater and every park in Vienna? Would he not be made to dance and to crawl in the gutter in the very shadow of the great Cathedral which was erected in his name? Would he not be deprived of a bench when weary, of a drink when thirsty, of food when hungry, of medicine when sick? Would he not be avoided as a leper; and if he came into a public place, would he not be kicked out amidst the jeering of the crowd? Would he not be thrown out of his home, deprived of his work and livelihood, sentenced to starvation, driven from his homeland and not admitted into any other? Would he not be declared a louse, a rat, a verminous parasite who must be exterminated without mercy? Tell me, was there ever a time in history since his own days when he was crucified more readily and with greater sadistic joy than he is being crucified now, every day and every hour? When was he and his teaching more deliberately trampled under foot, jeered at and degraded, than now? What was the scoffing of the Roman soldiers on Calvary as compared with the jeering of the mobs in Vienna and Berlin? The horrors of Golgotha compared with the horrors of the bombing of Guernica and Warsaw and London? The whole world now is one big deliberate mockery of him. Yes, a mockery, more than a cruelty. It is as if some infernal imagination had deliberately invented the whole of the present scene for the sole purpose of jeering and mocking at God and of showing the utter futility and failure of Calvary. And yet, you continue to whisper your prayers and to pour out sermons about the coming of the Kingdom of God upon the earth and about the victory of the Cross. Where is that victory? Where is the glory, strength and beauty of that Kingdom? Why does it not rise from the gutters of Vienna and Prague, of Warsaw and Berlin, to strike terror into the hearts of its blasphemers? Why do not its defenders come forth to smite those who drag the dignity of Man through the mud and humiliate God as He has never been humiliated before?"

The silence in the room was heavy now and oppressive, laden with that heaviest of all loads, the anguish of a human soul. Not only the voice of the fire, but the movement of the shadows on the wall and the very whisper of the man's bitter thoughts, seemed to have stopped. The entire world gathered in this little room was hushed in stupefied despair; was this man's destiny upon the earth?

"Something is wrong somewhere," the man at the hearth groaned in the confusion of his mind. "Was it all a mistake: Golgotha, Calvary, the Cross? Did the Son of Man err on the eve of his passion and throw away his life for nothing? Perhaps, had he really become a refugee in Egypt and experienced the long-drawn-out agony of being pulled up by the roots; had he felt his sap drying up, his roots shrivelling, his whole self withering and dying without yet being physically dead; had he sat long and wearily in the anterooms of the Refugee Committees, seen the look of contempt in the eyes of the supercilious young women and heard the loud rebuffs of the overbearing smug men; had he been made to feel continually that he was a stranger, an alien, living on the mercy and generosity of others, that he was taking away someone else's job, eating someone else's bread, treading on someone else's soil, breathing someone else's air; had it been dinned into him that he was a failure, that his life was superfluous, and that he was probably more responsible himself for his situation than the brutes who had caused it; had he dragged on for many dreary years an existence which was neither life nor death; had he known longing which finally exhausts itself as a child sobs itself to sleep; had he had all faith in men, hope in life, and belief in himself stamped out in him; were he able to survive only by forgetting his reality in front of a dying fire—then, perhaps, the Son of Man would have known more of human misery than he ever knew on Calvary, and history might have taken a different course."

Defiance suddenly began to ooze out from the fire-gazer's thoughts, like air from a punctured tire. Having hurled his greatest challenge into the heavy silence and shadows of the room, he became calm, and his pensive mood returned. Once more his old doubts and regrets, driven off by his outburst like a flock of frightened birds, were coming back and settling comfortably again on their usual perch in his mind.

"Surely, we cannot escape our fate," he mused, but no longer with bitterness. "We only think we can escape by crossing frontiers and oceans. But in reality we never escape, for we all carry our cross within ourselves, and when we think that we have left it far behind us, we suddenly find it rising before us from the fire on an open hearth."

The fire-gazer suddenly realized with a familiar pang that his elaborate dream of the evening had petered out like everything else in his life. At the beginning, it was to be a bitter revolt, a mighty call for a new and brave Gethsemane; but it was turning out to be a poor little whimper of a naked soul which had ventured for a moment into the raging storm outside, and had turned quickly back into the warmth of an attic room with a faithful coal fire. Even in his growing drowsiness he could not help but see clearly that the fine web he had woven all evening, out of the phantoms of his mind with the shadows of the night, was nothing but a screen behind which he had sought to hide regrets and sorrows he feared to face. He saw the tenuous fabric of his fanciful screen breaking in many places, and through the rifts dreaded monsters pushed ugly wagging heads, demanding: "What right have you to be warm and snug in front of a fire while out there

the others are trudging through deep snow on wintry roads, are huddled into ghettos and driven through the streets with a badge of shame? What right has one part of mankind to enjoy a single ray of light and happiness while the other is steeped so deeply in darkness and in pain?"

Quickly and deliberately he switches off the flow of his thoughts, as one switches off an electric light, and sinks into a heavy, silent reverie, his eyes blankly fixed on the fire. The drowsiness gets bigger and heavier; it is now like a big, kind, pregnant woman, moving softly and gathering into its apron everything in the room: the shadows on the walls, the leaping flames on the hearth, the castles, the spires, the domes, the fairyland with streets of gold, the weird fancies and visions of man, and the soft, mellow voice of the fire crackling its long tale of wisdom and error, regret and grief. Only the human mind, still struggling weakly, resists the sweet sensation of rest and peace that is descending slowly upon a tired spirit worn out by a long night of its own Gethsemane. It is as if man's mind alone, of all things in the world, is not yet fully convinced that the greatest and sweetest of all human truths is sleep, and is still restlessly seeking some other answer. But finally he too sees that there is no other solution to the torturing problems of men; and waving a faint little goodbye to the waking, warring world, he too sinks into the sweet bosom of merciful sleep.

2. WAR AND PEACE

A CHRISTMAS CAROL

For the Sunday-School Children of
The Church of the Disciples

James Russell Lowell

"What means this glory round our feet,"
   The Magi mused, "more bright than morn?"
And voices chanted clear and sweet,
   "To-day the Prince of Peace is born!"

"What means that star," the Shepherds said,
   "That brightens through the rocky glen?"
And angels, answering overhead,
   Sang, "Peace on earth, good-will to men!"

'Tis eighteen hundred years and more
   Since those sweet oracles were dumb;
We wait for Him, like them of yore;
   Alas, He seems so slow to come!

But it was said, in words of gold
   No time or sorrow e'er shall dim,
That little children might be bold
   In perfect trust to come to Him.

All round about our feet shall shine
   A light like that the wise men saw,
If we our loving wills incline
   To that sweet Life which is the Law.

So shall we learn to understand
   The simple faith of shepherds then,

And, clasping kindly hand in hand,
   Sing, "Peace on earth, good-will to men!"

And they who do their souls no wrong,
   But keep at eve the faith of morn,
Shall daily hear the angel-song,
   "To-day the Prince of Peace is born!"

LITTLE CHILD OF MARY

From the Negro Spiritual "De New-Born Baby"

H. T. Burleigh

Baby born in Bethlehem—
O little Child of Mary—
O little Child of Mary—
Glory be to the new-born Babe!

Make room for the Child of Mary—
Make room for the Child of Mary—
Room in your heart for the Child of Mary—
Glory be to the new-born Babe!

He will bring good-will to men,
This little Child of Mary.
Open your heart to the Child of Mary—
Glory be to the new-born Babe!

O Holy Child, give peace to all men!

THE CHRIST OF THE ANDES

Florence Earle Coates

Far, far the mountain peak from me
Where lone he stands, with look caressing;
Yet from the valley, wistfully
I lift my dreaming eyes, and see
His hand stretched forth in blessing.

Never bird sings nor blossom blows
Upon that summit chill and breathless
Where throned he waits amid the snows;
But from his presence wide outflows
Love that is warm and deathless!

O Symbol of the great release
From war and strife!—unfailing fountain
To which we turn for joy's increase,
Fain would we climb to heights of Peace—
Thy peace upon the mountain!

THE WOODEN CHRIST

Martha Foote Crow

At the high ridge
Of a wide war-stricken realm
There stands an ancient wooden Christ.
Hollow the tottering image towers,
Eyeless, and rotten, and decrepit there,
His smile a cruel twist.
Within the empty heart of this old Christ
Small stinging insects build their nests;
And iron-hearted soldiers cross themselves
The while they pass
The hollow-hearted figure by.

I think there is no Christ left there
In all those carnage-loving lands
Save only this of hollow wood
With wasp nests
Hiving in its heart.

THE WHITE COMRADE

After W. H. Leatham's *The Comrade in White*

Robert Haven Schauffler

Under our curtain of fire,
Over the clotted clods,
We charged, to be withered, to reel
And despairingly wheel
When the signal bade us retire
From the terrible odds.

As we ebbed with the battle-tide,
Fingers of red-hot steel
Suddenly closed on my side.
I fell, and began to pray.
I crawled on my hands and lay
Where a shallow crater yawned wide;
Then,—I swooned . . .

When I woke it still was day.
The pain was fierce in my wound;
But I knew it was death to stir,
For fifty paces away
Their trenches were.
In torture I prayed for the dark
And the stealthy step of my friend
Who, staunch to the end,
Would creep to the danger-zone
And offer his life as a mark
To save my own.

Night came. I heard his tread,—
Not stealthy, but firm and serene,
As if my comrade's head
Were lifted far from that scene
Of passion and pain and dread;
As if my comrade's heart
In carnage had no part;
As if my comrade's feet
Were set on some radiant street
Such as no darkness could haunt;
As if my comrade's eyes
No deluge of flame could surprise,
No death and destruction daunt,
No red-beaked bird dismay,
Nor sight of decay.

Then in the bursting shells' dim light,
I saw he was clad in white.
For a moment I thought that I saw the smock
Of a shepherd in search of his flock.
Alert were the enemy, too,
And their bullets flew
Straight at a mark no bullet could fail;
For the seeker was tall and his robe was
    bright;
But he did not flee nor quail.
Instead, with unhurrying stride,
He came,
Still as the white star low in the west,
And, gathering my tall frame,
Like a child to his breast. . . .

Again I slept;—and awoke
From a blissful dream
In a cave by a stream.
My silent comrade had bound my side.
No pain was mine, but a wish that I spoke,—
A mastering wish to serve this man
Who had ventured through hell to revoke my
    doom,
As only the truest of comrades can.
I begged him to tell me how best I might aid
    him,
And urgently prayed him
Never to leave me this side of the tomb
When I saw he was hurt—
Shot through the hands that were joined in
    prayer!
Then, as the dark drops gathered there
And fell in the dirt,
The wounds of my friend
Seemed to me such as no man might bear.
Those bullet-holes in the patient hands
Seemed to transcend
All horrors that ever these war-drenched lands
Had known or would know till the mad world's
    end.
Then suddenly I was aware
That his feet had been wounded, too,
And, dimming the white of his side
A dull stain grew.
"You are hurt, White Comrade!" I cried.
His words I already foreknew:
"These are old wounds," said he,
"But of late they have troubled me."

ABOVE THE BATTLE'S FRONT

Vachel Lindsay

St. Francis, Buddha, Tolstoi, and Saint John—
Friends, if you four, as pilgrims, hand in hand,
Returned, the hate of earth once more to dare,
And walked upon the water and the land,

If you, with words celestial, stopped these kings
For sober conclave, ere their battle great,
Would they for one deep instant then discern
Their crime, their heart-rot, and their fiends' estate?

If you should float above the battle's front,
Pillars of cloud, of fire that does not slay,
Bearing a fifth within your regal train,
The Son of David in his strange array—

If, in his majesty, he towered toward Heaven,
Would they have hearts to see or understand?
. . . Nay, for he hovers there tonight we know,
Thorn-crowned above the water and the land.

WHERE IS
THE REAL NON-RESISTANT?

Vachel Lindsay

Who can surrender to Christ, dividing his best with
    the stranger,
Giving to each what he asks, braving the uttermost
    danger
All for the enemy MAN? Who can surrender till
    death
His words and his works, his house and his lands,
    his eyes and his heart and his breath?

Who can surrender to Christ? Many have yearned
    toward it daily.
Yet they surrender to passion, wildly or grimly or
    gaily;

Yet they surrender to pride, counting her precious
and queenly;
Yet they surrender to knowledge, preening their
feathers serenely.

Who can surrender to Christ? Where is the man so
transcendent,
So heated with love of his kind, so filled with the
spirit resplendent
That all the hours of his day his song is thrilling and
tender,
And all of his thoughts to our white cause of peace
surrender, surrender, surrender?

THE TERRIBLE MEEK

Charles Rann Kennedy

———————

A PEASANT WOMAN
AN ARMY CAPTAIN
A SOLDIER

THE TIME
A TIME OF DARKNESS

THE PLACE
A WIND-SWEPT HILL

———————

*Before the curtain rises, a bell from some distant
place of worship tolls the hour. Nine brazen notes,
far off, out of tune. Then a heavy peal of thunder,
and the sharp, cracking strike of a bolt; yet, above
all, one other sound, more piercing—a strange, unearthly Cry. There follows a mighty howling of
wind, blended with a confused clamour of voices and
the hurrying of many feet. The noises have almost
all died away, when the Curtain rises upon inky
darkness.*

*A sudden hush. The silence deepens. There is a
sense of moorlands and desolate places.*

*Far off, a cow lows in her stall. Some lost sheep
down in the valley bleats dismally. Silence again.*

*It is broken by the Voice of a Woman, weeping
bitterly. A* PEASANT WOMAN.

WOMAN. Oh! . . .
    [*Another voice: the gentlemanly, well-bred
    voice of an army man, now under some stress
    of emotion. A* CAPTAIN.]
CAPTAIN. My God, this is awful. I can't stand it.
WOMAN. Oh! . . .
CAPTAIN. Come, my good woman, it's all over now.
There's no earthly help for it. You can't remain here,
you know.
WOMAN. Leave me be. Leave me be.
CAPTAIN. All the others left long ago. They hur-
ried off home the moment—the moment the storm
came. . . .
    Come, it's bleak and quite too dreadful for you
up on this hill. Let me send you back to the town
with one of the soldiers.
WOMAN. One of the—soldiers! . . .
CAPTAIN. Yes: come, come now . . .
WOMAN. Leave me be. Don't touch me. There's
the smell of death on you.
CAPTAIN. Well, since you . . . And, after all
. . . [*The clank and rattle of his sword and uniform
mark his moving away. He sits.*] The smell of death.
My God, it's true.
    [*A bitter wind comes soughing up from the val-
    ley. The sheep bleats once, piteously. Then all
    is quiet again.*
        *Some one else is coming. He is heard stum-
    bling blindly up over the hill, the steel butt of
    his weapon ringing among the stones. A* SOL-
    DIER.
        *Groping in darkness, he collides suddenly
    with the* CAPTAIN. *His voice is that of a com-
    mon man, city-bred.*]
SOLDIER. Gawd blimey, wot the 'ell . . .
    Oh, beg pawdon, sir. Didn't know it was you,
Captain.
CAPTAIN. That's all right, sentry.
SOLDIER. 'Pon my word, sir, you give me a start,
fust go orf. Wot with the storm an' the darkness,
an' this 'ere little job we been doin', I tek my oath
I thought for a moment as you was . . . well, sum-
mat else.
    Wasn't quite a nice thing wot 'appened up 'ere
just nah, sir, was it?
CAPTAIN. It wasn't.

SOLDIER. I'm on guard myself, sir; or I don't know as I'd 'a 'come up, not for choice.

You bin 'ere all the time, Captain?

CAPTAIN. Have I? Yes, I suppose I have. I've been here . . . ever since.

SOLDIER. It's not exackly the place ter spend a pleasant arternoon, is it, sir?

CAPTAIN. No, I suppose not.

SOLDIER. O' course, there's company, as you might say; but not quite congenial company, eh wot?

CAPTAIN. That depends entirely upon the point of view.

SOLDIER. Dam' creepy, I call it! . . .

Well, we done for 'im good an' proper, any'ah.

CAPTAIN. My God, yes. We builders of empire know how to do our business.

SOLDIER. Pretty bloody business, too, ain't it, sir?

CAPTAIN. Yes, that's the word.

[They consider it for a moment. Presently the SOLDIER laughs at some amusing recollection.]

SOLDIER. It's an ill wind wot blows nobody any good. I got summat aht o' this, orl said an' done.

CAPTAIN. What's that?

SOLDIER. I got some of 'is togs.

CAPTAIN. His togs. How do you mean?

SOLDIER. Why, I'll tell yer. 'E didn't want no more togs, not the way 'e was goin'; nah did 'e? So me an' the boys, we got our 'eds together, and arter we'd undressed 'im an' put 'im to bed, so to speak, we pitched an' tosed for the 'ole bag lot, one by one, till they was orl bloomin' well divided aht. I got 'is boots.

CAPTAIN. You got his boots, did you?

SOLDIER. Yes, pore devil. 'E don't want them no more. Not quite my fit; but they'll do to tek 'ome for a keepsake—that is, if we ever do get 'ome aht of this 'ere stinkin' 'ole. My little missis 'll think a lot of them boots.

CAPTAIN. They will be a pleasant memento.

SOLDIER. Just wot I say, sir. Oh, my missis, she got an 'oly nose for 'orrors: she reely 'ave. Tellin' abaht them boots 'll last 'er a lifetime.

CAPTAIN. She must be an attractive young woman, your—missis.

SOLDIER. Oh no, sir, just ordinary, just ordinary. Suits me, orl right. . . . [Some memory holds him for a moment.] Funny thing, Captain, 'ow this 'ere foreign service keeps you—well, sort of thinkin', don't it? S'pose it's the lonely nights an' the long sentry duties an' such like. . . .

CAPTAIN. You've felt that too, then, have you?

SOLDIER. Yessir; meks me think abaht my missis. 'Er was in the family way when I left 'ome, sir—expectin' just a couple of month arter I sailed. . . .

The little beggar 'll be gettin' on by nah—that is, if 'e come orl right.

CAPTAIN. You've made up your mind for a boy then, eh?

SOLDIER. She allus 'oped for a boy, sir. Women's like that. S'pose it's orl right; it's men wot's wanted these days, wot with the Army an' the Spread of Empire an' orl that.

CAPTAIN. Yes, they make better killing.

[The SOLDIER is rather stupid, or he would have laughed. He goes on.]

SOLDIER. Yessir, 'er's bin 'ankerin' arter a kid ever since we was married six year ago; but some'ow or other it never seemed to come orf. 'Ealthy woman, too, sir. You unnerstan' 'ow these things is, Captain: there's no tellin'. Little beggars come by guess an' by Gawd, it seems to me. . . .

I wonder if it's a boy. There's no gettin' no news aht in this blarsted . . .

Good Gawd, wot's that? . . .

CAPTAIN. What?

SOLDIER. Be'ind us. Summat sort of . . . There, 'ark!

[The WOMAN's voice rises, sighing like wind.]

WOMAN. Oh! . . .

SOLDIER. My Gawd, wot is it?

CAPTAIN. It's a woman.

SOLDIER. A woman! Up 'ere?

CAPTAIN. She has every right to be here. This is her place.

SOLDIER. But does she know? Does she know wot's . . . danglin' up yonder, over 'er 'ed?

CAPTAIN. She knows more than we do. She belongs to him. She is his mother.

SOLDIER. 'Is mother! . . .

CAPTAIN. Yes, he was her baby once.

[The SOLDIER is affected by this. He speaks with real compassion.]

SOLDIER. Pore devil!

[Their minds go wandering through many troubled by-paths of thought. Presently the SOLDIER speaks again.]

Wot was it 'e done, Captain?

CAPTAIN. Don't you know?

SOLDIER. Not exackly. I got enough to look arter

with my drills an' vittles withaht messin' abaht with politics an' these 'ere funny foreign religions.

CAPTAIN. And yet you, if I mistake not, were one of the four men told off to do the job.

SOLDIER. Well, I 'ope I know my duty, sir. I on'y obeyed orders. Come to that, sir, arskin' your pawdon, it was you as give them orders. I s'pose *you* knew orl right wot it was 'e done?

CAPTAIN. No, I don't know exactly, either. I am only just beginning to find out. We both did our duty, as you call it, in blindness.

SOLDIER. That's strange langwidge to be comin' from *your* lips, Captain.

CAPTAIN. Strange thoughts have been coming to me during the last six hours.

SOLDIER. It's difficult to know wot's wot in these outlandish places. It's not like at 'ome, sir, where there's Law an' Order an' Patriotism an' Gawd's Own True Religion. These blarsted 'eathens got no gratitude. 'Ere's the Empire sweatin' 'er guts aht, tryin' ter knock some sense inter their dam' silly 'eds; an' wot do you get aht of it, orl said an' done? Nuthin'! Nuthin' but a lot of ingratitude, 'ard words, insurrections, an' every nah an' then a bloody example like this 'ere to-day! Oh, these foreigners mek me sick, they do reely!

CAPTAIN. Yes, perhaps that has been the real mistake all along.

SOLDIER. Wot 'as, Captain?

CAPTAIN. Taking these people—men like this one, for instance—for foreigners.

SOLDIER. Well, you'll excuse me, sir, but wot the 'ell else are they?

CAPTAIN. I'm not quite sure; but supposing they were more nearly related? Supposing, after all, they happened to be made of the same flesh and blood as you and me? Supposing they were men? Supposing, even, they were—brothers?

SOLDIER. Brothers! Why, that's exackly wot 'e used ter say—'im up there. . . .

Did you ever 'ear 'im, sir?

CAPTAIN. Once. Did you?

SOLDIER. Once. [*They remain silent for a little.*] It was politics when I 'eard 'im. On'y it sahnded more like some rummy religion.

CAPTAIN. When I heard him it was religion—sounding curiously like politics.

SOLDIER. Them two things don't 'ardly seem to go together, do they, sir?

CAPTAIN. They don't. Perhaps they ought to.

SOLDIER. I don't know. Seems to 'ave led '*im* into a pretty mess. . . .

It's a queer world! . . .

I wonder wot it was 'e reely done.

CAPTAIN. It's rather late in the day for us to be considering that, seeing what *we* have done, isn't it?

SOLDIER. Well, I don't know. P'r'aps it's funny of me, but I never done a job like this yet withaht thinkin' abaht it arterwards. . . . An' I done a few of 'em, too.

If you arsk me, sir, it was them—well, them long-faced old jossers dahn there as begun the 'ole beastly business. You know 'oo I mean.

CAPTAIN. Yes, I know whom you mean. But haven't they a name?

SOLDIER. Well, I 'ardly know *wot* ter call them, sir. They're like a lot of old washerwomen. Allus jawin'. We got nuthin' exackly like that sort at 'ome, sir.

CAPTAIN. Oh, I don't know that there's all that difference.

SOLDIER. They was allus naggin' the pore fellow, one way an' another. Couldn't leave 'im alone. They started the 'ole business.

CAPTAIN. Why, what fault did they find with him? What was it they said he did?

SOLDIER. It wasn't nuthin' 'e done, far as I could mek aht. It was summat as 'e said, wot riled them.

CAPTAIN. Something he said?

SOLDIER. Yes, summat 'orrible; that's wot they said. Summat too bad ter be spoken, summat they wasn't a-goin' ter stand from anybody. Least, that's wot I 'eard. . . .

Wasn't so very 'orrible, neither. Not ter me. Sahnded a bit mad, that's orl.

CAPTAIN. Oh, then you know what it was?

SOLDIER. Yessir. They 'ad a name for it, too: on'y I can't quite remember. One of them big jaw-crackers, you unnerstand. Seems a bit orf for a bloke ter come ter this, just for usin' a few words.

CAPTAIN. There is great power in words. All the things that ever get done in the world, good or bad, are done by words.

SOLDIER. Well, there's summat in that, too. On'y this thing 'e said—blimey, it was nuthin'! There ain't a loony alive wot doesn't say the same thing 'e said, an' more, a thahsand times a day, when 'e's reel bad in 'is 'ead. At the most, it sahnded like a bit of langwidge, that's orl.

CAPTAIN. And *you* don't mind that, do you?

SOLDIER. Me? 'E could 'a'done it till 'e was blue in the face an' welcome, far as I'd care.

CAPTAIN. You yourself, of course, had nothing at all against him? Nothing personal, nothing political, I mean. No more than I had.

SOLDIER. Lor' bless you, no, sir. Rawther liked 'im, the bit I saw of 'im.

CAPTAIN. Only they—the long-faced gentlemen—found him guilty. So, of course, they had to hand him over to the magistrate.

SOLDIER. Yes, blarst them. What did they want ter go an' do that for?

CAPTAIN. It was perhaps their—duty, don't you see?

SOLDIER. [*taken aback on the sacred word*] Oh, was it? Well, since you put it in that way, o' course. . . .

CAPTAIN. Then, again, came the magistrate's duty. I suppose he found he had some duty in the matter? Did *he* very much object to this horrible thing that had been said?

SOLDIER. Not much! 'E ain't that sort, not this fellow! . . .

That's the funny thing abaht it. Far as I could 'ear, there weren't no mention of that, by the time the case come into 'is 'ands. No, it was riotin' an' stirrin' people up agen the government, as 'e on'y 'ad ter deal with.

CAPTAIN. Was that charge proved against the prisoner?

SOLDIER. They 'ad witnesses, I suppose. On'y you know wot witnesses are, in a case like this, sir. Got their orders, you unnerstand.

CAPTAIN. And, of course, they all did their duty. That sacred obligation was attended to. They obeyed.

SOLDIER. I don't know. Don't arsk me. I know nuthin' abaht it. [*He is a little nettled at the turn the conversation is taking.*]

CAPTAIN. Was there no one, from among all those crowds that followed him, to stand up and say a word for him?

SOLDIER. Well, wot do *you* think? Them greasy blighters! You saw 'ow they be'aved just nah, when we done the job.

CAPTAIN. *Their* duty, as voicers of public opinion, I suppose.

SOLDIER. [*sullenly*] I don't know.

CAPTAIN. Had they any very strong feelings against this monstrous thing he said? Were they so stirred with affection for the government? Or didn't their duty cover those unessential points?

SOLDIER. I don't know.

CAPTAIN. Well then, this magistrate? Having examined this poor wretch in the presence of all that exemplary, patriotic, obedient mob of people, he soon found out where *his* duty lay? It was his duty to hand him over to us—to you and me.

SOLDIER. [*shortly*] Yessir.

CAPTAIN. [*insisting*] To you and me.

SOLDIER. I said, Yessir.

CAPTAIN. Whereupon, though we were practically ignorant as to the charge upon which this man was convicted: though we had grave doubts as to whether he were guilty at all; and while it is perfectly certain that we had nothing against him personally, that we even liked him, sympathized with him, pitied him: it became *our* duty, our sworn, our sacred duty, to do to him—the terrible thing we did just now.

SOLDIER. I can't see wot you're drivin' at, sir. You wouldn't 'ave a man go agen 'is duty, would you?

CAPTAIN. I'm trying to make up my mind. I don't know. I'm blind. I don't think I know what duty is.

SOLDIER. It's perfectly plain, sir. Arter all, duty *is* duty, ain't it?

CAPTAIN. Yes, it doesn't seem to be very much else.

SOLDIER. 'Ow do you mean, sir?

CAPTAIN. Well, for instance, it doesn't seem to be love or neighborliness or pity or understanding or anything that comes out hot and fierce from the heart of a man. Duty! Duty! We talk of duty! What sort of devil's duties are there in the world, do you think, when they lead blindly, wantonly, wickedly, to the murder of such a man as this!

SOLDIER. Well, far as I'm concerned, I on'y obeyed my orders.

CAPTAIN. Orders! Obeyed orders!

SOLDIER. Well, sir, it was you as give them to me.

CAPTAIN. Good God, man, why didn't you strike me in the blasphemous teeth, the hour I gave them?

SOLDIER. Me, sir? Strike my superior orficer!

CAPTAIN. You struck this defenceless man. You

had no scruples about his superiority. You struck him to the death.

SOLDIER. [*hotly*] I on'y did my duty!

CAPTAIN. We have murdered our brother. We have destroyed a woman's child.

SOLDIER. I on'y obeyed my orders. When my superior orficer says, *Kill a man*, why, I just kill 'im, that's orl. O' course I kill 'im. Wot's a soldier for? That's duty! [*With sudden lust.*] Blood an' 'ell! I'd kill 'im soon as look at im, yes, I would, if 'e was Gawd aht of 'Eaven, 'Imself! . . .

Not as I 'ave anythin' personal agen this pore devil. On'y I *do* know my duty.

[*They are silent for a little while. Then the* SOLDIER, *feeling that he has gone too far, begins assuaging the situation;*]

There's one thing certain: it's no use cryin' over spilt milk. 'E's dead an' done for nah, wotever comes. Dead as a door-nail, pore cuss.

[*The* CAPTAIN, *who has risen during his excitement, now sits down again. His sword clatters against a boulder.*]

[*A pause.*]

'E ain't the fust man I done for, neither; an' I bet 'e won't be the last. Not by a long way.

[*He speaks in an aggrieved tone. It is the way in which shame comes to a soldier.*]

[*A pause.*]

CAPTAIN. [*deeply*] So you think he is dead, do you?

SOLDIER. Well, wot do *you* think? A man don't live forever, 'ung up as 'igh as we got 'im yonder. Besides, we did a bit of business with 'is vital parts, arter we'd got 'im up there.

CAPTAIN. And all that, you think, means—death.

SOLDIER. Well, don't it?

CAPTAIN. That's what I'm wondering.

SOLDIER. Six hours, mind you. It's a long time.

CAPTAIN. There is something mightier than time.

SOLDIER. Well, they don't supply little boy's playthings, not from our War Office. One of these 'ere beauties. . . . [*He rattles his weapon in the darkness and continues*] . . . when they *do* start business, generally touch the spot.

CAPTAIN. It would have to reach very far, to touch —this man's life.

SOLDIER. Nah, wotever do you mean, Captain?

CAPTAIN. I mean that life is a terrible, a wonderful thing. You can't kill it. All the soldiers in the world, with all their hate, can't kill it. It comes back, it can't die, it rises again.

SOLDIER. Good Gawd, Captain, don't you talk like that!

CAPTAIN. Why, what are you afraid of? We have shown great courage to-day, you and I. Soldiers should be brave, you know.

SOLDIER. That's orl very well, when it's a matter of plain flesh an' blood; but Lor'! Ghosts! . . .

Do you believe in them, sir?

CAPTAIN. What?

SOLDIER. Ghosts.

CAPTAIN. Yes. It came to me to-day.

SOLDIER. [*slowly*] If I believed there was reely ghosts abaht. . . .

CAPTAIN. They are the only realities. Two of them ought to be especially important to you and me just now.

SOLDIER. Two? Blimey! 'Oose?

CAPTAIN. Why, yours, man, and mine. Our ghosts. Our immortal ghosts. This deed of ours to-day should make us think of them forever.

SOLDIER. Yours an' mine? I didn't know we 'ad ghosts, you an' me.

CAPTAIN. It makes a difference, doesn't it? There have been millions of our sort in the long history of the world. I wonder how many more millions there will be in the years to come. Blind, dutiful, bloody-handed: murderers, all of us. A soldier's ghost must be a pitiable thing to see.

[*The cloudy darkness slightly lifts from the ground. Their forms can be dimly discerned— vague shadows upon a deeper gloom. Up above there still dwells impenetrable night.*]

Tell me, brother murderer, have you ever prayed?

SOLDIER. Me, sir? . . . [*Ashamed.*] Well, sir, nah you arsk me, yes I 'ave—once.

CAPTAIN. When was that?

SOLDIER. Why, sir, abaht a couple of month arter I set sail for this blarsted little 'ole.

CAPTAIN. I understand. You prayed then for the birth of an innocent child?

SOLDIER. Yessir.

CAPTAIN. You will have need to pray again to-night. Both of us will have need. This time for the death of an innocent man.

[*The* SOLDIER *is embarrassed. He does not know what to say. Something about "duty" comes into his head; but somehow it seems in-*

appropriate. A brighter thought occurs to him;]

SOLDIER. Well, it's time I was dahn yonder, lookin' arter the boys. Any orders, sir?

CAPTAIN. Orders? No, no more—orders.

SOLDIER. Orl right, sir.

[*There is heard the rattle of his salute, and the dying away of his footsteps, as he stumbles blindly up and over the hill.*]

[*The* CAPTAIN *does not speak until all is still again.*]

CAPTAIN. My God! My God! Oh, my God!

[*He buries his face in the dirt and stones.*]

[*The faintest moaning of wind. The sheep bleats. A dog, disturbed by the sound, barks, far off. Then there is a deep silence, lasting one minute.*

[*The Voice of the* PEASANT WOMAN *is heard, speaking at first in dull, dead tones, very slowly;*]

WOMAN. Thirty-three year ago he was my baby. I bore him. I warmed him: washed, dressed him: fended for him. I fed his little mouth with milk. Thirty-three year ago. And now he's dead.

Dead, that's what he is. Dead. Hung up in the air like a thief: broken and bleeding like a slaughtered beast. All the life gone out of him. And I'm his mother.

[*A gray, misty light creeps over her face and hands. Moment by moment, her features limn out faintly through the darkness, one pale agony.*

Her garments still blend with the general gloom.]

That's what they done to my son. Killed him like a beast. Respectable people, they was. Priests, judges, soldiers, gentlemen: even common folk like me. *They* done it. And now he's dead.

He didn't hold with their kind, my son. He was always telling them about it. He would stand up open in the market-place, at the street corners, even in the House of God itself, and tell them about it. That's why they killed him.

He had a strange way with him, my son: always had, from the day he first come. His eyes. . . . They was wonderful. They held folk. That and his tongue and his tender, pitiful heart.

They didn't understand it down here. None of us understood it. We was blind—even me. Many a time I got in his way and tried to hinder him: I was afraid for him, ashamed. And then he'd look at me. . . . They was always wonderful, his eyes.

He wasn't particular, my son. He would go with anybody. He loved them so. There wasn't a drunken bibber in the place, not a lozel, not a thief, not a loose woman on the streets, but called him brother. He would eat with them, drink with them, go to their parties. He would go with grand folk, too: gentlemen. He wasn't particular: he would go with anybody.

And I tried to hinder him: I got in his way, because I was ashamed. I kept pushing in. I was afraid of what the people might think. Like I was blind. Like I didn't understand. I never told him as I understood. And now it's too late. He's dead.

[*A gust of anguish takes her, overwhelming her;*]

Oh, my son, my own son, child of my sorrow, my lad, come back to me! It's me, it's your mother, calling to you. Cannot you hear me out of the lone waste and the darkness yonder? My lad, come back, come back to me! . . .

He's gone. I shall never know the touch and the healing gladness of him again, my son, my little lad. . . . Hark! . . .

[*The wind rises and falls away like a whisper.*]

On'y the wind blowing up over the moors. God's breath, men call it. Ah! It strikes chill to the bones. . . .

Is it cold you are, my lad? I cannot reach you yonder—on'y your feet, your poor broken feet and the ankles hanging limp toward me. My bosom warms and waits for you, hungering, yearning like the day I bare you; but I cannot get up to you: I am cramped and cold and beaten: I cannot reach you yonder. . . .

[*There is heard a low fluttering as of wings;*]

The night-birds and the bats may come anigh you, they with their black wings; but not your mother, the mother that gave you life, the mother that held you warm, my son, my son, my little cold lad.

[*Her speech breaks away into sobs for a little while. As she recovers, she goes into a dazed dream of memories;*]

That was a cold night, too—the night you was born, way out in the country yonder, in the barn with them beasties. My man, he was sore about it. He covered us over with his great wool coat, and went and sat out in the yard—under the stars—till them three gentlemen come.

Them three gentlemen. . . . They talked wonderful. I have it all here in my heart.

Ay, it was rare and cold that night. Like now. Like it is now. . . .

Wonderful. They was not common folk. They was like lords, they spoke so fine. About my little lad. About you.

And then, that other night, before you come. It was a kind of light: it was a kind of glory. Like sunshine. I remember every word he said. About you. About my little lad.

[*The agony begins to prick through again, stab by stab, as she continues;*]

It was all promise in them days, all promise and hope. Like you was to be somebody. Like you was to be a great man. I kept it inside of me: I fed on it: day by day as you sprung up, I learned you about it. You was to be no common man, you wasn't. You was to lord it over everybody. You was to be a master of men, you was. And now you'm dead.

Oh! . . . Oh! . . . Oh me! . . .

That day of the fairing, when we went up to the big city, your father and me and yourself. The wide asking eyes of you, your little hand, how it would go out so and so, your little tongue all a-clatter, the ways, the wonderings of you, and the heartbreak, the heartbreak when we had you lost. Talking to the good priests, you said. Good priests! My God! . . .

It began that day, that bitter day of the fairing when we went up to the big city. I lost you then. I have lost you ever since.

Oh, the big city, the cruel city, the city of men's sin! Calling, calling the sweet life of a man and swallowing him up in death. There was no doing with you from that day. No home for you in the little village from that day. Your father's trade, your tasks, your companions, all fell off from you that day. The city, the big city called you, and the country thereabouts. It was your kingdom, you said. You must find out and build your kingdom. And the people thronged about you and followed you wherever you went in them days. They hung upon your words: they worshipped you. In them days. It was the way you had—your strange way. A power went out from you. You was always like nobody else. A

king! A king! It was me as put it first into your head. You looked like a king. You spoke like a king. You ruled like a king. You, the little peasant lad I bore. I never told you: I never lifted up my hand to help you: I hindered you; but I was proud of you, my lad, proud and ashamed, and afraid, too! And now it's too late. You'm dead. All come to nothing. You'm dead. . . .

Dead. Killed by the soldiers and the judges of the great city. I'll tell them about it. I'll go through all the earth telling about it. Killed by the men you called your brothers. Killed by the children of your kingdom. Killed, and the golden crown of your glory torn off, battered, and cast to the ground. Beaten, mocked, murdered by the mighty masters of the world. Hung up, high up in the air like a thief. Broken and bleeding like a slaughtered beast.

[*She has come to the bottom of her grief. Her voice dies away through strangled sobs into silence.*]

[*A pause.*]

[*The* CAPTAIN *rises. He halts irresolute for a moment. Then he can be heard moving over to where she lies prone on the ground.*]

CAPTAIN. Woman, will you let me speak to you?

WOMAN. Who are you?

CAPTAIN. I am the captain who spoke to you just now. I am in charge here. I am the man who gave the order that killed your son.

WOMAN. Ah! . . .

CAPTAIN. Won't you hear me? I must speak to you.

WOMAN. What do you want to say? What is there for you to say?

CAPTAIN. It is about myself. . . . I. . . .

WOMAN. Go on. I'm listening.

CAPTAIN I am a murderer. I want you to forgive me.

[*She does not answer.*]

I did it. I did it with a word. It was like magic. One word, one little word, and I was a murderer. There is nothing more terrible in the world than to be a murderer. . . .

And now I want you to forgive me.

[*She does not answer.*]

I suppose it's impossible. Forgiveness is impossible for a wretch like me. Because I killed him.

For God's sake, speak to me!

[271]

WOMAN. [*in a stupor*] I want to. I'm trying to. But you say you killed my son.

CAPTAIN. Oh! . . .

WOMAN. Why did you do it?

CAPTAIN. I did not know. Killing's my trade. It was the only thing they brought me up to do.

[*She does not answer.*]

I have been mixed up with it ever since I can remember. My father did it before me. All my people did it. It is considered the thing—the sort of thing a gentleman ought to do. They call it glory: they call it honor; courage; patriotism. Great kings hold their thrones by it. Great merchants get their beastly riches by it. Great empires are built that way.

WOMAN. By murder?

CAPTAIN. By murder. By the blood of just men. Women and little children too.

WOMAN. What makes them do it?

CAPTAIN. They want money. They want power. They want kingdom. They want to possess the earth.

WOMAN. And they have won. They have it.

CAPTAIN. Have they? Not while your son hangs there.

[*She is bewildered.*]

WOMAN. What do you mean? My son. . . . My son is dead.

CAPTAIN. Is he? Not while God is in Heaven.

WOMAN. I don't understand you. What were you saying yourself, just now? On'y a little while ago I heard his blood dripping down here in the darkness. The stones are dank with it. Not an hour ago. He's dead.

CAPTAIN. He's alive.

WOMAN. Why do you mock me? You'm mad. Are you God, as you can kill and make alive, all in one breath?

CAPTAIN. He's alive. I can't kill him. All the empires can't kill him. How shall hate destroy the power that possesses and rules the earth?

WOMAN. The power that. . . . Who?

CAPTAIN. This broken thing up here. Your son.

WOMAN. My son, the power that. . . .

CAPTAIN. Listen. I will tell you. . . .

I am a soldier. I have been helping to build kingdoms for over twenty years. I have never known any other trade. Soldiery, bloodshed, murder: that's my business. My hands are crimson with it. That's what empire means.

In the city I come from, it is the chief concern of the people. Building kingdoms, rule, empire. They're proud of it. The little children in the schools are drilled in obedience to it: they are taught hymns in praise of it: they are brought up to reverence its symbols. When they wave its standard above them, they shout, they leap, they make wild and joyful noises; like animals, like wolves, like little brute beasts. Children! Young children! Their parents encourage them in it: it never occurs to them to feel ashamed: they would be treated like lepers if they felt ashamed. That's what empire does to human beings in the city I come from. It springs from fear —a peculiar kind of fear they call courage.

And so we go on building our kingdoms—the kingdoms of this world. We stretch out our hands, greedy, grasping, tyrannical, to possess the earth. Domination, power, glory, money, merchandise, luxury, these are the things we aim at; but what we really gain is pest and famine, grudge labour, the enslaved hate of men and women, ghosts, dead and death-breathing ghosts that haunt our lives forever. It can't last: it never has lasted, this building in blood and fear. Already our kingdoms begin to totter. Possess the earth! We have lost it. We never did possess it. We have lost both earth and ourselves in trying to possess it; for the soul of the earth is man and the love of him, and we have made of both, a desolation.

I tell you, woman, this dead son of yours, disfigured, shamed, spat upon, has built a kingdom this day that can never die. The living glory of him rules it. The earth is *his* and he made it. He and his brothers have been moulding and making it through the long ages: they are the only ones who ever really did possess it: not the proud: not the idle, not the wealthy, not the vaunting empires of the world. Something has happened up here on this hill to-day to shake all our kingdoms of blood and fear to the dust. The earth is his, the earth is theirs, and they made it. The meek, the terrible meek, the fierce agonizing meek, are about to enter into their inheritance.

[*There is a deep, solemn silence for a moment or two, broken only by the tinkle of sheep-bells, which are gradually approaching.*]

WOMAN. Then it was not all wasted. It was the truth, that night. I have borne a Man.

CAPTAIN. A man and more than a man. A King.

WOMAN. My peasant lad, a king: Yes. And more yet. He was what he said he was. He was God's Son.

CAPTAIN. It will take a new kind of soldier to serve in his kingdom. A new kind of duty.

WOMAN. A newer courage. More like woman's. Dealing with life, not death.

CAPTAIN. It changes everything.

WOMAN. It puts them back again. What he done, puts all things back again, where they belong.

CAPTAIN. I can see the end of war in this: some day.

WOMAN. I can see the joy of women and little children: some day.

CAPTAIN. I can see cities and great spaces of land full of happiness.

WOMAN. I can see love shining in every face.

CAPTAIN. There shall be no more sin, no pain. . . .

WOMAN. No loss, no death. . . .

CAPTAIN. Only life, only God. . . .

WOMAN. And the kingdom of my Son. . . .

CAPTAIN. Some day.

WOMAN. When the world shall have learned.

CAPTAIN. Mother! . . . I am a murderer! . . .

WOMAN. I have been with Child. I forgive you.

[*It grows a little lighter.*]

[*Some one is heard stumbling blindly over the hill. It is the* SOLDIER. *His form emerges gray out of the gloom.*]

SOLDIER. 'Ello! Are you there, Captain?

CAPTAIN. Yes. I'm here.

SOLDIER. The fog's liftin' dahn below there—liftin' fast. It'll soon be up orf this 'ill, thank Gawd! The General wants ter see you, sir.

CAPTAIN. What does he want with me? Do you know?

SOLDIER. Another of these 'ere bleedin' jobs, I think, sir. Been a bit of a disturbance dahn in the tahn. The boys 'ave their orders, sir. General wants you ter take command.

CAPTAIN. Tell him I refuse to come.

SOLDIER. Beg pawdon, sir. . . .

CAPTAIN. I refuse to come. I disobey.

SOLDIER. I don't think I quite 'eard, sir.

CAPTAIN. I disobey. I have sworn duty to another General. I serve the Empire no longer.

SOLDIER. Beg pawdon, sir, it's not for the likes of me; but . . . Well, you know wot that means.

CAPTAIN. Perfectly. It means what you call death. Tell the General.

SOLDIER. Tell 'im as you refuse to obey orders, sir?

CAPTAIN. His: yes. [*Half to himself*] How simple it all is, after all.

SOLDIER. [*after a moment*] I'm sorry, Captain.

CAPTAIN. Thank you, brother.

[*The* SOLDIER *has no word to say.*]

[*The darkness is rapidly melting away. All three figures are now beginning to be seen quite clearly.*]

SOLDIER. Look sir, wot did I tell yer? It's comin' light again.

CAPTAIN. Eternally.

[*An unearthly splendour fills the place. It is seen to be the top of a bleak stony hill with little grass to it.*]

[*The* WOMAN *is dressed in Eastern garments; the* CAPTAIN *is a Roman centurion; the* SOLDIER, *a Roman legionary. Above them rise three gaunt crosses bearing three dead men gibbeted like thieves.*]

[*At the foot of the crosses a flock of sheep nibble peacefully at the grass. The air is filled with the sound of their little bells.*]

Curtain

PART SIX

The Passion Drama

See where Christ's blood streams in the firmament!

MARLOWE: DR. FAUSTUS

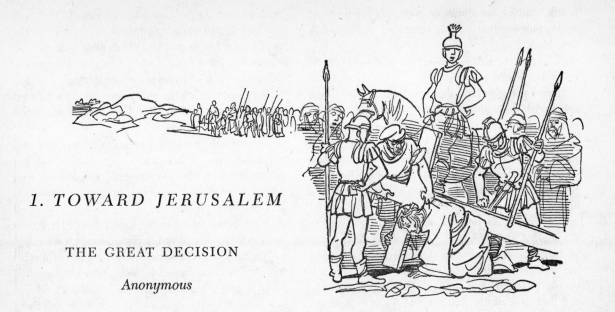

1. TOWARD JERUSALEM

THE GREAT DECISION

Anonymous

Why was Jesus crucified? What were the forces that brought him to the Cross? Such a question cannot be discussed *in extenso* here; the interested reader may be referred to Henry Sloane Coffin's book, *The Meaning of the Cross* (Scribners, 1932). But both this selection and the one which immediately follows—both from the anonymous fiction, *By an Unknown Disciple*—have a bearing on the question. In "The Great Decision" Jesus rejects a political Messiahship, refuses compromise, and commits himself to the method of non-violence. In "Nicodemus Sums It Up" the nature of the forces which opposed Jesus is clearly set forth. Both titles have been supplied by the Editor.

It was full summer before the disciples returned to Capernaum. Judas Iscariot was the last to come in. As I went down the Way of the Sea I met him at the fork of the road stalking along from Rameh. His flesh had fallen away from his bones, and his face was gaunt and grim. Some purpose seemed to fill his mind and drive him forward, for his features worked as he walked, and he talked to himself. When I greeted him he stopped and looked at me half-bewildered as if he had never seen my face before, and then suddenly he seemed to fit me into a place in his memory, for he called out eagerly,

"Is Jesus at Capernaum?" And when I said that he was, he forged forward again as if his purpose so filled his mind that there was room for nothing else. His eyes were bent on some point far ahead of him,

and, like a dog on a trail, he made straight for that. He walked so fast that it was hard to keep up with him. Once he turned to me, and said,

"What is he doing?" And when I answered,

"He is working at his trade," his eyes darkened and he muttered,

"He works at his trade when Israel is perishing." He did not speak again, but went forward faster than before.

When we reached Capernaum Judas turned aside for no one. Though several men spoke to him he paid no heed to their greetings, but made straight for the house of Jesus. And behold, when we reached it, the courtyard was empty and the space under the palms where the ox-yokes were stacked was vacant. The door of the house was shut and there was no one about. But Judas, after a glance or two around like a dog seeking scent, made for the beach, and here we found Jesus with three or four other men. The men, bent on their daily tasks, were about to launch a boat when Judas, travel-worn and thin, his beard and every line of his weary face heavy with dust, burst into their peace. They stopped their work and stared at him as if something in his aspect struck fear into them.

But Jesus seeing him, spoke,

"You have just returned? You look very tired."

"I have somewhat to say to you," Judas answered.

"When did you last eat?" Jesus asked him, but

Judas brushed the question aside, his mind so set on his purpose that he was regardless of his bodily weariness.

"I do not remember. This morning. What matter!" he said. "Where can we talk?"

"I was going to the other side of the lake. Come apart with me and rest awhile," said Jesus, and he put his shoulder to the gunnel of the boat, and I helping, we pushed her off. As she took the water I jumped in to steady her, and Judas followed. The other men would have clambered in, too, but Jesus put them aside, saying Judas would speak with him alone, and so they gave it up, and when Jesus had got in, helped to push us off with oars. Whether it was that they thought I was joined with Judas on his business, or whether they were used to seeing me with Jesus I know not, but they made no remark on my presence, and, indeed, the boat so quickly slid into deep water that I could not have got out of it if I would without leaving her guideless. So it came about that I heard what Judas had to say.

The wind was fresh, and Jesus and I set the sail. Judas did not help, but sat in the stern silent and absorbed while the boat raced across the blue lake to the other side. Here we landed, and tied the painter to a great stone. Jesus brought bread and dates from the boat, and we climbed to the wide grassy plain above, but Judas would not eat.

"Later," he said, and, for a time, he lay face downwards on the bleached grass as if he thought of what he had to speak. Then suddenly he sat upright, and turned his haggard face to Jesus.

"Master," he said, "I have preached the kingdom as you told me. Throughout all Galilee I have found the same misery and slavery. Everywhere the hold of the Romans is tightening. Our statesmen do not care. They will never win us back our freedom. In a short time it will be too late."

His voice broke, and he covered his eyes with his hands. At the sight of his woe a lump came into my throat, and I turned away my head, but the tranquillity that lay in the eyes of Jesus did not waver. He sat patient, helping Judas with silence till he should recover himself.

In a moment Judas had mastered himself. He uncovered his eyes, and looked Jesus straight in the face

"When I asked you before, you turned a deaf ear to me. But now I have seen the misery of the people, their oppression and starvation. Will you not listen? You alone can free them. You have but to lift your hand, and thousands will flock to you. Never has there been such a ferment. The people will follow you anywhere, even to death."

His voice was hoarse with passion, and he pleaded as a man pleads for what he desires most upon earth.

"I cannot do it myself," he said. "The people will not follow me. I lack something. I have not the power to win men's hearts as you have, Master. And you care for them. You have seen their misery. Will you not help? Restore to us our nation."

A great compassion shone in the eyes of Jesus, and there was reverence in his voice as he answered,

"Judas, it is not the way. Listen. Once before this temptation came upon me. When the message first came to me, when I looked round on the world and saw men as they are, and God told me to tell them what they might be, then I was driven into the wilderness, and there I fought with devils. God gives the message. It is for the Messenger to learn how to deliver it. Your question was before me, Judas, and to find an answer I wrestled with the powers of evil. All the kingdoms of this world and their splendour seemed to pass before me, and a voice within me said, 'These will all acknowledge your kingdom, and the rule of the God who sent you. But you must first unite the people and drive out those who stop them from living as God would have them live. Then will God have the kingdom, the power, and the glory.' In my soul I pondered, and then I saw the meaning of the devil that spoke within me, and I said, 'Oh, Satan, if I by your evil help drive out evil, then will you, not God, be Ruler. I will not fall down and worship you. For if I by force drive out force, will not the strong reign? And if I by cruelty drive out cruelty, will not the cruel be master?' I tell you, No, Judas, I will never hand this world over to the Master of cruelty and force. It is not the way."

He ceased speaking. Judas did not answer. He sat silent, shaken, but not convinced; his body crouched together, and in his stress he gnawed his knuckles. Suddenly he looked up from beneath his pent brows, and said,

"Under our present rule the people starve. It is in your power to give them liberty. If you will not have them fight for that high ideal, will you lead, that they may have bread?"

Jesus put the taunt aside, and answered gently,

"That temptation, too, has been before me. God has given me power, but if I use my power to give bread only I should be a traitor. Man does not live by bread alone, but by the breath of God within him. If God gather to himself his spirit and his breath, all flesh would perish and man turn into dust. No, Judas; neither is that the way. Men must seek first the kingdom of God and his righteousness, and all these things will be added to them."

Judas was not vanquished. His head drooped on his chest, and with one hand he plucked restlessly at the tufts of grass beside him and, unseeing, flung them from him. After a moment he sighed and glanced at Jesus, and there was craft in his eye.

"God guards his servants," he said. "It is natural to shrink from sacrifice that seems too great to bear. But God would preserve his Messenger. Your power is great. You could escape."

Jesus met his look, and in his own there was so much of sadness and of pity that the cunning glint died out of the eyes of Judas.

"Judas," he said. "What I have taught shall I not stand by? God will not alter his laws to save even the most beloved servant. What a man sows that shall he also reap. If I, using my powers carelessly, trust to God to make a success of my failure, I am again in the power of the Devil. Thou shalt not tempt the Lord thy God."

There was silence. Judas frowned as if his mind was working hard, and suddenly, as if he abandoned his purpose, he rose to his feet.

"Master," he said, "if you will not lead in Galilee, will you go to Jerusalem?"

Jesus replied,

"But, Judas, I have been to Jerusalem. Was it not in Jerusalem that I first met you?"

"You have never preached the kingdom in Jerusalem," said Judas, and the lines of his face twitched and then hardened as if he sought to hide his thought. Jesus, still seated on the grass, searched his face, and Judas, bracing himself, met his eyes. A long look passed between the two, and then Jesus, too, rose to his feet and said,

"I will go to Jerusalem."

Judas stared at him.

"You will go to Jerusalem?" he asked, as if amazed at his own success.

"I will go to Jerusalem," Jesus repeated, and half to himself he added, "It is not meet that a Prophet should die out of Jerusalem."

Judas caught the words and answered hastily,

"You will not die. You will go to a triumph"; and, suddenly, as if seized with suspicion, he cried,

"You mean it? You have promised? You will not fail me?"

Jesus stooped and gathered up the bread and dates which Judas had rejected. Then he turned and said,

"I will never fail you, Judas."

And with that the talk ended.

NICODEMUS SUMS IT UP

Anonymous

My days went swifter than a post that winter, and I heard nothing of the doings in Jerusalem nor did I see Jesus. In South Galilee gossip ran along every road, but my villages in the north were cut off from this traffic; and though the talk in them still raged about the teaching, no man knew what fate the doctrine had met in Judea.

It was Nicodemus who first told me that Jesus was in danger. By this time spring was nearly here again, and I had sent to Judea to ask for some monies that I needed. Now Nicodemus was an old man, and when the mule train came in and I saw him riding at its head, I was astonished that he should have come himself when he might as easily have sent a steward. But when he had alighted from his mule and, after delivering to me the monies, had washed and refreshed himself and we were alone in the room, he said,

"I have grave news for you. I have come straight from Jerusalem, where your friend Jesus has been teaching all winter. His fame has spread through all Judea. He has gone back to Capernaum now, and I have come to warn you that if he returns to Jerusalem for the Passover the Priests and Council will have his life."

"Why, what has he done?" I cried.

"The Council thinks he is dangerous," answered Nicodemus. "There is great division amongst the people, and as his followers grow, so do his opponents. There is no open discussion in Jerusalem because of the authorities, but the city is full of whispers, and rumours fly about in secret. Some say he is a good man, while others insist he is leading the people astray. Many say that he is the Prophet spoken of by David, and others are sure that he is the Messiah. Some people argue that he cannot be the Messiah as he comes from Galilee, and the Scriptures say the Messiah must come from Bethlehem, David's village, and be of David's race. It is said that men went and asked Jesus himself about this last, and he answered that as David in the Psalms called the Messiah Lord, how could it be that the Messiah was David's son? But even with this from Jesus, many people look to see in him the fulfilment of prophecy, and the tumult grows. The Rulers are afraid. They have no wish to see the Kingdom of God established on earth. The good news that Jesus preaches is not good to those who bear rule."

"It would be," I said, "if they would only forego their ordering of other men and be content to serve."

Nicodemus looked at me out of his wise old eyes.

"The last thing men will forego is that," he said. "Jesus is too clear-sighted not to know the risks that lie in such teaching. They will kill him for that alone."

"They cannot kill him for his teaching of the Kingdom," I said.

Nicodemus shook his head.

"They will find an excuse."

"They cannot," I cried.

"A way will be found. Do I not know? Am I not also a Ruler of Israel? But let me tell you all, and you can judge for yourself."

"Tell on," I answered, and sat silent to listen.

"The matter has not yet come before the Council as a whole, but I hear others of the Seventy talk, and so I know. Some of the Rulers have already tried to embroil Jesus with the Romans. If they could prove an offence against the Imperial law, then the Romans would deal with him, and the blame of the people would fall upon them. So they have sought to show that the teaching of Jesus is the same as that taught by Judas of Gaulonite. You are too young to remember the rebellion led by this Judas, but Jesus must have heard of it. It was when the Romans first put a tax on us, in the days of the Procurator Coponius. Our people took his taxation heinously until the High Priest persuaded them to cease opposing it. But this Judas never ceased his opposition, proclaiming that the taxation was the beginning of slavery, and that the Jews were cowards if they endured to pay a tax to the Romans, seeing that God was our only Ruler. I mind me well of the misfortunes that came of all this. One violent rising after another, robberies and murders and famine. But the Romans prevailed."

"I have heard my father speak of it when he was alive," I said.

"All men spoke of it," said Nicodemus. "This Judas inflamed our nation to an extraordinary degree. Even now his followers are not all dead. But they keep quiet. If they raised a voice, the Romans would not let them live a day. They will as quickly slay Jesus, if they have proof that his doctrine is that of the Gaulonite. Now I will show you the full craft of the Priests and Rulers. They sent men to Jesus to seek out such evidence. These men spoke fair to him and pretended to be in sympathy with his teaching. They said, 'We know you teach God's way truly and that you are no respecter of the masks of men, but see straight through all outward shows to the inner man.' When they had thus hinted that Jesus had the like attachment to liberty that Judas preached, they said, 'Now, tell us honestly, are we right in paying taxes to Cæsar or no?'"

"It was a vile trick," I said.

"Jesus was not taken in by it," said Nicodemus. "He asked them to show him a denarius, and the men, somewhat wondering, handed him the coin. 'Whose head and inscription is this?' he said, and the men answered, 'Cæsar's.' 'Then pay to Cæsar what belongs to Cæsar and to God what belongs to God,' said Jesus."

"He is too clever to be caught," I said, and Nicodemus answered,

"Yes. But that does not endear him to the Priests and Council."

"I hate them for their enmity," I cried with passion, but Nicodemus said,

"Your friend would not have you feel thus. How can you help God to undo the evil such men do if you are so blinded by hate that you canno' see what was in their minds when they did it? Look you, I am old and have seen much of life, but I try to put myself in the place of these men and know what they feel. Cannot you do likewise?"

I was abashed and said,

"Jesus rebuked them. I have seen his anger."

"When Jesus rebuked them was it not because they refused to show kindness? Has Jesus ever preached any but one way into the Kingdom? Your friend is gentle and great and humble. I am not as he," said Nicodemus. "I do not say you should love the Pharisees, but I ask you to show understanding of them. If they kill Jesus it will be from the best of motives."

"And not because they hate him?" I cried, unbelieving.

Nicodemus smiled sadly.

"Think you there is room in the soul of Caiaphas for so wild a passion as hate? His heart is cold. There is no fire within him. How can such a one understand Jesus? He can but think him a fool."

"No man ever looked in the face of Jesus and thought him a fool," I cried.

"To Caiaphas a clever man preaching folly is more dangerous than a fool. As you live your life, you judge your neighbours. How can these men, whose thoughts are only of bearing rule upon earth, judge of Jesus, whose message is to mind men of the spirit? There are limits to what a man may hold in his thoughts, and theirs are only of this world."

"It cannot be that Jesus will lose his life because of a misunderstanding?" I said.

"No ruler will admit that he does not understand," answered Nicodemus. "And indeed, if God's Kingdom were here there would be much change. Jesus himself says the last will be first and the first last. The Rulers do not want change. They are satisfied with the power they hold under the Romans. They think it their duty to keep our religion and customs as they were handed down to us. Jesus does not regard matters of the law as the Rulers do. He preaches more liberty than our customs have allowed. He knows that if you give a man the right to choose for himself, you give him the right to make mistakes, but he has a boundless faith that God will teach if men but listen. The Priests have not this faith. They say he is upsetting all law and order. Take the question of the Sabbath. The Priests say that Jesus preaches against the Sabbath, and

that, if he destroys the Sabbath, the Romans will force conscription into their armies upon us. They cannot train men who keep the seventh day as strictly as do the Jews. Even the Roman discipline would be broken by that custom. It is only the strict observance of the Sabbath that has hitherto kept us from serving."

Nicodemus was much perturbed, and my anxiety grew as I listened.

"That is the danger for Jesus," he went on. "He will be killed by men who believe in their own good intentions. The Rulers are sure they do the will of God. They think now, and they are sincere—remember I am one of them and come straight from Jerusalem—that if Jesus goes on preaching there will be a tumult in Galilee. The Galileans have always been turbulent. They may try to establish the Kingdom by throwing off the Roman rule. If there is a rising, whatever its result, the Priests and Rulers will lose. If Jesus wins, he is no friend to their power and they will go. If the Romans win, then also our Rulers must lose, for the Romans will blame them for the rising and will take away the powers of the Council."

"But it is not in the heart of Jesus to lead a rebellion," I said.

"It is in the heart of some of his disciples," said Nicodemus. "If the Priests do not understand the teaching, neither do the disciples. Judas Iscariot has done him much harm. It is in my mind that he tries to make a tool of Jesus. I do not trust him."

"He has tried, but Jesus would not listen," I said.

"He will try to force his hand," said Nicodemus. "Judas is blinded by hate of the Romans. From what I have seen of Jesus he will not be able to sway his will. But if Judas joined Jesus, hoping for the deliverance of our nation, what will he do when he learns that Jesus does not mean rebellion? Judas is as bitter at heart as a camel. He is a dangerous man to disappoint."

My heart was sick as I listened. Nicodemus was so balanced and wise and yet so anxious.

"But there is Pilate," I cried, seeing a ray of hope. "The Council cannot kill without the Roman permit. Pilate is no friend of the Priests."

"Pilate's position is not so secure that he can risk a conflict either with the people or with the Council. He has few troops in Judea. The Rulers will bring such evidence that he cannot resist, even if he distrust it. Men say, too, that the Emperor looks at him with suspicion since he failed to bring the ensigns with Cæsar's effigies to Jerusalem. The Jews defeated Pilate in that. Here again is misunderstanding. Cæsar does not know the strength of our feeling against graven images, but if he learn that his ensigns now pass Jerusalem by a back way, he may demand the worship of his effigy. The Jews will die rather than render it, and this Pilate knows. If he cannot make Cæsar understand our customs, and if, on top of this, there is tumult, and troops have to be sent from Syria, Pilate will be recalled, and perhaps lose his head. There is another matter, too, that men speak of—Pilate needs the favour of the High Priest in his plan for bringing water by aqueduct to Jerusalem. These Romans like to leave such memorials of their rule. Pilate wants to pay for this out of the Temple treasury. Where else can he find the money? If he is to use the Corban must he not be friends with the High Priest? But you know Pilate, even as I do."

"I have always found him a just man," I said.

"Just, but hard," said Nicodemus. "What is one life to him if he can purchase order by sacrificing it? He has shed much blood before and will again."

We fell silent again, I pondering, and then another hope, weak indeed, struck me, and I said,

"Jesus is not under the jurisdiction of Pilate. He is of Galilee and under Herod. Herod has shown great interest in him and sent for him."

Nicodemus shook his head.

"Herod is like all men of his sort and curious of novelty. Did Jesus go to see him?"

"No, he refused," I answered.

"Then Herod will do nothing to help him. He may be angry if Pilate usurps his authority, but he does not want sedition in Galilee. If he killed Jesus the people would blame him, but Herod is a fox. He will let Pilate do it, and put the blame on the Romans. And in any case the Priests will arrest Jesus in Jerusalem, and he is under Pilate there."

"They cannot arrest him without evidence that he preaches rebellion," I persisted.

"You do not understand their craft," said Nicodemus. "If they fail in that, as they must fail, Jesus being so wise, they have another contrivance. They will indict him for treason."

"Treason? How can that be?" I asked.

"Our Priests maintain that the laws under which they hold their power were given us by God. There-

fore to teach the breaking of them is blasphemy. The desecration of the Sabbath may seem a small matter to Pilate, but the Priests will then say that Jesus preaches that he is the son of God and that the divine lives in him."

"Of course he does," I said. "It is part of his teaching that God is our father and has his dwelling within us. I have often heard him teach so. And if God is our father, must we not be his sons?"

"Our rulers are blind," said Nicodemus. "If they had feeling they could burst the scales that blind their eyes. But cold-hearted they listen to Jesus, and when he tells of a spiritual kingdom, they think he desires to found an earthly one, and when he tells of the divine in man they say he teaches that he himself is God. The punishment for blasphemy is death. They mean to kill him. Let me tell you more. There is a man, a mason, who had a withered arm. Jesus healed him."

"I know. I saw him do it," I said.

"The man is working at his trade again. The Pharisees were angry with him for his gratitude to Jesus, and to stop his mouth they told him that Jesus claimed to be God, and the man answered that of a certainty he was more than man, for such kindness was never shown by a man to men. The Pharisees are full of wrath with the man, but he blazons it abroad, and his testimony will help to kill Jesus. That is not the only thing. There has already been an attempt to arrest Jesus. The Chief Priest sent some of the officials to bring him before the Council, but the men found him teaching, and waited until he had finished, wanting to bring him away quietly for fear of the people. I was at the Council myself when the men returned without Jesus. The Chief Priest asked them why they had not brought Jesus, and all the excuse the men could offer was that they had never heard any man speak as he did. The Chief Priest was so taken aback that he could only say,

"'Has he deceived you too, as he has the common people, who are ignorant of the law?'

"Another of the Pharisees said to the men,

"'The common people are cursed in their ignorance. None of the Rulers or Pharisees have been taken in by him.' I thought all this so unfair that I asked if it was according to our Law to judge a man without having heard his defence, or even knowing anything of his deeds. They all turned on me then, and Jonathan, the son of Annas, said, sneering, 'Are you also from Galilee? Search the Scriptures and see whether they say that a Prophet is to come out of Galilee!'"

I laid my hand on the hand of Nicodemus, the bravery of the frail old man so touched me, and for a time we sat silent. Then he went on,

"There was another day when Jesus was teaching in the Temple Court and the Priests themselves came to confront him. They said to him, 'Tell us by what authority you act? Who gave you your authority?' Jesus answered them, 'I too will ask you a question. Give me an answer first. Was the baptism that John gave of divine or of human origin?' You see what a dilemma this put them in? If they said divine, Jesus would ask them why they had refused to believe in it, and they dared not say human because of the people around them, who all believed that John was inspired."

"What did they do?" I asked.

"Oh, they gave it up. They said they did not know, and Jesus at once answered that then he, too, would not answer them as to his authority for his deeds."

"Is there no way to save him?" I asked.

"I have done what I could and failed," said Nicodemus. "It was for that I came north. For you may do something. Your father was a friend to Caiaphas and you know Pilate. You must go to Jerusalem. At the least you can warn Jesus and perchance withdraw him for a time."

For a moment hope lit up my heart. Then I remembered, and the flame died away.

"Jesus will never flee," I said. "He has it in his mind that he may have to suffer. I mind me of things he has said. He knows that if he goes to the Passover he goes most surely to his death."

"Nevertheless, we may save him. And if not——" Nicodemus paused.

"If not?" I repeated.

"Death is the right of all," said Nicodemus.

"Must he die?" I cried out in anguish.

"If he resist, the people will rise. Jesus would never thus cause desolation. But how can he resist? Has he not taught that wrong is never to be repaid by wrong, or violence by violence? If he resists, the Pharisees will soon point out that his teaching has a flaw. Has he not said that they taught what they did not mean to follow?"

I buried my face in my hands.

"Son," said Nicodemus, and in his voice was the great tenderness of the aged who have learnt wisdom in the service of God, "Lift up your heart. We will do what man can. It may be possible to persuade Caiaphas to take no action against Jesus, seeing that the teaching means peace and love only. Let us go to Capernaum and see Jesus, and then we can travel on to Judea."

And so we set out for Jerusalem. But we rode under black shadow, the shadow of misunderstanding, a shadow that darkened the world.

2. THE DAY OF FALSE HOPES

THE RIDE TO JERUSALEM

Norman Nicholson

And he answered and said unto them, I tell you that, if
these should hold their peace, the stones would immediately cry out.

LUKE XIX, 40

The colt is tethered at the appointed gate,
The password known: "The Lord hath need of him";
The trees are ready—this year Easter's late—
And willows wave their feather-fronds of palm.

The starlings practise on the chimney pots;
The thoroughfares of time are open wide;
Soon, now, the eyes shall weep for the blind streets,
The healing voice shall speak to the deaf road.

The window-sills are empty; no crowds wait;
Here at the pavement's edge I watch alone.
Master, like sunlight strike my slaty heart
And ask not acclamations from the stone.

THE DONKEY

G. K. Chesterton

When fishes flew and forests walked
    And figs grew upon thorn,
Some moment when the moon was blood
    Then surely I was born.

With monstrous head and sickening cry
    And ears like errant wings,
The devil's walking parody
    On all four-footed things.

The tattered outlaw of the earth,
    Of ancient crooked will;
Starve, scourge, deride me: I am dumb,
    I keep my secret still.

Fools! For I also had my hour;
    One far fierce hour and sweet:
There was a shout about my ears,
    And palms before my feet.

THE TRIUMPHANT ENTRY

Henry Vaughan

Come, drop your branches, strow the way,
    Plants of the day!
Whom sufferings make most green and gay.
The king of grief, the man of sorrow
Weeping still, like the wet morrow,
Your shades and freshness comes to borrow.

Put on, put on your best array;
Let the joyed road make holy-day,
And flowers, that into fields do stray,
Or secret groves, keep the high-way.

Trees, flowers, and herbs; birds, beasts, and stones,
That since man fell, expect with groans
To see the Lamb, come, all at once,
Lift up your heads and leave your moans!
  For here comes he
    Whose death will be
Man's life, and your full liberty.

Hark! how the children shrill and high
  "Hosanna" cry;
Their joys provoke the distant sky,
Where thrones and seraphim reply;
And their own angels shine and sing
    In a bright ring;
      Such young, sweet mirth
      Makes heaven and earth
Join in a joyful symphony.

CHRIST'S COMING
O JERUSALEM IN TRIUMPH

Jeremy Taylor

  Lord, come away;
    Why dost thou stay?
Thy road is ready; and thy paths made straight
  With longing expectation, wait
  The consecration of thy beauteous feet.
Ride on triumphantly; behold, we lay
Our lusts and proud wills in the way.
Hosanna, welcome to our hearts! Lord, here
Thou hast a temple too, and full as dear
As that of Sion; and as full of sin;
Nothing but thieves and robbers dwell therein:
Enter and chase them forth, and cleanse the floor;
Crucify them, that they may never more
    Profane that holy place,
    Where thou hast chose to set thy face.
And then if our stiff tongues shall be
Mute in the praises of thy deity,
    The stones out of the temple-wall
    Shall cry aloud and call
Hosanna! and thy glorious footsteps greet.

THE ENTRY INTO JERUSALEM

Anonymous

The anonymous work, *As Others Saw Him, A Retrospect, A.D. 54,* is purportedly written from the point of view of one Meshullam ben Zadok, a member of the Council of Twenty-Three who voted for the death of Jesus. Meshullam sends his record to his friend Aglaophonos, physician of the Greeks at Corinth.

I heard naught and saw naught of Jesus the Nazarene till the very last week of his life, and that was the week before the Passover. The winter had been a severe one, and much misery had arisen among the folk through the exactions of the Romans; indeed, an attempt had been made to throw off the Roman yoke. In several places the people had assembled in arms and attacked the soldiery, and in some cases had slain their sentries. Pilate had but sent off a cohort into the district, and all signs of discontent went underground. One of the leaders of the revolt, Jesus Bar Abbas, had been captured and thrown into prison. He, indeed, had attempted an insurrection in Jerusalem itself, where he was well known and popular among the common folk. When he was arrested, a riot had occurred, and one of the soldiers was slain who had been sent to arrest him; wherefore he lay now in prison on the charges of rebellion and murder. Yet many thought that this man had been put forth to try the temper of the people and the power of the Romans, in preparation for a more serious attempt to shake off the oppressor.

Yet who should lead the people? Jochanan, the only man whom of recent times the people followed gladly, had been done to death by Herod. One man alone since his death had won the people's heart, to wit, Jesus the cousin of Jochanan. He, and he alone, could lead the people against the Romans, and all men wondered if he would. In the midst of their wonder came news that Jesus the Nazarene was coming up to the Holy City for the Feast of Passover, the feast of redemption from Egypt. Would it prove this year a feast of redemption from the Romans? All hope of this depended upon this Jesus.

It was twenty-one years ago, but I can remember as if it were yesterday the excitement in Jerusalem when the news came that Jesus of Nazareth had arrived in the neighborhood and was spending his

Sabbath at the village of Bethany. All those who were disaffected against the Romans cried out, "A leader! a leader!" All those who were halt, sick, or blind, cried out, "A healer! a healer!" Wherever we went, there was no talk but of the coming deliverance. As I approached one group of men I heard them say, "When will it be? When will he give the sign? Will it be before or after the feast?" "Nay," said one of the crowd, a burly blacksmith he, "what day for the deliverance but the Passover day? But be it when it may, let him give the sign, and I shall be ready."

"And prove a new Maccabee," said one in the crowd, referring to his hammer, whereat a grim laugh arose.

The next day being the first of the week, which the Romans call the Day of the Sun, I was pondering the words of the Law in my little study chamber near the roof of my father's house in the Street of the Bakers near Herod's Palace, which at that time was inhabited by the Procurator, when suddenly I heard the patter of many feet in the street beneath me, and looking out, I saw them all hurrying, as it seemed, to the Temple. I put on my sandals, and, taking my staff in my hand and drawing my mantle over my head, hurried out after the passers-by. But when they came to the Broad Place before the Water Gate, they turned sharp at the right, and went down the Tyropoeon as far as the Fountain Gate, where I overtook them. There I found all the most turbulent of the city population. Some of the men I knew had been engaged in the recent riot under Jesus Bar Abbas. Others were the leading zealots in Jerusalem, and all were men eager for the freeing of the city from the Romans. And among them, too, were others who cared not for freedom, nor hated the Romans, but would only be too pleased if the city were given up to disorder and rapine. While these waited there, we heard cries from behind us, and looking back, saw filing out from the Temple courts on to the Xystus Bridge, and down into the Tyropoeon, the brigade of beggars who pass almost their whole life in the Court of the Gentiles. These came down slowly, for among them were many halt and some blind, and all were old and feeble of limb. "Why come they forth from the courts?" I asked; "and why are we waiting?" Then said one near me, "Knowest thou not that Jesus the Nazarene enters the city to-day? And men

say he is to deliver us." And at that moment a cry arose among the folk, "Lo! there he is." Looking south, for a time I could see nothing, for the midday sun of the spring solstice was shining with that radiance which we Jews think is only to be seen in our land. But after a while I could discern, turning the corner of the Jericho Road near En Rogel, a mounted man, surrounded by a number of men and women on foot. "It is Jesus—it is Jesus!" all cried; "let us go to meet him!" And with that, all but the lame rushed forward to meet him, and I with them.

It is but three hundred paces from the Fountain Gate to En Rogel, and the Nazarene and his friends had advanced somewhat to meet us, but in that short space the enthusiasm of the crowd had arisen to a very fever, and as we neared him one cried out, and all joined in the cry, "Hosanna Barabba! Hosanna Barabba!" and then they shouted our usual cry of welcome, "Blessed be he that cometh in the name of the Lord!" and one bolder than his fellows called out, "Blessed be the coming of the kingdom!" At that there was the wildest joy among the people. Some tore off branches of palms, and stood by the way and waved them in front of Jesus; others took off each his *talith* and threw it down in front of the young ass on which Jesus rode, as if to pave the way into the Holy City with choice linen. But when I looked upon the face of Jesus, there were no signs there of the coming triumph; he sat with his head bent forward, his eyes downcast, and his face all sad. And a chill somehow came over me. I thought of that play of the Greeks which thou gavest me to read, in which the king of men, driving to his own palace at Argos, is enticed to enter it, stepping upon soft carpets like an idol of your gods, and so incurs the divine jealousy.

As we approached the Fountain Gate, the beggars from the Temple had come down to it, and joined in the shouting and the welcome; and one of them, Tobias ben Pinchas by name, who had, ever since men had known him, walked with a crutch, suddenly, in his excitement, raised his crutch and waved it over his head, and danced before Jesus, crying, "Hosanna Barabba! Hosanna Barabba!" and all the men cried out, "A miracle, a miracle! what cannot this man perform?" And so, with a crowd surrounding him, Jesus entered Jerusalem and went up into the Temple. But I that year had been appointed one of the overseers who distributed the unleavened bread to the poor of the city for the coming Passover, and I had then to attend the meeting of my fellow-overseers.

That night there was no talk in Jerusalem but of the triumphant entry of Jesus. The city was crowded by Israelites who had come up to the capital for the festival, and a whisper went about that many of the strangers had been summoned by Jesus to Jerusalem to help in the coming revolt. During that night, wherever a Roman sentry stood, a crowd of the unruly would collect round him and jeer at him; and in one place the sentry had to use his spear, and wounded one of the crowd. So great was the tumult that, when the sentries were changed for the midnight watch, a whole company of soldiers accompanied the officer's guard and helped to clear the streets. Meanwhile, where was Jesus? And what was he doing in the midst of this tumult? I made inquiry, for perchance he might have been holding disputations about the Law, as is the custom with our Sages; but I learnt that he had left the city at the eleventh hour, and gone back to the village of Bethany, where he was staying. But I was thinking through all that evening of the strange contrast between the triumphant joy of his followers and the saddened countenance of the Nazarene.

Men knew not what was to become of this movement in favor of him. Most of the lower orders were hoping for a rising against the Romans to be led by this Jesus. Shrewder ones among the Better thought that the man was about to initiate a change in the spiritual government of our people. Some thought he would depose the Sadducees, and place the Pharisees in their stead. Others feared that he would carry into practice the ideals of the *Ebionim*, and raise the Poor against the Rich. Others said, "Why did he not enter by the gate of the Essenes, for he holdeth with them?" All knew that the coming Passover would be a trying time for Israel, owing to the presence of the man Jesus in Jerusalem, and the manifest favor in which he was held by the common folk. But amidst all this I could see only the pale, sad face of Jesus.

3. THE CLEANSING OF THE TEMPLE

THE ANGER OF CHRIST

Richard Watson Gilder

On the day that Christ ascended
　　To Jerusalem,
Singing multitudes attended,
And the very heavens were rended
　　With the shout of them.

Chanted they a sacred ditty,
　　Every heart elate;

But he wept in brooding pity,
Then went in the holy city
　　By the Golden Gate.

In the temple, lo! what lightning
　　Makes unseemly rout!
He in anger, sudden, frightening,
Drives with scorn and scourge the whitening
　　Money-changers out.

By the way that Christ descended
　　From Mount Olivet,

[*287*]

I, a lonely pilgrim, wended,
On the day his entry splendid
  Is remembered yet.

And I thought: If He, returning
  On this high festival,
Here should haste with love and yearning,
Where would now his fearful, burning
  Anger flash and fall?

In the very house they builded
  To his saving name,
'Mid their altars, gemmed and gilded,
Would his scourge and scorn be wielded,
  His fierce lightning flame.

Once again, O Man of Wonder,
  Let thy voice be heard!
Speak as with a sound of thunder;
Drive the false thy roof from under;
  Teach thy priests thy word.

TOLD IN THE MARKET-PLACE

Edwina Stanton Babcock

That day the doves with burnished breasts
  Uneasy were; we, halt and blind and lame,
Within the temple waited, ugly guests,
  Hoping, in spite of filth, disease and shame;
Outside the multitude waved branches green,
Calling, "Hosanna to the Nazarene."

I shrank close to the roof-prop, for my eyes
  Were dead to seeing: but I heard the clink of coins,
The piles of silver shekels steadily rise,
  Poured from sheiks' bags and belts 'round merchant loins;

I heard the purple priced; and in between
Far off,—"Hosanna to the Nazarene."

I could not see Him enter, but I heard
  The multitude and smelled the dusty throng:
Old Anab brushed me with his ragged beard,
  Muttering, "Kneel, thou! He will speak ere long."
Yea—thou five times more leprous I had been
I would come here to implore the Nazarene.

But then the woman Terah, ill of pox,
  Began to whimper. "See, he bringeth woe!
He overturns the booths, the treasure-box;
  His eyes blaze on the dove-sellers. Let us go!
He'll scourge us, smite us. Tush! It is well seen
We shall be cursèd of the Nazarene."

A form swept past us, we in terror caught
  A man's clear voice of anger: then the sound
Of fleeing feet of traffickers, onslaught
  On booths, and tables crashing to the ground.
I heard the money scatter and careen
Under the spurning of the Nazarene.

Rachel, a maiden, clutched my sleeve, and shrank
  With me behind the curtain, and the crowd
Surged wildly past. For us, our dear hopes sank
  Under that stern voice cutting like a goad,
Judging, arraigning, charging; 'mid the spleen
Of money-changers, stood the Nazarene!

"This temple is my house, the House of Prayer!"
  (His voice was like the wind that whips the leaves)
"But with your buyings and your sellings there
  Ye—ye have made my house a den of thieves!"
Then little Rachel sobbed; "Awful his mien;
His eyes are flames; I fear the Nazarene."

But when the temple silenced—while a dove
  Fluttered and soared and beat against the roof,
We frightened beggars heard a voice of love
  Calling us gently; then his tender proof
He gave. He healed us! I, who had been
Blind from my birth—I *saw* the Nazarene!

4. THE LAST SUPPER

THE FEAST IS PREPARED *

Edwin McNeill Poteat

Early in the afternoon of Thursday, Salome, wife of Zebedee and mother of James and John, raised herself on her couch, and listened to what she thought was a rap on the outer door. She had been resting during the hot two-hour period that stifled the crowded city as the sun began its slow descent from the meridian; and her room, carefully shuttered against the glare, had been both quiet and cool. The rap was repeated outside, impatiently. She slipped her feet into her sandals and was on the point of answering the summons when she heard the shuffling feet of a servant girl crossing the court. Moving to the window, she swung the heavy wooden shutter half open and looked out into the white sunlight. As the outer portal creaked open, a tall man, his head protected against the heat by a looping fold of his tunic, entered the yard. He balanced a large water jar on one shoulder, and as he stooped slightly to avoid the low lintel, a few drops of the water spilled, and spattered in a silver cascade over the servant girl. The water carrier laughed as he set the jar down, quite undisturbed by the sharp words of the young woman who, flicking uselessly at the dark spots that mottled her robe, turned to the gate again, and closed it.

She did not slip the wooden bolt into the socket. The moment the door swung to, a sharp knock and the noise of voices stopped her. She opened the gate

---

* The title of this selection has been supplied by the Editor.

slightly again, and looking suspiciously through the narrow crack, saw two men.

"We were told," said one of them, somewhat out of breath, "to follow the man with the water jar, and to ask the master of the house . . ."

"The master is not in," the maid replied curtly.

"To ask the master," the man went on, "where the room is, in which we are to prepare the Passover."

She scrutinized the faces of the men for a moment, and then slowly drew the gate open again, wide enough to allow their entrance.

"Come in," she invited; "you are from Galilee?"

"Yes," they answered, and stepped quickly inside. The maid slipped the bar noiselessly into place and started toward the house.

Through the half-opened shutter, Salome had seen her two sons step inside the gate, and was waiting at the low door of the house when they reached it. She touched her lips with her finger, to warn them lest their surprise at seeing her there betray them into noisy talk.

"The mother of the Teacher is sleeping in there," she said. "We must not disturb her. She has been very tired, and sleeps fitfully. Come into my room." She led them back to her cool chamber, and bade them sit on the long couch near the window.

"We did not know you were here," John said mysteriously. "He said nothing of Mary's being here either. Only the command to follow the man with the water jar. Is it here that we shall eat the feast?"

"Yes, and it is nearly prepared. All that lacks is getting the food. The room is ready; it is a large and comfortable place." She raised her eyes and pointed to the ceiling as she spoke. "An upper room, where you can sup in quietness and in safety."

"You say his mother rests not well?" asked James solicitously.

"Nay, she scarcely sleeps at all," replied Salome. "Since Monday she has been afraid. Last night at midnight, she cried out, and when I went into her room she was sitting up, her hands gripped tightly over her heart, and a look of terror in her eyes. 'A pain, like to the sharp thrust of a sword, racks me here,' she said. I gave her a breath of camphor leaves to smell, and she quieted at length."

"Yes," said James, "we are all of us afraid, all except him. If he is afraid, he betrays it by no word or sign. Perhaps when she awakes, we can tell her not to fear since he is unafraid. Or when he comes tonight, he can comfort her. That were better."

"Tell me," Salome demanded gently of them, "what is he going to do?"

"After the supper tonight, he will return to the Garden of Olives," answered John.

"Can he not stay here; is it not safer here than there?"

"To one who has no fear, one place is as safe as another," laughed James.

"But, I was thinking not of tonight," corrected Salome, "but of—well, of the years ahead. Those who are his followers expect so much of him; and they that hate and fear him—they will surely not suffer him forever. Monday morning in the temple . . ."

"I think," interrupted John, "he wishes that had not happened."

"Perhaps," countered his mother, "but it did happen; and it drove a wedge between his friends and his enemies. His mother is full of misgivings. She would have him return with her to Nazareth. I—I would see him seize the power that waits but for his grasp . . ."

"Nay, good mother," warned James. "Do you forget his word to you when you sought positions for us on his left and right when he was to grasp—as you put it now—his Kingdom?"

"I forget nothing," she answered animatedly. "He promised you a cup to drink and a baptism to undergo. Did that not mean that after our cup was drained, you would be rewarded?"

"I think it was not thus that he intended," John answered. "He promised us nothing. He reminded us that rewards and positions and such like were not his to give."

"So you have not urged him to seize power, and promised your support to him?" asked Salome. "And is there still bitterness to drain from new cups; and must this baptism of his engulf us all, his weary mother and me and . . . ?"

James took the hand that had been stressing her fretful words with brisk, impatient gestures, and his touch quieted her.

"You are the mother of the sons of thunder," he said smiling. He looked at his brother and continued: "It is hard to know sometimes the source of the clouds and the lightnings, and the winds that ruffle the waters of the lake. But here . . ."

John nodded and laughed understandingly, and took hold of her other hand, lifting her gently to her feet. He slipped his arm about her, and let her head rest on his ample shoulder. She understood the rebuke, and was quiet for a moment. Presently she looked up into the face of her strong son and said:

"But if it is not to be brought about thus, how can his mother's puzzled heart be set at peace?"

"I do not know," John answered wearily. "I asked him once about his home in Nazareth, and he spoke that strange word about leaving father and mother and houses and lands for the sake of the gospel. I do not think he will abandon us to danger, but I do not think he will endanger the gospel by seizing power. We have talked much with him of late. He talks of wars and rumors of wars, of broken homes and divided families, of friends who prove false, and of faithfulness to the end."

"And yet he will not stop it with a sign, or avert it by proclaiming himself as King? There is nothing he cannot do . . ."

"Nothing, indeed, except those things which his love forbids. There is much I do not understand; but this I know: he will not fight for power."

Salome looked from one face to the other. Both men seemed slightly stooped with weariness, and the lines about their faces indicated that they had been keeping long and sleepless vigils in their meeting place under the olive trees. And for the moment her vigorous and anxious mind was quieted by tenderness and solicitude, and she searched her heart for some intimation of ministry she might bring to her sons. At length she said, as if her concern for Jesus were quite forgotten:

"Will you not rest here for an hour? There is time, and it is quiet; and sleep will refresh your bodies. I will fetch water that you may bathe your faces. Have off your sandals, let me wash your feet."

She pushed them gently down on the divan, and they submitted to her attentions by kicking off their sandals and rolling back their sleeves. As Salome stooped to pick up an earthen basin, she heard a sound in the door, and turning, saw Mary the mother of Jesus standing, framed by its rough outlines. Her eyes, somber and dark with weariness and the intuitions of tragedy, lighted for a moment as she recognized the two men; and her greeting though cursory was cordial.

"The feast," she said, looking toward Salome who had not risen from her bending posture, "the feast. Must we not put it in readiness? He will be here at the set of sun, and wishes not to be delayed. He says that he will have other business after supper, beyond the brook. He will meet someone in the garden. I hope it is a friend."

"Yes," the other woman said, indulgently, "there is but little to be done. I have already arranged the couches, and the boys will presently go out to buy some wine."

She stood up and moved toward the door. "There is a jar of water freshly brought. It is cool. Will you not also be refreshed by it?"

"Nay," said Mary, "it is my heart that is weary, and what water—what water—" She stopped as though challenged by a recollection—"what water can refresh the heart?"

She turned and disappeared into the shadows. In a moment more there were sounds as of someone stirring in the room above. James and John looked at the ceiling and then at each other, but did not speak.

THE UPPER ROOM *

Toyohiko Kagawa

Venus, poised in the clear sky above Jerusalem, was luminous. There was a perfume subtle as mist in the

* The title of this selection has been supplied by the Editor.

spring air, the scent of green things reaching upward from the earth. Mary had been aware of it all the way from Bethany. The olive trees in the garden of Gethsemane had whispered of it. The brook Cedron had sung the full sweet song of April as she crossed it. She had come eagerly the two miles from Bethany to assist in serving supper to Jesus and his disciples who had gathered in the upper room of the house of young John Mark and his mother.

But when she turned at last into the narrow twisting streets of Jerusalem, the early darkness ceased to be a friendly and familiar thing. Instead, suddenly and inexplicably, it became a threatening presence. Or perhaps it was the city itself which menaced, and the shadows crouched crookedly before the houses and shops but shared the emotional coloring.

Mary of Bethany began to walk faster and faster in rhythm with the hurrying of her heart. What was it that brooded tonight over the holy city? What forces had gathered within its walls, that a village girl happily on her way to serve her Master, as she had done so many times before, must feel a choking in her throat and her breath coming short? Under this strange feeling of pressure, of a weight pressing down, down, she found herself running. Dear God, she might be too late. The thought was involuntary, sprung of itself. Too late for what? She could not tell.

"Jesus! Master!" His name came in gasps from her straining throat.

Mary Magdalene and the mother of Mark looked up in surprise as she burst into the kitchen.

"Mary, is something wrong?" Mary Magdalene, reaching into the oven for bread, paused. Mark's mother stopped stirring the young herbs she was boiling.

Mary looked about her. The familiar scene. The smell of warm food. Two women going calmly about ordinary tasks. Nothing different. Nothing to fear.

She laughed unsteadily. "I was afraid I might be too late!"

The face of Mark's mother crinkled into a relieved smile. "Too late? Nay, you are come in good season. My son has not yet returned with the wine he was sent to buy."

"But—Jesus—is he——?"

"He and the disciples are all gathered upstairs,"

said Mary Magdalene. She bent down again to look into the oven, her face flushed with the heat. Mary crossed to stand beside her, glad of the fire's warmth, as if somehow it might take from her a thin foreboding, like a physical chill, which would not leave her.

"Master! Is something lacking?"

She looked up at the sound of the anxious voice of the mother of Mark. Jesus had come quietly down into the kitchen.

"I would have a basin of water," he said. "My disciples are weary and their feet dusty."

"I will wash them," said Mary of Bethany eagerly.

Jesus smiled slightly, shook his head. "Nay, Mary, tonight that is my task."

She started to protest, astonished, but could not speak against the gentle determination in his manner. Yet all the way upstairs with the basin she rebelled at the thought of Jesus ministering to those who rightfully should have ministered unto him in such a menial task. Certainly, they would not allow it.

She returned to the kitchen to find young John Mark entering from the street with a large keg of wine. He greeted her, pleasurable excitement in his young face, as always when the Master whom he so admired accepted the hospitality of the house. Simon Peter, Mary knew, was well-acquainted with the family, through a distant relationship, some said, and for this reason Jesus often came here to spend an hour or more while in Jerusalem, though rarely did he stay the night. He preferred their own more humble dwelling at little Bethany where he might rest and refresh himself away from city noises, smells, and other confusion. Mary never ceased to be joyous that this was so, that the Master passed by the splendid comforts of larger homes and the prestige of their owners to dwell with Martha, Lazarus and herself. Their tiny garden, even when he was absent in Galilee, was fragrant with the memory of his presence. Often, when she sat there alone in the cool of the evening, her mind would go back to talks they had had there sometimes far into the night while stars seemed to burn closer, while thoughts grew, stretched—and reached with confidence into eternity.

She took the wine keg from Mark. "I will carry it upstairs, lad," she said.

It was heavy, but she took no thought of that.

Little enough burden to bear for Jesus, who continually bore so much for others. Jesus who had raised Lazarus, calling her beloved brother forth from the dismal tomb with sure authority, divine authority. This had been to her the final proof. Never doubting his goodness and humanity, that demonstration of power convinced her that he was more than a righteous mortal—he was, as he said, the Son of God. The Messiah!

In the upper room, she set the keg down with a bump. Jesus was indeed washing the disciples' feet. They were permitting it. Bewilderment, even consternation, sat on every face—but, yea—they were permitting it!

Jesus finished with the drying of the feet of Judas Iscariot, whose face alone was expressionless, and turned to Peter who was next.

Peter, unable longer to control himself, said violently:

"Master, do you wash my feet?"

Jesus paused, looking at him quietly. "What I do, you do not now understand. But you will hereafter."

Peter pressed his lips together and said righteously: "You shall never wash my feet." He looked about at the others rebelliously, critically.

Jesus' answer was swift. "If I wash you not, you have no part with me."

On Peter's face the inner struggle was written in line and muscle. At last he said humbly: "Lord, not my feet only, but also my hands and my head."

Pondering deeply, Mary of Bethany went down the stairs. She told Mary Magdalene what she had seen. The latter opened her eyes wide, then nodded, but said nothing.

The bread and herbs were now ready, and Mary and young Mark took them upstairs. The washing of the feet was finished, and all were seated around the long table. Jesus was in the center with John on his right hand and James on his left. Judas Iscariot sat next to James. Peter, apparently still embarrassed because of the recent episode, had chosen to sit on the end seat at the left.

As Mary picked up the water jug and basin to take them down to the kitchen, Jesus was speaking gravely to the disciples.

"If I, then, your Lord and Master, have washed your feet; you also ought to wash one another's feet.

For I have given you an example, that you should do as I have done to you."

Mary went downstairs again, grateful that she had heard these words, and came back shortly with vinegar for the herbs. This time, she became aware of a change in Jesus' expression and tone.

"He who eats bread with me has lifted up his heel against me," he said sorrowfully.

Mary stood still. She was halfway to the stairs, but could not take a step, nor lift her hand. It was as if all the evil, all the revenge, the lust, the greed of Jerusalem had settled like a great brooding shadow upon this upper room. Yet it was a feeling that came to her, as before in the streets, rather than the words he spoke. For often he spoke in terms not easy to comprehend, and what he meant exactly by these words, no one could tell with certainty.

The disciples looked around the table at one another, and back at Jesus, uneasily.

Jesus said: "I tell you this before it comes to pass, that afterward, when all is fulfilled according to the scripture, you may believe that I am he."

"Master," said Andrew, "speak plainly. We know not what you mean."

There was silence—thick and impenetrable. No voice ventured into the dark stream of it. Mary put her hand to her throat. In its hollow, she could feel the beat of her pulse, loud and swift.

Then Jesus lifted his head. "Even that I must tell you, that afterward you may believe." His eyes went slowly from one to another, dwelling at last upon Judas Iscariot looking darkly at a bit of bread which he was crumbling in nervous fingers. Then the Master's eyes lifted upward, away from them all.

"Verily, verily, I say unto you, that one of you shall betray me."

Immediately, there were protestations.

"Nay, not I!"

"Master, do not believe it!"

"Never!"

But Mary saw that each looked doubtfully at the others, suspicion and incredulity mingling in his countenance. While all talked, while all remonstrated, filling the room with words as if to drown foreboding, Mary saw Peter beckon John who leaned against Jesus' breast. His gestures were clear. Peter was asking John to find out from the Master who the traitor was.

Now, uncertainly, the disciples were asking, each in turn: "Is it I?"

John was questioning Jesus quietly, but she could not hear what he said, nor Jesus' answer. The Master, after a moment when he seemed to be in prayer, broke off a piece of unleavened bread and, dipping it into the vinegar, handed it to Judas.

Judas Iscariot, after a moment's hesitation, took the bread, crushing it in his fist. He did not look at Jesus whose eyes were upon him, stern—yea—but somehow compassionate. Later, with awe, Mary was to remember that look and marvel at it.

Jesus said: "What you do, do quickly."

None seemed to know what Jesus meant, save John alone, upon whose face a strange expression dawned, unbelief struggling against apprehension. Mary, trying to evolve some clear thought from her chaotic emotions, argued that no doubt Judas had neglected some important errand for the Master, as lately he was wont to do. Perhaps he had forgotten to purchase the lambs for Passover, or to make some distribution to the poor. This seemed plausible, for Judas rose at once and, brushing by her without a word, went down the stairs.

Mary followed, but when she reached the kitchen he had gone. Mary Magdalene was standing in front of the oven with a stranger, a young girl in rags with no sandals upon her torn dusty feet. Tears had furrowed, like spring freshets tumbling from the mountains, down her dirty cheeks. Her hair was a dark tangle and dry as baked hay.

Answering the query in Mary's eyes, Mary Magdalene said: "This is Drusilla, whose father Jehu is imprisoned in the Tower of Antonia."

The girl's mouth worked, and fresh tears trembled on her lids.

Mary Magdalene put a comforting hand on her shoulder.

"She has been tending sheep near the Master's birthplace of Bethlehem in order to raise the two hundred shekels necessary to release her father from the dungeon. At night her bed was a pile of dried grasses in a cave——"

"But I didn't mind that!" burst out Drusilla. "Little by little I was saving money to save my father, and when the lambs are born this spring—ah, but then it will be too late!" She began to sob, the weary rhythmical weeping of one who has done much mourning, and sank down upon the floor.

The eyes of Mary of Bethany grew wet in sympathy. "What does she mean—too late?" she asked Mary Magdalene.

"She has received word that her father is to—is to be executed tomorrow," said Mary Magdalene.

"I have saved one hundred and fifty shekels," gulped Drusilla, lifting great drenched eyes. "Only fifty more—only fifty more would save him!"

Mary said swiftly: "My sister has gone to Ephraim with Lazarus to sell some sheep. There should be enough from the sale when she returns——"

Drusilla looked at her, faint hope in her face. "You mean you will let me borrow fifty shekels from you? You will, really?" She got to her feet. "Then I shall not have to bother the Master after all." She came to Mary, plucked at her sleeve. "When will your sister return—when?"

"I expect her any time," said Mary reassuringly. "Of course, if the shepherd were out with his sheep she might have had a little trouble locating him— but she should be back soon now. Even if she were to come tonight, though, the prison wouldn't be open, would it?"

"Not after dark," said Drusilla.

"Then nothing can be done until tomorrow, I fear," said Mary.

Drusilla knelt suddenly and picked up the hem of Mary's tunic. She pressed her lips to it in mute gratitude. "Then I'll come back early tomorrow morning." She stood, her chin quivering. "I—I cannot tell you!" She fled from the kitchen, and out into the city darkness before either of the Marys could protest.

"But where will she stay the night?" asked Mary of Bethany in concern.

"Perhaps she will return to Bethlehem and her flock," said Mary Magdalene, smiling sadly, "or it may be that she knows of a nearer cave. Indeed, this daughter of the outcast, Jehu, is a little like the birds of the air which the Master speaks of. She will find a nest, and our Father will watch over her."

The eyes of the two women met in deep, sweet understanding. Mary felt reassured. Mary Magdalene was always so sure, so certain that God would take care of His own. There was in her a strength of conviction hard won and fast held to.

Mary, thinking she might be needed to serve, returned again to the upper room with young Mark.

THE SOP

Anonymous

It was no enemy which did this wrong,
But one who held with him communion sweet;
Chosen and trusted, taught and cherished long—
Had he not humbly stooped to wash his feet?
This was the man! and now the hour was nigh;
And Judas, who betrayed, said, "Master, is it I?" . .

But when from out the dish the sop he drew
Which to the traitor his dark soul betrayed;
All bitterness from all the herbs that grew
Since man lost paradise, that sop conveyed.
The bruisëd palms of more than mortal death
Combine to furnish forth the Saviour's haroseth!

THE LAST SUPPER

Joaquin Miller

"And when they had sung an hymn they went out into the Mount of Olives."

What song sang the twelve with the Savior
When finish'd the sacrament wine?
Were they bow'd and subdued in behavior,
Or bold as made bold with a sign?

Were the hairy breasts strong and defiant?
Were the naked arms brawny and strong?
Were the bearded lips lifted reliant,
Thrust forth and full sturdy with song!

What sang they? What sweet song of Zion
With Christ in their midst like a crown?
While here sat Saint Peter, the lion;
And there like a lamb, with head down,

Sat Saint John, with his silken and raven
Rich hair on his shoulders, and eyes
Lifting up to the faces unshaven
Like a sensitive child's in surprise.

Was the song as strong fishermen swinging
  Their nets full of hope on the sea?
Or low, like the ripple wave, singing
  Sea songs on their loved Galilee?

Were they sad with foreshadow of sorrows,
  Like the birds that sing low when the breeze

Is tiptoe with a tale of to-morrows,—
  Of earthquakes and sinking of seas?

Ah! soft was their song as the waves are
  That fall in low musical moans;
And sad I should say as the winds are
  That blow by the white gravestones.

5. THE GARDEN

THIRTY PIECES OF SILVER FOR JESUS

Helene Mullins

I think you know, Annas, the price is low
  For such a man; there is not in Judea
So fair a face to rest your eyes upon,
  So smooth a breast to shatter with a spear.

Besides He's young and has been well-beloved;
  There was a woman once who left the street,
And followed Him into a hostile house,
  And knelt and pressed her lips against
    His feet.

He has no wealth, yet men have gone with Him,
  And left their homes and wordly goods behind,
Because His voice was gentle when He spoke,
  And when He looked at them His eyes
    were kind.

Admit the price is low; for thirty coins
  One buys a plot of ground, a harlot's kiss,
A cask of wine, perhaps, a negro slave,
  But seldom such a comely man as this.

IN GETHSEMANE

Giles Fletcher

Sweet Eden was the arbor of delight,
  Yet in its honey flowers our poison blew:
Sad Gethsemane, the bower of baleful night,
  Where Christ a health of poison for us drew,
  Yet all our honey in that poison grew:
So we, from sweetest flower, could suck our bane,
And Christ, from bitter venom, could again
Extract life out of death, and pleasure out of pain.

A LEGEND OF GETHSEMANE

Teresa Hooley

"O, Who is this that seeks at night
The ways of green Gethsemane?
O, Who is this that prays at night,
Face to the ground in agony?—

Sorrow of Sorrow, Grief of Grief."
Uneasy whispered blade and leaf.

Sudden the Garden understood.
The grasses, on His garment's hem
Laid sighing lips—and even as blood
Were the great drops that fell on them;
The flowers all bowed their heads one way;
The wild things cared no more to play.

But there were those of herb and tree
Forbore to worship, murmuring thus:
"Nought but a suffering man we see
And what is human grief to us?"—
He turned, the Holy and the Wise,
And looked on them with anguished eyes.

They trembled, stricken and aware—
The aspen and the quaking-grass:
"All, all Creation's woe is there.
Master, forgive! Alas, alas!"
Too late. Moved by remorse forever,
The grasses shake, the aspens quiver.

GETHSEMANE'S GIFT

Katherine Brégy

When is He nearest to all of us,
  Our Brother and God's Son?
Why is He dearest, how is He most
  Inalienably our own?

Is it as little wondering Babe,
  Innocent, impotent, wise,
Turning from angels and shepherds and kings
  To laugh in His Mother's eyes?

Or during the hidden, mysterious years
  When the Light of the World went veiled and dim,
When he walked with the village women and men
  That their hearts might be open to Him?

Very close is the Christ Who wept
  For his friend struck quiet by Death:

Who to ruler's daughter and widow's son
  Gave back the incredible breath.

Who pitied our humblest hunger and thirst,
  The tired flesh spent in the race—
And from water and wine and bread and love
  Made Sacraments of His grace.

Our lips are pressed to His feet on the Cross,
  And the heart of the world is pierced with his own,
And out of the Tomb, since He has led,
  We follow the Easter sun

To the Dream come true, to the Word fulfilled,
  To the Life stretching endlessly, everywhere.

But I would not forget what the olive-trees heard—
  His one unanswered prayer!

THE DISCIPLES IN THE GARDEN *

Edwin McNeill Poteat

"Rock," said Simon the Zealot, contemptuously; "to call Simon, son of Jonas, a rock is to insult rocks in general." He slapped the massive stone on which he was sitting. Around him in the semi-darkness the resting forms of seven men were dimly visible. Peter, James and John were out of earshot under a heavy shadow of olive trees. Jesus was a stone's throw beyond them. What had happened to Judas Iscariot no one seemed to know. It was the rest of the twelve who were grouped around the Zealot.

"Guard well your words, Simon," warned a voice hid by a shadow. "How do you know there is no enemy close enough to hear you?"

"Enemy?" Simon stood up and counted slowly, pointing to each recumbent figure. "We are seven here; there is no enemy except he be one of you," he answered sourly.

"Seven, indeed," the voice continued quietly, "but during the last watch of the night did not one leave

---

* The title of this selection has been supplied by the Editor.

us? And he is gone we know not whither, though I, for one, fear the worst."

"Fear?" retorted Simon, his voice rising, forgetful of the admonition to silence, "Fear! That's the trouble, always fear. And what is it tonight that rattles your feeble shanks? Is it the late hour, and this patch of shadow? Is there none that can stand up but me? Can you not keep your knees from smiting save by lying down?"

"Your friend the Rock is not afraid," came another voice. "Less than two hours ago did he not say that no matter if all of us should forsake the Master, he would stand by him?" The Zealot detected that a sneer inflected the words.

"Bah," he snorted in reply; "the Rock will not flee? Mark you; this night we may see a strange sight—a rock that runs." He laughed roughly at his crude jest.

"Is it well that you should talk of your own courage while you laugh at another's boast?" Andrew had risen slowly to his feet. He was standing about ten paces behind the rock by which the Zealot stood. There was no rancor in his voice, neither were his words angry or pained. Simon the Zealot turned his body halfway around and faced his questioner. Andrew continued:

"My brother speaks hasty and boastful words—"

"Aye; but he speaks not only for himself. Before he boasts of his own courage, he must accuse us of cowardice."

"Truly spoken," answered Andrew. "I cannot defend him; but I can explain him." There was something in the steadied and subdued manner of his speech that quieted the group. "This is no place to boast of our bravery, nor is it the time to rebuke the rash promises of others. These are hours that shake the hearts of the stoutest men. It is no evil thing to be afraid. He who knows not fear, knows not courage. He only is brave, who, threatened by fear, yields not his heart to it."

There were low murmurs approving these quiet words. Andrew was little given to speech, and the men who were surprised by his mild rebuke to the Zealot, felt themselves also sobered by his moderation and his wisdom. He was so little like his erratic and outspoken brother that it was not infrequently whispered among his fellows that he deserved his brother's sobriquet. Simon was more like sand; it was Andrew who was massive, immobile, and silent as a

rock. That his name meant "manly" was singularly fitting; nor was the fact forgotten that his brother's name meant "a hearing," by those who accused him occasionally of listening to things to which other ears were deaf.

The ill-temper of the Zealot had subsided as suddenly as it had arisen; and he sat down again on the stone. His manner of speech was hardly less volatile than the man he had been abusing. More than once he had been twitted that the reason he disliked Peter was that he was so like him. He saw in Peter disagreeable qualities that he would not confess in himself.

"How did it come about that you and Simon are so different?" It was Thomas who put the question.

"It is not strange," replied Andrew. "It must, I agree, seem odd to one who is a twin; but is it not true that blood brethren are, more often than not, as different as Cain and Abel?"

"Perhaps," Thomas answered. "Strange are the ways of God."

"Yes; but we do not always reason well to say that such differences are the doings of God's hands. To argue thus is to lay both blame and praise at the same altar."

"Yet who but God can order the making of a man?"

"That no one can surely say. But the fire and the vaunt you like not in my brother is surely not the handiwork of God. Did not the Master bid him be called Rock to undo the bungling error of another?"

"This is strange talk," broke in the Zealot, "such as I have not heard before. Do we judge him unkindly, not knowing him well?"

A faint sound of conversation drifted from the direction where Jesus and the three had withdrawn. It sounded like the voice of one in distress. The men stopped speaking, and for a brief interval, held their breath, listening. The murmur was repeated. It was clearly the sound of agonized speech, but the words were indistinguishable.

"Does he plead with an interloper?" one asked.

"Nay; I think he prays," came a whispered answer.

The sound died away. A gust of humid air rustled the olive leaves, and a drifting mantle of thick cloud veiled the face of the declining moon.

"Simon's bluster is a mask for fear." Andrew's voice retrieved the group's wandering attention, and brought them back from a confusion of pity and apprehension to renewed interest in their comrade. "When he was quite a small child, one day, trying to lean too far over the gunwale of a boat to see the men pull in a net, he fell into the sea. Fortunately for himself he dropped into the net, and that saved him. But it broke a great hole in the net and lost most of the fish. When he was finally pulled aboard, half full of water and quite full of fright, one of the men scolded him angrily and told him it was a demon of the sea that had pulled him in. For years after that he would not get into a boat. In fact, it was not until he was fully grown, and it was necessary that he make his living either fishing or at some other craft, that he could be induced to leave the shore."

"Did he ever get over his fear?"

"Well, the strange thing is that he never acknowledged being afraid of anything. The older he grew the more ways he discovered for avoiding dangerous situations; and whenever he got into the neighborhood of trouble, he would invariably talk noisily about his deeds of valor."

"But how could such a coward become a fisherman? It is not the safest of lives—not on the Sea of Galilee."

"Perhaps it was fear of starving to death," laughed the Zealot.

"Do you remember," Andrew broke in, "when we were caught alone in the storm on the sea? What a night it was! We hardly dared to hope that any of us would reach the shore alive. And then the Master appeared near by. You did not notice it perhaps, but I watched Peter during the height of the tempest. He whined and gibbered like a lunatic, but managed to keep mumbling an improvised incantation, as was his habit."

"And then the Master—" Thomas spoke up.

"Yes, the Master! Simon suddenly coming to his senses resolved that the stigma of fear should not attach to him, and asked to be allowed to walk on the water! He, who of all men feared the water most, wanted to step out on it! That, I think, was the most daring thing he ever did to disguise his fear."

The cloud that had mantled the moon for a darkening interval passed, and the pallid light, sifting through the trees showed the figures more distinctly. Andrew was smiling. On the faces of the others a sense of momentary respite from their anxiety, softened the lines etched by weariness.

"Then you think," asked the Zealot, "that his boast early in the evening was no honest offer of loyalty in the event of trouble?"

"Certainly not dishonest," answered Andrew, "but it is exactly what those of us who grew up with him would expect."

"And yet I do not understand," said Philip, "why the Master should call him Rock. He cannot know him as you do. You would surely give him no such name."

"I am not sure that he does not know him better than I do," answered Andrew. "Simon is bad enough now, but he is a different man from the fisherman who feared the sea. And it was the Master himself who taught me to understand and love a blood brother I had misunderstood and hated."

"Hated?" echoed the Zealot in surprise.

"Yes, hated," said Andrew humbly. "One day I heard the Master talking with him after one of his fiery outbursts. 'Satan has desired you,' he told him, 'that he might sift you as wheat. But I have prayed that your faith fail not.' I asked him afterward what he meant. 'Satan is the spirit of fear,' he said. Simon was once Satan to me; he was trying to frighten me. The Satan of fear is the father of a whole brood of sins, those sins of passion that are committed in hot blood—"

Andrew did not complete his sentence. The other men were so intent on what they were hearing that Jesus and the three were almost in their midst before they saw him. His three companions were rubbing their eyes like bewildered children roused suddenly in the deep of the night. Jesus walked with a firm and vigorous step and stopped at the side of the stone where the Zealot had been sitting. All of the men rose instantly to their feet and followed the direction in which the hand of the Master pointed. The dancing light of a lantern leaped back and forth amid the trees, stopping every now and then like a discarnate spirit searching the darkness. As it leaped again, the noise of many voices hummed about it. The men looked at each other anxiously in the dimness.

"Let us be going," Jesus said, "the hand of him that betrays me is near." He began walking steadily toward the interlopers, as if to acknowledge the drunken curtseyings of the lantern. For ten paces he walked alone. The disciples stood drawn close together by the sense of sudden peril. Simon Peter stepped out of the circle and followed Jesus. His mind was like a vortex of spinning devils. He was choking with terror. In half a dozen stumbling strides he accosted the man carrying the lantern. Malchus was his name, the servant of the high priest. The fear that palsied Peter's mind gave the strength of desperation to his arm. Blindly he struck out. In his fist was gripped the hilt of a broad sword. The man with the lantern staggered as a heavy blow split his ear. As he fell forward, the light went out, and the wild confusion was muffled by the darkness. The only sound was of heavy feet running through the olive trees.

MALCHUS' EAR

Richard Crashaw

Well, Peter, dost thou wield thy active sword;
Well for thyself, I mean, not for thy Lord:
To strike at ears, is to take heed there be
No witness, Peter, of thy perjury.

APPEAL TO CLAUDIA PROCULA *

Toyohiko Kagawa

"He is taken!"

Mary of Bethany and the mother of Mark looked up from their dish-washing. The door was flung violently open. Young Mark sprang into the kitchen. He was entirely naked. Blood, from a cut over one eye, was caked upon his temple. Upon one shoulder was a red angry welt.

His mother ran to him, moaning. "My son, what has happened?"

But Mary could neither move nor speak. Her

* The title of this selection has been supplied by the Editor

hands and feet were cold. She could feel the moisture starting on her forehead. A dish slipped from her nerveless fingers, crashed to the floor. The boy, clinging wild-eyed to his mother, began to sob. Great gulping sobs of pure terror. Mark's mother was repeating over and over: "Son—son, what has happened? What has happened?"

"Jesus has been captured!" gasped the boy.

Mary cried out. Her fears were become reality. Her mind accepted it as one accepts, against the will, a blow. But her heart rebelled. Not yet . . . not yet! Despite the Master's prophetic words at supper, she had hoped that the time of fulfillment was not yet come, that there were days, weeks, perhaps years ahead. . . .

She wrenched at her apron. The cloth tore. She did not care. She was in a frenzy to get it off. She would not stand idly by—she would not! He was taken—but he should go free!

She ran from the house. Joanna, wife of Herod Antipas' former steward, lived but a few blocks away. She could help. She had influence with the great.

Crooked streets and crooked shadows. People jostling, impeding her progress. Every breath a pain. Oh, Jerusalem, Jerusalem, do your people now rejoice because the holy Passover is at hand? Weep, rather—weep!

Chuza's house was behind the palace of the king. Mary hurried around to the kitchen door, and asked a maid to call her mistress.

Joanna appeared at once. She was dressed elaborately, apparently for some important function. Mary was, for a moment, abashed. Rarely had she seen Joanna so attired. When she was with the other women serving the Master, her raiment was like theirs, simple. To Mary, blinking in the glow of the olive lamps hung from the ceiling, this was but another part of the night's strangeness.

Joanna moved into the light, her damask robes gleaming. "Why, is it you, Mary? Do come in."

Mary stumbled inside. "You—you haven't heard?"

The answer was in Joanna's puzzled face.

"They have taken Jesus, our Master!"

Joanna's face went white. "It—it can't be!" She took a step forward and shook Mary by the shoulder. "It can't be!"

Mary choked. Like the first bearer of the evil tidings, young John Mark, she wanted to throw herself into comforting human arms, and weep. She swallowed hard. No time now for tears.

"I had the news from Mark," she said heavily. "He escaped naked from Jesus' captors and ran home to tell us."

Joanna's fingers gripped Mary's arm painfully. "But who—where?"

Mary shook her head blankly. She had not waited to hear the details. The main, stark fact had been sufficient to send her flying here.

"I'm not sure," she faltered. "The Romans, perhaps—or the chief priests. Probably in the garden of Gethsemane, where he often goes for prayer and refreshment." What did it matter, how or where? It was enough that he was taken, the most loving and beloved man who ever trod the earth. Mary said pleadingly: "Don't you know a way to save him?"

"Just a minute," said Joanna quickly. "I'll go and speak with my husband." A whisper of her skirts, like the chill sound of wind, and she was gone.

Mary of Bethany was alone, more alone than she had ever been before. In body and in spirit. She was aware of her fingers clenching and unclenching, the ache of her throat, the tremble of her limbs. But it was as if these things were no part of her. They did not belong to her, nor she to them. Only her rushing, headlong thoughts were hers—and the terrible agony of her fear. She moved her lips numbly. "Master . . . Master . . ."

It seemed a starless eternity before Joanna's return.

"We've just sent a messenger to investigate." Joanna's usually calm voice was jerky with repressed feeling. "You had better come in. Indeed, I think you should spend the night here. It isn't safe for a young woman to be out alone this late."

Before Mary could reply, a tall slave came through the back gate carrying a letter. Snatching it from him, Joanna hurried again into the inner room. This time, she returned almost at once, and spoke to the slave. "There is no answer. Greet your master, please, and give him our thanks."

The slave bowed wordlessly and slipped like a shadow through the rear gate.

Joanna turned to Mary, her face strained. "It is true. The Master has been taken to the high priest's house. That letter was from Jonathan, Annas' youngest son."

Almost, Mary had begun to entertain the wild hope that young Mark had had a terrrible nightmare, which, in boyish terror, he believed to be true. But now—if Jonathan, an avowed admirer of Jesus, verified the report—she knew with heaviness that it was so.

What was Joanna saying? "They—they are planning to put Jesus out of the way."

"Nay!" cried Mary. Jesus—out of the way? Jesus, of the free step, the joyous laughter, the healing hands and piercing fearless eyes—Jesus out of the way? What insanity! "Nay!" she said again, and her voice was high and unfamiliar in tone.

Joanna smote her hands together in sudden angry violence.

"I, too, say nay!" But after a moment, she said more moderately: "Come in now, Mary. The celebration here is over and we can talk matters over. What shall we do?"

Although she was vaguely embarrassed by her rough working clothes, Mary allowed herself to be led into the guest room. Hardly were they seated, however, when there was a loud knocking at the front gate.

When the guest was ushered into the room, Mary recognized him as Nicodemus, a member of the Sanhedrin. Seeing Joanna, he began to talk excitedly, his fingers clawing his long graying beard.

"Madam, the prophet of Galilee has been taken by the soldiers and led away to the house of the high priest. I'm afraid they seek his life."

"We have heard," said Joanna. "It is a terrible thing!"

Chuza entered and, after a brief greeting, Nicodemus went on in a strained voice. "I have just received a letter from Annas' son, Jonathan, who believes as I do."

Chuza nodded gravely. His usually kindly lips were tight, the lines about his mouth were stern.

"We, too, have had word of this from Jonathan."

"What a mistake, this arrest!" said Nicodemus in exasperation. "But it has happened, and now we must see what can be done about it. You are on intimate terms with the governor Pilate, and I implore you to use your influence with him. According to the law, only Pilate has the authority to send a man to the cross." Nicodemus' eyes gleamed anxiously between sparse lashes. "Will you not see him and beg him to return a verdict of not guilty?"

That was it! Of course, that was the solution, thought Mary. Without Pilate's consent, the priests were helpless to accomplish the worst.

Another visitor entered. He was Joseph of Arimathea, wearing a Roman toga, and princely in his bearing. He and Nicodemus clasped hands, their eyes meeting earnestly. Then, in the dialect of Galilee, Joseph spoke to Chuza.

"They are calling an emergency meeting of the Sanhedrin. Annas and Caiaphas, I am convinced, will force a decision to crucify Jesus." His lips twisted scornfully. "The prophet has interfered too much with their—business."

Joanna urged everyone to be seated. No one heard her.

"If they do this thing," said Joseph with decision, "it will but increase the sins of the people in the sight of God. There will be no alternative, save the destruction of the people of Judah. King Herod Antipas killed John the Baptist because of his condemnation of the adultery of Herodias, and now this year if the high priest, who in national life holds a higher position than king, kills the prophet of Galilee, the future of our people is black indeed." He sat down on the formal Roman chair to which Joanna directed him, but rose restlessly a moment later, and began to pace the floor.

Chuza said: "I know well how those in authority seek to make vice, virtue and virtue, vice. For that reason, we moved from Sepphoris palace to Jerusalem, braving the dangers of Herod's anger." His eyes met Joanna's. "The peace we have had since my resignation has made our loss gain."

Nicodemus said impatiently: "No doubt. No doubt. But you are still in favor with Pilate, are you not? You can intercede for Jesus?"

Chuza rubbed his chin thoughtfully, then nodded. "Yea, I can. But there is still a better way. Pilate listens to anything his wife says and, instead of going directly to him myself, I think success would be more certain if my wife Joanna speaks with Claudia."

Joseph said promptly: "A wise thought. Let us have Joanna go."

Mary looked at Joanna whose lips were parted, and whose dark eyes were luminous with determination. Joanna would do her best for the Master, there was no doubt of that. When Chuza's wife rose, Mary rose, too—suddenly conscious of her drab attire and disheveled hair. Wearily, she swept a lock back from her forehead.

Because it was dark, they went out to the broad street through the Joppa gate. Turning to the left in front of the west gate of the temple, they came out on the wide Damascus road which they climbed in silence for some distance before turning into the very narrow lane in which two people could not walk abreast and which led to the Tower of Antonia. Pilate's residence was directly northwest of the tower.

Because it was the night before the eve of the Feast of the Passover, every house was lighted in celebration, and the streets were, even yet, quite lively.

When they reached Pilate's mansion, Mary bade farewell to Joanna.

"Nay," said Joanna, clinging to her. "You must come with me, Mary."

"But I can't go before the governor's wife in these clothes," protested Mary.

She wanted to get away, to run in all haste back to Bethany. Lazarus must hear of this, and Martha, if she were returned from her journey. Her brother would have words of courage for her. In his eyes, ever since his resurrection, there had been the calm of complete assurance.

But Joanna's hands held her. "Nay, leave me not. I need the comfort of your presence, Mary. As for raiment—here, put on my coat. I am wearing a ceremonial robe, so it matters not if I have a coat or not."

Joanna was so insistent that Mary agreed, and together they entered the courtyard. The surroundings were very strange to Mary of Bethany. Her friends were all girls from the lower ranks of society and tonight was her first glimpse of the environment of the upper classes of Rome and Jerusalem where dress and formality were strictly observed.

They were ushered into a large room on whose mosaic floor was spread a rich red carpet. Mary's sandaled feet sank into it. But she was hardly impressed, save that, for a moment or two, the awful fact of Jesus' arrest ceased to possess its full measure of reality. This was merely the pleasanter part of the night's dream. She, humble Mary of Bethany, treading the crimson rugs of the governor's palace!

Pilate's wife appeared at once. Whether for the festival or not, she was dressed like a Greek goddess in a gold-embroidered gown, her hair in Grecian style held up by gold pins.

"Joanna!" She clasped her guest's hands and spoke in Latin. "It is long since we have met. I heard but recently from Pilate that you had left the household of Herod. How was that?" She searched Joanna's face with concern.

Joanna answered hesitatingly, not as fluent in Latin as Claudia, making a brief explanation. Then she introduced Mary. "She is one of the disciples of the prophet of Galilee. It is about him we have come. Have you heard what has happened?"

Claudia shook her head.

"He has fallen into the hands of the high priest Caiaphas and his father-in-law, Annas."

"We have heard nothing of it," said Claudia, concerned. "When was he taken?"

It took so long, Mary thought. All the questions, all the answers. While they talked, sand was running out of the glass. Time was sliding like water between the fingers, and none could stay it.

"I think it was early this evening," Joanna was saying.

"That Annas!" said Claudia explosively. "He's a great trial to my husband. The man is really responsible for the aqueduct revolt of last spring. At first, he promised a share of the temple revenue for the project, and a start was made, but before long he made the excuse that it was costing too much, and made my husband the culprit!" She gestured expressively. "And he himself started the revolt! And now what is he up to?"

Jesus was bound in the house of the high priest. Jesus was in the hands of his implacable enemies. Pilate's wife ranted about aqueducts, temple revenue, and revolts—and the Master was captive. Mary tried not to think what might be happening to him. That he would be treated with the respect due him was too much to hope. She had seen too clearly the envy and hatred in their eyes as they baited him in the temple. She had seen them daily growing more desperate for words to catch him with. She had heard, too, their mumblings and threats at Jesus' denunciations of their hypocrisy and greed. Well, they could not trap him with phrases, however skillfully knit, nor with staves, had they dared take him bodily in the city. But, in a lonely place, surrounded by but few followers, they had captured him. And now—now that they had him—what?

"That man!" said Joanna. "That man, Annas! You know, he says that as long as the prophet of Galilee is alive, the coffers of the temple will never be full, and tonight he has seized him." She wrung her hands. "I know he plans to crucify him. Doubtless tomorrow he will be brought before your husband, and we beg you to intercede on his behalf. Ask your husband, I pray you, to discharge him as guiltless."

Claudia, her face grown serious, left her guests and went into the next room. The sound of an octachord, which had been playing throughout their conversation, was immediately stilled. Then, after a little, Pilate entered the room with Claudia.

The governor carried his octachord with him, and looked annoyed at being disturbed. He sat down on a chair nearest the door, and waited impatiently for Joanna to speak.

Mary had often heard that the frequent uprisings of the Jews had affected Pilate's health, but she was unprepared for the nervousness of the Roman. He moved continually, head, hands and feet. Muscles jerked in his cheeks. He bit his full under lip. His thin hands plucked at the strings of the octachord, filling the room with weird inharmony.

Claudia, apparently resigned to her husband's difficult temperament, spoke soothingly: "Won't you listen to Joanna's request? You remember, she once talked to us of that famous prophet of Galilee. Now she is much disturbed about his arrest by Annas."

Pilate straightened. He put his harp down on the chair beside him. "What's that? Annas has seized the Galilean prophet? Annas hasn't any such authority. Haven't you confused him with Caiaphas?" His mouth twisted. "That Annas is a sly fox. Just the sort to try something like this." He looked around at them petulantly. "He broke his promise to me and then linked himself with the Zealots and stirred up trouble in the city. A wily fellow. You can't tell what he may do. Evidently that good prophet, Jesus, was interfering with him in some way." He smiled mirthlessly, as if liking the thought of interference with Annas, from whatever source.

Mary was tempted to speak out, to bring him back to the important matter under consideration. In her mind now, there kept flashing sharp and dreadful pictures. Scenes in Caiaphas' house, in which Jesus played the victim's role. Scoffing. Insults. Perhaps, she shuddered, even physical abuse. Ah, lord of

Rome, cease your petty, selfish reminiscing, forget your own troubles for a moment, and think on the enormity of this crime against God. His Son in the hands of evil men!

Claudia said: "Joanna has come to ask me to intercede for him. They think his captors will send the Galilean to you tomorrow to ask formal judgment, hoping you will sentence him to death."

Pilate started. "Death!" he snorted. "Nonsense. What evil has he done? The fellow may have been unwise—yea—but from what I hear it was courageous foolishness. He walked openly in the temple and denounced the thieving Sadducees and the sanctimonious Pharisees." He slapped his knee. "By the gods, I would that I had seen it!"

Claudia said: "These followers of his know that you are an upright judge, and they beg you to pronounce him innocent of the charges against him. That's your request, is it not, Joanna?"

Joanna bowed. "That is our great desire. I believe it probable that Annas will accuse the prophet of something like stirring up a revolution, but as Claudia well knows, he is far from being an insurrectionist. As a matter of fact, last spring, when about five thousand Zealots were gathered together and wanted him to be their leader in revolt, he hurried away to Tyre and Sidon instead, and would not allow himself to be involved." Joanna's voice trembled in her earnestness. "He is a strong and peaceful man, and that is why Annas and Caiaphas, chafing under their loss of temple profits, will doubtless demand some unreasonable punishment. Please do not listen to anything they may say but judge him fairly and uprightly."

Pilate looked convinced. "I'll do my best for you. As you say, Annas is a wicked fellow, and there is no prophesying what he may try to do." He sighed gustily. "He gives us a lot of trouble." He got up, nodded briefly, and, with his octachord, disappeared into the adjoining room.

Mary of Bethany was weak with relief. He had promised. Pilate had promised. He would take the Master's part against the chief priests. And without Pilate's consent, as representative of Rome, there could be no death verdict against the Nazarene. No death verdict!

She hardly heard Joanna thanking Claudia, barely remembered her own manners. Claudia was escorting them to the door. Stopping, she took Joanna's hands in her own.

"Joanna, do come again when you have not such business as this. When Cypros was in Jerusalem, she came often, and I was not lonely, but since Agrippa quarreled again with King Antipas and has had to go to Egypt, there has been no one. I have been so lonely of late! Won't you come tomorrow?" She turned courteously to Mary. "And bring your friend."

Mary heard Joanna promise, and she herself murmured something—she was not sure what. As they went out through the courtyard, she thought that once such an invitation from the governor's lady would have meant a great deal to her. Now it was subordinate to the thought that perhaps the Master might be freed tomorrow. That perhaps he would share with them the Passover. Her anxiety that he was still in the hands of the priests remained, but the great terror for his ultimate safety had lifted.

She murmured: "Master . . . Master."

6. THE PROCURATOR

CHRIST BEFORE PILATE

George Herbert Clarke

(He is a man—magnanimous broad brow;
   The seer's eyes, tragical, These dogs of Jews
   Endure no liberal mind: their priests accuse
Christus of aims impossible.) Art thou
A King then, as thine enemies avow?
   Thou sayest. Truth is my Kingdom. All men whose
   Spirits are of the Truth hear it and choose
Its light, its benediction. He ceased now.

How may we know the unknown? Pilate sighed.
   None answered. Time stood still. The eternal
     Deep
     Flowed round about the twain that strangely
       yearned
     Each to the other. . . . At last, like men asleep
Waking—the thorn-crowned to be crucified,—
     Roman and Galilean slow returned.

TROUBLED BY DREAMS

Edwin McNeill Poteat

Procula, beloved wife of Pilate, woke with a start. For a full minute she stared at the canopy over her bed, until its outlines, gradually taking shape in the darkness, reassured her that she had been dreaming. Her sense of great relief manifested itself by a deep intake of breath, and a sharp, convulsive exhalation. She heard no sound in her room except the regular breathing of the slave girl sleeping on a low cot at the foot of the great bed. She lay still for a while, listening to the nocturnal scurry of tiny sounds that pattered like frightened feet over the vast carpet of silence. Presently the voice of the palace watchman drifted in from a distant parapet. It was the third watch, three hours yet till cock-crow.

She turned over and tried to fetch her departed sleep by tricks she had hitherto found successful. She marked the steady rhythm of her heart and counted a legion of soldiers parading through her mind in the slow tempo of her pulse beat. But the imaginary army display made her restless and she moved impatiently. She rose to her elbow and looked toward the heavy curtain that mantled the window. Through a bladelike rift she noted that the moon was not yet gone. Dropping again to her pillow she returned in recollection to Rome, to the court of Tiberius. How many times she had put herself to sleep turning over in her mind the scandals of Julia, the shameless daughter of the emperor! The tangled intrigues of Livia, the queen mother, had often served as a soporific; and to trail some court gossip about Agrippina, the proud and passionate empress, was to follow an easy path to the gates of sleep.

After an hour of fruitless effort that only made her more restive, she sat up in bed.

"Rhoda," she called quietly to the girl. The maid sat up suddenly with the slavish promptness she had cultivated, but she could not dissemble either her anxiety or the weight of sleep that was not to be put off, merely by a change of posture. She rubbed her eyes bewilderedly, and got heavily to her feet, acknowledging the summons with a deep, though uncertain obeisance.

"Rhoda," Procula repeated. The voice was sympathetic, and oddly whimsical. "What do you think of dreams?"

The girl was either too astonished or too sleepy to respond at once, so Procula continued as if in explanation: "Dreams, do you never dream? Do not frights or fancies trouble your head? Or do you Jews dream no more? I heard my master once say the Jews had stopped their silly dreaming since he became their governor."

The slave had had a moment in which to recover from her sudden rousing, and after lighting a tall taper by the bed from the flaxen wick that burned all night out of sight behind a screen, answered modestly:

"Yes, my lady, sometimes I dream. But tonight I have been sleeping too sound for dreaming."

"And what mean the dreams that visit you when your sleep is light?"

"I do not know. There are soothsayers by the city wall in the bazaar of Annas who understand such things. They say that dreams are sometimes the voice of God, and sometimes the voice of the evil one."

"Have you ever visited these men with your dreams?" asked Procula eagerly.

"Nay, my lady," replied the girl with an intimation of embarrassment in her tone. "There are old crones who sell love philters to love-sick maidens, I have been told; but one as young as I should not dream or think of such things. Perhaps when I am older—"

"Of course; but then, one can hardly help dreaming. Dreams come unbidden to young and old alike. Would you seek the soothsayers if you dreamed a strange and terrible thing?"

"Not I, my lady. I am but a slave girl; and such things are too great for me. I have heard men say that in ancient times armies won victories and rulers were chosen because interpreters of dreams spoke true words of wisdom. And a kitchen maid once told me that every daughter of Abraham dreams she is to bear a king when the first pains of her travail are

upon her. But I do not believe such things. Perhaps the dream of bearing a king is the whisper of a midwife to give courage in the hour of pain."

Pilate's wife sat up and hugged her knees to her breast. The slave girl threw a fold of the linen sheet solicitously about her shoulders, against the chill of the early morning. The sound of their conversation had roused one of the guards of Pilate's bedchamber who moved to the door. The two women heard his step, followed by a pause.

"Go part the arras and whisper to him that it is we. Ask him if Pilate sleeps well."

The girl moved noiselessly across the stone floor and did as she was commanded. There was whispered exchange, and when she returned to Procula's bedside she said: "The Procurator has not turned over since midnight."

"I have never borne a child," Procula went on, satisfied with the report of her lord's bovine-like slumber. "But of late I have thrice dreamed of a king. I have no pain to make me dream such things, except it be a pain here." She laid her hand on her heart. "I wonder what a dream-teller would make of it."

The girl made no reply. The light of the taper flared brightly for an instant. The woman turned and looked at it, as if there were a mysterious answer to her question in the leap of flame. Her dark eyes glowed with impatience. She narrowed them thoughtfully.

"Come hither, child," she said to the girl. "I shall tell you the dream that woke me an hour ago. Sit near me lest our voices disturb the governor's sleep." The girl moved toward her, took the pillow that was offered, and settled herself upon it at the feet of her mistress.

"Strange, it was. I saw a place of death outside the city, beyond the Damascus gate. Three crosses topped a rocky hill, shaped like a skull that grimaced as if in pain." Procula pulled the sheet more securely about her shoulder and shivered. "And as I watched, three men were hung upon the crosses, and a crowd of people set up a great shout, making sport of the suffering victims. And then the cross in the middle began to grow like a tree, only much faster—fast as the little trees the magicians grow under a napkin. It grew, and grew, taller and taller, and the man on it grew larger and larger—"

She spread her arms out wide as she could to

illustrate the cross's growth, and the little girl, watching her intently, said: "See how your arms make great shadows on the wall."

The candle sputtered again, and the woman looked behind her timidly. "There is nothing," she said.

"Nay," answered the slave; "but when you spread your arms—"

"Oh, I see," Procula resumed. "And the cross and the man upon it grew until they touched the heavens; and the arms of the man seemed to reach out to enfold the earth in an anguished embrace; and wherever the shadow of the cross fell there was blight. And the tip of the cross kept growing till it pierced the heavens and let fall a shaft of light, brighter than the noonday. And then I saw that the places where the dark shadows had fallen were smitten as if by a plague—Rome, Alexandria, Athens, and even the waters of the sea. But, when the light fell from heaven, these stricken places and those who had fallen prostrate and weeping in the shadows, rose again. New cities like alabaster gleamed in the light; and the people danced and sang with new joy. And then the cross was lifted out of its pit and slowly disappeared into the flaming glory of the sun. There was a sound of heavenly music as it was lost to sight. When I looked at the earth again, the two other crosses were turned into beautiful flowering trees, and the place of death was covered with a garden."

She paused, her face alight with wonder and distress. The girl got up and lit a fresh taper. Outside the voice of the watchman announced the fourth watch and the coming of the day. Procula reclined on her elbow for an instant, watching the soundless movements of the slave girl, and then sat up again. Eagerness edged her voice as she spoke excitedly.

"Rhoda, when the day has come, you shall go with my dream to the soothsayers in the booths and learn of them its meaning. I would go myself, but Pilate must not know that my spirit is so sorely troubled."

"But why should such a dream distress you? Is it not fancy, and nothing more?"

"Nay, for it has visited me twice before, and each time the cross grows higher and the man upon it grows greater and the light is more blinding. If I dream it again, the man and the cross will fill the whole earth, and the light will blind me."

"Surely," replied the girl, "such things cannot be. Is it not a dream, this man, this cross, and this light?"

"It is that that I must know. Go to your room now and come again in an hour. Fix my pillow; I shall rest a while until Pilate is awake. When you come back, be ready to go to the bazaar."

The girl bowed low as she went out, but on her face there showed nothing of the resentment and confusion that agitated her heart. She had no wish to go to the booths so early. The streets would be crowded with pilgrims. There would be noise and confusion and brawling around the food stalls. She was unused to such disorder; and held soothsayers and their like in a distrust that was akin to fear.

When she returned to her mistress an hour later, there was very little said between them. Pilate was stirring about in his quarters talking noisily to a soldier who had gained entrance to report a riot in the streets. Procula was anxious to have the girl away on her errand, so putting a leather wallet in her hand, urged her to hurry, and be back as soon as possible with her message. As the girl took leave, there was misgiving in her heart. She scolded herself as she slipped down the dark corridor to the great portal, for having mentioned soothsayers by the city wall.

As she stepped shyly into the street, she was surprised to see the city so lively with early risers. It was not yet the hour for crowds to be abroad; and there was something in the air that was portentous of danger. The great street which led to the Damascus gate was so crowded that she made her way forward with difficulty. A turn to the east offered no easier going. She was annoyed, and then afraid. Her mistress had urged haste, and yet, she reasoned, if the rabble was as thick in the bazaars as in the city streets, there would be little chance of her discharging her duty at all.

She stopped for a moment behind a protecting corner to reconsider her route. Only two or three of the busier streets were familiar to her, so she decided to go back and try the great street again. As she reached the intersection near Pilate's palace whence she had so recently come, she saw a mob of men pressing toward the balcony of the governor's offices. In front of them they shoved a man bound with heavy cords, who, in spite of their jostling and threatening behavior, seemed to move ahead of them in unhurried dignity, as if heedless of their shouting. Rhoda was terrified and the sight of the crowd erased in an instant the commission on which she had been dispatched to the booths. Forgetful of everything save her own safety, she broke and ran like a wild creature. As she sped the distance between the advancing mob and the door to the palace, she heard the rioters shouting, but could make out only one or two words. "King," "crucify" they seemed to yell, and yet she thought, as she pushed into the door, that they were strange cries. King, crucify—what could it mean?

She hurried to the chambers of the governor's wife and as she rapped for entrance, she was overcome with the realization that she had miserably failed to do what Procula had so anxiously commanded. Before she could decide what excuse to make, the door opened, and she stood before her mistress.

"Back so soon?" Procula asked her eagerly. For a moment Rhoda couldn't speak. She thought furiously what to say, then penitently replied as she knelt before her:

"Nay, good lady. I couldn't get to the gate. The people are rioting in the streets. They bring a culprit hither to the governor that they may be granted permission to kill him. They shouted so furiously that I could not make out what they said except 'King,' 'crucify.' I was so frightened I came back. When the crowd scatters, I can go to the booths."

To Rhoda's immense relief, there was no rebuke, following her confession. Instead her mistress parted her lips as if about to speak, and then covered her mouth with her hand. From her inner chamber she could dimly hear the noise of the mob outside. Above its sullen murmur she heard voices calling for Pilate. Procula turned toward the rising flood of sound, stopped a moment in indecision and then rushed through the heavy curtains that separated her from the hall leading out to the balcony. As she hurried forward the noise of the people struck her like a blow. She stopped again, and then noticed that Pilate, having heard the disorderly summons, was standing before them on the balcony.

He was no less surprised than the mob when a slave girl suddenly appeared beside him in the bright sunlight. Her eyes were wide with fear and burning with the fire of excitement. She plucked his sleeve and dropped on her knees before him. His heavy face twisted in a scowl of annoyance and he lifted his hand as if to strike her when she said:

"I bring you word from my mistress. She sent me hither to say to you 'Have nothing to do with that innocent man, for during the night I have suffered terribly in a dream through him!'"

Pilate looked from the girl into the darkened corridor. He saw Procula standing, half concealed behind a curtain. She looked at him appealingly, but as he started to speak, disappeared and was gone.

※

JESUS AS PILATE SAW HIM [*]

W. P. Crozier

The late Editor of *The Manchester Guardian* delighted many readers with his brilliant posthumous novel of ancient Rome, *The Fates Are Laughing*, published in 1945. Nearly twenty years earlier, he had already revealed a powerful imagination in his much less widely-read *Letters of Pontius Pilate*. In the selections reprinted here we view the Passion-drama through Pilate's eyes.

PILATE COMES TO JERUSALEM
FOR THE PASSOVER

Jerusalem

I have come up as usual for their great festival, the Passover. It amused me, when I received your letter just before leaving Cæsarea, to find you complaining of the congestion in Rome. You should be here. Judæa has been filling up for weeks past. They come by tens of thousands, weeks in advance, and spread over the country, visiting their friends and relatives, searching out the villages their fathers came from, and making pilgrimages to the places where their history began.

During the last week they have been concentrating on Jerusalem. Every ship that has reached Cæsarea has been crowded inside and out. The conditions on board some of them must have been disgust-

[*] The title of this selection has been supplied by the Editor

ing. You never saw such a medley as passes out from these ships. Some of them must have spent their last penny in paying the fare; not a few have got here without paying any fare at all. You know the sort of mixture that comes out from the Games in Rome—riffraff from the slums and blue blood cheek by jowl. It is the same here and Jewish blue blood has no more liking for riffraff than blue blood has in Rome. They smell abominably. You should see the aristocrats turning up their rich or learned noses.

The whole lot throng the roads. The stream is continuous from the coast, from Samaria and from Jericho. Many of them sleep in the open. Some of the wealthier bring tents and bedding with them. In Jerusalem and the neighborhood everybody who can takes in lodgers. They charge a pretty price. Foodstuffs are doubled and trebled in price. I believe the language that the foreign Jews use about their brethren in Judæa shocks even the Greeks. To-day, when I approached, there was a complete block for a good mile from the city, and had it not been for some stout work by my escort I should still be kicking my heels outside the walls.

I have half my total force in readiness—2,000 men. There is no reason to anticipate anything beyond the usual brawls, but one must be prudent. You know how religion always excites the lowest passions. The Jerusalem Jew is at his worst at these times and the visitors resent his arrogance. They are most apt to brawl in the Temple, that being the heart and kernel of their worship! In the synagogues they are not so dangerous, because most of these foreign communities have each a synagogue of their own, where they can agree fairly well, but in the Temple they all meet together and can quarrel about priority in offering sacrifice, or about the inadequacy of the other people's gifts, or about being more Jewish Jews than one another.

Having got through earlier Passover without serious disturbance I have no reason to be anxious. The danger lies in the immense suppressed excitement that underlies the festival. They work themselves up to a state of ecstasy. With all these thousands gathered from the far ends of the earth, they imagine themselves a free and independent people, they live again in the old days, they think that their Yahveh has only to perform one of his preposterous wonders and we Romans would vanish in the wind. If the spark were handy, a fire might easily be lit.

Do you know that since I arrived to-day, the Jews have been complaining that I have not expedited the carriage of foodstuffs to the city? They block the roads and then complain that the food carts don't come through. But that is their way. They are intractable. If the place were full of pigs they would sooner starve than eat.

I will let you know how we go on.

REAPPEARANCE OF JESUS

Jerusalem

Do you remember the preacher Jesus, who fled to Syria some months ago to save his life from Antipas? He has appeared again. What is more—you may think it incredible, but it is true—he is on his way to Jerusalem. My spies report that having passed hurriedly through Galilee he has crossed the frontier. I have dispatched agents to keep in touch with him. According to present information he denounces the priests and Pharisees at every step and avows his intention to be in Jerusalem for the Passover. He brings a following with him. I suppose there are always people who are tired of life.

It was good of you to find me an expert on vine culture so quickly. These Jews have wits—none sharper—and they are industrious, but they are sadly lacking in scientific knowledge. If they were not bled by their priests they would have much more money for modern knowledge and equipment, but what can you do when a bloated corporation of priests fattens on an impoverished people? Send your expert at once, I pray you, by way of Alexandria and he shall go straight out on a round of country visits.

JESUS IN JERUSALEM

Jerusalem

So far all goes well. I derive a modest amusement from what I hear of the divisions and jealousies among these different Jews. Remarkable enough at any time, they are much more so when the foreign Jews are here. To begin with, the extreme Pharisees despise even the Jews in their own country who do not belong to their special sect. To them a man is good, that is to say virtuous, if he observes the law minutely, and not otherwise. I assure you that if they have a woman of the common folk to work in the house, they think the house and all the inmates are made unclean by it. You may imagine how much greater is their contempt for the Jews from Egypt or Syria who actually mix with heathen folk like you and me, or Sejanus and Cæsar.

The foreign Jews resent this arrogance. Many of them are extremely rich, many of them (especially those from Egypt) are more learned than their Pharisaic critics, and, of course, they are civilized. Yet when they go into the Temple, mix with the Pharisees and listen to the lectures of the learned, they find themselves treated with sneers and insinuations that they are little better than the Greeks whose language they speak—and often enough, it is the only language that they do speak, since they have neither Hebrew nor Aramaic. On several occasions the rank and file have almost come to blows, but this is a harmless recreation and I do not interfere.

You will expect to hear more about the preacher Jesus. I am, for two reasons, proceeding cautiously. My first thought was to arrest him before he entered Jerusalem and came in contact with the crowds. But that course would have its dangers, at a time like this. Since he crossed the frontier he has done nothing openly to justify it, his followers would spread the report that I had seized a noble patriotic Jew, and so, figuring once more as the oppressor, I might have on my hands a sudden outburst of passion of the kind which I desire to avoid.

Besides, Annas and Caiaphas have both been to see me. It was at once apparent that they, and especially Annas, were extremely desirous that I should remove what they consider a danger to themselves. They hate the man and no doubt with good reason. The Pharisees and lawyers are really disturbed about the attacks on the Law; the priesthood scents a danger to its livelihood; while Annas, Caiaphas and the other noble Sadducees are not only concerned for the maintenance of the whole priestly system (they are pretty indifferent themselves about the Law), but fear some sudden turn of affairs which might convert this Jesus into a national hero—and then what would become of them and their power? (I suggest to you, as a subject for one of your plays or meditations, that the greatest stimulant of all to a man's activities is the desire for Power.)

They suggested to me that, remembering what had happened in Galilee, it would be wise for me to seize Jesus quietly and put him out of the way. I am not, however, so stupid as to pull the chestnuts out of the fire for them and bring on myself an unnecessary odium. I replied that the trouble was primarily their affair but undoubtedly it might concern me at any moment. I wished to avoid a tumult and presumed that was also their desire. They were emphatic that it was so. I said that I should hold my hand for the present, but that if there were any disturbances I would act at once and I expected their loyal coöperation. This they promised me.

If nothing happens during the festival it is my intention, though I did not tell them this, to wait until the crowds disperse again and then make an end of Jesus. I cannot allow him to stir up Judæa as he stirred up Galilee. If he provokes trouble during the festival—whether by his own act or by the people losing their heads over him, even against his will—I shall strike at once. But the priests must coöperate and I am certain they will. Do you understand fully why they will? Not only because they hate this particular man, though they do, but because, if they stand out, the case may easily become one of the nation against the wicked Governor, which does not suit their plans, and because also there are some of them whose names I know—and they know that I know—who are tarred with the anti-Roman brush and had better show themselves zealous to assist me when the chance is offered them.

Jesus is in Jerusalem. He entered yesterday. His entry, if he had any intention of raising the populace, was a failure. Few of them knew about it. He came up by the road from Jericho. It was crowded with Jews from the Euphrates region and from Syria, who had never heard of him. If there were any Galileans who recognized him, they would only remember that he had failed them in Galilee last year. His own immediate followers are poor stuff. (I had Alexander following the group and Joseph mingling with the general crowd.) They are ignorant and superstitious men who are only dangerous because they share the usual delusion about leaders of this kind. They are always expecting Jesus to perform a "wonder," whether it is bringing to life a dead man or killing a live one, and they think about him just like the peasants and workmen of Galilee, expecting him at any moment to set about delivering the nation and bringing in a new age. I know by this time that a Jew in his own country can scarcely think in any other terms.

There was no evidence yesterday, any more than there has been before, that the preacher takes this view of himself. He entered with no more than the stir that there usually is when a party escorts some local notability. His followers shouted themselves hoarse and a few others, seeing them do it, shouted too. If six men throw their caps up for a reason, six others of the herd will follow suit. I had taken all precautions. I had some disguised soldiers walking with the crowd from Jericho and some more ready at the entrance to the city. Marcius had orders, if any attempt was made to rouse the mob, to cut down Jesus and his followers at once, but nothing happened. That is not to say that nothing will happen. Alexander wormed himself into the confidence of some of the preacher's followers. He says they have the most extraordinary ideas about the brilliant change that is going to come over their fortunes, but that all that their leader intends—Alexander is positive about this—is to pursue in Jerusalem his quarrel with the priesthood and the Law. It is enough.

I hope I am not mistaken in believing that you are interested in these long explanations. Were I writing to anyone else, I would say merely that I have cause to fear another pestilent agitation and that I mean to crush it while I may.

SCENE IN THE TEMPLE AND
DECISION TO ARREST JESUS

Jerusalem

Both Herod Antipas and brother Philip are in Jerusalem. These princelings behave as though they owned the East. They have brought rich presents for the Temple, they pose, they cultivate the Jews. They go in procession to and from the Temple services and the mob, which has forgotten how many Jews old Herod tortured, burned or crucified, claps and cries out for them as though it would be a fine thing to have a Herod instead of me at the Antonia. I have not met the princes, but I have stationed a guard of Roman soldiers at their gates. It is a proper mark of respect; it is also a hint that we keep an eye on them. Some of the noble families who supported the father have sent representatives to wait on the sons and accompany them to the Temple, but the ruling coterie, those who have office and those who hope to have it, hold aloof. They know on which side their bread is buttered.

The affair of Jesus is coming to a head. Yesterday, accompanied by his immediate followers, he visited the Temple. He stopped in the outer court, which is an enormous place like a fair ground, full of the paraphernalia for Temple-gifts and sacrifices, and thronged by thousands of Jews chaffering and arguing at the top of their voices in a score of languages and dialects. You know that market of theirs in Rome which one takes visitors to see from curiosity. It is like that, with a hundred times the hubbub. Suddenly Jesus began to assail his enemies the priests and all their works in the most violent terms. So far as I can learn, he denounced the whole ritual-mongering business of the Temple. Very sensible, too, except for his own safety. Had he been understood or attracted wide attention he would have been murdered on the spot.

If you remember that the life of these Jews, not only here but to the far ends of the earth, centers in the Temple-worship and that it is a highly organized business controlled by a powerful and jealous corporation, you will see that only a madman or a suicide would act like this. As it went, there was only a scuffle and the thing passed off. It was rather like his entry into the City. He himself speaks Aramaic and a large part of his hearers would have no idea of his meaning. Besides, the noise is appalling. You know the Jews; if you are not noisy they think that you are ill.

Nothing whatever came of the affair and, if it was intended as a demonstration, it was another failure. Jesus soon left the Temple again together with his followers who, according to my reports, are getting nothing out of their visit to Jerusalem but chagrin and disappointment. This is not at all the sort of thing which they anticipated. Denunciations of the Temple-worship in the Temple are likely to have an unfortunate end for them, as they probably suspect.

This incident has played into my hands. The man is an avowed failure. Ignored at first, he has now offended beyond forgiveness. Few people may have heard and seen his outburst, but a great many will know about it before to-night. You may say that if he has failed so signally, he is also negligible. Possibly, but there is a risk, and I do not take risks. Consider the audacity of this action. To me, who know these people, it is almost inconceivable. To challenge the priesthood in their sacred citadel and at the Passover, backed by a handful of peasants more ignorant even than himself—I could laugh at the thought were it not that a man so rash and passionate, and at the same time so determined, might make another sort of appeal to-morrow which might have a different ending. I have determined to suppress him. Public opinion, thanks to his folly, will support me. Still, I shall have the arrest carried through as quietly as possible in conjunction with the Sanhedrim. His companions will give no trouble.

After the scene in the Temple the old fox Annas sent an envoy to me. More than anyone he has a vested interest in the maintenance of peace; as you know, he has several sons whom he intends for the highest offices. At the same time, he has his finger on the pulse of the Pharisees who are rebels at heart against us and would help any seditious movement if it had a serious foundation. His point is the same as my own, that Jesus is not an actual but a potential danger. He urges that we should strike while few people know of him, and while those who do —and they will increase hourly—are shocked by his gross impiety (Annas's words). He adds that, if necessary, they will produce one of Jesus's own followers who will give damning evidence about certain ambitions which his master has avowed in private conversations. That does not concern me. I don't doubt they will provide themselves with the evidence they want, but I have already all that I require. The top and the bottom of it is that the man is, or might be, a political danger to me, as Antipas thought he was in Galilee last year, and as Antipas recognized the preacher John to be, when he cut his head off at Machærus and so saved me the trouble.

I am concerting with the priests. Jesus and his following spend their nights outside Jerusalem; we know the place. He will be arrested quietly and executed without undue delay.

I had not thought of it before, but I think I shall give my friend Antipas the opportunity of condemning Jesus. The trouble began within his jurisdiction, so that it is the correct and polite thing to do. Besides, it would be pleasant to show Antipas both that a mischief-maker has slipped through his hands but not through mine, and also, that when he

has condemned his subject, he has to hand him over to the superior authority, the Roman Governor, for execution of sentence. Yes, I will send him to Antipas.

ARREST OF JESUS

Jerusalem

Your freedman Krito has arrived this morning bringing your letters and others which he had picked up for me at Cæsarea. He starts back again at once, so that the letter I write you now must be a short one. I wish it had been only your letters he had brought me, for they gave me the pleasure which I always experience in hearing about you and Rome. But no sooner had I read them than I was thrown into ill temper by the news from Cæsarea. You know—I am sure I have told you this before—that when the Passover is finished and a large part of the foreign Jews troop back to the coast on their way home, I hold Games in Cæsarea for several days. It is a relaxation for me as well as for them, and it is good for trade. Do you ask whether they come to my Games? Of course they come. They are not Pharisees. They are Greek Jews, Cyrenaic Jews, Asiatic Jews, merrier and humaner folk than their harsh Judaic brethren.

Could anything be more exasperating than the blow which has befallen me? In the first place a ship bringing six lions from Cyrenaica has foundered. The crew had not even the good grace to go down with the ship. Still, lions are cheap and I do not make too much of it. What is more serious is the loss of my gladiator Aduatucus, a Gaul. He was the best swordsman in the East. Since I came out here he had fought nearly fifty contests and had never been beaten. The women love him. The Governors of both Syria and Egypt had tried to buy him from me —once or twice I lent him as a great favor, but I always refused to sell—and I had told him that when he completed fifty contests I would give him his freedom and make him trainer of the troop. He might have become manager of the Games, he might have gone back with me and become first favorite of the crowd at Rome. Why, he might have caught Cæsar's eye, entered his Household and controlled provincial governors. With this career before him, and knowing the value that I attached to him, he was inconsiderate enough to enter into a tavern brawl about a girl with two Thracians. They stabbed him to death and then took their own lives, so that

I have not even the poor consolation of using them for the Games. By Jove, I am annoyed.

You were asking about the aqueduct. It works admirably and I have reason to know that the foreign Jews applaud me for it. They disapprove, as they are bound to do, of my use of the Temple-money, but they see that I am not behind the Governors of more important provinces in my care for the Roman name and the health of my people. The Jews here also use the water, even the Pharisees. The only difference is that they show no gratitude.

Jesus was arrested late last night. I provided a troop of soldiers who accompanied the officials of the Sanhedrim. The advantage is that as the news spread this morning—if it did spread—it would be known that Procurator and Sanhedrim had acted jointly. The Sanhedrim are not popular with the most zealous Jews, but the general impression would be that if all the authorities, Roman and Jewish, were acting together, this must be a troublesome fellow who was better out of the way. The arrest was made without disturbance. Jesus himself gave no trouble and his followers ran at once. I believe some of them are well on their way home.

The prisoner was taken to the High Priest's quarters until this morning when he was handed over to my people. I believe Caiaphas got a few of the leading priests together and they examined him for themselves. The case is a perfectly simple one, from my point of view, and will give no difficulty. Since Antipas will not handle the matter—I am coming to that in a moment—I shall execute Jesus as a maker or a cause of sedition against Cæsar. But these priests have always to remember that sedition against Cæsar is usually a merit in the eyes of the populace (and of a good many Pharisees too), and they will want to make out a good case for themselves. They will insist, I suppose, on Jesus's defiance of the Law, attacks on the ritual and outbreak in the Temple. Probably they will say that he regarded himself as the expected Messiah (of which there is no evidence), and the people, with their mouths agape, have no use for a Messiah who cannot keep himself out of the hands of the despised Romans. That is not the kind of deliverer the Jews want any more than his own followers.

I have not seen the man myself, though I shall do so presently. I gave orders for him to be taken to Antipas, as I said I would, with a polite statement that as the disturber of the peace was a Galilean, he would perhaps consider the matter came within his jurisdiction. I received a reply, equally polite, that Antipas recognized my courtesy but waived any right that he might have over an offender in my City of Jerusalem. A touching exchange of courtesies! I shall finish the matter off to-day.

Your freedman waits, but one word more. Is it true, as I hear from Lentulus Spinther, that Sejanus's nephew has been refused an audience by Cæsar and that Sejanus has doubled the Prætorian Guard at Rome? What if Sejanus falls? What if he refuses to fall? Do not become famous too hastily, my friend. Obscurity, though inglorious, is safe. When the master walks through the fields with stick in hand, fortunate is the poppy with inconspicuous head.*

TRIAL AND EXECUTION OF JESUS

Jerusalem

I must complete the letter which I began this morning. Immediately after dispatching Krito, I confirmed with Marcius the military arrangements for the Passover, which begins to-morrow. I heard reports from Joseph, who thinks that acts of violence against individuals amongst the ruling Sadducees will grow. In his opinion it does not much matter whether the province is as quiet as I contrive to keep it or whether there is constant friction between us and the Jews; his feeling is that the extreme men are tired of peace.

Afterwards I tried and condemned the prisoner Jesus. He was crucified at once along with some other prisoners who were awaiting execution. It is not a bad thing to have an object lesson of this kind on the eve of the Passover because, in such a nondescript gathering as we have here, there must always be dangerous characters who have exceptional opportunities for their special qualities. By this time Jesus is buried. It is their custom to bury an executed offender the same day and, besides, the Sabbath begins at sunset—has, indeed, already begun. The Sanhedrim asked permission to bury the body this afternoon. It suits them, having got Jesus out of their way, to dispose of the whole matter before the Passover begins and so to damp down any discussion which might arise, especially after

---

* Sejanus was summarily executed in the next year and his friends were involved in the catastrophe.

the inscription that I ordered to be attached to the prisoner, about which more presently.

The trial was short but in due form and order. Jesus was accused of disturbing the peace, stirring up disaffection and claiming to be King of the Jews. There was evidence both from our side and from that of the Jews, both from Galilee and from this city. Caiaphas, Annas and the leading Sadducees were prominent and so were some but not all of the chief Pharisees; some of the Pharisees would lend no assistance in convicting a rebel against Cæsar however much they desired his death as a rebel against themselves.

However, that did not help him. The priests had much to say of his attacks on their religion, but I cut them short on that. They cannot have it both ways. If we are not allowed to interfere in their religion, they cannot appeal to us when their observances are attacked; as soon as the offense becomes political, directly or indirectly, then we take note of it. They may squabble about Yahveh, like the Egyptians about Isis, till they burst, but when a man brawls in the Temple he tends to provoke a general explosion and that concerns us closely. The charge against Jesus of disturbing the peace was proved to the hilt and he could not deny it.

I inquired of the prisoner, through Alexander, whether he admitted the more serious accusations. The Jews alleged that he regarded himself as the destined deliverer of the nation, which involves the end of both their authority and ours. This would constitute a much more direct offense than that for which Antipas put John to death. They cited both the public utterances in which Jesus had spoken of a new kingdom as being imminent and also certain admissions about himself which they said he had made to his own followers. This was, I suppose, the special evidence which Annas said that they intended to produce.

I put the question to him. I asked him whether he considered himself to be the deliverer. "So THEY say," he answered, indicating the High Priest and his neighbors, with a curt gesture of contempt. I pointed out to him that he was accused also of representing himself as King of the Jews. I asked him whether he considered himself to be that. He made the same answer—"So YOU say," meaning, I suppose, that in neither case was there anything in his own conduct or motives to support the accusa-tion, but that he knew well enough that we meant in any case to fix the charge upon him. He realized that he was trapped, and that there was no way of escape, but he was bold and resolute, defiant, almost insolent.

They are all alike, these Jews, bitter and unyielding, whether to us or to each other. Standing alone he might be, forsaken and with enemies on every side who meant his death, with his own countrymen delivering him to the Roman executioner, but he was cool and determined, like the men who engineered an attempt on the life of the great Herod and suffered the extremes of torture sooner than yield an inch. A dangerous breed!

I condemned him to death. I could, of course, do nothing else. All roads lead to that conclusion. Alexander, who has a cool and detached way of regarding his countrymen, insists that this man, so far from posing as Messiah, or King, like most of the mischief-makers during the last thirty years, did all that he could to prevent the stupid people from fastening that part on him. Alexander thinks that there was nothing that Jesus sought to avoid so much as this, knowing that if such a conception of him spread abroad, it would deliver him into our hands and be fatal to his campaign—a hopeless campaign in any case—against the priesthood and its system.

Alexander has talked to some of his followers and says that the preacher had unquestionably warned them often and in the severest terms that they were not to regard him or speak of him as the Deliverer whom all these Jews expect, and that it was only when he thought that the old conception of him had died away in Galilee that he decided to come up to Jerusalem.

It may be. But I am sure that if he was not a dangerous rebel yesterday, he would have been to-morrow. For either he would have succeeded in his assault on the priesthood or he would not. If he had not, how long would a man of his temperament, so passionate, headstrong and bold, have abstained from making that appeal to the patriotic feelings of these Jews which always—always—meets with a quick response, even when made by men of much less powerful character than his?

You remember Procula's and Alexander's description of the scene in Galilee? And supposing that he had conceivably made headway against the priests and all the mummery of the Temple ritual, how long would it have been before he turned upon Cæsar and the sacrifices to Cæsar and to Rome? Would he have respected the cult of Divus Augustus, do you suppose? But long before we had to consider that eventuality we should have had to intervene with force between their contending factions. Why, as it is, they are almost in a state of suppressed civil war, ready to fly at each other's throats. Give them a bad governor—a governor even half as bad as they say that I am—and the feud between those who tolerate us and those who despise the tolerators will break into open war. This is an unfruitful soil in all respects but one. The seeds of disorder will grow if you only scratch the soil. My policy is to destroy them the moment that they sprout.

But I had forgotten: allow me one word about the inscription announcing the offense of Jesus. It was "King of the Jews," set up over the cross. The Pharisees were indignant. They themselves want a King of the Jews. It would give them the greatest pleasure to see Cæsar overthrown to-morrow and a Jewish King installed—not a half-Jew like Herod— who would rule the country through them and sup-press their Sadducean rivals. But it angered them to see the precious title, "King of the Jews," held up to ridicule; it was too plain a reminder of their servitude. Besides, they thought it an insult that a crucified criminal, a presumptuous countryman who had defied them, should be labeled "King."

I took a short way with them. "What I have written I have written," said I, and bade them begone. I know the breed. From the moment that this Jesus set up his individual judgment against theirs they meant to have his life. Scratch a priest and find an autocrat. All the world over, if a man says that he will use his own intelligence about things divine, the priests prick up their ears and feel their knives. If he goes further and tells his fellow men that they also are entitled to use their own intelligence— off with his head and there's an end of it!

I run on so, my dear Seneca. The subject carries me away. I must apologize to you again; I am afraid that even you will find the subject tedious. For, after all, what does it matter? What does it matter—one Jew more or less?

I wish I could find a substitute for Aduatucus.

7. THE CROSS

THE PRAETORIANS

Edwin McNeill Poteat

The Raven, so named by his fellow legionaries because his voice was singularly rasping, stirred lazily in the straw. The men of his company lay about him disposed in various attitudes and degrees of sleep. The sun was only just high enough to have begun pouring its lazy warmth into the open court, and as the light began its slow trespass across the sprawl-ing figures, they began to stretch, sit up, yawn, and rub their heavy eyes. They had scarcely moved since the second watch when the noisy exit of two squads of the guard for emergency duty had disturbed their torpid slumber for a moment. They had known little comfort and less leisure since their arrival from Cæsarea, and beds improvised of loose straw and flagstones afforded them scanty rest and ample reason for grumbling. While not on active patrol in the city, they spent most of their time, out of earshot of the captain, complaining. Dislike of police duty in Jerusalem during the Jewish feast exaggerated their recollections of the pleasures of seaside detail from which the Passover festival had temporarily removed them.

The Raven discovered that his nearest neighbor, a youth newly recruited to the legion, still slept heavily. Jealous of the reprieve the lad's weariness had won from the early sun, he tickled the sleeper's nose maliciously with a straw, and smiled at the convulsive reflex. It was harmless fun and he kept repeating it until his victim brushed awkwardly at the annoyance and turned over. As the sunlight fell upon him, he tightened his eyelids defensively, covered his eyes with the pit of his elbow and settled again into steady, rhythmic breathing. The Raven surveyed the supine form contemptuously and then observed that one unsandaled foot protruded beyond the disordered blanket covering his legs. He grinned mischievously, picked up his broad sword, and drawing it slowly from the scabbard, smote a resounding whack with its flat side against the sole of the exposed foot. There was a howl of surprise and anger from its injured owner but it was drowned in the noisy laughter of the other men who, having seen the maneuvers of the Raven, were waiting gleefully the shocked awakening.

"You dirty. . . ."

"Get up, Carrion," croaked the Raven, laughing. "See what day it is? Here we have holiday, and you snore for its observance."

The recruit rubbed his foot ruefully and blinked in the direction his tormentor was pointing. Across the wide courtyard, on the opposite wall hung the calendar for the day, suspended there at the break of dawn by the adjutant's orderly. He read the large angular Roman initials:

PRID NON APR MEGALENSIS *

Ludi Megalensis was the greatest of the Roman holidays, the birthday of Cybele, *Magna Deum Mater*, Great Mother of the gods. Wherever citizens of the empire met on that day they saluted each other in her name. In 204 B.C. as an aid in the war against Hannibal, worship of this phallic goddess had been instituted in Rome. She was said to have come from central Asia Minor and was believed to dwell in a huge black meteorite which had been

---

* Pridie Nonas Apriles. The day before the nones of April—April 4th.

brought to Rome with an extravagant display of pomp and devotion. The festival was elaborately celebrated with games for and by the populace, and amphitheater and street were filled with rioters from sunup until far into the night. The captive enemies of the empire were saved from one year's end to the other for that day to die in hopeless combat with wild beasts or gladiators in the arena; and the blood lust of thousands of excited spectators from Spain to the Indus was sated with the magnificence of the holiday's slaughterings.

To others the day was hardly less bloody, though their observance was an act of pious worship. Initiates into the cult of Cybele received their ceremonial bath that day, a gruesome affusion of the blood of a bull, slain over a grating beneath which the novitiate crouched to receive the cleansing cataract, and from which he emerged, sticky with dark clots as a testimony to his devotion to Magna Mater. So whether it was a day of sport or of sanctification, it was for all a day of blood.

Other eyes in the court had responded to the Raven's sharp command and blinked at the notice. It was not easy to keep two calendars in their heads, and since they were compelled to live under the Hebrew order of days while in the holy city, they passed up their Roman holidays with little ceremony. In Cæsarea there would be games in the circus, but nowhere in or about Jerusalem was there a place for heathen celebrations. A few of the Jewish leaders who endlessly curried favor with Roman officials affected interest in some of their feast days, but now it was the Passover, and no Roman day could dispute with the people of Israel the prior claims of that feast. Moreover, the Jews were not a sporting folk; their games were gentle and for children. They were revolted by blood shed to amuse the crowds, for bloodletting was to them solely a symbol of birth or of expiation.

"Why should we not keep Megalensia?" The voice was the Raven's raised to a strident pitch. "Did I not win a chaplet once in Rome before Great Julius? It was thirty years ago. Have I told you how the wild thrust of a frightened jackel cost me this tooth?" He spread wide his lips and put the tip of the third finger of his left hand—the thumb and two other fingers were gone—where a cuspid was lacking; "And this"—he pointed with another finger at his left eye disfigured by an ugly white scar across the pupil. He looked comically grotesque as he posed thus exhibiting his scars, but few of the men appeared interested. It was an old tale to most of them, repeated on every possible occasion.

"Jackal?" asked the youngster who a moment before had felt the sting of the broad sword. He had stood up, and was balancing himself on one foot. "Jackal," he repeated incredulously.

"Aye, a jackal, Carrion," the Raven taunted. "And take care of your own stinking flesh; there may be others about!" He laughed at his own jest. "But he was a jackal that stood on two legs until I cut him down. That day I paid proper respect to the Great Mother, and the Great Julius paid proper respect to me." He thumped his thick chest and bellowed in gusts of raucous laughter.

There was a sound at the gate and as a messenger accompanied by an orderly bearing the ensign of the Procurator entered, every soldier in the court struggled briskly to his feet. The Raven was annoyed at the interruption of his boasting, but years of soldiering brought him by habit to immediate though aggrieved attention. The messenger unrolled a parchment no wider than his two hands and read in high staccato tones: APRILIS IV MEGALENSIS ORDER OF CRIMINAL DEATH TO JESHUA OF NAZARET STROKES THIRTY NINE BY SCOURGE DEATH BY CRUCIFIXION PONTIUS PILATE PROCURATOR. He handed the parchment to his attendant, who in turn handed him a smaller scroll which he proceeded to intone in his artificial pitch of voice: "Marius known as the Raven, Master of the Scourge. Thirty-nine strokes, no more no less. Error by scourge-master punished by twice the margin of mistake." He turned sharply and disappeared through the gate.

The Raven grinned broadly but the missing tooth and sightless eye imparted a mirthless quality to his smile. He was not a little pleased at his appointment, though he had seen many men shrink from applying the lash. And suddenly he realized a singular appropriateness in the coincidence of his proposal to celebrate the feast of Cybele and his appointment as scourge-master. He rubbed his hands together greedily.

"Stand on both your feet, Carrion," he ordered the youth at his side. "Did you never see a taurobolium? Today you shall see one after a new fashion. The Raven will bleed no bull; you shall see him

bleed a man." He scratched his stubble chin reflectively and squinted his scarred eye. "And you, Carrion, may have a bath of blood for the Great Mother. Ho, ho," he roared, "the Raven will do her honor again, and you shall become her disciple." He plucked the sleeve of the young guardsman and started to obey the summons of the messenger. No one else moved toward the door; scourgings were routine matters, to be attended to as a duty, not as a spectacle. And as the Raven and his somewhat bewildered companion made their exit he stopped and picked up a handful of loose straws, while the rest of the men indifferently made themselves comfortable again in the sun.

The scourging that preceded the death of condemned felons took place in a small enclosure at the rear of the praetorium. There was only room enough for the guard of six lictors who acted both as witnesses and as precaution against any possible act of violence by the prisoner. The regimental doctor stood by to interfere if the victim seemed likely to die under the lash, and to administer a restorative if needed during the ordeal. When it was over he applied an unguent of camphor oil to staunch the bleeding. The scourge-master was allowed, if he wished a counter whose duty it was to stand and tell the strokes after they fell. The law that provided that an error must be doubly recompensed, allowed the penalty to be laid on by the counter, or by one of the lictors. The Raven had never been sure of his ability to count. Once before he had failed by two strokes to administer the full thirty-nine, and he had not forgot the four blows applied to his own back by a fellow legionary with whom, as ill-luck would have it, he had quarreled two days previous. It was quick thinking on his part that called the lad out as his aid. He was young, new to the legion and afraid of him. At least so the Raven thought. If an error occurred, the consequences therefore would cause him a minimum of discomfort.

When they reached the court of scourging, the victim had already been trussed up on a post the thickness of his own torso, and as high as his waist. He was bent forward over the post; his hands extended downward and were bound with leather thongs that tightened about his arms above the elbows and his legs above the knees. The Raven and his counter stopped a moment outside the gate.

"Here," said the Raven, "take these straws. They

will help you keep count." He extended his hand and thrusting forward his heavy jaw, glared savagely at the lad.

"Can you count?" he asked, suddenly withdrawing his hand.

"Aye."

"How far?"

"To more than an hundred."

"Without straws?"

"Aye, and without fingers." The Raven detected the note of insolence in the words, and raised his maimed hand as if to strike him. The boy did not wince.

"I do not trust you, you impudent swine," he said extending his hand again. "As each stroke falls— and I shall bring blood with each blow; there is no gentleness in this Raven's pecking—after each stroke, break off a length of straw and lay it on the stone, like this." He broke off an inch and stooped and with the heel of his hand brushed clean a spot on the flagstone, and put down the piece of straw. Then he broke off another length, and another, until ten lengths were set in a row before him.

"Make three rows, like that," he said, straightening himself up. "But the fourth row must have only nine. And if you make an error—" he grasped the boy's shoulder with his good hand and spun him around till he faced him—"if you count wrong, Carrion, I'll break your back." He shoved the boy viciously through the gate, and with one long stride, followed him into the enclosure.

The Raven saluted the little company, threw off his tunic, rolled up the sleeves of his leather jacket and took the scourge that was handed him. He could not see the culprit's features. His long dark hair fell in a soft cascade around his head, obscuring his closed eyes and his face darkly flushed by the downrush of blood. The Raven noted the white unblemished firmness of the skin that molded the shoulder and dorsal muscles with a powerful and sinewy grace, and he wondered, for a moment, who he was and what his crime. He waited for the boy to brush a stone clear of dust. The doctor nodded, and the officer in charge lifted his hand as a signal to begin.

He stretched the three lead-tipped thongs to test their elastic strength and took his stance. There was a second of uncomfortable suspense, and then the scourge fell in a whistling circumflex and creased the back with three white lines. He raised his arm for

the second blow, the wales reddening with oozing blood. Wh-h-h———tt fell the lash again. The scourger's nostrils dilated and his lips tightened. He noted, after the second blow, that the welts on the white back formed a crude pattern. It looked like the numeral IV. "Four," he muttered, audibly. The boy looked up in surprise. "Two," he corrected. The lictors laughed, and the Raven lunged awkwardly as he struck, off balance, a glancing blow.

After the involuntary convulsion at the first blow, the victim did not move. His body was limp with relaxation; the thongs thumped pitilessly against ribs weirdly resonant, but there was no outcry. The scourger breathed noisily as he cut the air and the reddening flesh. Blood began to run in little trickles down the sides of the whipping post; they started along the shoulders, ran under the armpits, down the arms and into the limp hands. Once the doctor raised his hand and stopped the torment of lead and leather to examine the culprit. He pushed back an eyelid. The man turned his head and looked at him from his awkward, inverted position. He was alive and aware. The blows began again.

But not before the Raven had cast an oblique glance at the straw fragments on the flagstone over which the boy was bending. He had already lost his relish for his job. *Mater Deum Magna* was forgotten; the jest about the taurobolium unrecalled. He had meant to count the strokes himself, but the patterns his blows had cut in the white flesh before they became a confused and bloody laceration, had disturbed his figures. The boy, he feared, might also be confused. So when the doctor had assured himself his patient was still conscious and signaled for continuance, the Raven speeded up the tempo of his rhythmic lashing, stopping less often than was customary to grip more securely the handle of the flagellum. At the end of what he vaguely thought was about thirty strokes he stopped, looked toward the boy, hoping against a fear-born furious hope, that he would descry, beneath his bent figure, three rows of ten short straws each.

He cocked his good eye anxiously, but his vision was blurred. Edging toward the lad, he stepped carelessly into a pool of black blood and slipped, and before he could catch his balance, his foot had left a smear across the spot where the counter's scattered straws had been. He stood up angrily and raised his lash above the boy. The doctor moved toward him, and placing himself between the two, pointed significantly to the victim. The Raven turned. Nine times more he laid the rending whip across the motionless back, the blows whistling with increasing fury as they fell.

"Thirty-nine," he croaked excitedly at the last blow. He was breathing rapidly. "Thirty-nine," he cawed again, pointing inquiringly with the whip to the spot where the boy should have kept the score.

"Forty-two," the lad finally replied, quietly.

"You dog," snarled the scourger. "You kept no count; show me your straws." He stepped toward the boy threateningly.

"Nay," said the lad. "I needed no help to keep the tally; have I not two good eyes and ten good fingers?" The boy was as unabashed by the angry threat as was the centurion in charge who ordered the Raven to stand aside and took from him the bloody lash which trembled in his hand.

A guardsman stepped unceremoniously over to the prisoner and with a deft stroke of his broad sword severed the thongs that held him. Space was cleared by the wall, and he was laid down on a mat of straw with a tunic folded under his face. The doctor, a Greek from Corinth, bent over him and cleaned away the blood with a moist napkin before applying the cooling and healing unguent to his wounds. The fragrance of the camphor oil revived the man, and he opened his eyes weakly and said: "Thank you, friend."

Meanwhile the Raven broke out defiantly, "If I gave him three more than his desert, they were three more than I deserve. Ask that young pig again of his count—" his tone was a whine, as if almost pleading—"to see if he be not repaying me a debt he thinks I owe him."

"Take off your shirt," ordered the officer brusquely. "There is more important business here than listening to your whimpering." And to the lad: "Will you pay his score, or shall I ask another? There are several men here who would be pleased to take your place." By the way of answer the boy reached for the whip the officer held.

Two guardsmen were helping the scourged man to his feet. He stood precariously, leaning heavily on the arm of the man on his left. He steadied himself for a moment while the doctor draped his seamless tunic gently over his shoulder. He looked searchingly at the sullen and threatening scourge-master slowly getting out of his leather shirt, and then looked at the whipping post. Straw had already been kicked about its base, covering the stains of blood so newly spattered. His escort of two men began to urge him roughly toward the gate. They were under orders to return him to the praetorium, and were eager to do so. They knew it was not safe for him to see the Raven punished. They feared he might collapse and have to be carried out. Furthermore, they were in a hurry to turn him over to their superiors, and get back in time to see the sport with the new victim.

The Raven had already been placed in position over the post. Alternately he cursed the guard and importuned the Great Mother. As Jesus passed him, he turned to the officer and said:

"I know not the laws of Rome, but to do the will of God is my meat, day and night; and his laws are the ways of mercy and forgiveness. Cannot the wounds I suffered through this man's error, be atonement for his sin?"

The Raven straightened himself in astonishment and looked at Jesus. He dropped his jaw, as if about to speak, but the wan smile that met his gaze silenced him.

The centurion laughed gruffly, shook his head, and pointed toward the exit. Jesus felt his arms seized by his escort. They turned and helped him slowly through the gate that swung shut behind them. As they started toward the praetorium he heard over the wall the whistle of a lash and a heavy thud, and the sharp, convulsive cry of a man, torn by pain.

SODOMA'S CHRIST SCOURGED

George Edward Woodberry

I saw in Siena pictures,
  Wandering wearily;
I sought not the names of the masters
  Nor the works men care to see;
But once in a low-ceiled passage
  I came on a place of gloom,

Lit here and there with halos
    Like saints within the room.
The pure, serene, mild colors
    The early artists used
Had made my heart grow softer,
    And still on peace I mused.
Sudden I saw the Sufferer,
    And my frame was clenched with pain;
Perchance no throe so noble
    Visits my soul again.
Mine were the stripes of the scourging;
    On my thorn-pierced brow blood ran;
In my breast the deep compassion
    Breaking the heart for man.
I drooped with heavy eyelids,
    Till evil should have its will;
On my lips was silence gathered;
    My waiting soul stood still.
I gazed, nor knew I was gazing;
    I trembled, and woke to know
Him whom they worship in heaven
    Still walking on earth below.
Once have I borne his sorrows
    Beneath the flail of fate!
Once, in the woe of his passion,
    I felt the soul grow great!
I turned from my dead Leader;
    I passed the silent door;
The gray-walled street received me;
    On peace I mused no more.

HIS SAVIOUR'S WORDS GOING TO THE CROSS

Robert Herrick

Have, have ye no regard, all ye
Who pass this way, to pity me,
Who am a man of misery!

A man both bruised and broke, and one
Who suffers not here for mine own,
But for my friends' transgression!

Ah! Zion's daughters, do not fear
The cross, the cords, the nails, the spear,
The myrrh, the gall, the vinegar;

For Christ, your loving Saviour, hath
Drunk up the wine of God's fierce wrath;
Only, there's left a little frost,

Less for to taste than for to show
What bitter cups had been your due,
Had He not drunk them up for you.

THE CROSS

Thomas Bancroft

Our Saviour's cross, begilt with guiltless blood,
Was framed (as some write) of four kinds of wood,
Palm, cedar, cypress, olive; which might show
That blessings thence to the four parts should flow
Of the vast world, and from the four winds should
Christ's flock be fetched to his thrice-blessèd fold.

THE NAILS

Charles Wharton Stork

So, you're stretched on the planks, you schemer,
Earth disturber, heaven blasphemer.

You've been a wonder for getting in wrong.
Somebody fetch the nails along!

What's the first one? Envy, is't?
Spread out his fingers, clamp the wrist

To steady his palm for the ragged point.
No, don't set it too near the joint!

There, that's better. Keep it firm.—
Funny he doesn't begin to squirm.—

Hate is the hammer to pound it through.
Strike! . . . Aha! how's that for you?

He don't wince now much, but he will
Perhaps when his numb flesh feels the chill

Of the bitter metal's tearing bite.
At least his left hand will no more spite

His betters by feigning it can hold
More than rank or power or gold.

Next his right hand. What's the nail?
Scorn. I see his lips go pale.

Well he knows that its iron tooth
Is worse than Envy's barb uncouth.

Strike! Do you flinch to hear him groan? . . .
Hark! how it crunched the brittle bone.

Silly hand, it's well you're fast, or
You might again be cheating your master,

Giving away what most he needs,
Egging his wits into spendthrift deeds.

Now for the nails to stop his feet
From gathering dust on the common street.

Here is Malice, an ugly spike,
Long with a good broad head to strike.

Send it in straight! . . . No more of your tumbling,
Vagrant foot, so apt at stumbling

In shady places—you know what I mean,—
That pretty street walker, the Magdalene.

As for the other foot, fetch out Fear.
Ho! you have dogged us many a year,

Foot, with your plodding patience, have you?
And all the while with no head to save you.

Drive the nail deep there! . . . Good! that's done.
Now, feet, I think you will hardly run

About so freely to stir the rabble
And wake dull mouths to a senseless babble.

Often you used to trouble our peace
With a strange soft tread that never would cease

Night or day. We heard it pursuing
Like a shepherd that drove us to our undoing,

Turned us out of our pleasant ways
To lonely pastures of dangerous days,

Urged us on till we lost our breath
Toward sorrow and toil and shame and death.

But, thank our stars! we've escaped at last,
Pursued you in turn and nailed you fast.

Brothers to-night we may all sleep fair
And each be proud to have done his share.

Look how we have him, helpless, dumb;
And the worst of his torment is still to come.

Lift him up. Let the show begin.—
Which was the nail, friend, that you drove in?

GOOD FRIDAY

A. J. M. Smith

This day upon the bitter tree
Died One who had He willed
Could have dried up the wide sea
  And the wind stilled.

It was about the ninth hour
He surrenderèd the ghost,
And His face was a faded flower
  Drooping and lost.

Who then was not afraid?
Targeted, heart and eye,

Struck, as with darts, by godhead
  In human agony.

For Him, who with a cry
Could shatter if He willed
The sea and earth and sky
  And them rebuild,

Who chose amid the tumult
Of the darkening sky
A chivalry more difficult—
  As Man to die—

What answering meed of love
Can finite flesh return
That is not all unworthy of
  The God I mourn?

THE WOMEN OF JERUSALEM

Gabriel Miró

"And there followed him a great company of people, and of women, which also bewailed and lamented him."
ST. LUKE XXIII, 27

"And he, bearing his cross, went forth into a place called the place of a skull, which is called in the Hebrew, Golgotha, where they crucified him, and two others with him, on either side, and Jesus in the midst."
ST. JOHN XIX, 17, 18

Fruitful of virtue and of good works was the hearth of the prudent Hebrew woman of old.

Her daughters fashioned garments and girdles; her slave-women, fluttering about the sunlit court, bleached cloth, spun and wound yarn, ground meal, kneaded dough, and tended the oven; and such as had had an ear pierced, as slave-women who had renounced their right of freedom on the befalling of a Sabbatical Year, sold products of the household to the non-Israelite, and kept the jewel-cases containing their mistress's armlets and pearl *thorim* and finger-rings and ear-rings and ankle-chains of amber-and-gold-mounted walnuts, almonds, and lotus fruit

which tinkled musically against the feet. And the mistress of the household superintended the sewing, and renewed the perfume in the alabaster phials worn in their bosoms by her daughters, and the ivory needles of those daughters' *stibia* for artificially pricking and enlarging their eyelashes and eyebrows, and plied the spindle, and dispensed the linen, and tended the lamp which "burneth throughout the night," and studied such of the Lord's precepts as might "open her mouth unto wisdom," and kept the chests containing her husband's and sons' clothing, and laid out their freshly-washed changes of mantle and tunic and stout outer-girdle and soft inner-girdle (for wear next to the skin) and shoulder-scarf and ablutions-napkin and oversleeves and breeches and night-robe and turban and *koufieh* and straw sun-cowl. Also, she repaired the clothes of the women-folk—the plain white tunic, the fringed and embroidered tunic, the undershift, the veil, the hood, and the cloak capable of containing six measures of meal. In short, she lived "clad in righteousness and orderliness," and followed, overlooked, the routine of her establishment, and opened her hand to the needy, and earned praises even in those city gateways which, in the East of that period, constituted a hot-bed and breeding-ground of slander, and the hub of that tendency to ribaldry and discord and backbiting which was all too little forbidden in Israel, and a sink for the scraps and waste of every hearth and roof-tree, and a rendezvous whither the slave repaired with his mistress's chamber secrets, and the client with criticisms of his patron's meanness, and the parasite with calculations of his regalings, and the Rabbin with plans for stamping the mark of his own school upon dialectical triumphs achieved by another; a place where fraud was mooted, and adultery, and the tears of the barren woman, and there assembled the fuller, and the soldier, and the gold-beater, and the water-carrier, and the out-at-elbows Levite deprived of a share in the offerings and tithes, and the vicious scion of a noble house, and the whore, and the journeyman prepared to doze until some steward should hire his services; a place where the Phœnician set up his stall, and the cripple advertised his disability, and the *portitor* or tax-gatherer lurked behind his desk, though he was an object of such general detestation that even the leper who lifted ragged sackcloth to give warning of his ulcers refused charity of such a hand, and the traveller seeking a lodging contrived special lies for his benefit, and applauded his own cunning if he should succeed in passing off upon him a slave for a son, or in swearing that the contents of his purse stood exempt from toll, as destined exclusively for the Holy Treasury, even though within an hour they might be spent upon gambling, or squandered amongst whores. Yes, the gateways of the East were the square, the deck, the sample-room, and the exchange of every walk in life. And in particular they were the lounge and assembly-room of venerable wiseacres and prominent citizens who came thither during the sunny hours of a winter's day, or during the cool of a summer's evening, to defame their neighbours, or to gloat over indecencies, or to extol the attractions of a bride discovered without her veil, or to exchange comments and opinions upon divorce—the followers of the Shammaite doctrine looking upon divorce as sanctionable only when the wife had actually committed adultery, or when the husband desired to seek progeny from a more fruitful spouse, whereas the Hillelite school considered divorce to be justifiable even on a ground so little serious as that the wife had served her husband with an unpalatable dish. Hence he who heard the mother of his children praised in a city gateway was the more entitled to say with the sage of old that "the loss of her would be more bitter even than the downfall of Jerusalem."

But one day all, both old and young, both tolerant and intolerant, found themselves suddenly united in general protestations against a Rabbi who had pardoned a woman taken in adultery.

For it was the pardoning of the sin, rather than the sin itself, that had scandalised these persons.

And with one voice Priests and Scribes and Pharisees "of the sort who do make long speeches in widows' houses, that they may devour their goods," fell to raining curses upon the man who had dared to contemn one of the Commandments of the Chosen Race.

But certain women left their household tasks to listen, and inquired in bath-chamber and prayer-house concerning the man, and concerning his word of love wherein lay a sword and a searchlight able to pierce to the very heart. And they learnt that, though at first his following had comprised only twelve disciples from the land of Gennesaret, it had since spread through Decapolis and Samaria, and reached

the confines of a Judea that was still exclusive and averse to the smallest relaxation of Israel's frontiers, until, finally, the prophet had sent out seventy missionaries—a number equal to the number of Israel's families—and gained adherents in the City of the Lord herself, and in the villages round about her.

Hence it came about that, though execrated in every synagogue, the name of Jeshua of Nazareth was mentioned on every hearth. And even the slave-women guarding the house-door's entrance-screen would be able to tell of his movements, and say: "I did see him come through the strait-ways where hangeth the smoke of the forges, and thence cross the place where thunder the mills of the fullers, and ascend into the ward of the grinders and its savour of wood and of meal, and depart unto Zion."

Particularly did certain women of Israel evade husband or father to approach latticed window and gaze upon the prophet who, so worn and melancholy of bearing, yet also so keen and comprehensive of glance, would stretch forth his hands above children's heads, and above the wheeled litters of cripples being taken to await the Stirring of the Pool, and bless them in a voice warm and charged with emotion.

And then the women would return to their household duties with a new sense of pleasure and ecstasy, and a zest at once painful and sweet.

For every word uttered by the Rabbi breathed a charm able to lull a weary heart to sleep. And, in direct opposition to men arid, harsh, and encased in egotism, this man, whilst declaring himself to be the Son of God, could show sympathy for women, and forgive even the most abject! Not that Rabbi Jeshua did not rebuke the very thought of sin: it was rather that he heaped scorn upon the injustice of accusers who themselves were lecherous, yet so presumptuous as to cast the first stone. Hitherto there had always stood between the Hebrew woman and her God a spouse, or a parent, or a master, or the shadow of some Doctor of the Law of the sort who "laid burdens upon others which he himself would not touch with so much as a finger": but now the Rabbi, whilst in no way seeking to detach the Hebrew woman from her duties, placed her beside the man, that upon both might stream the radiance and the protection of "our Father which abideth in Heaven," and opposed to the utterances of a rancorous, withered, Pharisaical oratory, to the utterances of a facile, ostentatious piety, that prayer of the Patriarchal Age which had maintained between the Creator and the created the loving, intimate bond of a forgiving parent with a child needing bread.

Yet, whenever any such Jewess expressed confidence in the promises of Jeshua's doctrine, at once the gloomy voice of husband or father thrust her back upon such jealous aridities as that the Rabbi was trampling upon the Law, and omitting its rites, and perverting its truth, and eating the bread of strangers and Gentiles.

At the same time, it was rumoured that no less a man than Nicodemus-ben-Gorion, a Master of Israel, and a Pharisee of the strictest and purest views, had sought the prophet's counsel, and that Joseph of Arimathea, a Sanhedrite of the most punctilious erudition, had entertained the Rabbi, and listened respectfully to his discourse.

And the soul of those women of Israel wavered between hope and fear.

Then there came a spring morning of such joyousness that the very gateways and arches of the city seemed to be lifted up, and all Jerusalem to become as a burgeoning field, or a verdant mountain, in the sunshine.

And "Hosanna!" again and again cried a band of countrymen who left everywhere behind them a fresh fragrance of olive and palm boughs. And "Hosanna to the Son of David!" they cried again.

And this joy of Nisan penetrated even to close-locked hearths, now that the Rabbi from Galilee was riding in triumph through the hitherto hostile city, and weeping with the anguish of his love as he listened to the people's benedictions and the songs of jubilation which entwined themselves around the walls of the Temple like mist.

Yet that evening, when returning homeward, some of the Rabbi's late glorifiers could be seen walking in weary silence, and trailing in the mire the same olive and palm boughs which recently had been flashing above the Rabbi's head.

And Jesus Himself returned to Bethany with the Twelve Disciples.

And again the women of Jerusalem saw their happiness overcast.

Then came another day of exultation when Hosannas to the Rabbi were heard floating down from the Sanctuary's porticoes, with canticles sung by the pure and tender tongues of children dedicated to the Lord. Yet even as the childish hymns were arising like perfumed vapour they gave place to a roar like the roar of a red, ruthless conflagration, and men were seen to be fleeing from a crashing of broken jars and tables, overturned desks and coin, bird-cages whence the captives had escaped, and animal bellowings and bleatings. For now Jesus' voice was ringing through the Cloisters like a thunderbolt.

Yet still, whenever one or another Jewish woman referred to the bold Nazarene, there intervened a husband or a father to confound her faith by saying that such a display of vainglorious austerity would ruin humble traders, and that in his haste the Nazarene had uttered an abominable blasphemy against the Temple.

The objectors added that this time not even his own disciples would venture to defend him.

Upon that followed the excitement of the Paschal Festival, when a turmoil of multitudes ensued, and the splendour of Antipas' Court, and the puissance and the grace of the Procuratorial train, were to be seen.

And every family got out its festival robes, and set forth board and lodging in readiness for guests, in that the Scriptures had commanded that "the Lord your God loveth the wayfarer, and therefore do ye also love him and receive him, in that even as he were you yourselves in Egypt."

The result was that there set in a fading of the emotional impression recently created by Jesus; and some even ventured glibly to depreciate His demonstrations and controversies in the Temple, until the Rabbi's triumph came to seem a thing remote, a mere obscure, rustic episode.

And then came the news of his taking, effected in an olive-garden after that all His Disciples had fled. Whence at dawn on the following day the Prophet who had fluttered so many cloistered feminine hearts was walking a being even more abject and forlorn than some of those who had recently fallen at His feet, and implored His compassion.

Nevertheless, certain women of Jerusalem sent their slave-girls to wait in the neighbourhood of the Prætorium, and themselves sat at home in torment because of the slowness of the legal process, and disposed to chide their dependents, and to start at the mere click of a wicket. And at length, when there came from the *Lithostrotos* a blast of trumpets and a tempest of shouting, the women's hearts leapt within them, and, for all the sorrow caused by the news of the death sentence, felt almost relieved through the fact no longer the tortures of fancy would have to be borne, but that the anxiety and the emotion which had been lurking in their breasts, and racking their every thought, were ended. For at least the women's accumulated pain now could join with despairing resignation, and with a frenzy of compassion at the Rabbi's downfall, in the relief of sweetly charitable tears, and of remembrances that He had such a mother as themselves, and of speculations as to where that mother might be, and as to whether she was fair of face, and as to whether she would be present at her son's execution, and as to what might be her feelings. And with that the women embraced their children with sobs, and once more betook themselves to the tasks of establishments blessed by the Lord God of Israel with eminence, fortune, and plenty.

But the women who found the sorrow the least easy to bear were the women who dwelt upon the actual line of route. In that route were included three streets: a street long and wide which in places was covered over with archways and buttresses, and lined with the awnings of eating-houses and booths; a street running to the Tyropeon, and having its lintels hung with, in addition to the usual *mezzuzahs* or little cases of the Commandments, the oil and drug-jars and festooned-herbs of herbalists and perfumers, of a community of men with elderly, withered features, and wheedling tongues, and woman-like hands, and hidden stores of wealth; and, lastly, a street steep and chalky which ascended to the Gate of Gennath, and ran between landowners' villas of burnt brick beside whose walls rose staircases of limestone, or of pinewood planking with palm-wood uprights.

And that day there was not a portico or gallery or dining-chamber that was not alive with guests come to view the passage of the condemned. Only within those houses were certain women sitting listening to beating hearts in little rooms the atmosphere of which hung heavy and oppressive with its musky smell of garments, with its smoke from braziers, with its "herbs of virtue," with its cedar-wood of bedsteads and cupboards, and with its fragrance of fruit-baskets. And whenever an utterance or a laugh

came from the crowd those women would run to the streak of light which the jealous lattice admitted, in a conviction that danger threatened. And then they would sigh, and once more kiss one another, and resume a fretting evidence by a flashing of almond eyes amid the darkness, and a swaying to and fro of jewelled forms. And if some bold hand or forehead happened to thrust itself against the bulrushes of the window-fringe, anger and fear would break forth again, and also a yet keener desire to know what was passing. And only after a while would the women resume their comments upon the gauds and the cosmetics of the courtesans able to flaunt themselves openly along the line of route, and upon the effrontery of the young men from the Greek colonies, and upon the acuteness of the lithe Phœnicians who bawled wares from every country—cinnamon-coloured apes from Central Asia, ruddy amber from the Baltic, and embroidered fabrics from Ionia—and upon the diffidence of Libyan shepherds who, tall, clad in white, and tattoo-marked in blue, had melancholy, handsome features, hair divided into two queues and braided above the eyebrows, and the back of the neck clipped close, and foreheads bound with ostrich plumes.

But at length an end was put to the tremors of the obscurity by the sound of approaching footsteps of husbands. And all started from their divans. And approaching also was the blast of a *bucina*, a sound which brought back to the women's minds an image which smote them with consciousness, and reddened their cheeks, and made them remember the haste with which the disciples had fled, and led them to ask one another, without actually opening their lips, which of their number were to be chosen for proffering the "wine of myrrh."

For, ordinarily, the women selected for holding that draught to the lips of the criminals included some of Jerusalem's leading matrons. And subsequently those matrons were supposed to go and condole with the hearths left desolate and impoverished by the crime, and assist the widows or the children or the parents to leave the land which had witnessed their kinsman's stripping and agony.

The wine in question—the "wine of charity" of the Book of Proverbs, and the *vinum languidum*, or "wine of heaviness," sanctioned by the Greater *Sanhedrin*—was a brew made of grape-must into which a few grains of the gum of *balsamodendron myrrha* had been cast. And its purpose was sufficiently to stupefy, to cause *sopor*, or lethargy, in men dying slowly on the cross to make them lose consciousness sooner than otherwise they would have done.

Only if the crime had contained elements of special horror or ill-omen would no Hebrew woman, no matter what her rank might be, minister to the given criminal, so that he had to be handed the "bitter draught" by an executioner.

Yet, though, ordinarily, the draught was proffered by leading matrons, on the present occasion it befell that the Sanhedrites felt equally unwilling to run the risk of denying the criminals this relief and to see it provided from their own homes: wherefore they forbade their wives to attend the ceremony, and only the just Elishama, the father of the young Elipheleth who, loving the Prophet, had nevertheless fled from before His gaze and the terrors of Gethsemane, proved sufficiently strong and sufficiently pious to consent to his wife being present at the Paschal executions.

Wherefore, avoiding her son's eyes, the patrician lady left her mansion on Mount Olivet, repaired to Jerusalem, and there joined certain wives of small land-holders and petty traders.

And together all set forth through alley-ways and by-ways with the solitude rendering them all too conscious of the beating of their hearts and pulses, and their lips uttering never a word rather than let their voices go echoing through the stillness which their feet were cleaving.

Once an old camel turned round with a grunt from a doorway, and for a moment the little band scattered in dismay, and in an agony to increase their speed, yet also in a consciousness that for a failure to do so they must blame the shortening of their stride with the ankle-chains. But on the present occasion no jewel or other garniture adorned their clothing— their figures lay swathed beneath plain, stout grey or mulberry-coloured cloaks which effectually concealed all grace of outline, with, pulled over their brows, hoods, and, falling from their temples, the stiff, close-fitting veil.

Never hitherto had the wife of Elishama, through exclusiveness, and the other women, through humbleness of origin, been chosen to fulfil the lugubrious office. Yet now they knew that soon they would be surrounded with soldiery, and forced to receive upon their faces the direct gaze of the condemned, and feeling themselves beside quivering bodies which still were treading the earth as they bore onward the trees to be planted for those bodies' reception. And these thoughts caused the women to press yet closer around the mother of Elipheleth, and that mother's fingers to tremble more and more convulsively upon the foot of the iron cup which shortly she was to hold to the lips of him who had blasted her son's youth.

A slave laughed at them from a roof where he was curing jackal-skins, and the women darted forward like a flock of sheep, descended a flight of steps, and issued into an alley-way ruddy with sunlight, and flanked with ancient walls and caper-trees of the sort whose seeds the Jew of the period was accustomed to pickle and consume.

And though at length a gust of shouting dissipated the women's terror of the solitudes, it replaced it but with a terror born of the populace, and of the knowledge that their task was imminent.

And even when the clamour died down for a moment the women found themselves shuddering at the sound of horrible footsteps overtaking them. The footsteps were those of an old beggar and a girl as lean and dirty and dishevelled as a starving dog, with the two linked together with a cord, and plastered over with befoulments. And amid the silence the old man's fists could be heard descending upon the girl's frail shoulders whenever she stopped to pick up, and to gnaw, some fragment or strip of fruit-peel or stalk, and in one instance to clutch at a bitten-into bean-pod. The man, tall and crooked, had a turban like a strand of yellow rope, features studded with blotches and pimples, a body clad in a coarse, rough tunic, with a wisp of bass serving for a girdle, bare legs like the shanks of a sheep, and huge sandals of palm-fibre and leather. And whenever he shouted at the girl he dribbled upon her bare neck from a long, hooked nose thrust almost into her ear.

Before him the women shrank back. And as he passed them he left upon them a horrible impression of sockets mutilated and rendered vacant with the branding-iron of a barbarous justice.

Just as the couple plunged into the human mass beyond, and the old man's turban began to nod and zigzag a way through it with a sort of dull, frenzied pertinacity, before disappearing, the women also reached the clamorous street.

And, arrived, they wavered—they felt as though caught in the eddies of a turbid river. But when the wife of the patrician raised aloft the vessel of *mesek* they were recognised, since they had fallen amongst retainers of the Prætorium.

And, near-by, a gate opened, and a cry arose, for there came forth from the gate an old woman who, keen and blue of eye, with hands as dead white as ivory, unfolded a napkin, and wiped the face of one of the criminals.

And the crowd, seething to and fro, gave vent to applause of or derision of the compassionate act according as mood dictated. But when a street-trader bawled: "She is of the Rabbi's company," and all sought the more to look at her, the centurion, the *exactor mortis,* came riding back to give her protection, since she was known, and her name was Berenice—she was a stranger come to Jerusalem to see her son, a mercenary in the Tetrarch's bodyguard.

And so the little band of women reached the broad, tumultuous space which the Gate of Gennath shaded, and there passed through the masses of humanity with arms raised to shield their eyes, and hands clutching at, and clinging to, the smooth stones, and lips uttering smothered cries. Until finally the human wedge in the Gateway shot them forth into the outer precincts.

And there there were sun-bathed gardens, and blue, distant vistas, and tents and outstretched garments and campfires and camels of nomads, and waves of attendants thrusting back people as they issued from turnings and by-ways, and spears of mounted men, and splendour of arms, and crooks upraised to guard flocks, and standards, and bleatings, and flute playings of minstrels, and shoutings of persons disputing with, or calling to, one another.

For the paved roads from Jaffa and Damascus were congested with humanity packed between detachments of the cohort. And every garden fence had upon it a seething mass of male and female field-workers, and everywhere there was a note of jubilation.

The cavalry, Golgotha reached, made for the hill's northern slopes, and allowed the other shelving, clay undulations to become thronged with a rabble which waved its arms, laughed, threw stones about, pelted folk with thistle-heads and fragments, and stripped from itself the rags and ordure of squalid sewers and latrines of that Acra where hordes of vagabonds huddled together in ditches, and dogs roamed by night to burrow in the refuse draining into two great cesspools from a declivity which, as bare as a carcase, lay ever blurred with steam of burial vapour and swarms of gadflies.

Persons unable to overcome their repugnance to the spectacle remained on the outskirts of the crowd, but the sunken track-way to Golgotha's summit—an eminence of no great height, and converging to a platform of bare and barren rock—soon became scintillant with legionaries and tiaras and ceremonial robes. Leaping his horse over thistles and rubbish, the centurion disappeared for a moment behind a bend of the path, to reappear as a figure red and gleaming in its *chlamys,* with a flashing elbow projected against the sky, and a hand resting gracefully upon a belt whence the suspended sword-sheath looked like a torch. Last of all, like the antennæ of a gigantic caterpillar burrowing its way into the mass of smocks and cloaks and tunics, came the grim, tragic branches of the crosses.

And so all came to a solemn halt.

The women bearing the "wine of mercy" had ascended the ridge by a different path—a path which issued at the extreme end of the rising; and now the centurion motioned them towards the centre with his baton, and there they stood feeling surrounded with the legionaries' looks and laughter and comments. Suddenly a criminal passed them, glistening with sweat, stumbling, and being pushed forward by slaves upon whose heads his cross kept throwing its horrible shadow. And to him succeeded another of the condemned, a man rounded of outline, with a mien like that of a tired mule.

And next came the figure of the Cyrenian shepherd, oaken-hard, robust with toil, and clattering his iron-shod sandals as he scraped the foot of Jesus' Tree across the rock.

At its upper end the main path debouched upon a glacis of shingle which completed the distance to the summit; and up this glacis the Sanhedrites pressed their mules, and were followed by a heavily-cloaked group with, at its head, a man with pale features, beard of youthful down, and hairless underlip. And as this man twisted his fingers into his turban, with his auburn locks fluttering upon the wind, and making him look like a young eagle, he kept sobbing, "O Rabbi! O Rabbi!" And even when flecked with foam from the bit of the centurion's horse he still continued his way through the turmoil of the throng.

Only when the members of his group had drawn clear, and were standing with cloaks ungirdled and unclasped, could it be seen that their breasts were heaving, their eyes strained, their mouths sublime with anguish, and their hands clasped to the same heavens as still were looking down upon burgeoning gardens and smiling hills and all the track-ways of the Promised Land.

Amongst the group facing the multitude was Jesus' Mother—a figure silent and motionless and pale. On beholding her, the mother of Elipheleth sank back, half-swooning, amongst her friends.

And then came Jesus Himself—His locks fallen over His face, and dripping and clotted like the hair of a drowned man, His neck tense with suffering, and His shoulders hunched owing to the brutal violence with which His arms had been lashed behind His back. And, on seeing Him, the women of Jerusalem broke forth into a lament in which cries of sorrow for the fate of Him whom their thoughts still glorified and reverenced mingled with compassion for the grief of a mother like themselves.

And when certain Rabbins approached them to say that the *Sanhedrin* had interdicted all mourning for the criminals the women repelled the rebukers, and counter-rebuked them, and still followed after Jesus—strong and uplifted in their affliction. For into that affliction there lay thrown the whole strength of a life-long seclusion of tender hearts, so that the rush of sobs beat cruelly upon their frail flesh, and had mingled with it both the accumulated terror and fatigue and mental anguish born of the journey through the streets and the ascent of the Hill of Golgotha, and memories of Jeshua's youth and humiliations and trials, and a maternal tenderness which leapt from the bosom compact of tears. Hence the pain of that lamentation was like a physical pain in the side, and, though hidden, terrible, and not to be relieved save through heaping lament upon lament in protest against the rest of humanity.

And the wife of Elishama, who ever had feared and hated Jeshua on behalf of her son, whilst trusting Him on behalf of her daughters, wept with the rest—wept with all the bitterness of a mother.

And Jesus turned and looked at them. And as He did so they felt (for they could not see His eyes) that already He had probed the hidden wound. And from them His gaze passed onward, over the hillside. And as it did so a groan of longing burst from His lips. For again He saw Himself ascending a hillside so lush with cyclamen and anemone as to dye red the feet of a multitude; a hillside where once two ants had approached His feet, and gently He had lifted them up, and placed them in a flower; a hillside whence larks had sunken into the richness of a plain; a hillside where He had turned back the flap of His turban to receive the full glory of the morning sun upon His brow, and the full savour of a grain-crop; a hillside where He had cried to His father in an agony of supplication; a hillside where He had proclaimed: "Blessed are the poor, like unto yourselves, for unto them shall belong the kingdom of heaven."

And now, of all that raging, mocking city, none had a tear of compassion to shed for His plight save only this poor handful of women!

And He turned to those women, and, shaking His head to clear His eyes of the hair that was blinding Him, forced His twisted lips to the hoarse cry:

"Weep not for me, but for yourselves!"

And the women answered with a passionate outburst of emotion.

And the dragging voice went on:

"Weep likewise for your children, for the day is at hand when ye shall say: Happy is the barren womb!"

And the voice (broken with thirst and exhaustion) spread over the slopes of Golgotha, and concluded with the words of Hosea:

"Ye shall cry unto the mountains, cover us, and unto the hills, fall upon us!"

Around His form, picked out against the blue sky above the summit of the ridge, there were the Syrian slaves of the cohort, a few soldiers, and the Sanhedrites, with the hooves and trappings of the latter's mules jingling, and their riders' stern brows exuding sweat.

On the summit also could be seen, prominent amongst the legionaries guarding the site of execution, the blind mendicant's yellow turban.

Suddenly such of the multitude as had gained the top opened out to allow of two posts arising in its midst. The posts wavered for a moment, and then stood fixed, and stark and massive. And as the mob surged around them again the centurion moved his horse in the congenial task of digging his iron-shod toes into the rabble's sides. Then he rode to, and halted at, the edge of the rock which resembled a skull, with the hooves of his charger throwing up the stones, and the rider puckering his eyes to peer into the depths before straightening himself in his saddle to look also at the city beyond.

A slave approached him with the basket containing the hooks for sealing the mouths of malefactors who should blaspheme against the Imperial justice. But the Roman shrugged his well-set shoulders under their mail, and said:

"They can do no hurt to Rome. Let them blaspheme if they list."

Then he approached the women bearing the narcotic, and, bending down, bade them approach nearer, and himself escorted them to the place of punishment.

As yet the slaves had not completed the task of hollowing out the socket for Jesus' Cross, and in their vicinity the blind old mendicant was moaning with a sort of endearing note, and peering with empty eye-spaces in the direction of the leaner of the two malefactors. A gasp of anguish burst from the criminal's throat, and led the ragged girl to turn her attention to his swollen, tremulous hands, to the abrasions on his feet where they were exuding matter upon the rock, and to the feverish, convulsive writhings of his form.

At length a soldier approached, and divested the man of his sackcloth smock—tearing open, in the act, the weals left by the flagellation. And, thus stripped, Genas looked as frail and fragile as a piece of basketwork, as hugging his pointed elbows, he stood lifting alternate feet, and swaying his body to and fro. And the old man moaned blindly in his direction with a half-demented mien, and the ragged girl eyed derisively the old man's hands as they twitched in the sunlight.

The women with the "wine of mercy" reached Jesus' side just as the soldiers were unfastening His girdle, and He Himself was removing His one remaining sandal. But, on savouring the odour of the bitter draught, He put it from Him, and gazed into the eyes of the patrician woman.

And a tear fell from those eyes into the cup as though it had been another grain of myrrh, and then she tendered the vessel to the more withered of the two malefactors, who reached forward with

such bestial eagerness to swallow that his teeth closed and clattered upon the rim.

In the meantime the wrists of the other malefactor had been lashed to the bars of his cross—the object of such lashing being to prevent jerks of agony from subsequently impending the transfixing of the palms: yet, when offered the "cup of mercy," he dashed it roughly from him with the rusty ring thrust through his nostrils, and upset its contents.

"Ye shall see," he cried, "that I will yet have courage to sing on the cross even whilst ye yourselves are comforting and warming your hearts with wine of the Passover."

And his hoarse laughter and fœtid breath drove the women away.

Then, dexterous and debonair, an executioner, approached the man, and opened his right hand. And a dull blow resounded.

At the second stroke the nail could be heard penetrating the wood, whilst the loins of the condemned cracked as though twisted, and his pupils dilated into a hard, glassy stare, and from his features (still set in the expression which had accompanied the jest) there issued a yell.

And when the blind mendicant heard that yell he turned about, and, plucking hairs from his scabby beard, struck his fists against his dead-white forehead, clasped his fingers over his ears, and rushed away down the slope.

And even when the ragged girl shrieked after him: "It is not he, thou old fool! It is not our Genas! It is another that they are nailing!" he continued his flight amid shower of thistle-heads and stones and clots of dung, with the ducts of his eyeless sockets exuding tears, and the folds of his throat swollen with sobbings until they looked like the gills of a dead fish.

Then soldiers posted on ladders, and hauling upon ropes, raised the cross-bars which had had the quivering hands of Gesias nailed to them: and then they lifted the man's thighs, set them astride of the *sedile* or rest which projected from halfway up the upright, and was designed to afford sufficient support to prevent the flesh from tearing away at the points of transfixion, and, lastly, doubled back the legs until the soles of them lay prised against the wood.

Then the mallet struck home again, and the man's toenails could be heard rasping together as the toes twitched under streams of blood trickling down upon them from the shredded tissues.

Next, the wisp-like Genas was hoisted aloft by two slaves. At first he hung as in a syncope, with his transparent lips parted in a smile. But presently the lips opened wider, and vented a gulp like a sob, whilst the mouth pursed itself like the mouth of a child sucking at its mother's breast. And when the soldiers drew nearer, in jesting expectation that he would awake and relate to them dreams of his childhood, they had to step back hastily, for the crucified began to send ordure spattering down the trunk of the cross.

Barabbas also was there. He had come thither with the idea of beholding in the execution of the two malefactors merely their own, but in the death of the Rabbi *his own*.

And presently the soldiers raised Jesus ready nailed, and crossed and recrossed a rope about His body.

Thus three crosses stood turned towards the path of the westering sun. And, of them, the one in the middle was higher than the other two, and bore upon its branches Our Lord.

And gently a warm air, redolent of gardens, came blowing over the hill, and stirred the hair upon the faces temporarily blurred through pain and loss of blood.

But soon the nails checked the outflow from the ruptured veins. And then consciousness began to return, and moans could be heard, and sides be seen expanding, and ribs gaping and jerking. For returning consciousness meant consciousness at once of torture and of absolute inability to move under it.

And as a white, glorious, fleecy cloud passed over the sun it dulled coldly, for a moment, the flesh of the figures on the crosses. Then the sun returned again, and the flesh leapt back into relief.

The pious women returned to the city, for there were evening meals to be prepared, and guests to be entertained.

And if they met husband, or father, or brother near the gaiety of the city walls they gave them no more than the hasty greeting of the Jewish woman of the period. For in those days she had all eyes fixed upon her, and, if she were seen lingering with men, murmurings speedily arose.

ON THE DAY OF THE CRUCIFIXION

Leonid Andreyev

In *The Old Wives' Tale* Arnold Bennett taught us that there were people during the siege of Paris who were far more interested in keeping their small businesses running than they were in the fortunes of war. But it may be that we do not yet realize that not all the inhabitants of Jerusalem at the time of the Crucifixion placed themselves in the presence of the cosmic drama. To Leonid Andreyev's hero, the terrible thing about the day was his toothache. In the brief play which follows Frank Harris conceives Simon of Cyrene, quite unbiblically, as a man preoccupied with getting on in the world. Unlike Ben-Tovit, however, Simon realizes before the end the true significance of the occasion.

On that terrible day, when the universal injustice was committed and Jesus Christ was crucified in Golgotha among robbers—on that day, from early morning, Ben-Tovit, a tradesman of Jerusalem, suffered from an unendurable toothache. His toothache had commenced on the day before, toward evening; at first his right jaw started to pain him and one tooth, the one right next the wisdom tooth, seemed to have risen somewhat, and when his tongue touched the tooth, he felt a slightly painful sensation. After supper, however, his toothache had passed, and Ben-Tovit had forgotten all about it—he had made a profitable deal on that day, had bartered an old donkey for a young, strong one, so he was very cheerful and paid no heed to any ominous signs.

And he slept very soundly. But just before daybreak something began to disturb him, as if some one were calling him on a very important matter, and when Ben-Tovit awoke angrily, his teeth were aching, aching openly and maliciously, causing him an acute, drilling pain. And he could no longer understand whether it was only the same tooth that had ached on the previous day, or whether others had joined that tooth; Ben-Tovit's entire mouth and his head were filled with terrible sensations of pain, as though he had been forced to chew thousands of sharp, red-hot nails. He took some water into his mouth from an earthen jug—for a minute the acuteness of the pain subsided, his teeth twitched and swayed like a wave, and this sensation was even pleasant as compared with the other.

Ben-Tovit lay down again, recalled his new donkey, and thought how happy he would have been if not for his toothache, and he wanted to fall asleep. But the water was warm, and five minutes later his toothache began to rage more severely than ever; Ben-Tovit sat up in his bed and swayed back and forth like a pendulum. His face became wrinkled and seemed to have shrunk, and a drop of cold perspiration was hanging on his nose, which had turned pale from his sufferings. Thus, swaying back and forth and groaning for pain, he met the first rays of the sun, which was destined to see Golgotha and the three crosses, and grow dim from horror and sorrow.

Ben-Tovit was a good and kind man, who hated any injustice, but when his wife awoke he said many unpleasant things to her, opening his mouth with difficulty, and he complained that he was left alone, like a jackal, to groan and writhe for pain. His wife met the undeserved reproaches patiently, for she knew that they came not from an angry heart—and she brought him numerous good remedies; rats' litter to be applied to his cheek, some strong liquid in which a scorpion was preserved, and a real chip of the tablets that Moses had broken. He began to feel a little better from the rats' litter, but not for long, also from the liquid and the stone, but the pain returned each time with renewed intensity.

During the moments of rest Ben-Tovit consoled himself with the thought of the little donkey, and he dreamed of him, and when he felt worse he moaned, scolded his wife, and threatened to dash his head against a rock if the pain should not subside. He kept pacing back and forth on the flat roof of his house from one corner to the other, feeling ashamed to come close to the side facing the street, for his head was tied around with a kerchief, like that of a woman. Several times children came running to him and told him hastily about Jesus of Nazareth. Ben-Tovit paused, listened to them for a while, his face wrinkled, but then he stamped his foot angrily and chased them away. He was a kind man and he loved children, but now he was angry at them for bothering him with trifles.

It was disagreeable to him that a large crowd had gathered in the street and on the neighboring roofs, doing nothing and looking curiously at Ben-Tovit, who had his head tied around with a kerchief like a woman. He was about to go down, when his wife said to him:

"Look, they are leading robbers there. Perhaps that will divert you."

"Let me alone. Don't you see how I am suffering?" Ben-Tovit answered angrily.

But there was a vague promise in his wife's words that there might be a relief for his toothache, so he walked over to the parapet unwillingly. Bending his head on one side, closing one eye, and supporting his cheek with his hand, his face assumed a squeamish, weeping expression, and he looked down to the street.

On the narrow street, going uphill, an enormous crowd was moving forward in disorder, covered with dust and shouting uninterruptedly. In the middle of the crowd walked the criminals, bending down under the weight of their crosses, and over them the scourges of the Roman soldiers were wriggling about like black snakes. One of the men, he of the long light hair, in a torn blood-stained cloak, stumbled over a stone which was thrown under his feet, and he fell. The shouting grew louder, and the crowd, like colored sea water, closed in about the man on the ground. Ben-Tovit suddenly shuddered for pain; he felt as though some one had pierced a red-hot needle into his tooth and turned it there; he groaned and walked away from the parapet, angry and squeamishly indifferent.

"How they are shouting!" he said enviously, picturing to himself their wide-open mouths with strong, healthy teeth, and how he himself would have shouted if he had been well. This intensified his toothache, and he shook his muffled head frequently, and roared: "Moo-Moo. . . ."

"They say that He restored sight to the blind," said his wife, who remained standing at the parapet, and she threw down a little cobblestone near the place where Jesus, lifted by the whips, was moving slowly.

"Of course, of course! He should have cured my toothache," replied Ben-Tovit ironically, and he added bitterly with irritation: "What dust they have kicked up! Like a herd of cattle! They should all be driven away with a stick! Take me down, Sarah!"

The wife proved to be right. The spectacle had diverted Ben-Tovit slightly—perhaps it was the rats' litter that had helped after all—he succeeded in falling asleep. When he awoke, his toothache had passed almost entirely, and only a little inflammation had formed over his right jaw. His wife told him that it was not noticeable at all, but Ben-Tovit smiled cunningly—he knew how kind-hearted his wife was and how fond she was of telling him pleasant things.

Samuel, the tanner, a neighbor of Ben-Tovit's, came in, and Ben-Tovit led him to see the new little donkey and listened proudly to the warm praises for himself and his animal.

Then, at the request of the curious Sarah, the three went to Golgotha to see the people who had been crucified. On the way Ben-Tovit told Samuel in detail how he had felt a pain in his right jaw on the day before, and how he awoke at night with a terrible toothache. To illustrate it he made a martyr's face, closing his eyes, shook his head, and groaned while the gray-bearded Samuel nodded his head compassionately and said:

"Oh, how painful it must have been!"

Ben-Tovit was pleased with Samuel's attitude, and he repeated the story to him, then went back to the past, when his first tooth was spoiled on the left side. Thus, absorbed in a lively conversation, they reached Golgotha. The sun, which was destined to shine upon the world on that terrible day, had already set beyond the distant hills, and in the west a narrow, purple-red strip was burning, like a stain of blood. The crosses stood out darkly but vaguely against this background, and at the foot of the middle cross white kneeling figures were seen indistinctly.

The crowd had long dispersed; it was growing chilly, and after a glance at the crucified men, Ben-Tovit took Samuel by the arm and carefully turned him in the direction toward his house. He felt that he was particularly eloquent just then, and he was eager to finish the story of his toothache. Thus they walked, and Ben-Tovit made a martyr's face, shook his head and groaned skilfully, while Samuel nodded compassionately and uttered exclamations from time to time, and from the deep, narrow defiles, out of the distant, burning plains, rose the black night. It seemed as though it wished to hide from the view of heaven the great crime of the earth.

THE KING OF THE JEWS

Frank Harris

HUSHIM. *A woman of the tribe of Benjamin; wife of Simon and mother of his two sons, Alexander and Rufus.*

SIMON. *Of Cyrene, who owns a field in the country outside Jerusalem, on the way to Bethel.*

The Scene: Jerusalem.
Time: The First Hour on the day of Preparation.

HUSHIM. Now you know what to do, don't you? You go to the Temple by the second hour and wait for Joad. You'll know Joad, he'll be dressed as a priest. Tell Joad he's the handsomest man you've ever seen; he's small, you know, and likes to think he's captivating. Compliment the High Priest on his sense of justice; say it is the finest in the world; anything. . . . Don't be afraid of overdoing it; all men love flattery.

SIMON. [*nods his head*] I'll do my best.

HUSHIM. If I've not heard from you by the fourth hour I'll send Alexander to you to know the result, for I shall be very anxious. And the boy'll find out, he's so sharp. Don't spare compliments. You must be doorkeeper in the Temple, and flattery is like honey, even if you don't deserve it, it's pleasant.

SIMON. [*going*] I'll try to do what you say, Hushim.

The Eleventh Hour on the day of Preparation.

HUSHIM. Well? Have you got the post? You have been a time. Are you a doorkeeper of the Temple; have we a house in the Inner Court?

SIMON. [*passing his hand over his forehead*] I don't know.

HUSHIM. Don't know; you must know. Was Joad there? He promised to speak for you. Did you see him?

SIMON. I didn't see him. [*Sits down wearily.*]

HUSHIM. Didn't see him? Wasn't he there? My uncle's brother, too, and he promised me: the liar. What did you do?

SIMON. I did nothing. I'm tired, Hushim.

HUSHIM. Tired! What happened? Why don't you speak? What's the matter with you? Are you dumb or ill?

SIMON. I'm not ill, I'm only tired.

HUSHIM. Tired, you great hulk. Where have you been? What have you been doing? What's the matter with you? Can't you speak?

SIMON. If you knew—

HUSHIM. If I knew what? Oh, you make me mad. What is *it*? [*She takes him by the shoulder and shakes him.*] What's happened? Oh, you brute.

SIMON. You've no cause for anger, wife.

HUSHIM. No cause! Have you got the place? What did the High Priest say? You must know that.

SIMON. I don't know.

HUSHIM. You don't know. You must be mad. This comes of marrying a foreigner, a fool, a great brute. They all said I'd repent it. Oh! Oh! Oh!

SIMON. Don't cry, Hushim. I'll tell you everything.

HUSHIM. [*drying her eyes*] Tell me, did they make you doorkeeper? That's what I want to know. Tell me that. You promised you'd be in the Temple at the second hour, and here it is the eleventh. Where have you been all day? Where?

SIMON. I'm sorry, wife; I forgot.

HUSHIM. Forgot, sorry! What do you mean? Joad promised me to get you the place if the High Priest liked you. Did you get it? What did they say? Talk, man.

SIMON. I'm so sorry. I forgot all about it. I have not been to the Temple.

HUSHIM. You've not been to the Temple, and why not? Where were you? Don't say that Eli got the post. Don't say it or I'll strike you.

SIMON. I'm very sorry. I forgot. I don't know who got it. I wasn't there.

HUSHIM. [*sitting down*] Oh! Oh! Oh! He wasn't there! Oh! Oh! Oh! Where have you been all these hours? What have you been doing? Where did you go? Where did you eat?

SIMON. I've not eaten. I've—

HUSHIM. Not eaten! Why not? What's happened? Oh, why won't you speak? Talk, tell me!

SIMON. I'll tell you everything; but I'm very tired.

HUSHIM. Tell me first, who got the post? You must have heard.

SIMON. I don't know. I've not heard.

HUSHIM. At the fourth hour I sent Alexander to the Temple to find out whether you were chosen or not; when it got so dark I sent Rufus to my sister-in-law, Hoshed. I could not bear the suspense. They've both come back without news. You must know who got the post.

SIMON. No, I don't know. I didn't ask, but—

HUSHIM. You didn't ask?

SIMON. I'm thirsty.

HUSHIM. [*giving him wine*] There! Now tell me everything. You went out to the field?

SIMON. [*nods while drinking the wine*] I was at the field till nearly the second hour working, then I came into the city. When I reached the street which leads from the Temple to Golgotha I could not get across it, there was such a crowd. They had all come to see some prisoners who were going to be crucified.

HUSHIM. But didn't you push through?

SIMON. I got through to the first file, but there soldiers kept the passage. I had to wait. No one was allowed to cross. . . . They told me there were three criminals. The people were talking about them. Two were thieves and one was a rebel from the north, who had tried to make himself king. It was to see him the people had run together. Some said he was a Holy Man. . . .

After a little while the prisoners came by. The two thieves first, and then slowly the man, whom some called a prophet. He looked very ill. . . . [*After a long pause.*] They had platted a crown of thorns and pushed it down on his head, and the thorns had torn the flesh and the blood ran down his face. When he came opposite to me he fell and lay like a dead man; the Cross was heavy. . . . The Centurion ordered some of the Roman soldiers to lift the cross from him and he got up. He seemed very weak and faint: he could hardly stand. . . . The Centurion came across to me and pulled me out, and pointed to the Cross and told me to shoulder it and get on. . . .

HUSHIM. But why you?

SIMON. I suppose because I looked big and strong.

HUSHIM. Didn't you tell him you had to be at the Temple?

SIMON. Of course I told him, but he thrust me forward and warned me if I didn't do as I was told, I'd have to go to the Temple without feet.

HUSHIM. Oh, what bad luck! No one ever had such bad luck as you. No one. Why didn't you run away?

SIMON. I didn't think—

HUSHIM. Well, you carried the Cross? And then—

SIMON. I went to lift the Cross; it seemed as if I were helping to punish the man. While I stood hesitating, he looked at me, Hushim. I never saw such eyes or such a look. Somehow or other I knew he wanted me to do it. I lifted the Cross up and got my shoulder under it and walked on. I did not seem to notice the weight of it, I was thinking of his look, and so we went through the crowd past Golgotha to the Hill of Calvary. On the top I put down the Cross.

HUSHIM. When was that? It must have been about the third hour. Why didn't you go to the Temple then? You see, it was all your fault. I knew it was! But go on, go on.

SIMON. I forgot all about the Temple. I could think of nothing but the Holy Man. He stood there so quiet while the priests and people jeered at him. . . . When they nailed the others up they shrieked and screamed and cursed. It was dreadful. . . .

When they were getting ready to nail him to the Cross I went over to him and said, "O Master," and he turned to me, "forgive me, Master, for doing what your enemies wished." And he looked at me again, and my heart turned to water, and the tears streamed from my eyes, I don't know why. . . .

He put his hands on my shoulders and said, "Friend, friend, there is nothing to forgive. . . ." [Lays his head on his arms and sobs.]

HUSHIM. Don't cry, Simon, don't cry. He must have been a prophet!

SIMON. [choking] If you had seen him. If you had seen his eyes. . . .

HUSHIM. [beginning to cry] I know, I know. What else did he say?

SIMON. He thanked me, and though I was a foreigner and a stranger to him, and quite rough and common, he took me in his arms and kissed me. . . . I was all broken before him. . . .

He was wonderful. When they nailed him to the Cross he did not even groan—not a sound. And when they lifted the Cross up—the worst torture of all—he just grew white, white. . . . All the priests and the people mocked him and asked him if he could save others why he couldn't save himself. But he answered not a word. . . . I could have killed them, the brutes! He prayed to God to forgive them, and he comforted one of the thieves who was sobbing in pain. . . . Oh, he was wonderful. Even in his anguish he could think of others, and yet he was the weakest of all. . . .

And then the storm burst, and I stood there for hours and hours in the darkness. I could not leave him, I wanted. . . . Later some of his own people came about the Cross, weeping, his mother and his followers, and took him down, and they called him Master and Lord, as I had called him. They had all loved him. They all loved him. No one could help loving him, no one. . . .

Above his head on the Cross, they had written, "King of the Jews." You Jews have no king, I know; they did it to mock him. But he was a King, king of the hearts of men.

HUSHIM. And with all that, we've lost the place! What was his name?

SIMON. Jesus of Nazareth.

HUSHIM. What was it he said to you? I want to remember it to tell Hoshed.

SIMON. He called me "Blessed, for that I, a stranger, who did not even know him, was the only man in the world who had ever helped to bear his burden."

8. THE JUDAS TRAGEDY

ACELDAMA

Henry Wadsworth Longfellow

JUDAS ISCARIOT

Lost! lost! Forever lost! I have betrayed
The innocent blood! O God! if thou art love,
Why didst thou leave me naked to the tempter?
Why didst thou not commission thy swift lightning
To strike me dead? or why did I not perish
With those by Herod slain, the innocent children
Who went with playthings in their little hands
Into the darkness of the other world,
As if to bed? Or, wherefore was I born,
If thou in thy foreknowledge didst perceive
All that I am, and all that I must be?
I know I am not generous, and not gentle,
Like other men; but I have tried to be,
And I have failed. I thought by following Him
I should grow like Him; but the unclean spirit
That from my childhood up hath tortured me
Hath been too cunning and too strong for me.
Am I to blame for this? Am I to blame
Because I cannot love, and ne'er have known
The love of woman or the love of children?
It is a curse and a fatality,
A mark, that hath been set upon my forehead,
That none shall slay me, for it were a mercy
That I were dead, or never had been born.

Too late! too late! I shall not see Him more
Among the living. That sweet, patient face
Will never more rebuke me, nor those lips

Repeat the words: One of you shall betray me!
It stung me into madness. How I loved,
Yet hated Him! But in the other world
I will be there before Him, and will wait
Until he comes, and fall down on my knees
And kiss his feet, imploring pardon, pardon!
I heard Him say: All sins shall be forgiven,
Except the sin against the Holy Ghost.
That shall not be forgiven in this world,
Nor in the world to come. Is that my sin?
Have I offended so there is no hope
Here nor hereafter? That I soon shall know.
O God, have mercy! Christ have mercy on me!

Throws himself headlong from the cliff.

THE GOSPEL ACCORDING TO JUDAS

William E. Barton

Written Saturday, the day following the Crucifixion.

I do not write to excuse myself. I know full well that I have sinned beyond the possibility of pardon here on earth and I know not if it be possible in the mercy of God that I shall have forgiveness in heaven. I am not writing with any thought that I shall be able to set aside or even greatly to modify, the merciless judgment which coming generations must pronounce against me; nor can any condemnation by whomsoever uttered surpass that of my own conscience. I have betrayed the innocent blood. I have seen Him hanging on a tree whom I had chosen as my leader and Lord and whom I believed to be the noblest and best of men, and I know that largely it was my fault. I am little concerned with the judgment of history upon me, knowing as I do that I am under the righteous condemnation of God and the bitter reproach of my own conscience. The thirty pieces of silver, until yesterday in my possession, are a mill-stone round my neck, which it seems must drag me to the bottom of the abyss. My lips are blistered with the memories of the treasonable kiss I gave Him. Life has become unbearable. If I do not die of remorse I shall surely take my own life. Great would be my joy this minute if I could feel myself nailed, not to His cross, for I am not worthy of that honour, but to the cross of one of the two robbers who were crucified beside Him. Neither of them was so base as I. Think not that I write to excuse myself. All that I write and all that anyone else will ever write will serve only to increase my condemnation.

Nevertheless there are some things which ought to be said, not in apology for me, but as giving from a different point of view an account of the ministry of Jesus. I am sure that none of the other disciples will ever do this as I think it should be done, even if men so illiterate should ever write their recollections of the ministry of Jesus. If I write at any point in criticism of them, or any of them, let it not be thought that I am seeking to exonerate myself.

I was born in Judah; my very name Judas is the glorious name of Judah, with the Greek ending. It meant in the language of our fathers, "One who deserves to be praised." It is more than an honourable name; it is a glorious name. It is the name of the "Lion Tribe." It is the name of the most noble and illustrious of all the twelve tribes of Israel. Jesus himself traced his birth through this tribe. Ten of His disciples were Galileans: Simon the Zealot and I shared with Jesus the honour of descent from Judah. Simon and I were born in Judah and I was named for that most stalwart of the sons of our father Jacob.

We two were born in Judah, Simon and I, and we two are mentioned last in the lists of the apostles. We who came from the proudest of the tribes had this perpetually to irritate us, that we were looked upon as having hardly any right even to a place among Galileans. Whenever people asked how many apostles Jesus had and what were their names, the lists always began with Simon Peter and Andrew his brother, and the next names were those of the two sons of Zebedee. Then after all the rest, most of them commonplace and insignificant men, came the two names from the one really great tribe, the names of Simon the Zealot and Judas Iscariot.

I know very well that I had no right to even the lowliest place among the disciples of our blessed Lord. I am not deserving of even the least of the honours that came to me in the months of my association with Him. Nevertheless, it is not a light thing to a proud man, a man who is justly proud of his birth and social position, that in every compilation of a list of names of men with whom he is associated, the names of fishermen and publicans should stand above his own. I know that in intellect and training and business ability and knowledge of the world I was their superior. If scholars in the future shall examine the records with care they will find some readings in which I am spoken of as the "first," or "chief," among the disciples. I will not pretend that I ever deserved any such title, and I am confident that no one will be deceived by any such fortuitous survival of an incidental record. Nevertheless, there have been those who were in no wise partial to me who did not hesitate to say that in family prestige, native ability and education, I was not behind the very chief of the apostles. Certainly I must have had some abilities which they all recognized, or I never should have been chosen as treasurer, nor should I have been retained in that position for months after rumours had come into circulation that I was pilfering from the treasury. Whether these reports were true or false I shall consider later. I am speaking now of my position as a member of the apostolic group. It was an uncomfortable position from the start, and if in any degree it was my fault, that fault was not wholly mine.

I wonder if anyone would believe me when I say that my motives in becoming a follower of Jesus were not wholly bad. My character had in it traits enough that were and are unlovely, but I was sincere in my love for my country. The traditions of the old days, when Israel had a name and a place among the nations, and Judah was chief among the tribes, were very precious to me. From boyhood I was thrilled when I heard about them. I longed for an opportunity to show my devotion to that which had made my nation great. Does anyone suppose that I joined the society of Jesus for the mere sake of the little money which I might possibly be able to filch from the bag? They underrate my ability as a thief, to say the least. I could have found more profitable places to win confidence and betray it for the reward of money. The love of money was strong in me, but had that been my only motive it would have kept me away from the company of that little band of fishermen with the paltry contents of their small treasury. I believed myself a patriot and had some reason for this opinion.

I had no real associate in the apostolic group, excepting Simon, the Cananæan. He was a patriot, and fought with Judas of Gamala, who headed the opposition to the census of Quirinius. He bitterly resented the domination of Rome and contested with the sword every assumed right of aggression. He risked his life for the glory of Israel when the other disciples of Jesus were quietly fishing in the Sea of Galilee. Jesus Himself said that no man had greater love than he who laid down his life for his friends; Simon the Zealot put his life in peril for the principles of the Kingdom of God and he was the only man among them who had ever risked anything for the sake of the kingdom.

I was not a soldier like Simon, but I was a Judean as he was. I loved my country as he did; I associated myself with Jesus from the same motive that carried him into that uncongenial group. I gave up a better home than most of the apostles and better worldly prospects and business opportunity, but my name always appeared at the end of the list, and Simon came next to the bottom, he who had risked the most.

The apostolic group was made up of cliques. Simon Peter and the two sons of Zebedee became a kind of self-appointed committee, to whom should be entrusted all the innermost confidences of the company. Matthew the publican had no large group of friends among the apostles, but he was popular outside with people of his own rank, and that gave to him a kind of prestige, even though in some respects it was one of doubtful honour. The whole group of Galileans nagged and annoyed me. They who came from that province, whose blood was mixed with that of the Gentiles, that province utterly unknown by name in the days of our national glory, looked upon us who came from Judah with unremitting jealousy and never ceased to snub us.

I know it may seem unworthy to mention this and things like this, and these are indeed things insignificant in comparison with my own great sin; but at least it can do no harm that men should know that my position has been one of constant discomfort.

If ever any of the disciples of Jesus should tell the story of his ministry, they would be compelled to tell how again and again the disciples quarrelled among themselves as to who should be the greatest among them. It happened over and over. Jesus rebuked us once by calling a little child and saying that he was greatest in the kingdom. We all understood what that meant, but that was not the end of the matter. Jesus had this in mind when He said to us, "See that ye fall not out by the way." Whenever our minds were free from pressing cares, that was the question that came up. I was ambitious and so was Simon; so were all the rest. James and John were insufferable in their ambition. Only a few days ago, as we were approaching Jerusalem, their mother, Salome, came to Jesus and they with her, begging Jesus that they might sit the one on His right hand and the other on His left in His kingdom. I will not deny that Simon and I coveted those places for ourselves, but we had better sense than to get our mothers to tease Him to give them to us. If I was any more ambitious than the others I think I may say that it was because I was more intelligent. They had come to Jesus from his own neighbourhood, from the vicinity of Capernaum, where He had established His residence. They did not at the outset look on their discipleship as involving their permanent leaving of home to be with Him, but when I turned my back on my home in Judea I knew that it meant something like a permanent departure from my life-long associations. I was ambitious; of course I was ambitious. I believed that Jesus was to establish a kingdom and that He would choose as His foremost officials those who from the beginning of His ministry had left their homes and become His followers. I believed that I had something that I could contribute to the movement and that I should deserve both recognition and reward. If this was sinful it was a sin which I shared with all the other disciples, and I am sure that I could not have exhibited it any more hatefully than did the men from Galilee.

Those Galileans had mostly known each other before. They were brothers or cousins or partners one of another, holding their common interest against outsiders, like Simon and me, but still jealous of each other. Unlike Simon and myself they had no large idea of sacrifice in coming to Jesus. They measured their sacrifice in terms of lost time from their fishing, but Simon measured it in terms of danger which he had encountered and I measured it in terms of possible bloodshed. Simon and I were consistent revolutionists. If the kingdom ever came it must come by the overthrow of Rome. If Rome was overthrown it must be by military force. Inasmuch as a little country like ours could never hope to rally an army great enough to stand against Rome, I knew that there must be favourable circumstance, either political or supernatural. I came to Jesus because I believed He had the power to rally men to Him and to organise them into a successful army of resistance against Rome. If we could begin a revolution in our own country, we might hope that we could rout the local Roman guards and hold our territory successfully against forces that Rome could immediately send for our subjection.

Let me confess that I never really loved Jesus. It was not affection for Him that drew me to Him. On the contrary, there was in Him that which made me ill at ease. I felt that He was able to read my character as no other man. In His presence I felt a sense of self-reproach such as no one else ever gave me; but if I did not love Him, I admired Him and was willing to follow Him; for I loved the kingdom, which He preached.

I have said that I am not seeking to justify myself. I realise that what I am saying may seem to contradict that statement. I do not intend to do anything that can truthfully be called self-justification, but I want to make it plain that my coming to Jesus was not wholly the result of evil motives. I have said that Simon and I were consistent revolutionists. Jesus knew this when He accepted us as disciples. He knew that Simon had fought with the sword against the Romans and that I, a Judean, had come into His Galilean company because of my very strong sympathy with our national hope. I still think that we ought not to be too severely blamed for not understanding Jesus better in this particular. How could we have been expected to know what Jesus meant when He talked about the Kingdom of Heaven? He knew what meaning we gave to that term. If He chose to give it a new meaning, how could we be expected to know it? He was continually putting

new wine into old wine-skins till the wine-skins burst. Was David's kingdom wholly a spiritual kingdom? Was the kingdom of God as the Psalmists sang of it a kingdom wholly of the soul? Did they not tell of the Messiah coming to break the nations into pieces like a potter's vessel? Was the kingdom of God which the prophets promised us entirely a matter of spiritual comfort? Did they not see the Messiah coming from Edom with garments dripping and spattered with the blood of the enemies of Jehovah? How was I to be blamed for an idea of the kingdom which I learned from the holy prophets? John the Baptist believed in the kingdom not very different from that in which I believed. And so did the other apostles of the Lord.

I think perhaps my view of the Kingdom of God was more definite than that of most of the other disciples because I had thought more about it; and for this reason it may have been harder for me than it would have been for them to believe that the Kingdom of Heaven is within, but none of them ever came to realise that, even up to the hour when Jesus was crucified.

I have spoken of a sense of self-reproach which I felt in the presence of Jesus. One time He addressed us and said, "Have I not chosen you twelve, and one of you is a devil." At first I could not believe that He meant me. Yet there was something in the word which caused my heart to sink within me. I felt that He knew that while the others had come to Him as full of wrong ideas as I, they had come with a more genuine affection. When the poor woman of the street washed His feet with her tears and wiped them with her hair and He forgave her all her sins for the greatness of her love, I felt that love such as hers was something in which I could have no share. My devotion had been of a calculating sort. I had reckoned with more of deliberation than the other disciples on the substantial rewards of the kingdom.

I have been accused of stealing. Yesterday I would have resented the charge. To-day I confess it, for it seems to me a small sin compared with that which now I have committed and must shamefully confess. From time to time I took money from the common purse. But I was suspected of stealing a long while before I stole, and I think suspicion made it easier for me to be a thief. I am by nature a covetous man, yet for a long time I knew of these suspicions and did not steal. Latterly I have stolen, whether more or less than they suspect I cannot tell.

John, the son of Zebedee, never liked me. I have never heard of his saying a gracious word about me. I have been told that he has attributed to me the discontent among the disciples last Friday night, when Mary of Bethany broke her bottle of perfume and poured it upon His head. I did complain. So did all the others. It seemed to me the most extravagant thing I had ever witnessed. That perfume represented a working man's wages for a year. We had been living none too abundantly, and here was opportunity to replenish our own treasury for the stern days ahead of us, or to make a notable gift to the poor, who at the time of the feast are thick as flies in Jerusalem. There has been no incident in all the ministry of Jesus, which seems to me more incomprehensible than his willingness to have so much money wasted upon Him for the satisfaction of a single hour. I confess that I protested, and so did all the others. Indeed, it was that very incident which threw me into such a passion that I began to consider for myself how I could turn our situation into financial advantage. So I went to the High Priest, and I earned those thirty pieces of silver to my everlasting shame.

But while covetousness has been with me a lifelong fault, and this money adds to the blackness of my sin, it was not solely for money that I proved false to Jesus. That became the occasion of my crime, but the causes lay deeper.

I betrayed Jesus. I confess it to my everlasting shame. I plead no excuse, yet with it all I did not mean to murder Him. It never occurred to me that such a result would follow the information which I gave to the priests. They were anxious to arrest Jesus at a time when He could be taken into custody without raising a popular disturbance. They dared not arrest Him while He was speaking in the temple. They undertook to do this last October, when He was in the city at the Feast of Tabernacles. The officers of the law came back without Him. They were overawed by the people and half converted by the words they heard Him speak. Spies had been watching the home of Lazarus where Jesus went every night. Jesus made a secret arrangement for a place to eat the Passover Supper and I felt sure that after that He would be likely to go to some other place than to the home of Lazarus. I thought the olive orchard, Gethsemane, was where He would be likely to go and spend the rest of that moonlight night. I told the priests of this probability and offered to be their guide.

But I did not mean to murder Him. I believed that He had grown timid. He had never used His mighty power for His own protection. I believed that I could force Him to do so. On Sunday morning He had ridden into Jerusalem in triumph, and our hearts leaped for joy as we saw Him thus proclaiming Himself the Messiah. But after that He seemed more cautious. The days were slipping by, and He was not asserting Himself. He left the Temple Tuesday evening with no indication that He intended to return.

This seemed to me an appalling situation. We had come to Jerusalem, menaced by a great danger and inspired by high ardour. Sunday and Monday everything went His way. He drove the money changers from the Temple and no man dared lay hands on Him, but all day Tuesday He fought a losing battle, and when He left the Temple in the afternoon I realised that the end had come unless we could rouse Him to some new act of self-assertion.

How could I force Him to utilise the power which He possessed? All day Wednesday He hid in Bethany. On Thursday He made His secret arrangements for the eating of the Passover and afterward hid in the orchard. To guide the soldiers to His place of hiding would be to force an issue. I was sure that He would rise to the emergency. I said to myself that in a way my betrayal was the expression of my faith. When Jesus went up to Jerusalem, I, in common with all the others, thought He would be killed. When Thomas said, "Let us go with Him that we also may die with Him," my heart responded to the suggestion, but I soon began calculating how if the situation should become as serious as that I could at least save my own person free from harm. But when I saw His courage and the rising enthusiasm of the people I thought I had begun to understand the motive of Jesus. He had been farther sighted than I had. He had repressed us until He saw that the time was ripe. Now He was asserting Himself. We forgot that we had started to die with Him and resumed our discussion, as to who should be the greatest. I began to say to myself that I was the best business man in the company; that my buying at wholesale had saved Jesus and the disciples a good deal of money and that I was entitled to a commission on my purchases. When I saw Him indulging in what I thought reckless extravagance, I saw no reason why I should continue to practice petty economies. So I became a thief; rather I will say, I manifested the fact that I already was a thief. But I was not solely a thief. I was a man of good business ability whose talents were under-rated and who turned a passing occasion to commercial advantage.

I acted in covetousness, but far more in resentment. It was my opportunity to vent my long cherished hostility toward the whole crowd of the Galileans, but I never thought that Jesus would die.

On that last night my heart warmed to Jesus in an act which I understood to be one of appreciation. I had the seat of honour at the table. I was next to Jesus, and when He dipped the sop He gave it to me in token of friendship. Yet somehow that very act had in it a quality which I resented. I felt that He read my character and knew my lack of love for Him and realised that He could not trust me. His very kindness turned in my soul to bitterness and it seemed as though the spirit of evil grew more definitely personal within me at that very moment.

My shame grows deep when I remember the sign by which I betrayed Him. I kissed Him. I agreed with the priests upon this as the token of betrayal. From that hour until now my lips have burned as though they were hot coals in the memory of that shameful act. And now as I look back upon it my shame grows greater as I see that this possibility had long been inherent in my lack of love, my covetousness, my sinful and selfish and sordid spirit. And the worst of all is the memory of the kiss I gave Him.

I stood aside after the kiss and waited for Jesus to manifest His divine power. I thought He would summon twelve legions of angels. I thought they would smite down the guard and that Jesus would return in triumph to the Temple. I thought that He would proclaim himself king and drive the Roman soldiers from the city. I had a vision of the blessing it would bring to the people of Jehovah. Our people were perishing under oppression; their national hope was dying, and the religion was losing its hold upon their lives. I thought of Judas Maccabaeus, for whom I was named. He was a mighty deliverer of the people of God, and Jesus was mightier than he. I had looked upon the misery of my people and my heart waxed hot. I calculated the greatness of the

power of Jesus and I dared even to fancy that He would thank me when all was over that I had forced Him into a position where He would use that power, assert His Messiahship and deliver His people. Then I thought we should see who is the greatest in His kingdom. I said within myself, "The greatest of the apostles will not be any of those Galileans who smell of fish; it will be I, Judas, of the royal tribe, the man of affairs and business experience. I shall be recognised as having brought in the kingdom."

Alas! No legion of angels came. The mob bound Him and led Him away. They jeered Him and they scoffed at Him; they blindfolded Him and mocked Him, and all the mighty power which I expected Him to use remained quiescent. If He had it He did not use it. He saved others; Himself He could not save.

They brought Him before Pilate, and He was condemned to die. They led Him forth beyond the wall of the city and crucified Him and with Him two robbers. Would that one of them had been I.

And now He is dead, and the world has lost Him who might have been its Saviour had I not betrayed Him. I with my covetousness and resentment and pride and selfish patriotism, I delivered Him to be crucified. I betrayed Him with a kiss. I sold Him for thirty pieces of silver.

Thank God I did not keep the money. While yet He was hanging on the cross I hastened to the Temple and offered it back to the priests. They would not take the money. They shrugged their shoulders when I proffered it and said I had earned it and it was no further concern of theirs. When I cried out in agony of soul that I had betrayed the innocent blood, they said, "That is your own affair and no concern of ours." I flung it on the floor and came away. A little while later I went back and I heard them talking among themselves as to what they would do with it. They had been bargaining with an old man, a potter, for a piece of ground to use as a burial place for the poor. It was good for nothing else. He had dug off all the soil to get at the clay for use in his business. They had driven a hard bargain with him and had an option on the property for thirty pieces of silver. The money which I received for the betrayal of Jesus was just enough to buy this scarred and sterile tract, with hardly enough of soil left upon it to provide graves for the outcast and the stranger. Let me be the first to lie in it. Let me go thither and see if there be in it a tree where I may hang myself and there be buried among the paupers and the outcasts.

I cannot live with the memory of my guilt and the consciousness of my shame, yet before I die let me leave this record that He to whom I came under the impulse of the glad hope that He should redeem Israel seems to me still to have been the noblest and the greatest of men. What He meant by the Kingdom of God I do not know, and I am a stranger to love such as He taught and manifested. But in Him I have seen the power and compassion and the grace of God, and in Him have I beheld the power and the glory of God, which I hoped would be for the redemption of Israel.

Can it be that the redemption is larger than I have dared to hope? May it be that after all His kingdom is coming as He said, not with observation but as a spiritual power that is to transform the world? I do not know. I cannot understand. I cannot even think. Behind me is the mocking memory of lost opportunities. Within me are the tortures of a soul self-condemned and to be condemned by all coming generations of mankind. Before me is the blackness and hopelessness of death.

But might it be that His love, which is unto the uttermost, could forgive even me? I must not presume upon such great mercy. Let me fall into the hands of God and not into the hands of man. I heard His word to the penitent robber upon the cross, for I was hiding near. I longed to run and hide my face at His feet and plead for His forgiveness, but I knew I was not worthy. I know His love can save even unto the uttermost, and I wonder if in the life beyond there may be for me one faintest gleam of hope. I do not know. Alas! I do not know.

THE WIFE OF JUDAS ISCARIOT

Cale Young Rice

The wife of Judas Iscariot
  Went out into the night,
She thought she heard a voice crying:
  Was it to left or right?

She went forth to the Joppa Gate,
  Three crosses hung on high,
The one was a thief's, the other a thief's,
  The third she went not nigh.

For still she heard the voice crying:
  Was it to right or left?
Or was it but a wind of fear
  That blew her on bereft?

She went down from the Joppa Gate
  Into the black ravine.
She climbed up by the rocky path
  To where a tree was seen.

And "What, sooth, do I follow here?
  Is it my own mad mind?
Judas! Judas Iscariot!"
  She called upon the wind.

"Judas! Judas Iscariot!"
  She crept beneath the tree.
What thing was it that swung there
  Hung so dolourously?

"Judas! Judas Iscariot!"
  She touched it with her hand.
The leaves shivered above her head,
  To make her understand.

"Judas! Judas! my love! my lord!"
  Her hands went o'er it fast,
From foot to thigh, from thigh to throat,
  And stopped—there—at last.

"Judas! Judas! what has He done,
  The Christ you followed so!"
More than the silver left on him
  Made answer to her woe.

"Judas! Judas! what has He done!
  O has it come to this!
The Kingdom promised has but proved
  For you a soul-abyss!

"Was He the Christ and let it be?" . . .
  She cut him from the limb,
And held him in her arms there
  And wept over him,

"None in the world shall ever know
    Your doubts of Him but I!
'Traitor! traitor! and only traitor!'
    Will ever be their cry!

"None in the world shall ever know—
    But I who am your wife!"
She flung the silver from his purse:
    It made a bitter strife.

It rattled on the ringing rocks
    And fell to the ravine.
"Was He the Christ and let it be?"
    She moaned, still, between.

She held him in her arms there,
    And kissed his lips aright,
The lips of Judas Iscariot,
    Who hanged himself that night.

9. ETERNAL CROSS

VOX ULTIMA CRUCIS

John Lydgate

Tarye no lenger; toward thyn heritage
Hast on thy weye, and be of ryght good chere.
Go eche day onward on thy pylgrymage;
Thynke howe short tyme thou hast abyden here.
Thy place is bygged above the sterres clere,
Noon erthly palys wrought in so statly wyse.
Come on, my frend, my brother most entere!
For the I offered my blood in sacryfice.

THE HYMN OF THE HOLY CROSS

Richard Crashaw

Look up, languishing soul! Lo, where the fair
Badge of thy faith calls back thy care,
    And bids thee ne'er forget
    Thy life is one long debt

Of love to Him who, on this painful tree,
Paid back the flesh He took for thee.

Lo, how the streams of life from that full nest
Of love, thy Lord's too liberal breast
    Flow in an amorous flood
    Of water wedding blood!
With these He wash'd thy stain, transferr'd thy
        smart,
And took it home to His own heart.

But thou, great Love, greedy of such sad gain,
Usurp'd the portion of Thy pain,
    And from the nails and spear
    Turn'd the steel point of fear,
Their use is changed, not lost; and now they move
Not stings of wrath, but wounds of love.

Tall tree of life! Thy truth makes good
What was till now ne'er understood,
    Though the prophetic King
    Struck loud his faithful string;
It was thy wood he meant should make the throne
For a more than Solomon.

Large throne of Love! royally spread
With purple of too rich a red;
   Thy crime is too much duty;
   Thy burthen too much beauty!
Glorious or grievous more? thus to make good
Thy costly excellence with thy King's own blood.

Even balance of both worlds! our world of sin,
And that of grace heav'n weigh'd in Him,
   Us with our price thou weighed'st;
   Our price for us thou prayed'st;
Soon as the right-hand scale rejoiced to prove
How much death weigh'd more light than Love.

Hail, our alone Hope! let Thy fair head shoot
Aloft; and fill the nations with Thy noble fruit.
   The while our hearts and we
   Thus graft ourselves on Thee,
Grow Thou, and they; and be Thy fair increase
The sinner's pardon, and the just man's peace.

Live, O, for ever live and reign,
The Lamb whom His own love has slain!
And let Thy lost sheep live t'inherit
That kingdom which this Cross did merit.
              Amen.

THE CORONET

Andrew Marvell

When with the thorns with which I long, too long,
   With many a piercing wound,
   My Saviour's head have crowned,
I seek with garlands to redress that wrong,—
   Through every garden, every mead,
I gather flowers (my fruits are only flowers)
   Dismantling all the fragrant towers
That once adorned my shepherdess's head:
And now, when I have summed up all my store,
   Thinking (so I myself deceive)
   So rich a chaplet thence to weave
As never yet the King of Glory wore,
   Alas! I find the Serpent old,
   Twining in his speckled breast,
   About the flowers disguised does fold,
   With wreaths of fame and interest.

Ah foolish man, that would'st debase with them,
And mortal glory, Heaven's diadem!
But thou who only could'st the Serpent tame,
Either his slippery knots at once untie,
And disentangle all his winding snare,
Or shatter too with him my curious frame,
And let these wither so that he may die,
Though set with skill, and chosen out with care,
That they, while thou on both their spoils dost tread,
May crown thy feet, that could not crown thy head.

THE DREAM OF THE ROOD

Anonymous

Hark! of a matchless vision would I speak,
Which once I dreamed at midnight, when mankind
At rest were dwelling. Then methought I saw
A wondrous cross extending up on high,
With light encircled, tree of trees most bright.
That beacon all was overlaid with gold;
And near the earth stood precious stones ablaze,
While five more sparkled on the shoulder-beam.
Gazing on it were angels of the Lord,
From their first being's dawn all beautiful.
No cross was that of wickedness and shame,
But holy spirits, men on earth, and all
The glorious creation on it gazed.
   Sublime the tree victorious; while I,
Stained with iniquity, was galled with sins.
There, clothed as with a garment, I beheld
That tree of glory shining joyfully,
Adorned with gold, enriched with precious stones,
Which covered worthily the Ruler's cross.
However, through the gold I could perceive
That wretched ones had battled there of old;
For on the right side once it had been bleeding.
Then all my spirit was with sorrow stirred;
Fearful was I before that radiant sight.
There I beheld that beacon, quick to change,
Alter in vesture and in coloring;
Now dewed with moisture, soiled with streaming
   blood,
And now with gold and glittering gems adorned.
   A long time lying there I sadly looked
Upon the Savior's cross, until I heard

Resounding thence a voice. That wood divine
Then spake these words:
                    "It was long, long ago—
Yet I recall—when, at the forest's edge,
I was hewn down, and from my stem removed.
Resistless were the foes that seized me there,
They fashioned for themselves a spectacle,
Commanded me to bear their criminals;
And on men's shoulders carried me away
Until they set me down upon a hill,
And stayed me fast; mine enemies indeed!

"Then I beheld the Master of mankind
Approach with lordly courage as if He
Would mount upon me, and I dared not bow
Nor break, opposing the command of God,
Although I saw earth tremble; all my foes
I might have beaten down, yet I stood fast.

"Then the young Hero laid His garments by,
He that was God almighty, strong and brave;
And boldly in the sight of all He mounted
The lofty cross, for He would free mankind.
Then, as the Man divine clasped me, I shook;
Yet dared I not bow to the earth nor fall
Upon the ground, but I must needs stand fast.

"A cross upraised, I lifted a great King,
Lifted the Lord of heaven; and dared not bow.

"They pierced me with dark nails, and visible
Upon me still are scars, wide wounds of malice,
Yet might I injure none among them all.
They mocked us both together; then was I
All wet with blood, which streamed from this Man's
        side
When He at length had breathed His spirit out.

"Many a vile deed I suffered on that mount;
The God of hosts I saw harshly outstretched,
And darkness hid the body of the King,
With clouds enshrouded its effulgent light;
Forth went a shadow, black beneath the clouds;
And all creation wept, lamented long—
Their King had fallen, Christ was on the cross.

"Yet eagerly some hastened from afar
To Him who was their Prince; all this I saw.
Ah, then with sorrow was I deeply stirred;
Yet to the hand of men I bowed me down,
Humbly, with ardent zeal. They took Him then,
Lifted from His dire pain almighty God.
The warriors left me standing, swathed in blood,
And with sharp arrows wounded sore was I.
Him they laid gently down, weary of limb,

And stood beside His body at the head,
Gazing upon the Lord of heaven; while He
Rested a while, with His great labor spent.
Then in the slayers' sight men there began
To build a sepulchre, from marble hewn;
And laid therein the Lord of victories.
A song of sorrow then for Him they sang,
The desolate at eventide, when they,
O'erwearied, would depart from their great King.
And so companionless He rested.
                                "We,
After the warriors' cry uprose, yet stood
A long while there, on our foundations dripping.
The corpse, fair dwelling of the soul, grew cold.

"Then one began to fell us to the earth—
A fearful fate! and in the entombing mold
Deep buried us. Yet, undismayed, for me
The friends and followers of the Lord made search—
And when from out the earth they lifted me,
With silver they adorned me, and with gold.

"Now mayest thou know, O hero mine, beloved!
Unutterable sorrows I endured,
Base felons' work. But now hath come the time
When, far and wide, men on the earth, and all
The glorious universe doth honor me,
And to this beacon bow themselves in prayer.
On me a while suffered the Son of God;
Therefore now full of majesty I tower
High under heaven; and I have power to heal
All those who do me reverence.
                                "Of old
Was I a punishment, the cruelest,
The most abhorred by men, ere I for man
Had opened the true way of life. Lo, then
The Prince of glory, Guardian of heaven,
Above all other trees exalted me,
As He, almighty God, in sight of men
His mother honored, blessèd among women,
Mary herself.
                "Now, hero mine, beloved,
I bid thee tell this vision unto men,
Reveal with words that 'tis the glory-tree
On which almighty God suffered for sin,
The many sins of man, and Adam's deeds
Done long ago. There once He tasted death;
But afterwards the Lord from death arose
By His own mighty power, a help for men.
To heaven He then ascended, whence shall come
Once more upon the earth to seek mankind

At the last judgment day, the Lord himself,
Almighty God, surrounded by His angels.
And there shall He, who hath the power of doom,
Adjudge to every one the just reward
Which he on earth, in this short life, hath earned.
Then unabashed and bold can no one be
Before the word which He, the Ruler, speaks:
'Where is the man,' He asks the multitude,
'Who for the Lord would taste of bitter death
As He Himself once did upon the cross?'
Then are they fearful, little can devise
What they shall say to Christ. But need is none
That any at that time should be afraid
Who beareth in his heart this sacred sign;
For through the cross alone must every soul
Seek out the Kingdom from the earthly way,
Who hopes hereafter with the King to dwell."

Happy in mind I prayed then to the rood
With great devotion, where I was alone
Without companionship; my soul within
Was quickened to depart, so many years
Of utter weariness had I delayed.
And now my life's great happiness is this,
That to the cross victorious I may come
Alone, above the wont of other men,
To worship worthily. Desire for this
Is great within my heart, and all my help
Must reach me from the rood. Of powerful friends
Not many do I own on earth, for hence
Have they departed, from the world's delights;
They followed after him, their glorious King,
And with the Father now in heaven they live,
Dwelling in bliss. Each day I longing ask:
"When will the cross of Christ, which formerly
I here on earth beheld, call me away
From this my transient life, and bring me hence
To all delight, the joyous harmonies
Of heaven, where sit at feast the folk of God,
And gladness knows no end—so placing me
Where with the saints in glory I may dwell,
Enjoying greatly their glad minstrelsy?"
Be gracious unto me, O Lord, who once
For sins of men suffered upon the cross.
He freed us, gave us life, and home in heaven.

Hope was restored with blessedness and joy
To those who had erewhile endured the fire.
Triumphant in this journey was the Son,

Mighty and prosperous, when He advanced
Into God's Kingdom with a multitude,
A host of souls; when to His angels came
The almighty Master for their joy, to those
The holy ones in heaven, who from the first
Had dwelt in glory; when their Ruler came,
Almighty God, into His fatherland.

"THE LOVE OF CHRIST
WHICH PASSETH KNOWLEDGE"

Christina Rossetti

I bore with thee long weary days and nights,
   Through many pangs of heart, through many
      tears;
I bore with thee, thy hardness, coldness, slights,
   For three and thirty years.

Who else had dared for thee what I have dared?
   I plunged the depth most deep from bliss above;
I not My flesh, I not My spirit spared:
   Give thou Me love for love.

For thee I thirsted in the daily drouth,
   For thee I trembled in the nightly frost:
Much sweeter thou than honey to My mouth:
   Why wilt thou still be lost?

I bore thee on My shoulders and rejoiced:
   Men only marked upon My shoulders borne
The branding cross; and shouted hungry-voiced,
   Or wagged their heads in scorn.

Thee did nails grave upon My hands, thy name
   Did thorns for frontlets stamp between Mine eyes:
I, Holy One, put on thy guilt and shame;
   I, God, Priest, Sacrifice.

A thief upon My right hand and My left;
   Six hours alone, athirst, in misery:
At length in death one smote My heart and cleft
   A hiding-place for thee.

Nailed to the racking cross, than bed of down
　　More dear, whereon to stretch Myself and sleep:
So did I win a kingdom,—share My crown;
　　A harvest,—come and reap.

But after nineteen hundred years the shame
Still clings, and we have not made good the loss
That outraged faith has entered in his name.
Ah, when shall come love's courage to be strong!
Tell me, O Lord—tell me, O Lord, how long
Are we to keep Christ writhing on the cross!

GOOD FRIDAY

Christina Rossetti

Am I a stone and not a sheep
　　That I can stand, O Christ, beneath Thy Cross,
　　To number drop by drop Thy Blood's slow loss,
And yet not weep?

Not so those women loved
　　Who with exceeding grief lamented Thee;
　　Not so fallen Peter weeping bitterly;
Not so the thief was moved;

Not so the Sun and Moon
　　Which hid their faces in a starless sky,
A horror of great darkness at broad noon,—
　　I, only I.

Yet give not o'er,
　　But seek Thy sheep, true Shepherd of the flock;
Greater than Moses, turn and look once more
　　And smite a rock.

CALVARY

Edwin Arlington Robinson

Friendless and faint, with martyred steps and slow,
Faint for the flesh, but for the spirit free,
Stung by the mob that came to see the show,
The Master toiled along to Calvary;
We gibed him, as he went, with houndish glee,
Till his dim eyes for us did overflow;
We cursed his vengeless hands thrice wretchedly,—
And this was nineteen hundred years ago.

CRUCIFIED

Patrick Dacus Moreland

I saw them passing endlessly,
Their faces drawn with pain;
And they were lashed by a stormy wind
And a crimson rain.

I heard the deep, resurgent roll
Of the gun's thunderous blast,
And a shell burst in their ghostly ranks
Marching past.

It wounded one within the breast.
Another's hand was torn;
And One there was whose brow was red,
With crown of thorn.

WOOD OF THE CROSS

Violet Alleyn Storey

Wood of the Cross, you might have been
　　Pale-budded then for spring;
Wood of the Cross, you might have shared
　　New life with everything.

If there was need to cut you down,
　　They might have made of you
A little house in a silent town
　　Where dusky olives grew.

Lamb of the Cross, You might have been
    Alive for many a day,
Walking with those who held You dear
    Along some ancient way.

If there was need for You to die,
    Why did they kill You so?
Why did they make you tread the way
    That low men used to go?

Wood of the Cross, you might have died
    Ere many years had passed,
But now you will be blossoming
    As long as earth shall last.

Lamb of the Cross, You might have been
    A myth, a passing dream;
But now you are the Risen Lord
    Whom great and poor esteem.

GOOD FRIDAY NIGHT

William Vaughn Moody

At last the bird that sung so long
In twilight circles, hushed his song;
Above the ancient square
The stars came here and there.

Good Friday Night! Some hearts were bowed,
But some amid the waiting crowd
Because of too much youth
Felt not the mystic ruth;

And of these hearts my heart was one:
Nor when beneath the arch of stone
With dirge and candle flame
The cross of passion came,

Did my glad spirit feel reproof,
Though on the awful tree aloof,
Unspiritual, dead,
Drooped the ensanguined Head.

To one who stood where myrtles made
A little space of deeper shade

(As I could half descry,
A stranger, even as I),

I said, "Those youths who bear along
The symbols of their Saviour's wrong,
The spear, the garment torn,
The flaggel, and the thorn,—

"Why do they make this mummery?
Would not a brave man gladly die
For a much smaller thing
Than to be Christ and king?"

He answered nothing, and I turned.
Throned in its hundred candles burned
The jewelled eidolon
Of her who bore the Son.

The crowd was prostrate; still, I felt
No shame until the stranger knelt;
Then not to kneel, almost
Seemed like a vulgar boast.

I knelt. The doll-face, waxen white,
Flowered out a living dimness; bright
Dawned the dear mortal grace
Of my own mother's face.

When we were risen up, the street
Was vacant; all the air hung sweet
With lemon-flowers; and soon
The sky would hold the moon.

More silently than new-found friends
To whom much silence makes amends
For the much babble vain
While yet their lives were twain,

We walked along the odorous hill.
The light was little yet; his will
I could not see to trace
Upon his form or face.

So when aloft the gold moon broke,
I cried, heart-stung. As one who woke
He turned unto my cries
The anguish of his eyes.

"Friend! Master!" I cried falteringly,
"Thou seest the thing they make of Thee.

Oh, by the light divine,
My mother shares with thine,

"I beg that I may lay my head
Upon thy shoulder and be fed
With thoughts of brotherhood!"
So through the odorous wood,

More silently than friends new-found
We walked. At the first meadow bound
His figure ashen-stoled
Sank in the moon's broad gold.

THE BURNING-GLASS

Walter de la Mare

No map shows my Jerusalem,
   No history my Christ;
Another language tells of them,
   A hidden evangelist.

Words may create rare images
   Within their narrow bound;
'Twas speechless childhood brought me these,
   As music may, in sound.

Yet not the loveliest song that ever
   Died on the evening air
Could from my inmost heart dissever
   What life had hidden there.

It is the blest reminder of
   What earth in shuddering bliss
Nailed on a cross—that deathless Love—
   Through all the eternities.

I am the Judas whose perfidy
   Sold what no eye hath seen,
The rabble in dark Gethsemane,
   And Mary Magdalene.

To very God who day and night
   Tells me my sands out-run,
I cry in misery infinite,
   "I am thy long-lost son."

JUDGE ME, O LORD

Sarah N. Cleghorn

If I had been in Palestine
A poor disciple I had been.
I had not risked or purse or limb
All to forsake, and follow Him.
   But with the vast and wondering throng
   I too had stood and listened long;
   I too had felt my spirit stirred
   When the Beatitudes I heard.

With the glad crowd that sang the psalm,
I too had sung, and strewed the palm;
Then slunk away in dastard shame
When the High Priest denounced His name.
   But when my late companions cried
   "Away! let Him be crucified!"
   I would have begged, with tremulous
   Pale lips, "Release Him unto us!"

Beside the cross when Mary prayed,
A great way off I too had stayed;
Not even in that hour had dared,
And for my dying Lord declared;
   But beat upon my craven breast,
   And loathed my coward heart, at least,
   To think my life I dared not stake
   And beard the Romans for His sake.

CHRISTMAS

E. Hilton Young

A boy was born at Bethlehem
That knew the haunts of Galilee,
He wandered on Mount Lebanon,
And learned to love each forest tree.

But I was born at Marlborough,
And love the homely faces there;
And for all other men besides
'Tis little love I have to spare.

I should not mind to die for them,
My own dear downs, my comrades true.
But that great heart of Bethlehem,
He died for men he never knew.

And yet, I think, at Golgotha,
As Jesus' eyes were closed in death,
They saw with love most passionate
The village street at Nazareth.

THREE HILLS

Everard Owen

There is a hill in England,
  Green fields and a school I know,
Where the balls fly fast in summer,
  And the whispering elm-trees grow,
    A little hill, a dear hill,
  And the playing fields below.

There is a hill in Flanders,
  Heaped with a thousand slain,
Where the shells fly night and noontide
  And the ghosts that died in vain,—
    A little hill, a hard hill
  To the souls that died in pain.

There is a hill in Jewry,
  Three crosses pierce the sky,
On the midmost He is dying
  To save all those who die,—
    A little hill, a kind hill
  To souls in jeopardy.

THE CRUCIFIXION

G. A. Studdert-Kennedy

When Jesus came to Golgotha they hanged Him on
  a tree,

They drave great nails through hands and feet, and
  made a Calvary;
They crowned Him with a crown of thorns, red were
  His wounds and deep,
For those were crude and cruel days, and human
  flesh was cheap.

When Jesus came to Birmingham, they simply passed
  Him by,
They never hurt a hair of Him, they only let Him die;
For men had grown more tender, and they would
  not give Him pain,
They only just passed down the street, and left Him
  in the rain.

Still Jesus cried, "Forgive them, for they know not
  what they do,"
And still it rained the winter rain that drenched Him
  through and through;
The crowds went home and left the streets without
  a soul to see,
And Jesus crouched against a wall and cried for
  Calvary.

COST

Richard Watson Gilder

Because Heaven's cost is Hell, and perfect joy
  Hurts as hurts sorrow; and because we win
  Some boon of grace with the dread cost of sin,
  Or suffering born of sin; because the alloy
Of blood but makes the bliss of victory brighter;
  Because true worth hath surest proof herein,
  That it should be reproached, and called akin
  To evil things—black making white the whiter;
Because no cost seems great near this—that He
  Should pay the ransom wherewith we were priced;
  And none could name a darker infamy
Than that a god was spit upon,—enticed
  By those He came to save, to the accursèd tree,—
  For this I know that Christ indeed is Christ.

MATER DOLOROSA

John Banister Tabb

Again maternal Autumn grieves,
As blood-like drip the maple leaves
  On Nature's Calvary.
And every sap-forsaken limb
Renews the mystery of Him
  Who died upon a Tree.

STILL THE CROSS

E. Merrill Root

Calvary is a continent
Today. America
Is but a vast and terrible
New Golgotha.

The Legion (not of Rome today)
Jests. The Beatitudes
Are called by our new Pharisees
Sweet platitudes.

We tear the seamless robe of love
With great guns' lightning-jets;
We set upon Christ's head a crown
Of bayonets.

"Give us Barabbas!" So they cried
Once in Jerusalem:
In Alcatraz and Leavenworth
We copy them.

With pageant and with soldiers still
We march to Golgotha
And crucify Him still upon
A cross of war.

*O blasphemous and blind! shall we
Rejoice at Eastertide
When Christ is risen but to be
Recrucified?*

SHEEP AND LAMBS

Katherine Tynan

All in the April evening,
  April airs were abroad;
The sheep with their little lambs
  Passed me by on the road.

The sheep with their little lambs
  Passed me by on the road;
All in the April evening
  I thought on the Lamb of God.

The lambs were weary, and crying
  With a weak, human cry.
I thought on the Lamb of God
  Going meekly to die.

Up in the blue, blue mountains
  Dewy pastures are sweet;
Rest for the little bodies,
  Rest for the little feet.

But for the Lamb of God
  Up on a hilltop green
Only a cross of shame
  Two stark crosses between.

All in the April evening,
  April airs were abroad;
I saw the sheep with their lambs,
  And thought on the Lamb of God.

10. INTERIM

FROM FRIDAY TO SUNDAY

Mary Borden

Mary Borden's novel, *King of the Jews*, "is an attempt to reconstruct the history of what happened in Palestine immediately after and consequent on the death of Jesus." The last five chapters of Part One, which form a convenient unit, have been reprinted here.

I

Petronius, the centurion, strode to the centre of the great room, wheeled in front of the governor's table, raised his arm before him in salute and stood at attention.

"Did you carry out your orders?"

"Yes, sir."

"Well, what about it? What happened?"

"Nothing, sir."

Pilate slouched in his chair, looked the officer up and down; looked again, his eyes suddenly sharp with suspicion. He was a fine figure, this man of the East in his white tunic and burnished cuirass. Cæsar's stamp was on him. Long years of military service in the legions of Rome had moulded him, carved him to its type, obliterated almost all sign in him of the man who had been born by the waters of Babylon. Discipline, Pilate admitted, could make good stuff even out of a Syrian, almost good enough anyhow, and he admitted now that the man looked every inch a Roman. But there was something wrong with him. Not in his bearing. That was correct. He stood rigid as a statue, his head high, his shoulders square and the lions of Rome glinting on them were steady. But the crown of oak leaves on his head and the vine staff in his hand trembled very slightly, and his face was battered and smeared with exhaustion, as if he had been engaged all day in a desperate battle and had arrived with news of defeat. Pilate had seen that look before in natural circumstances. What did it mean now, to-day? This Petronius was one of his best officers. He had put him in charge of the executions, knowing that he could be counted on to deal promptly with any disturbance. And here the man was staring straight ahead of him, out of blind defeated eyes, while he reported that nothing had happened.

"Come, Petronius, what's wrong? Was there a hitch somewhere? Did you have trouble with the mob? Did they make a demonstration in favour of the prisoners?"

"No, sir. There was no trouble."

"The criminals were crucified promptly, without bungling or accident?"

"Yes, sir."

"And you got my further instructions to see to it that they died before sunset?"

"Yes, sir." The answer did not come quickly. In the scarcely perceptible pause, the scraping of a pen on parchment sounded loud suddenly, as a squeal.

"Stop that, Evenus; leave that writing and go fetch me a lamp." Pilate flung the words over his shoulder at the Greek slave and leaned forward.

"Did you break their legs as I ordered?"

This time the silence was so prolonged that the soft footsteps of the little Greek sounded all down the length of the room before the centurion answered. At last he said:

"We did not break the legs of Jesus of Nazareth." And there was another sound in the silence. It was as if some presence, hidden in the shadows under the high rafters, had sighed.

"Why not?" Pilate was shouting suddenly. "What do you mean by disobeying my orders? I commanded that all three criminals were to have their legs broken and be dead before sundown."

The centurion still did not look at his superior officer. He did not seem to notice the governor's anger.

"The man Jesus was already dead, sir," he said in a whisper, as if to himself. "He died at the ninth hour, the hour when it was very dark."

"What has the dark got to do with it? How do you know he was dead? Men do not die of being crucified in three hours." Surely there was no need for the Governor of Judea to yell like that, be beside himself with rage over so small a matter.

The answer, when it came, was almost inaudible. "He gave a great cry, and I saw—"

"What did you see? You saw what looked like a dead man. How can you know there is no life in him, even now? A crucified man can look like a corpse, yet go on living for days. You know that as well as I do. I put you in charge of this execution because I feared a hostile demonstration and trusted you to see that the affair was carried out in order. Now you come to me, looking as if you had seen a ghost, and tell me you didn't consider it necessary to obey my instructions."

Pilate left his chair, came round from behind his table, stood close to his subordinate, his eyes level with the other's eyes, and glared into that other dark, haggard visage that was suddenly become the strange, unknowable face of an oriental masquerading as a Roman officer.

The centurion seemed to notice him for the first time. His eyes rolled suddenly, horribly in his head, and he seemed to find it difficult to speak, for he moistened his lips as if his mouth were very dry. But all he said was:

"I made certain afterwards, when your message came, sir, that the man of Nazareth was dead. One of my men plunged a spear into his side. The body did not flinch." His face was rigid again as a statue's and as blind.

"Why didn't you say so before? By Hercules, Petronius, I was about to tell you to report yourself to the commandant of the garrison."

The other said nothing. He seemed no more interested in his own disgrace than if he were dead. What had got into the fellow? Just now, when his eyes rolled in their sockets, he had looked like a lunatic. He was frightened, that was it. He had been scared out of his wits by the eclipse of the sun, as Claudia's slave women had been. They were no good, these Syrians. A clap of thunder, a fiery star trailing through the heavens, the discipline of years was torn to shreds all in a second, and there they were, naked, quaking worms of men. Suddenly Pilate saw red. Suddenly the Governor of Judea lost control of himself. The blind, naked, idiotic face of the man was too much. He struck it with the hard palm of his hand, his own face distorted. "Do you answer nothing?" he shouted. "Do you not know that I have power to condemn you?"

What was he saying? When had he said that? What made those words leap again from his mouth?

The centurion didn't move, not a muscle in his face quivered. Pilate glared a moment longer, then turned his back on him with a snarl; crossed to his table and flung himself down again in his chair.

The scene of the morning came back to him. He found himself looking down again at the swarm of rats packed inside the great walls of the keep before his judgment seat. He saw the livid light on the heaving mass of their ugly snouts, heard the beast howl of their rage. "Crucify him! Crucify him!" And he saw the man Jesus standing there, facing them in the gorgeous robe Herod had put on him. The King of the Jews. His face was grey; there was blood on it. The mouth was bruised. He swayed on his feet with exhaustion and from his sunken eyes poured agony as light pours from lamps. But it had nothing to do with fear. That agony was different from any the Roman had ever seen.

There was no room in Pilate's creed for pity. He was too used to seeing men mauled to death to be moved by compassion. And he was a Stoic. Life for him was a battle waged under a great general who commanded his conscience and the outcome of the battle depended on a discipline that tolerated no softness. Soft beds, soft words, soft feelings that melted the heart, all such things were in his mind degrading. But a good fight, a good race, a man who died gallantly, or a horse that ran well, that moved him. He knew a good horse and a brave man when he saw one. The Nazarene had been a brave man.

It seemed he was the fellow who had taken a whip and driven the money-changers out of the Temple.

The officer in command of the garrison had seen the thing. "A fine performance, sir; you should have seen it." Pilate wished he had. He wished he had known it was the same man. But what could he have done? How could he have saved the fellow when no one came forward to witness in his defence and he refused to defend himself?

To take him seriously as a pretender to the throne was preposterous. The whole trial had been preposterous. The Jews had made a mock of Cæsar's tribunal, they had staged on it a barbaric comedy with himself as chief buffoon.

And Caiaphas himself had preferred the charge: "We found this fellow perverting the nation and forbidding to give tribute to Cæsar, saying that he himself is Messiah, a king."

The High Priest of Israel had shouted the words in a loud voice, so that all the people could hear. And the whole senate, Sadducee-priests and Pharisaic elders, united for once like brothers in their hatred of this villager from Galilee, had shouted with him till the mob was in a frenzy. He had done what he could to save the man. Three times had he declared that he could find him guilty of nothing deserving of death. But the more he argued, the more the priests shouted, "Away with the man! Let him be crucified! If you let this man go, you are not Cæsar's friend!" and the more frenzied the mob became. And the prisoner had said nothing. He had stood above that howling mob, utterly silent. No, not utterly. He had spoken at last, words of a madman, a dreamer, an idiot. When he, Pilate, was trying to save him. What was it he had said? "My kingdom is not of this world. If my kingdom were of this world, then would my people fight."

What people? His people hated him. The rats would have torn him to death with their teeth. Who was there to fight for him? His friends had gone to ground like rabbits.

A king without a single subject, a leader with no followers. The man was most certainly mad, but he had been a better fellow by far than his mighty accusers; and he, Pilate, had pronounced him guilty on a charge of which he was innocent. For the charge was treason and he had not been guilty of treason and Pilate, whose god was justice, had done this because he was afraid of the Jews.

Justice! "You must be out of your mind, Claudia, to think you can interfere with the course of justice."

—Justice!—Her face had been ghastly as she repeated the word after him. He had found her, after the trial, pacing her room in the unnatural, suffocating twilight, with her slave women cowering in a corner, praying to their gods to save them. He had shouted at them to bring lamps, light candles, see to their mistress. But they had only cowered there, paralysed by terror because of an eclipse of the sun, just as the centurion was paralysed.

Well, it was over now. The sky was clear, the air cool, the sun was sinking as usual below the ugly plateau of Judea, and what was done could not be undone.

Bah! What did the life of any Jew matter? He had washed his hands of the blood of this man. He was dead and that was the end of him. He must deal now with Petronius, get to the bottom of his trouble and make up his mind about the corpse. He could not keep the councillor waiting any longer; it was ridiculous to spend so much time fussing over a dead body. He was making far too much out of the whole business. The problem was a simple one. That this Jesus was a dangerous rebel was nonsense. Nor did he believe that there was much in the suggestion that his followers would attempt to steal the body from the cross and spread the tale that he was still alive, for his followers were evidently cowards. On the other hand, the prisoner had struck him as a man who might very well have inspired a burning devotion in the breasts of unbalanced, weak-minded men of his own race, and he must take into account the extreme gullibility of the Jews where miracles were concerned. It was just possible that the men who had run away when their leader was arrested might pluck up courage in the night and attack the guard in the gully. It was more than possible, if they did, that a fight around the cross of a crucified leader at this time, when religious and racial feeling ran high, would provoke the riot he had been at such pains to avoid.

The question therefore was this: Were there enough of the dead man's adherents hiding in the rabbit warren of the city to make serious trouble if they were roused? He must try to find out.

The centurion was still standing to attention. There was no mark on his face where he had hit him. What had possessed him to so forget himself? He must treat the man gently, address him quietly, if he were to get anything more out of him.

"Did you see any of the Nazarene's followers lurking near the place of execution when you left?" Pilate spoke as if talking of a casual matter.

"There were two women by the cross, sir."

"What were they doing?"

"They were weeping."

"That couldn't do much harm. Come, Petronius, you are keeping something from me. Out with it. Did the execution not pass off as quietly as I was given to understand?"

"There was no trouble, sir."

"Let us go back. When you left the guardroom with your prisoners, did you take the route I indicated, avoiding the main bazaars?"

"Yes, sir."

"But a crowd followed all the same; there was some ugly incident?"

"No, sir. The prisoner staggered and fell under his cross in the street and I thought for a moment that some attempt might be made to rescue him, but the crowd was mostly women and they only gathered round him, wailing."

"Fell, did he?"

"He got to his feet again, sir, but he couldn't carry the wood. I had to order a passer-by to carry it for him."

"And what did the Jews say, when they saw their king sprawling in the dust, with that crown your men made for him on his head?"

"They laughed at him from their windows, and the women went on wailing."

"A pretty procession. Yet not of a character to trouble the Empire. What happened when you reached the Place of a Skull?"

"Nothing happened, sir."

"What? Was there no movement among the Jews when their king was stripped naked and nailed to the cross? I was told that many noble priests gathered in the crowd on the wall above the gully to watch him being crucified. Did they say nothing?"

"They made sport of him. But there was no movement nor any voice lifted in his behalf."

"And he, what did he do when his dream was shattered by your soldiers' hammers? Did he scream when he was hoisted into the air? Did he yell back at the scoffers?"

"No, sir. He made no sound."

"What, did he answer nothing when they shouted at him to save himself?"

"Nothing, sir."

"Too drugged, I suppose, to suffer much."

"He was offered the drug, but he did not drink."

"Why not?"

The centurion hesitated. His face had gone grey under the questioning. His eyes now were like the eyes of a sick dog that is being tormented. And when he answered, the words seemed to be dragged from him.

"I think he was waiting. I think he expected up to the last to be saved. I think it was only at the very end that he gave up hope."

"In whom did he hope, if he had no friends?" Pilate spoke softly. "Whom did he expect to save him? You? Me? Herod?"

"He expected his God to come to his rescue. He cried out at the last, 'Eloi, Eloi, Lama sabachthani'."

"Which means?"

"My God, my God, why hast thou forsaken me."

"And you, Petronius, were afraid."

The man's eyes acknowledged the thing. He fixed them desperately on the hard face of his chief.

"He was, sir, a son of God." His voice was scarcely more than a whisper. It was followed by silence, a silence so deep that the far sound of singing down in the city was like the sound of the sea beating on a distant shore. Pilate was thinking. He didn't look up when the door opened and Evenus entered, carrying a lighted lamp. Yet it was impossible to tell from his face what he was thinking.

The centurion waited. The Greek slave put down his lamp and waited, looking curiously from one to the other. Beyond the door Joseph, the councillor of Arimathæa, waited. And the fate of the dead body of Jesus of Nazareth hung in the balance.

"My kingdom is not of this world— You would have no power to condemn me were it not given to you from above— To this end was I born, and for this cause came I into the world. . . ." The man who had said that was dead. He was dumb now for ever. So how could Pilate slouching in his chair under the high ceiling, or the little Greek slave crouching by the lamp, or the centurion standing rigid in the centre of the stone floor, hear his voice echoing in the silence? He was dead and accursed and gone down into hell or wandering the earth, as some believed, in search of a place to rest. Surely it were unreasonable to suppose that he influenced Pilate's decision.

Pilate, at any rate, did not think of this, when he roused himself from his silence and told the slave to show the councillor in. He was the servant of Tiberius Cæsar. It was as the representative of an Emperor who hated the Jews that he received this Jew and (when he took his decision) he acted as a civil servant, responsible to Rome for the quiet of a turbulent province, was bound to act.

His reasoning was wrong, all the reasoning of all the dead man's enemies was mistaken. If the great men of his day meant to wipe the Nazarene's memory and his name from the slate of Israel, they should have let him alone, once he was dead. The Greek who watched the thing shape itself before his weary, quizzical eyes, could have told those enemies of the dead man who still seethed with hatred at the thought of his lacerated body, that there was nothing to fear from it, if only they let it be. There was no magic in it now to heal or harm. The power in the man had been something more awful than the power of his heart pumping breath through his lungs. His soul had been strange, his body was like any other man's, and now that his heart had stopped beating his soul was gone—to perdition they said, and to everlasting torment. Then they should have been satisfied.

Nor need his bitterest enemies have feared his wretched disciples. They were broken, disbanded. One was by way of hanging himself that evening. Only three had stayed in Jerusalem; the rest were flying to Galilee, afraid for their lives. And the three who had stayed behind were huddled in a darkened room, incapable of thought, action or speech. They were waiting, but they did not know what they were waiting for. To die, perhaps, since they had nothing left to live for. Certainly no idea of stealing his body had entered their stunned, bewildered heads. Their leader was dead. He had failed. His name was infamous. They were marked men, branded with the brand of the outcast whom they had believed destined by God for a throne.

Who else was there in Jerusalem that night to form a conspiracy for his sake? There was that brother of his called James, but he had never believed in Jesus when he was alive. He had been convinced from the first that this eldest son of his father was possessed by the powers of darkness and would bring horrible disgrace on his family. How could he believe in him now that his worst forebodings were fulfilled? There was his mother, but she had gone from the hideous scene of death, leaning on a very young boy, the only man in Jerusalem who had stood beside her while her son was dying, and he was not yet a man.

But there was one man of influence among the Jews who was prepared to take his stand on behalf of the dead. He did now what he thought was right and saw to it that the crucified victim of the people's rage should not be denied a refuge in the soil of his native land.

Joseph of Arimathæa was a just man and remarkable. He was rich and he was good. He was a conservative member of the party of the Pharisees in the senate, and his views were liberal. He was a devout Jew and he dared to defy the synagogue by going to the Prætorium on a holy day, when doing so defiled him and made it impossible for him to keep the feast. It was said afterwards that he believed secretly in Jesus of Nazareth and was waiting for the Kingdom of God. But what exactly that meant to him it is difficult to say, for he had never come out openly as a follower of the revolutionary rabbi who had been excommunicated; he took no part in the strange events that resulted from his own daring action; it is doubtful whether he believed that the kingdom God would one day establish on earth was identical with the kingdom of Jesus of Nazareth; and he could not have known what he was doing when he went boldly to Pilate and begged the body. For he meant to bury it. He wanted to put it away quietly and decently in a safe place, so that the soul of his unacknowledged friend would be bound to his body and at rest.

And he did bury it. Not with all the care and ceremony that he would have liked. That was impossible, it being a holiday and the Sabbath eve, but he did what he could. He saw that it was wrapped in a linen cloth and laid in a tomb, and he rolled a stone to the door of the tomb to make it safe. And he went away, intending to give his friend the last honours of the dead, as soon as the Sabbath was over. Had he known that that spirit could not be bound in any tomb, had he dreamed that the exhausted body was not to be left in peace for more than two days, surely he would not have risked the anger of God in order to bury it? He did not know. He had no more idea of what he was doing to the world and to his own race than Pilate, who helped him accomplish the thing. He was an honourable Jew, ready to set aside the

Mosaic law in order to render a last service to a man he loved, that was all.

A world divided the dark bearded Jew in his rich robes and the Roman soldier in Cæsar's harness. They did not speak the same language, acknowledge the same ruler or worship the same God. They had, in fact, almost nothing in common, save their deep mutual racial antagonism, and they faced one another in the great stone-flagged room of the fortress through a fog of prejudice. But they were both honest men, and it was this that made an understanding between them possible. This and one other thing. They had both seen and talked to Jesus of Nazareth while he was alive.

The great room was filling with shadow when the councillor was shown in; the last rays of the sun coming through the narrow slits of windows lay in gold bands across the floor. The lamp on Pilate's table made a globe of light, in which the governor sat with the Greek at his feet, to be at hand in case an interpreter was needed; but the centurion and the Jew stood at a distance outside the circle of light, two shadowy figures who were to disappear from the scene, once their parts in this drama were played.

Pilate spoke with cold formality to the dark shrouded figure of the noble Jew; there was scarce a tinge of sarcasm in his voice:

"You have come to me, Councillor, to ask leave, so I understand, to bury the body of a traitor."

"I do not believe him to have been a traitor, your Excellency."

"Naturally, otherwise you would not be here. Still, your friend is a traitor in the eyes of your law and mine. You come, I presume, as his friend. Am I right?"

"Quite right, my lord." If there was a sarcastic twitch to the Jew's lips as he used the title of "lord," it was hidden by his beard.

"Hum." Pilate stroked his chin. "He didn't seem to have many friends when he came before me this morning. Where were they all, Senator?" The Roman watched the Jew's face closely, as if a deal hung on the answer, and it did. Had Joseph of Arimathæa attempted at that moment to minimize the importance of Jesus, hoping to gain his end by so doing, the result of the interview might have been very different. But he spoke the truth.

"Jesus of Nazareth has many friends, but they are amongst the poor. They could not hope to make their voices heard in the Sanhedrin or before your tribunal. They had no spokesman."

"What of yourself?"

"I was not warned about the proceedings. I didn't know of the trial till it was over. The priests kept the thing quiet."

"Still, there were Pharisees present in plenty in the courtyard, before my judgment seat. Don't they represent the common people in your senate? I thought your learned men were the leaders of the poor."

"Not of the very poor, your Excellency. We are a democratic nation, but there is a large part of our people who are considered outcasts, unfit to be represented in the council. They are little better than slaves. They have no leader."

"Save this Jesus?"

The Jew bowed. Pilate scowled as was his wont when he was pondering. The little Greek looked from one to another, a faint cynical smile on his emaciated face. Pilate spoke again.

"What did this miserable class believe their leader would do for them?"

"They believed he would save them."

"And how was he to do this without bringing about a revolution? You said a moment ago that he was no traitor. Do you admit he was a rebel?"

The Jew waited a moment before answering, but when he did it was with his head up, and a glint of defiance in his sombre eyes.

"It would be impossible for you, my lord, a Roman, to understand the power, or the purpose, of this man. Had he accomplished what he willed to accomplish, a revolution would undoubtedly have taken place within our nation, but not of a kind that would be of importance to Cæsar. He had no interest in politics, would have nothing to do with armed insurrection. He purposed to change the hearts of the nation and those whose hearts he touched, believed in him."

"Why didn't they rise up then to defend him? Why didn't they storm my tribunal this morning?"

"They didn't know what had happened. The priests took him prisoner in the middle of the night, as you, my lord, are aware, and tried him secretly and brought him to you before the news got abroad. Jerusalem is thronged with strangers to-day. It was easy to arrange the matter."

"Yes. Yes. But he had friends with him when he was arrested. If they believed in him, why didn't they run through the city and rouse these many followers of his?"

The councillor of Arimathæa was very evidently disturbed by the question. His hands gripped one another inside the sleeves of his robe. His laboured breathing was audible.

"I do not know why his disciples did nothing. They may have lost hope or they may have expected him to save himself by a miracle, as did so many of those other foolish ones."

"What others?"

"Those foolish followers of his who thought that he could not die, and who watched from a distance when your soldiers nailed him to the cross, expecting to see him come down."

"Were they many?"

"Yes, a good many." The Jew's voice was both sad and scornful. Pilate paid no attention to that. He wanted to understand the facts, not the feelings involved.

"How many were there, Senator?"

"I didn't count them, your Excellency."

"A hundred; a dozen?"

"There must have been several hundred."

"And all thought him a god, eh? Or a magician?"

"They did not think him a man like themselves."

"And there was no miracle?"

"No. There was no miracle."

"And now they are all gone happily to their homes to make holiday."

"No. There is mourning to-night in many a house in this city, not only in the homes of outcasts, but among many devout people of humble yet decent position."

And Pilate was silent again. Joseph of Arimathæa had told him what he wanted to know. It wasn't clear, nothing was clear that had to do with the Jews, but it was the vague, exasperating, nebulous truth.

That there was a superstitious feeling in some quarters about this man Jesus was evident. Where superstition came into play among the Jews, there were always numerous unpleasant possibilities. It would be best on the whole to have the man's body safely out of the way.

"One more thing, Senator." Pilate spoke quickly now, biting off his words as if impatient to be rid of the Jew and all that he stood for. "If I give you the body, where will you bury it, and how will you manage the matter? It must be done to-night and your people do no work on holidays."

"The place is ready. I own a piece of land near the execution ground where I have built a new tomb. I would put the body there."

"You would do this yourself?"

The Jew hesitated an instant. Pilate looked at him sharply.

"Why do you hesitate, noble Councillor? You are a brave man to venture to breathe the polluted air of Cæsar's Prætorium on a holy day. Are you by any chance acting for other men who are less courageous?"

"No." The Jew was proud. "I have come by myself. I faltered over your question, because of a religious scruple of my own. I would not handle the body with my own hands, if this could be avoided. I had thought to arrange matters so that it would not be necessary, but I would make myself responsible for the business."

"You are a rich man and you would pay others to do for you what would soil your own hands, is that it?"

The councillor of Arimathæa flushed under his swarthy skin, his eyes smouldered, but he spoke softly.

"There are infidels in plenty in Jerusalem who can be hired to do almost anything, my lord."

"Well answered, Senator." Pilate stood up. "Petronius, go with the councillor and have your men take down the body of this Jesus of Nazareth. If you will explain to my officer, he will have the body carried for you to your family vault.—Take a stretcher and a couple of bearers with you, Petronius—or make your own arrangements, Senator, with my centurion. But do not pay his men anything. They are infidels, yet not to be hired."

"I am grateful, your Excellency."

Joseph of Arimathæa did not smile as he bowed himself out, but Pilate's mouth wore its habitual sneer as he watched him go. Having made his decision and got rid at last of this fellow Jesus, he was himself again.

And so it was arranged that the man who had been condemned to become forever a man without a country was to be allowed, after all, to lie in a tomb for a little while, like any respectable citizen of Jerusalem.

II

Sunset on the shore of a lake, and a crowd gathered on the quai in front of a fisherman's house, a crowd of humble people, fishermen, shipbuilders, labourers and market gardeners with their wives and children. They are quiet. A man is speaking to them from a lighted doorway. Everything is quiet. All the world is listening to his voice.

The quai is in shadow, but the lake is still flooded with light. There is no wind. The surface of the water is smooth as glass. Far out some fishing boats are becalmed; voices can be heard calling faintly from one boat to another. The arc of the sky is ribboned with streamers of gold; the light clouds high above the lake are the colour of flamingos' wings, and the afterglow of the sunset illumines his wonderful face. It is Jesus of Nazareth, a prophet, mighty in word and deed; a master and leader of men who loves the poor and the sick and the brokenhearted. He is telling them about the Kingdom of Heaven, and the people are listening spellbound as if the voice of the deep lake or the silent mountains were speaking.

A woman is standing by the water's edge, staring at him from a distance, an evil woman, haunted, unclean, passion-driven to the verge of madness. Her face is white, her eyes are horror-struck. She is a dancer from Magdala, famed for her wickedness.

And more people keep coming, such strange people. From every street they come, hurrying as best they can, hopping along on their crutches, dragging themselves eagerly forward on all fours, and some are carried on their beds, and those in front make room for the sick and maimed who keep coming. They lie thick on the ground, close round his feet, their desperate eyes fixed on his face; and they keep edging nearer, keep stretching out timid withered hands, as if longing fearfully to touch him. The hope in those wasted faces is terrible to see. Can he heal them? Will he have pity on them? Yes. Every evening, when the sun is setting, they bring from Magdala and Emmaus and Bethsaida-Julias and from the towns on the far side of the lake all those who are diseased or crippled or tormented by evil spirits, and he heals many of them; and every evening he talks to them about the Kingdom of God.

"Hearken," he says, "every one of you and understand: The Kingdom of Heaven is at hand. Be changed and believe the good news. You who are poor shall be blessed, for you shall inherit the Kingdom. And blessed are you who are hungry, for you shall be filled, and blessed are you who weep now, for you shall be glad. But unless you become as little children, you shall not enter into its glory, for of such is the Kingdom of God."

And now it is morning, and he has come back from a journey and the lake sparkles like diamonds in the sun, and all his friends are running to meet him. They shout at the sight of him and fall on his neck, laughing and weeping for joy at having him back again. And the cripples who before dragged themselves along the ground come running now; they've thrown away their crutches, and the sick, who had to be carried to him on their beds, come carrying others, and that lewd woman of Magdala comes quietly and sits down among the children at his feet, for he has changed her; he has given her the heart of a child.

And he begins once more to talk to them about the Kingdom. He is always talking about the Kingdom. Every day he tells them a little more about it and explains how God, their heavenly Father, will set up the Kingdom on earth, if only they will turn to him with all their hearts. Sometimes the crowd by the shore is so great that he puts off in a boat and speaks to them from the sunny water. Sometimes he goes up onto the mountain slopes and sits down on the grass, and the people flock after him like sheep after a shepherd, and he tells them stories, always about the Kingdom, while the summer deepens round them, the fields that were full of lilies grow white with the harvest, and there is a humming in the air as if all Galilee were singing.

"Listen. Let these words sink into your ears. The end of the world is at hand, but the Kingdom of God is here now, in the midst of you."

And one would call, then another: "Yes, and you are our king; you shall reign over us." But he would shake his head and say, "Only God is King. It is written: Thou shalt worship the Lord thy God, Him only shalt thou serve." But they did worship him, and indeed it did seem to be true that the Kingdom had already come, there was such joy and peace in all their hearts. They would often say among themselves that heaven could be no happier than this. Even the birds seemed to agree. How they sang in the woods when he came walking by with Peter and

James and John. How the brooks laughed, tumbling down the mountain side to wash his feet. How beautiful and how safe the world was with him, and how wonderfully strange it all was to a woman who had wallowed like a pig in the sties of Magdala. The birds would come fluttering as if they wanted to hear what he was saying. Little sparrows would perch quite close, cocking their heads, and watch him just as the children did who climbed into his lap while he talked or sat in a circle at his feet, staring up into his face with great adoring eyes. And once a child went sound asleep in his arms, and that was a wonderful sight for Mary of Magdala.

But it grew dark. A great darkness came down and covered all the earth, and she lost him. He was gone, they said. There was a price on his head. He was the friend of Satan and God had cast him out. "But where has he gone?" she cried, and she went stumbling after him along the dark roads, groping. She was like a blind woman without him; men looked to her like trees walking and their voices sounded in her ears like the voices of demons that inhabit magic groves. They laughed hatefully when she asked if they had seen him. "He is dead," they said. "Your king has been cast into hell." And then a great wall rose before her, with huge battlements and towers that loomed against the sky, and a crowd was gathered on the wall, and all the people were screaming and shouting at some one down below.

"Hail, King of the Jews! All hail, gluttonous wine-bibber! Look, he rolls like a drunken man! Hail, oh, mighty Messiah, your buttocks are bleeding." And crowds filled the street, and a throng of women were wailing and singing the song of the dead. But she fought her way through the crowd and saw him at last. He was staggering through the darkness under a heavy bar of wood, and he fell on his knees in the dust and the people surged round him, and their faces were livid with hate like the faces of fiends. She tried to get to him. She beat her way through to him with her fists, but the soldiers held her back when she got there. She could only look.

They had crowned him, but the crown was made of thorns that cut into his head and the blood from the pricks was trickling down over his sweating face, and he was panting like a suffering beast. He knelt there a moment in the dust while the women crowded round, wailing, and his face, when he lifted it, was so battered and swollen that it was un-recognizable. He couldn't carry the wooden bar. The soldiers picked it up and gave it to some one else to carry for him. Then he got to his feet again and staggered on, reeling between the windows of the houses that were full of jeering people, till he came to the City Gate and passed through it; and a Roman in the watchtower over the gate looked down and spat on him.

It was finished now. His agony was over. They had all gone away, and he was asleep. She must stay with him till he awoke. It was lonely here, with night coming on. He might not know where he was when he woke up. He might think for a moment that he was back in Capernaum. He might call Peter or James or John. If he called and no one answered, he would wonder what had become of them all. And when he saw the two soldiers sitting there by their little bonfire, playing dice, it would all come back to him. He would remember what they had done to him. That mustn't happen, not that.

He didn't remember now. He was at peace. All his poor racked body was relaxed; his head had dropped on his breast after that awful upward straining, and his twitching face was still. She could look up into his face. She dared not go too close, because of the guard; they had cursed her twice for coming too near. But even from her distance, she could see that he looked almost himself again. Was it only because the light was dim, or had the swelling truly gone down? He was dreadfully pale still, but there was no more bleeding from the thorns and she was sure that the bruises were healing. Indeed, he didn't look so very different from the way he sometimes looked when he had been exhausted by the crowds of sick who flocked to him to be healed. Sickness, sorrow and evil drained his life from him. When he had healed many diseased people, he would be at night as one dead, just as he was now. But the hatred of men cut him like knives. He had writhed a little while ago under torture, till the joints of his thighs had cracked. And all the while the crowd on the wall had scoffed at him. Now they were gone and he could sleep. Oh, merciful Father in Heaven, let him sleep and forget. He must never be allowed to remember.

But it was growing chilly and he would be cold in the night with nothing to cover him. If only the guard would let her come near, she could warm his feet in her hands. They were placed one on the other and nailed to the wood. She could see the nail driven through the fragile bones. Why had they driven a nail through his feet? He wouldn't be able to walk again until the wounds were healed, and he liked to walk. He walked everywhere. And it was spring, the season in the year that he loved best. The almond trees were in bloom in Galilee. The lambs were frisking over the hills. He would want to go back to his happy kingdom. But he wouldn't be able to go just yet. He must be healed of his wounds first. Oh, poor, tired, broken feet!

What was that? O God, what was that? She crouched quickly as the great wing swept across her face, then leapt up and struck out wildly with her arms.

"The vultures!" she cried. "The vultures have come!" And the woman who knelt beside her in the dust rose quickly and began as she did to cry out and beat the air with her arms.

"Take off your cloak," shouted Mary of Magdala. "Take your cloak and wave it. They will pluck out his eyes!" And she tore the long cloak from her shoulders and standing firmly with her bare feet wide apart, she began to lash the air with it, swinging it round and round her head.

Her master was dead. But she could not think that it was so. She had watched him die, had heard his last loud cry of agony, had seen his head drop on his breast. But her mind, her heart, her soul refused to acknowledge what she had seen and heard. She was a strong woman, a woman of the soil of Galilee, passionate, primitive, fearless and reckless under excitement. Her chest was deep, her shoulders were broad, her thighs were sinewed as a man's. And she had been, so men said, possessed of seven devils in the days when she was a dancer. Now she was possessed by love for the man who had saved her and lifted her into heaven. What did she care for the sight of her eyes and the knowledge of her brain? Let her eyes drop out of their sockets; let her brain crack in its skull, she knew that he could not die.

Even if the vultures got him, even if she couldn't keep them off and they tore the flesh from his face with their claws, she would not believe him dead. He was immortal. He was the giver of eternal life. He was only asleep. He had only slipped away out of his body for a little time. He would come back. She would be with him again. She must protect his body till he came. He had promised never to leave her. She believed him with all her might.

So she stood, her bare feet planted firmly and lashed the air, her head uncovered, her hair streaming back from her haggard face. And she looked more like an avenging fury than a dancing girl.

"Ai ee! Ai ee! Shout, Sister! Scream louder or cry to God if you cannot shout. Maybe he will hear you"; and the other woman, who was also called Mary, cried as loud as she could to Jehovah to rescue his son, waving her cloak in the air till it was like a frantic banner in the wind. But Mary of Magdala's powerful voice rang down the gully like a battle cry and her face was savage as she fought to save the body of her Lord.

Joseph of Arimathæa heard her as he reached the gate in the city wall, and he made haste at the sound and came quickly out onto the road above the gully where the crosses were, followed by Pilate's centurion and a number of men. He had a friend with him named Nicodemus, who also loved Jesus of Nazareth, and several servants; and the centurion had ordered two of his soldiers to bring a stretcher. And the other Mary, when she saw the band of men, sobbed out, "They have come. Praise be to God, they have come in time to the rescue." But Mary of Magdala went on lashing the air and yelling with all her lungs, for the vultures, which would be gone with the darkness, were growing more vicious every minute in the waning light.

And Joseph of Arimathæa, when he saw the two women below in the gully with the great birds wheeling overhead, ran down the slope followed by the others, and the centurion pulled a burning stick out of the soldiers' bonfire and ran, holding it aloft, shouting, "Bring lanterns! Light torches! Pile wood on the fire! Let there be light round the cross of Jesus of Nazareth!" And Mary of Nazareth dropped her arms at last and let her cloak fall to the ground, and stood watching.

The other Mary pulled her away to a further distance. She let herself be dragged back, but she did not take her eyes from the cross.

The light shone on him now. A flickering light played over his body. It bathed his feet that were nailed together; it licked at his side, where some one had plunged a spear; it touched his helpless hands that were stretched palms outward with a nail through each palm. And as the torches flared higher, it shone up into his face and, by some trick of the wind that eddied down into the gully, it seemed to make him smile. But he did not lift his head or look up to see what they were doing to him. Even when one of the soldiers climbed up the cross and began to undo the thongs that bound him, he made no sign of any kind.

The other Mary whispered: "They are going to take him down. Please God, they are going to bury him. Look, it is the centurion who was here before, the one who bowed his head when he was dying," and she plucked at the other's sleeve. But Mary Magdalene held her at arm's length and seemed not to hear what she said. Her eyes were starting out of their sockets and her breath came hissing between her lips like the hiss of a snake. They were drawing the nails from his hands and feet, and the soldier who was astride the top of the cross was about to tear the hand loose, for the nail was driven deep into the wood. Why not? Why should he handle the flesh of a dead criminal with care? Mary Magdalene crouched like an animal about to spring. But the centurion called in time, "Have a care. Go quietly, there, with those hands." And the soldier, though he gaped stupidly from his perch, did as he was told, drawing the nail out carefully enough, as such things go.

They had loosed all the ropes that bound him by this time and once the hands were free, the body slid sideways suddenly and, though the Roman grasped it quickly from above by the arms, it almost slipped from his grasp. But at last it was done. He was lifted down, and the soldiers laid him on the stretcher, where Joseph of Arimathæa and Nicodemus had spread a linen cloth.

Mary Magdalene was shuddering so that the other Mary dared not speak to her, and her teeth were rattling in her head. But when they began to wrap him in the cloth, she crept closer, crouching down again like an animal and suddenly she leapt for the bier, and such a shout of agony burst from her throat that it seemed as if it must wake the two crucified thieves that had been left hanging. They had covered his face.

She did not touch him. She knelt there on the ground beside his shrouded body, with all the astonished men round her. And her hands hovered fearfully over the cloth that hid him and all her strong body was shaking silently now and they dared not touch her, because of the awful look on her face.

"Who is she?" said one. "Where has she come from?"

"She must be the sister of the dead," said another.

"Do you know her, sir?" the centurion asked Joseph. But Joseph said no, he had never seen her before. And then they noticed the other Mary standing behind them and Joseph said, pointing to Mary Magdalene and speaking courteously:

"Who is this woman? Is she by chance of the family of the dead?"

"No, sir," the other Mary answered. "She is not of his kindred. She is only a follower. Jesus was her master. She came with us from Galilee in search of him."

"And you?"

"He was my husband's sister's child. I came with his mother to find him. But we were too late. We only saw him when he was crucified."

The centurion spoke then. "I remember now there were three women by the cross and a young boy."

"Yes, his mother and Mary Magdalene and I. The boy took my sister away when her son was dead."

It was growing dark. Mary Magdalene was still kneeling on the ground, her hands hovering over the shrouded figure and her body shaking. She didn't seem to be aware of anything round her. The men conferred together in low tones, then Joseph spoke again to the other Mary.

"You must take her away," he said. "We are going to bury Jesus by special leave of the governor."

So Mary, the sister of Jesus' mother, went to Mary Magdalene and touched her on the shoulder and spoke to the shaking creature as if to a child and said:

"Come, they are going to bury him. Come, we will see where he is laid."

But Mary Magdalene lifted her face in the light of the lanterns and looked round her and whispered:

"But he is not dead. They must not bury him when he is not dead."

And now the men were exasperated. They said to themselves that they had to do with a mad woman, and the centurion was about to take her by the arm and drag her away, but Joseph of Arimathæa came forward and spoke kindly, saying:

"He was my friend, Mary of Magdala. I also loved him, and I am laying him to rest in a chamber of stone, hewn out of a rock in my garden that is close by. If you will follow us, you will see that he will be safe there and better than here in this gully." And he took her by the hands and lifted her to her feet, and she let him have his way.

So the soldiers carried him on the stretcher up the bank and along the road, and a servant went before, carrying a lantern, and one walked to either side to give more light and the others followed with the two Marys behind the men. And they came to the new tomb that Joseph had had cut in the rock, and it was in a quiet garden and there was a sound of birds fluttering in the trees and the moon was rising behind the bushes as they put his body into the tomb and rolled a stone before the door of the tomb. And the two Marys stood in the shadow and saw where he was laid.

III

It was evident that a very important guest had been expected in that house between the Sheep Gate and the Pool of Five Porches. The table in the upper room was set for fifteen and a chair at the head of the table was all hung with garlands. But something clearly had gone wrong, for the house was silent. Of all the houses that crowded round it in that poor quarter of the town, it alone was dark and still. Indeed a passer-by might have thought it abandoned, for the great door that led from the street into its courtyard was not quite closed. It stood open a crack, as if the family that once lived there had left hurriedly, forgetting to lock up after them; and this evidence of carelessness or panic gave the house a stricken appearance. And yet, only the day before, all had been bustle and excitement in the house. The little black servant girl had been seen running a dozen times to the bazaar. Butchers and bakers and wine merchants had arrived, staggering under great baskets of provisions. The son of the house had come in from the country, wheeling a barrow full of wild roses and myrtle, and in the evening his mother had welcomed some dozen men to supper. It was as if all these people had mistaken the day, had celebrated the feast a day too soon, been visited afterwards with some awful punishment and had fled during the night, leaving the front door open to witness to their confusion.

The house, however, in spite of its deserted appearance, wasn't empty. Its mistress was upstairs in the room that had been the scene of the supper the night before and she had not left the street door open through carelessness. She herself had carefully placed it ajar so that a man who did not want to attract attention could slip in quietly without knocking. And three men had crept through it during the night. They were the three who were waiting in the closet back of the supper room. But she had evidently expected many more, for she twisted her hands together as she stood looking at the long empty table, and she was whispering to herself, "What shall I do? Oh, dear Master, tell me what to do," and then she caught her breath as if frightened by what she had said and stood there in silence, looking at the empty chair that had been made into a sort of throne with all those garlands of flowers.

A plump comfortable woman, well known in the neighbourhood for her hospitality, her pleasant face was anxious and sorrowful; her round eyes were frightened and red with weeping, her hands fluttered over the table in helpless agitation.

"Not less than ten; not more than twenty," she kept whispering to herself. "Oh, what shall I do? How can we keep the feast this dreadful day? All the good food will be wasted, such lovely lambs they were too. If only Mark would come. He would tell me. Oh, where can he be? What can be keeping him? Pray God no harm has come to him."

To keep the feast was the solemn command of God. Always all her life had she feared God and loved him and kept his commandments, and every year she had celebrated the joyous day of remembrance reverently, inviting her kinsmen and acquaintances from Galilee to eat with her, for she dearly loved to see happy faces round her table. But never had she made her preparations with such joy as this year, when she expected him, the one to whom she had appealed so naturally in her distress, forgetting that he could not help her now or ever again tell her what should be done.

He had sent word two days before that he was going to honour her humble house with his presence. Her son Mark had come with Judas Iscariot to bid her prepare a supper on the eve of the Passover for him and his disciples.

"He is coming to-night, Mother. He is bringing the twelve with him. He wants no one in the neighbourhood to know he is here. He would have supper with them alone."

"And will he stay with us over the morrow for the feast? Oh, will he stay with us?"

"He did not say, Mother, but I think he will, unless perhaps to-morrow—" The boy's eyes had flashed.

She had caught her breath. "Do you think he will proclaim himself king to-morrow?" she had whispered.

"I do not know, but we must be prepared."

"Oh, Mark, how wonderful! Oh, my dear son, to think that to-morrow he may be crowned in this city, and that he has chosen our house—"

Judas of Kerioth, who had stood by listening, interrupted her.

"Do you, Sister, get on with your preparations for to-night and let to-morrow take care of itself."

The look on his face came back to her now, but she had not noticed it at the time, she had been too uplifted by the wonder of it all. How could she have thought of treachery? How could she have been other than out of her wits with delight to think that he who was to reign in Jerusalem was to be her guest?

The table was set for fifteen and they were only five—herself, her son and the three disciples, Peter and James and John. Where were the others? Why had they not come? And where was Mark? Could he have been taken prisoner? Had the soldiers recognized him as the young man who had followed Jesus in the night and fled, leaving his cloak in their hands? He had come back stark naked across the roof tops and had dropped in through that window. Mary, the mother of the Lord, was there with her, and Mary, the widow of her brother, and Mary of Magdala. The three women had come looking for the Master and had arrived too late. He had already gone out with his disciples, and she was clearing away the remains of the supper when they knocked on her door. How weary they were; how bitterly disappointed, when they found he had been and gone; how it wrung the heart to think that the Master's mother had come all the way from Galilee in search of her son and had had never a word with him, until he spoke to her from the cross. What would she do, if they took her son, Mark, and crucified him before her eyes? Her plump face went grey at the thought, her round eyes were wild with anguish. Suddenly she ran to the closed door and pounded on it with her fists.

"Let me in," she cried. And then, when there was no answer, she cried louder, "O good sirs, let me in. I must speak with you." And at last there was the sound of a chair scraping on the floor and heavy uncertain footsteps approaching, and the door opened to show the disciple Peter standing there, staring out of bloodshot eyes. His hair and his beard were all matted with sweat, his rugged face was the colour of wax; his tunic was torn open to show his great hairy chest and there were bloody marks on his chest, as if he had gashed it with his nails. She faltered at the sight of him; even her fear for her own son seemed to her a small thing in the presence of this dreadful giant of grief. But she was truly very much afraid, so she said confusedly:

"Sir, forgive me, but my son Mark has not come home, and the feast is prepared, and I don't know what to do, for even if he were here, we would be only five."

Simon Peter seemed not to understand her. He stood there staring out of haggard, bloodshot eyes and muttered thickly the word "feast," as if it were an unknown word to him, and slowly wagged his head.

"Perhaps he is mad," she said to herself. "Maybe he has gone out of his wits with grief," but she tried again to reach him:

"It is the feast of the Passover, sir. Have you forgotten? And everything is ready, but no one has come save you three. Where is Andrew, your brother, and Philip and Nathaniel and Thomas Didymus, and Simon the Zealot? Where have they all gone? Why have they not come back? Do you think they have been taken by the police? Do you think that perhaps my son is taken with them and is even now in the dungeons of the governor's fortress? O sir, have pity. Give heed and tell me if you think my son Mark is in danger."

And Simon Peter seemed at last to gather his shattered mind together for he answered heavily, "The boy Mark was not one of us. He was not known to the authorities as a follower of Jesus. He can be in no great danger." And then his attention left her again and he stood there, helpless and senseless as a battered, broken-down ox. And there was no sound in the room behind him, save a sound of harsh breathing, and no light, though she knew there was a well-filled lamp on the table. "Have they been sitting all this time in the dark," she wondered, "with the shutters closed and no lamp?" But she dared not ask any more questions of the dreadful disciple. She dared not even mention the feast again, so she turned back into the room, and he closed the door after her. And it looked, she said to herself, when she saw the long table again, as if she were to be left to eat the feast alone.

The servant maid had set the table early that morning, not knowing what had happened. She had slept sound in her closet back of the kitchen all through the dreadful night. And in the morning no one had remembered her or thought to tell her that the Master, Jesus, was taken prisoner and condemned to death, for she was only a slave. So she had gone on with the preparations her mistress had ordered and had decorated his place at table while he was being crucified.

The garlands had been her idea. She had got out of bed before dawn to make them. She was busy plaiting them when Peter had crept into the house, so she hadn't heard him. They were not very pretty or very well made, but her mistress knew that the Lord Jesus would have been pleased and would have thanked the poor, black, ugly creature.

Should she take them down now and move his chair back against the wall? Should she take all the plates away? She couldn't bear to take his place from the table. Moreover, if she didn't keep the feast, she would be sinning against the holy law, and the rabbi of her synagogue and perhaps God himself would be very angry. Yet how could she sit down to eat, when he was dead? How could she sing hymns of praise to-night, all by herself, and drink the festal cup, when he had cried "I thirst" from his cross that afternoon? She clasped her fat little hands together and lifted her round eyes to the ceiling.

"Our Father, which art in Heaven," she whispered, "surely thou canst understand. Hallowed be thy name. Indeed, thy holy name is held truly sacred in this house. Thy Kingdom come. Always have we waited year after year for its coming. Thy will be done on earth. Was it done to-day? Oh, was it done to-day, Father, God?"

The Lord Jesus himself had taught her the prayer, but how could she say it now when he was gone and how could the kingdom come when he, the king, was descended into hell?

She was an ignorant woman of slow understanding. When her son in the old days came home of an evening from the synagogue college and expounded to her the subtle interpretation of some part of the holy law he had learned that day from the learned doctors, she was all bewildered and confused by the teaching. She would listen humbly, not understanding a word he said. But Jesus she could always understand, and when Mark had declared he would study no longer with any rabbi save Jesus himself, she had been glad. Indeed, she had been overjoyed to think that her son would one day be a disciple of the Master, as Peter was. But Mark's old master had been very angry. He had come to see them and Mark had accused the venerable man of hating Jesus because he taught the people the truth. It had been dreadful. And then last night Mark had declared that the rabbis and priests had all joined together to bring about Jesus' death. The priests were traitors, he said, to God and the nation; the rabbis were hypocrites. All were enemies of Jesus because they were afraid he would expose them. She had trembled to hear him. She knew it could not be God's will that Jesus should die. But she couldn't believe that all the holy men of Israel were, as Mark declared, in league with the devil to destroy him. They had misunderstood and misjudged him. She had tried to reason with Mark but the boy wouldn't listen. He had been beside himself with grief. He had dragged her to the place of execution like one demented. Then, when he saw Jesus die, he had rushed away and left her to find her way home.

She didn't know what to do. If she didn't keep the feast, the neighbours would point at her; they would pull their skirts aside when she went to the synagogue on the Sabbath. The rabbis might expel Mark from the synagogue; they might excommunicate them both. They had done the same thing to Jesus. He had been execrated in every synagogue in the land. He, Jesus of Nazareth, had been cursed with the curse of Joshua against Jericho and the curse of Elisha against those that mocked him and the curse of fiends of deadly power. "Let nothing good come out of him: let his end be sudden, let the whirlwind crush him, the fever and every other malady and the edge of the sword smite him. Let his end be unforeseen and drive him into outer darkness." Months ago she had heard these fearful words read out in her own meetinghouse over Jesus, and she had not faltered in her love for him. Should she falter now that his end was come? Did the brand of the cross make him a criminal in the eyes of God whom he had loved with all his soul? It did not; she knew it did not. She would always know, no matter what the world did to him, that he was a holy child of God. And if she and her son were made outcasts, then they must bear it for his sake. But in the meantime, she was not yet an outcast, nor had she ever willingly broken God's holy law. What would God do to her if she did not keep the feast? That was the important thing. What was God's will now in this matter? Did calamity and unutterable sorrow not free one from his command to rejoice? What would Jesus tell her to do if she could ask him? Would he say: "God has forsaken me. Remember me and forget God," or would he say: "Even though I may seem to be accursed, you must love God with all your heart and trust Him, even as you loved and trusted me. You must obey His holy law and give thanks to Him even to-day, for His infinite mercy, and not expect to understand."

Yes, that was what he would say, and that was what she must do. She must keep the feast; she must eat the Passover, even though the roast meat, whose smell made her sick, should choke her, even though the three disciples of the Lord Jesus would not join her, even though her son did not come.

She turned wearily to the door and went down the stair into the kitchen. The little maid was there, blubbering into the oven; she was basting the roast lamb with great salt tears.

"What shall we do?" the mistress of the house spoke to the bent back and black, kinky head. "None of the others have come."

"I don't know, m'm. Oh, dear, oh, dear, the meat is all burned to a cinder already. I can't see at all what I'm doing." She lifted her swarthy face, all smeared with tears and smoke. "It would be as well, to throw the feast out of the window."

"Hush, girl. Hold your wicked tongue. Those are blasphemous words."

"What do I care? What has your great God done for me?" sobbed the ugly little African, whose forbears had been camel drivers in the far desert beyond Egypt. "The Rabbi Jesus was my friend. He came into this kitchen only yesterday, it was, and I was singing and he put his hand on my shoulder and said, 'Child'—that's what he called me—'Child, you shall have a special place in the choir of the Kingdom of Heaven,' and he was laughing but not

to make fun of me; laughing, you know how he did, as if he loved you. And he knew all the time that he was going to be killed."

"What makes you say that? How could you tell such a thing?"

"It was when I took in the supper last night. He was talking to the other masters, his disciples; there was such a look in his eyes it broke your heart. I did not understand then but I know now. He was saying good-bye. He held the winecup in his hands. He knew it was for the last time. 'Do this,' he said, 'in remembrance of me.'" The slave covered her face with her apron and sobbed aloud. "He was my friend," she sobbed. "He loved me and he was like a god."

Her mistress was watching her helplessly when suddenly there was a sound of strong quick footsteps running in the courtyard, and her son burst into the kitchen.

"Mark, O Mark!" cried his mother, "where have you been?" And she flung herself on his neck.

"I've been down by the Horse Gate." His face was white, his eyes were dark with a desperate excitement. "I've been round by the arena. I've been scouring the town with young John and Stephen. Is any one here? Have the disciples come back?"

"Only Peter and the sons of Zebedee."

"Where are they?"

"They are upstairs. But, why, Mark? What is it? What have you been doing at this hour in those dreadful, dangerous quarters of the town? I thought young John had taken the Lord's mother home to his house."

"He did. She is there now. She has her sister and Salome the wife of Zebedee to tend her, and a great crowd of women are there to mourn with her. We had other work to do to-night."

"What work do you mean, Mark? What can you do now for the Lord Jesus, but mourn him? O Mark, dear, I have been so frightened"; she clung to the young man, trembling.

"Let me go, Mother. I must speak to the three upstairs. We've been trying to gather Jesus' friends together; we are going in a band to the house of Caiaphas to demand his body."

"But the feast, Mark, we must keep—"

He broke away from her and rushed from the kitchen. They heard him clattering up the stairs.

The servant blew her nose on her apron. "He'll

get no help from them," she said scornfully, with a jerk of her head toward the ceiling. "They are like dead men. When I took them some warm milk and a bit of bread at noon, they didn't look up or speak or notice that I was in the room. There, it's burning again." She made a plunge for the oven and whipped the roast out of it, and all the kitchen was filled with the smell of burnt meat and with steam from a pot that began to boil over at the same moment. Her mistress stopped wringing her hands and ran to remove it, crying all in one breath, "The herbs will be all dried up. If they go in a band to the house of the High Priest, they will be taken. Bring water! Pour water into the pot. Young John is only a lad. Stephen is such a frail young man. If they go with a band of beggars—"

"If they go where, Sister?" a quiet voice asked. It was Mary, the wife of Alphæus and mother of James and Joseph. Mark's mother turned to find her standing there.

"They would go to Caiaphas, my son and a band—"

"Are my sons with them?"

"No. I don't think so."

"Haven't you seen them? Haven't they been here? I came in search of them."

"They haven't been here that I know of."

How many mothers were looking for their sons that night. How strange it all was, Mark's mother thought, and the two women looked at each other; then the mother of the two disciples James and John said in a very quiet voice:

"Then they must have gone in the night."

"Gone?"

"Gone from Jerusalem. Gone back to Galilee. They were not at the trial. They were not at the cross. They were not with those friends of the Master who stood at a distance, watching when he was crucified. I was there and I looked for them."

"But none of the disciples were there, Sister."

"No, not one. There was only the boy John to stand by the Lord's mother."

"But they could not come forward. They would have been recognized and taken prisoner. You would not have your own sons taken?"

Mary, the wife of Alphæus, held her head high. "I would have my sons brave men," she said, "true to their master."

Mark had come back. He stood inside the door. "I can get nothing out of the three," he said. "They will do nothing. They wouldn't even answer me at first. But even without them, even if not one of the disciples will join us . . ."

"What would you have them do?" asked Mary. And Mark's mother broke in: "They have a mad scheme in their heads. The disciples are right not to listen to it. They purpose to go in a band to the palace of the High Priest to demand the body of the Master."

"You are too late, Mark."

"Too late?"

"Jesus has already been buried by order of the governor."

"When? Where? How can you know this is true?"

"The sister of the Lord's mother saw it. She stayed behind by the cross with Mary of Magdala. They saw the soldiers take him down and followed them. He is laid in a tomb belonging to a noble senator whose name I do not know. But I know the place; Mary of Magdala is watching there now. She would not come away."

"Then it is useless to go to Caiaphas?"

"Quite useless."

The boy leaned his head back against the kitchen door, all the fire and vigour gone out of him suddenly. He looked scarcely more than a child now, and his eyes filled slowly with tears.

"We had thought," he said, "that we could still do something for Jesus. I must go and tell the others."

"Yes, Mark, and bring them back. Bring young John to eat the feast with us, and Stephen too."

The young man stared. "How can we eat the feast, Mother? We've been in the hovels of outcasts and the dust heaps of beggars, searching for friends of the Master brave enough to go with us. We've been among the lepers who lie under the arches below Herod's arena. We are not fit to keep the feast." His young voice was bitter.

"But I must keep it, Mark. I must keep it. I know the Lord Jesus would not have us break the feast."

"Then you must keep it without me, Mother. And if you expect the three upstairs to join you, you will be disappointed. Better ask in old Aaron the cripple, who is lying with his accursed companions down by the pool, or Moses the blind beggar, who is crouching in the dust by the Sheep Gate. They have been waiting these many days for the Master."

"Why not?" It was the slave girl who spoke suddenly, her black eyes flashing in her dark face. "The

Lord Jesus would not have been too proud to invite them to his house. They were his friends. He told a story once, I heard it, about a rich man whose friends made excuses not to come to his feast, and who sent out into the byways and hedges and asked in the lame, the halt and the blind. Why shouldn't you, my mistress, do the same?"

They stared at the creature, astonished. Then Mary, the mother of James and Joseph, said gravely, "She speaks the truth. I too have heard Jesus tell this parable concerning the Kingdom of Heaven."

But Mark's mother was dumbfounded at the suggestion. She looked at Mary in amazement.

"You think the Master would like me to invite all these poor, unclean wretches to my table, to eat the holy feast?"

"I do."

"But where could they wash their hands? How could they be made clean?"

"If I remember rightly, Jesus had something very definite to say about that, Sister."

"So he did. Oh, so he did." A timid, wavering smile began to play round the mouth of Mark's mother. But still she hesitated. "It would be such a strange thing to do, such an unheard-of thing. What would our rabbi say, Mark, do you think?"

"I know very well, Mother, what the rabbi would say. He is one of those who killed Jesus."

And now his mother's eyes began to shine as she turned them on her son. "Let us do it, Mark; let us keep the feast for his sake, as he would have us do. Run to the pool: run to the gate: run and bring back any you find. There is food in plenty. I had prepared for fifteen, but there is an abundance. If there are more than twenty, God will forgive us."

The boy's face had lighted too at her words. "You are right, Mother. I'll bring them and John too, and Stephen. I'll tell them first. We'll go together to find the others." He dashed out of the door.

And now all was bustle in the kitchen. The breathless mistress of the house, who was doing this unheard-of thing and Mary, the mother of two disciples who had abandoned their master, busied themselves over the ovens, and the slave girl ran up and down the stairs, carrying plates piled with unleavened bread and jars of wine and bowls of bitter herbs. But the roast lamb, Mark's mother said, they would leave for the young men to carry up when they came; the meat, thank God, was not burnt so badly, after all.

And just when the women were ready, the guests arrived, and Mark threw the street door wide open to let them in.

What a strange troop they were. And yet, had Jesus of Nazareth been in the house, such a gathering would not have been at all strange, for the sick and the maimed and the blind always came wherever he was; and the crippled beggars who hobbled across the courtyard in their filthy rags were no more evil-smelling and hideous in appearance than many he had healed. It was a slow business for some of them to climb the stairs to the upper room, but Mark and Stephen and young John helped them, lifting the weakest ones in their strong young arms and guiding the steps of the blind. And presently they were all seated round that generous board, with the candles lighting up their queer twisted faces; and the empty chair that seemed indeed like a throne to them, all garlanded as it was with roses and myrtle, at the head of the table. None of them had ever seen such a glorious thing before, nor ever been bidden to a feast nor ever eaten the Passover. And some of them giggled foolishly and nudged each other, for they were weak in their wits as well as in their bodies, but their hearts that were as withered as their hands blossomed again that night in the warm light of that festal room. And when the son of the house said, "We will sing the song of praise written by David the King," and the young men and the women lifted their voices, they too who were outcasts joined in the singing as best they could. They didn't know the words very well and their voices were cracked and feeble, but they did what they could, and old Moses, who had hoped with such a great hope that Jesus would come and give him the sight of his eyes, raised his quavering voice desperately, as if he hoped even now for a miracle.

"Not unto us, O Lord. Not unto us, but unto thy name give glory, for thy mercy and thy truth's sake."

The young men's voices were strong and clear. The women sang with tears streaming.

"O give thanks unto the Lord; for he is good: for his mercy endureth forever."

Even the African girl opened her wide mouth and sang, but the Lord she remembered, as she threw back her head that was like a mat of black sheepskin, was the Lord Jesus, who was dead that day, not Jehovah, the Lord of the Jews.

And then silence fell on all the company, and the

son of the house stood up at the foot of the long table opposite the empty place that had been laid for Jesus of Nazareth. And he told the story of how God, the father of Abraham and Isaac and Jacob, had led his people out of Egypt, the land of bondage. And he lifted the cup in his hand and said the blessing of Israel over the wine, and then passed it to blind Moses who sat on his right and said:

"My Lord and Master who was crucified this day was here last night, having supper with his disciples. We have invited you to this feast for his dear sake. We offer you this cup in his name."

And the cripples and the blind men and the beggars in their rags repeated each one, as they drank: "In the name of the Lord Jesus." And Peter the disciple stumbled to the door of the room where he was hiding and opened it a little way and saw the strange company all gathered round the table. But they didn't notice him, for young John was just bringing in the platter with the roast lamb and Stephen was climbing the stairs with a second platter, and the women were busy breaking the bread and passing the bitter herbs to their guests.

IV

The three disciples were sufficiently recovered by next morning to begin to take account of what had happened to them. The day before they had been too stunned to think. Now, when the dawn began to filter into their hiding place, they struggled back to consciousness to face a world in ruins. Their master was dead. All their hopes were dead with him. Until yesterday they had been great men, the chosen friends of a mighty leader; to-day they were the associates of a sorcerer, branded with his guilt. And as devout Jews, they were bound to believe that he and they were guilty. That was the awful thing. The death of their leader made chaos of their faith in him; it made their love for him a sin. For the man they had believed in had been an impostor. His death proved it. The Messiah foreordained by God to be King of Israel could not be killed. But their Jesus, who had claimed to be Messiah, had been done to death. His claim therefore had been blasphemous and, as God-fearing men, they should hate him. But they found they could not hate him. Though he had been proved a false prophet he had been their friend.

He had loved them and they had abandoned him, and they were ashamed. It was shame that made them avoid each other's eyes. Yet according to what they knew of God, they should have felt no shame or remorse for having left Jesus of Nazareth when he was taken prisoner. Their God had condemned him. The Almighty God of their fathers demanded of them now that they should repent, not of having abandoned their master, but of ever having followed him. As good Jews, they stood condemned for the one; as plain men, they condemned themselves for the other. It was no wonder that their hearts and minds were sick with confusion and horror.

But they were alive. And it began to seem as if they might be spared to live many a day. The dangerous night had passed without alarm. The soldiers had not come for them. Indeed, they had slept like logs on the floor of their closet and woke furiously hungry. They couldn't help this. They were no more to blame for the gnawing pains in their vitals than for the overpowering need of sleep that had felled them like oxen toward the middle of the night. Their hearts might be sick; they were nevertheless brawny fishermen of the north country and life beat strong in their veins even though they had nothing left now to live for.

Twenty-four hours is a long time for three big healthy men to be shut up in a dark closet, and it is a long time to go without food. They had eaten nothing except a morsel of bread and a cup of milk since their supper with Jesus two nights before. So they crept from their little prison in the early dawn and stumbled down the stairs to the yard, and drenched their clammy, bearded faces with fresh water, then knocked softly on the kitchen door. The slave girl was there, warming some milk over the fire, and they drank the milk she put before them thirstily and devoured the cakes of unleavened bread that were left over from the feast, and if they were ashamed of making such a hearty meal when their Lord Jesus was scarcely cold in his tomb, this shame was a small thing compared to the other. Nor did the memory of his agony turn their stomachs, for they hadn't witnessed it. They knew almost nothing of what had happened since he had been taken. They didn't even know that he was decently buried till the mistress of the house came into the kitchen to drink a cup of milk before she went to the synagogue. Perhaps had they seen him hanging on his cross or watched him led through the streets like a beast, or even beheld him standing before the mob that yelled for his blood in the Prætorium, they might have acted differently. But they had seen nothing of all this. They had followed him to the place of execution only with their ears, and had only known he was dead when they heard the chatter of the excited crowd that streamed back from the crucifixion, under the window of the room where they were hiding. So they had no picture before their eyes of his humiliation; indeed they knew nothing about his death, save that it made him an accursed and unclean thing in the eyes of all Israel.

They had given up everything they held precious on earth to follow him. They had left their homes and families and means of livelihood to be founders with him of his kingdom. They had believed in his kingdom and, because of their belief, they had become, long ago, hunted men, with no safe refuge anywhere and no place to lay their heads. And they had often gone hungry for his sake, and had dogs set on them and been driven out of villages with stones. But they had been content because he had been there to keep up their courage, and had promised them that, when he set up his kingdom in Jerusalem, they, the twelve, faithful chosen ones, who had endured such tribulation with him, would sit on twelve thrones, judging the twelve tribes of Israel. This had been no figure of speech to them. They had counted on those thrones as children count on new toys promised them by their parents. They had seen themselves dressed in gorgeous raiment, sitting each one on a judgment seat like Pontius Pilate, and empowered by Jesus the King to deal out life and death as Pilate was empowered to do by Cæsar. These three, moreover, had been sure of some special glory in the kingdom, for they had been of all the twelve his most stalwart supporters and closest friends. Simon, he had named Peter, saying he was a rock; James and John the sons of Zebedee, he had called Sons of Thunder, so passionately had they defended him in the old days against his enemies. And he had often taken them with him when he withdrew himself from all the others.

But he had been unable to keep his promises. He was dead, and his death meant that all his talk of the kingdom was only a dream, that the kingdom itself was an illusion and that he had been a madman, possessed of the devil, who had told them not the truth but a lie. For the world of Rome quite evidently was not coming to an end, nor was the Temple going to be destroyed. Pontius Pilate and Caiaphas were stronger than ever; they had destroyed Jesus and for his disciples there would be no honour now nor any glory in this life or the life to come. Instead, they must go in fear of their lives and of their immortal souls, for they had been guilty of sacrilege; they had performed miracles of healing in the name of a sorcerer and even if their lives were spared on earth, they must live in terror always of the life to come. The most they could hope for now was to remain safe in this house till the Sabbath was over, then escape to their homes, mingling with the throng of pilgrims who would pour out of the city early next day. They could not even be certain that they would be received in their home town of Capernaum and allowed to take up their old occupations. Zebedee was a rich man. He perhaps could look after his sons, but what would become of Simon Peter, who had a wife and children and a mother-in-law to support, if all the townspeople treated him as an outcast? He and his were likely to starve.

It had been all very well for those lads, Mark and Stephen and young John, to rush about the city, inviting Jesus' friends to go to the High Priest and demand his body. The death of their leader was one thing to a group of boys and a crowd of beggars; it was quite another to men who had gone up and down the country preaching heresy and performing miracles in the name of this Jesus who was put to death for treason.

They knew only too well what happened to the recognized followers of a false Messiah. Had not Varus the Roman come through the country only twenty years before to hunt out the followers of Judah the Galilean and crucify them? One thousand men had been crucified after that uprising, and Varus had burned the native city of that leader to the ground. They knew well enough that Jesus, unlike Judah, had refused to lead the people in rebellion against Cæsar. But what good would that knowledge do them now that he was dead? Who would proclaim that truth to the world? The eleven disciples were perfectly right in being afraid for their lives. They were not mistaken in thinking they were compromised with him. They had acted like reasonable men in running away to save their own skins, when he was taken. If they had gone to the Prætorium to witness in his defence, they might very easily have died with him.

Peter and James and John could not blame the others for having fled already from Jerusalem. They were not astonished when the woman of the house told them that they were the only ones of the twelve who had been seen since the crucifixion. What amazed them was their own action in coming back to this suspect house. What amazed them even more was the attitude of its inmates to the man who was dead. Something had dragged them back to the place where they had last seen him. A hope, perhaps, a last flickering hope that he might even yet confound his enemies. But now there was no hope. The thing was done. He could never come back to them, never fill them again with the brave, radiant, blinding spirit that had deluded them. His spirit was gone down into hell. The world it had created round them was vanished like a mirage. Yet here were these people talking of him as if he were present, and there was his chair all festooned with fading garlands, as if waiting for him.

They went to the large upper room after breaking their fast, not daring to linger in the courtyard or kitchen; and they sat there all day. But they couldn't bear to look at the chair at the head of the table. One of the sons of Zebedee made as if to thrust it back against the wall; but Peter cried out in horror, "Don't touch it, leave it alone."

Simon Peter was far from being a reasonable man. He was always rushing ahead of himself and plunging into danger and doing things he was sorry for afterwards. His heart governed his head and often got him into trouble. It had nearly done so twice on the night his master had been taken. He had attacked one of the soldiers in the garden, then fled. Having fled, his heart dragged him after his master to the house of the High Priest. But he had remembered his danger in time, when he found himself surrounded by all those servants and soldiers in the courtyard of the palace. They were warming themselves by a fire and Peter had stood warming himself with them, wondering what they were doing to Jesus upstairs, when he realised that the servants were looking at him curiously and whispering to the soldiers. That brought him to his senses, and when one of the servant maids said, "You were with Jesus of Nazareth," he had denied it, declaring that he didn't know what she was talking about. And

when they all began to say to each other, "This man is one of them," he had denied it again. And finally, when they kept on accusing him and saying, "Surely you are one of them; you are a Galilean, your speech betrays you," he began to curse and swear, saying he didn't even know the man of whom they were speaking.

Queerly enough, his master had told him he would do this very thing. That last evening at supper Jesus had said to them, "You will all be ashamed of me tonight," and Peter had declared loudly that whatever the others did, he would never be ashamed of him. But Jesus had insisted, and had told Peter that that very night before the cock crowed twice, he would have denied him three times. And Peter had declared vehemently that he was ready to die with him, but never under any circumstances would he deny him. Indeed, they had all said the same thing. But it had happened just as their master had foretold, even to the cock's crowing. When they came to the test, they had not wanted to die with him, they had wanted to live; and they had been ashamed of him and had forsaken him, and Peter had sworn he did not know him, and the cock had crowed just as Jesus had said.

That was the frightening, uncanny thing. Even if Jesus knew exactly what they would do, how could he have known through human knowledge about the cock? The cock was a shrieking proof of what they would have given their right hands now to deny. If only they could believe that he had been a man like themselves. If only they could be assured even now that he had been like other men, with no awful power in him; a misguided, mistaken man, but not a fearful being. That was what terrified them, the knowledge of his unearthly power. He had touched lepers and made their flesh whole. Peter had seen him do it. He had put his spittle on the eyelids of blind men and given them back the sight of their eyes. He had commanded demons to come out of maniacs and the demons had obeyed him. He had taken a dead girl by the hand and brought her back to life.

They had seen him with their own eyes do all these things; they had seen him shaken like a tree in the wind by the awful power that poured through him. Sometimes when he had wrestled with demons, he would become strange himself as a demon and terrible to look at. And once they had seen him transfigured. On the side of Mount Hermon, far to the north on the borders of Tyre, when he was a fugitive

with a price on his head, they had seen him transfigured before them, and his face had shone as the
sun and his raiment had been white as the light, and
Elias and Moses had been talking to him. This, at
least, was what they had seemed to see. But it could
not have been Elias and Moses; it could not have
been the light of heaven that had illumined his face;
it had all been magic. Only the other day when he
had driven the money-changers out of the Temple,
it had been almost the same. The priests had been
paralysed; the guards had not dared interfere with
him, for there had been a fiery, starry light shining
from his eyes and a majesty that had seemed like the
majesty of the Godhead had illumined his terrible
face.

The throng had known then that he was their
king. He could have done with the city what he
willed, and they, his disciples, had believed he was
going to raze the Temple to the ground then and
there, and send the Tower of Antonia reeling into
the ravine below the city wall. But he had done
nothing, he had not even given the signal to fall
on the priests. He had stood watching the turmoil
with despair in his face, then had disappeared.

Judas had gnashed his teeth with rage at the
futility of the whole proceeding. He had expected
no miracles. Judas had never cared about miracles.
He was a hard man of Judea, much more learned
than they, and had often laughed at them for their
simplicity. But he had believed in the Master's
power and after the affair in the Temple, he had
run first to one then another of them, crying out
against him and saying, "Twice he has had the power
in his hands and failed to seize it; twice have the
people been ready to crown him; twice has he been
lifted to the pinnacle of success and has withdrawn
himself." Judas must have made up his mind after
that to betray him.

They spoke of this. Judas' treachery was one of
the things they could bear to speak of. It eased them
to hate the sinister man of the South who had turned
on their master in a fury of disappointment. They
too had been disappointed that day, but they had not
listened to Judas. They had had faith in their leader
in spite of everything.

"Not to the end," said John. "We were not faithful
to the end."

"He knew," muttered James, "that Judas would
betray him."

"How could he have known?"

"He knew," groaned Peter, "as he knew that I
would deny him, as he always knew everything."

But James, son of Thunder, shook his great head.
"Had he known he would not have let the thing be."

"But he told us, don't you remember? He said,
'One of you will betray me.' "

"And he told me I would deny him, and I did. And
he told us all, I remember now, that he would be
killed."

On that they looked at one another and were
silent. The fearful sense of his mysterious knowledge
and power was with them again. They could understand nothing; they could only tremble at this new
thought that he had known he must die.

It would have been a relief to them to believe that
Judas had merely betrayed a deluded man. But they
could not satisfy the thirsty agony of their souls with
draughts of hate for Judas, nor find any comfort in
the thought that he whom Judas, the bitter revolutionary, had delivered into the hands of his enemies
had been nothing more than a rebel. He had been
like no other man in the world. Even the rabbis who
came to scoff knew that he was unearthly. Not even
his bitterest enemies denied his miracles. No, he
was no ordinary being. He had been filled with a
power they had believed to be the power of God.
Since it could not have been the power of God, it
must have been the power of Satan.

They had not betrayed and abandoned a friend;
they had loved a devil. Let God have pity on them,
they loved him still. Satan had come in the guise of a
king who loved them, to ensnare their souls. Even
now that he had been exposed, the fearful charm of
his awful spirit lay on them like a spell to wring their
hearts and force them to remember things about him
that made them weep.

They remembered how he would laugh with them
and tell them stories, while they sat of an evening
round a little bonfire in some quiet spot on the shore,
grilling fish from the lake for their supper. And how
he had seemed to enjoy being with them and had
seemed to depend on their love. And they remembered how weary he often was and unutterably sad,
and how lonely he had seemed sometimes in the
midst of a throng who worshipped him. They remembered too how he had suffered when his family
had cut him off and his brothers had taunted him
with being a coward, and his own town of Nazareth,

where he had been brought up, had tried to kill him. And at the last meal they had eaten with him in this house, when they were all wrangling over who was to have first place in the kingdom, he had taken off his cloak and fetched a basin of water and knelt down in front of each of them and washed their feet. But worst of all was the memory of how he had asked them to keep watch in the Garden of Gethsemane while he prayed. For he had taken the three of them with him away from the others and had said to them, "My soul is exceeding sorrowful, even unto death; tarry ye here, and watch with me." But they had gone to sleep, and he had come back to them and found them sleeping and had said to Peter, "Simon, do you sleep? Could you not watch with me one hour?" And again he had gone away and prayed and they had heard his voice beseeching his Father in heaven: "Abba Father, take away this cup from me. If it be possible let this cup pass from me," and then they had fallen asleep again, and again he had come and waked them; and this time there were great drops of sweat, like drops of blood, running down his face. And they had not known what to say to him, and he had gone away to pray a third time, and for the third time they had slept. And then Judas had come with a crowd of men armed with swords and staves and carrying lanterns, and they had taken Jesus prisoner and bound him and led him away.

What did it all mean? If he were a great sorcerer, he could not have willed to die. Why had he not saved himself? They didn't breathe the question aloud, but they asked it of themselves and could find only one answer. God had killed him.

So they waited in the house of Mark's mother. And when their thoughts became unbearable, they watched the people from the window coming home from the synagogue in their fine Sabbath clothes, all chatting together, with their happy children clinging to their hands, and they felt as cut off from the pleasant normal world as if they were criminals under sentence of death. And presently their hostess came home in much distress, for a strange rabbi who had been asked to speak in the synagogue had preached a dreadful sermon about Jesus, the false Messiah.

"Do you know what he said?" she cried to the three disciples. "Do you know what the rabbi told the congregation? He told them that Jesus recanted on the cross and confessed his guilt before he died.

He said that when Jesus cried out that God had forsaken him, those words were a confession of guilt, wrung from him under torture, and all the people are talking about it."

Mark's mother was so upset that she kept talking on and on about it to herself as she set the table for dinner. But the disciples, Peter and James and John, could say nothing for they hadn't heard the cry, and they didn't know what to think. They could only sit there in silence and let the woman talk. And presently one, then another of those who had followed Jesus came knocking at the door. For word had gone round among the friends of Jesus that the three disciples were there, and all these poor, grief-stricken souls came and fell at the feet of Peter and James and John, just as if they were still the honourable representatives of a glorious leader. Indeed, they treated the three with a reverence greater than ever now that the Master was gone and only his disciples were left. They looked to the disciples to comfort them, but the three could give them no comfort; they could only murmur, "Peace be with you, Sister; Peace, Brother," when these simple people kissed them with tears running down their cheeks.

It was dreadful for Peter and James and John. As the day wore on, the room became filled with friends of the Master who came to them to have the awful calamity explained. Many had come all the way from Galilee to see him crowned king. All were humble folk who loved him with all their hearts. They kept weeping and talking about how wonderful he had been and how good. "He was so good." They kept coming back to that. "Never has there been a man so filled with love, for God and his fellow men. How could they have found any guilt in him? How is it possible that he should have been treated as a criminal?"

They kept asking the disciples to explain. Who had done this thing? Who was responsible? Was it Herod Antipas? And when the disciples said nothing, the other men argued among themselves as to who was to blame for the Master's death. For some said Herod had nothing to do with it; it was Pontius Pilate; and others said it was the High Priest and the Sanhedrin, and others again said that, if the Sanhedrin had done the thing, it was against the law. It was illegal to try a man in the middle of the night. But no one seemed to know the truth of the matter. And when they asked the disciples on what charge he had been condemned and who had witnessed against him, the disciples could not tell them, for they did not know.

It was fortunate that Mary, the wife of Alphæus, came in at this moment with a message from the Master's mother. Mary of Nazareth was very troubled, it seemed, in her grief, because they had laid her son's body away without anointing it, and she sent to ask if Mark's mother had what was needful. If so Mary, the wife of Alphæus, would come back with Mary Magdalene at sundown, when the Sabbath was over, to prepare the spices, and they would go to the tomb early in the morning and ask leave to anoint the body.

The disciples were thunderstruck at the news that the mother of Jesus was in Jerusalem. They could not understand it at all when they were told Mary of Nazareth had come all the way from Galilee in search of her son, for she had not believed, they said, in Jesus. None of his family had believed in him.

"I know nothing about that," Mark's mother said. "All I know is that she came to find him and arrived only in time to see him brought before Pilate, and watched the trial from the edge of the crowd, but never got near him till he was nailed to the cross."

"She stood by the cross?" whispered Peter.

"Yes, with young John, and the Lord spoke to them while he was dying and told John to care for her as if he were her own son, and she is with him now."

Simon Peter's face twisted as he heard this and the Sons of Thunder flushed dark red, even to their ears. And John groaned, grinding his teeth, but James said:

"A mother has a right to mourn her son and be near him, even when he is crucified. No officer in Israel would touch her."

"But the Lord's brothers?" Peter asked, in a hoarse voice. "Were they too at the cross?"

"No. But James came this morning to fetch his mother. He is in lodgings with the Rabbi of Nazareth. He besought her to come home with him to Galilee, but she will not go; she refuses to leave Jerusalem, and indeed she is too ill to be moved."

Then Salome, the mother of James and John, came bursting in with Zebedee their father, and she filled the house immediately with her loud lamentations, for she was a noisy, headstrong woman who had expected her sons to be privileged persons in the kingdom that had come to nothing. And she commiserated with them, crying out, "I thought to have seen you sitting to the right and left of his throne with crowns on your heads and sceptres, and now you are only fishermen again." And then she tried to comfort them, saying that once they were back in Capernaum, they would feel better. She and their father must set about finding them each a wife. Their father had business to see to in Jerusalem. He could not get away for a day or two, she would wait with him and go with the other women to anoint the poor dead Master. But they must not linger; the sooner they got back to their fishing the better: who knew what mischief the hired servants had got into, and so on and on, until at last Zebedee bade her be quiet, for he was a good man who had believed in Jesus and been kind to him in the old days with no idea of advantage to himself or his sons. But he too advised his sons to be gone early in the morning, for he had made enquiries in the city and had learned that a man called Saul was urging the priests to hunt out the followers of Jesus. And at last those two great sons of his, who had been very embarrassed by their mother before all the others, muttered yes. They might as well go back to Galilee.

And then at last Mary Magdalene came with Mary, the wife of Alphæus, who had gone to fetch her, for by that time evening was come, and all the others began to take leave of the three disciples, saying they must prepare for the journey home on the morrow. And many of them wept anew and said, "Till we meet again in Galilee. Till we meet again to talk of him." For they had been happy together gathered round their Lord Jesus, and now they felt they would be all scattered like a flock of sheep without out a shepherd, just as he had said.

But Mary of Magdala seemed not to notice any one. She just stood in the corner of the room, looking silently at the chair that was heavy with garlands of roses, and no one dared speak to her, because of the look in her sunken eyes. And she was standing like that and the others were all going, when the son of the house came in with Stephen and the boy John, to say that Judas Iscariot had hanged himself.

They stood transfixed at the news. Every one of them stood suddenly quite still, so still that one could almost have heard the petals fall from the wilted garlands. And then some one whispered, "Why? What had he done?" For there were those there who did not know about Judas. And Peter answered, "He betrayed Jesus," and covered his face with his hands and began to sob with sobs that seemed like to tear open his bowels.

The three young men had been to the tomb. "But we couldn't get near it," Mark said, "because of the guard. And there was a man prowling in the bushes. We caught sight of him staring at us out of the shrubbery; his eyes were so wild and bloodshot, his face so terrible, that at first we thought it was Judas."

"But it was James," put in young John. "James, the Lord's brother. He must have gone to the tomb after talking to his mother."

"But Judas?" they whispered. "How do you know he has hanged himself?"

"We found him," they answered, "hanging to a tree at the bottom of the garden."

And there was silence again in the room, for Peter's awful sobbing had stopped, and then some one asked, "Did you cut him down? Did you touch him?"

"No. We left him, but we told the guard; they will cut the body down."

"And throw it in the ditch," said some one, "with the two thieves that were crucified."

Vengeance. Did some one say that or was it only the awful unspoken thought in all their minds?

No. Not in all of them. Mary of Magdala seemed not to have heard. She was still standing as before, looking at the chair that was like a throne, looking as if she saw the Lord she adored sitting there. She did not notice when at last they all went away. But when the room was empty save for the three disciples, she went over to the chair and touched the flowers gently with her fingers, and said to Peter, "Did he sit here?" and Peter and James and John could not answer her. Indeed they could not bear to look at the little smile hovering over her haggard face, so they tiptoed back to their closet and left her alone. And it seemed to them, as they closed the door softly, that she sank on her knees by the empty chair, and leaned her cheek against it, and they thought they heard her crooning a song.

v

It was early in the morning when the women started for the tomb. The sun had not yet risen; the deep streets were filled with shadow; the great battle-mented walls were ghostly in the twilight. But dim figures with bundles on their back were already abroad; shadowy caravans of pilgrims were passing out into the country through the city gates, for people who had come to the feast from distant villages were already taking the road to their homes.

There were a number of women in the group that was going to the sepulchre. Some had met in the house of Mark's mother; others had waited for the morning, with Mary of Nazareth in the house of young John. Mary, the mother of James and Joseph was with Mark's mother, and Salome, the wife of Zebedee, and Joanna, the wife of Herod's steward, and several others. They had not expected to be so many. But the lady Joanna, when she heard what they were going to do, had sent word begging to go with them, for she had dearly loved the Lord Jesus. So she had slipped out of the palace through a little door and had come down through the Vale of the Cheesemakers to the house of Mark's mother on foot, accompanied only by a slave whom her husband had sent to take care of her till she reached the house. Mary, the sister of the Lord's mother, was waiting in the street outside the house where her sister was lying for those who came from Mark's house, and she had with her those who mourned all night with the mother of Jesus. They joined the first group with murmured greetings and went together quietly through the dim streets, all wrapped alike in black shawls, carrying carefully the baskets of fine linen and ointments and sweet spices they had prepared. But Mary of Magdala was not with them; she had gone on ahead while it was still dark.

"We will find her waiting outside the sepulchre," Jesus' kinswoman told Mark's mother. "She cannot bear to be far away from her master," and she smiled sadly, thinking of poor Mary Magdalene, who was like a dog bereaved of its beloved owner.

And Mark's mother murmured, "Poor thing, oh, poor thing, I wonder what will become of her? Do you think she would stay with us in Jerusalem? She seems to have no family in Galilee and no one to turn to now that the Master is gone."

"She will want to stay where he is," answered the other, "that is all that she wants. She watched outside the tomb all the first night. The boy John found her there in the morning and persuaded her to come back to his house, telling her that my sister longed to hear how they had buried her son; and we told her that Jesus would wish her to stay with his mother, so she stayed. But last night, when she had been with you preparing the things needful for the anointing, she came to sit with us again and we could see that she was straining like a dog on a leash to be back at her place by the sepulchre, so my sister told her not to wait any longer but be off to her master, and she went a little while ago, though it was still very dark."

The other women, when they heard it, were grieved for this Mary who had once been a harlot in the bazaars of Magdala and one said, "She loved him more than any of us. His death is more dreadful for her than for any one." And they wondered what they could do for the lonely creature whose life had been transformed by Jesus, and who was left now with nothing. For they knew that no woman who had lived in the presence of Jesus of Nazareth could go back to the life of a prostitute. Yet what could Mary Magdalene do if she went home to the country where she had once been famous for her wicked beauty? What would become of her if they did not befriend her?

"Perhaps she would come to me," Joanna said; "she could live with us in Tiberius and look after the children."

"She will do what she thinks her master would have her do," one said simply and the others agreed.

They were such simple women. Even the lady Joanna who lived in a fine house near Herod's castle in Tiberius was like one of themselves in her grief; even Salome who was usually so noisy and self-important felt as the others did, and was quiet. None of them were reasonable as men count reasoning. They were mothers in Israel whose understanding was in their bones, their breasts, their hearts. And their hearts were full and their breasts ached with sorrow. They did not think as the disciples thought about their master's infamous death. His crucifixion had not changed him for them. They didn't understand what had happened or try to understand it; they didn't believe that the man they had known and adored was an impostor who had deluded them. Nor did they suspect for a moment that he himself had been deluded in regard to his kingdom. They didn't understand about his kingdom, but obscurely, instinctively, illogically, they knew that it was something more mysterious than the ancient kingdom of David and Solomon, something heavenly and eternal

that could have been realised on earth if only the people had believed in him and they knew that he had died for it. At the same time, he had never been to them primarily a king. Even Salome, who had been so ambitious for her sons and entertained such childish dreams of glory, remembered him as did the others, now that he was dead, and could not find it in her big gushing heart to suspect him of having made blasphemous claims. The idea that he might rule the world had seemed to them all wonderfully possible, because he was wonderful. But to them all he had been first and last the beloved Master who had taught them to love God with all their hearts and their neighbours as themselves. And now in the early morning, after their long vigil, they remembered him as he had been and knew only that they worshipped him, and that he was gone.

It was growing lighter as they made their way toward the city gate. When they reached the gate, they saw through the arch that the sky was beginning to glow in the East, and when they came out on the high road that led down to Jericho they saw the pale daylight coming over the world, and they stood a moment all together, looking across the awful gulf of the Jordan valley. And the Dead Sea lay below them, though they could not see it. For the land sank swiftly, sluddering to a depth of which they could not see the bottom; but they knew it fell to the desert shores of that bitter water and they could see the grey wasteland spreading out like a vast rumpled blanket to the mountains of Moab. Soon, the sun would rise above that distant ridge and flood all the haggard land with golden light. But the gulf was awful. It yawned beneath them like the bottomless pit of death. They felt the rock of Jerusalem rising out of it like a ship riding the great deep of the unknown that had swallowed up their master. And they huddled together on the far side of the road, away from the gully where the crosses were, not daring to look down into that dreadful place, and looked out instead over the great distance with white faces, then turned and hurried up the path that led to the garden where he was laid. For they were afraid of death and afraid of the cruel mystery of the world, with its sun that rose each morning on the just and the unjust. And the only thing that could comfort them now was this little act of devotion to the one who had been to them like the light of the world. They would render to his poor body as best they could the last tender honours of the dead; they would touch it as they would touch a sacred thing, and wash it with their tears and anoint it carefully with sweet-smelling spices, then clothe it in spotless white, for it was all that was left to them now of a man they had felt was immortal. So they pressed forward eagerly, clutching their precious baskets tight as they scrambled up toward the garden, and one whispered to another breathlessly, for the path began to climb among steep rocks:

"Who will roll the stone away for us from the door of the sepulchre?" And another said, "Will he stay here, do you think? Will the noble councillor allow this to be his own tomb for ever?" And one, who was from Galilee, panted, "His mother will surely want to take him back to Nazareth to be buried in the tomb of his fathers." While one of Judea said, "Pray God he remains here with us, then we can visit him often." But the first said, "We can never roll away the stone by ourselves; it is too great."

And now they had reached the garden and there was a little gate leading into it between shrubberies, and the gate stood open. It was still dark among the trees. They could see nothing but shadowy masses of leaves and the path like a tunnel under them. But suddenly as they looked the figure of a woman appeared on the path, running toward them. It was Mary of Magdala and she cried out when she saw them, "The stone is rolled away! The tomb is empty! They have taken away the Lord and I know not where they have laid him! The stone is gone; the body is gone! I have looked everywhere. I have hunted the bushes." And indeed, all her clothing was stained with earth and there were bits of twig and leaves in her hair as if she had been through the undergrowth on her hands and knees. But she would not stop to tell them more. She only looked at them distraught when they took hold of her and cried, "I must tell Peter," and flinging them off, ran away down the path.

The pilgrims by now were pouring out of the city gate. By families and tribes and village communities, some with wagons piled high with luggage and women and children sitting perched on the luggage; some with laden donkeys, some with camels; they crowded through the gateway and their village rabbis walked with them like shepherds, each one leading home a flock of sheep; and all these travellers stared at the distraught woman who came running down to the gate, her red hair flying out behind her like a banner, and ducked between the wagons and donkeys and camels like an animal pursued, and ran on against the stream of people into the city.

Peter was there, when she reached the house of Mark's mother. He was coming down the stairs from the upper room with his bundle on his back and his stick in his hand, when she ran into the courtyard. But the Sons of Thunder were already gone. They had taken the road very early before the women had left, but Peter had lingered behind, for he had been very troubled by all the things he had heard and had been loath to leave Jerusalem. Indeed a battle had been raging all the night between his heart and his head, for he knew that he stayed in the city at his peril, and he knew that the man who kept him there was not what he had believed him to be, but he could not help remembering Jesus now as a friend whom he had betrayed, just as Judas had done, and he had writhed under the agony of the shame of it. If he fled back to Galilee, he knew he would be denying him again in death, as he had done in life, he, whom all those good people looked to now as their leader in the place of the Lord Jesus. His face burned when he remembered how they had kissed him, fallen at his feet, asked him to comfort them. They had not been afraid; they had not denied the man who was dead. The women—it was the women most of all who made him ashamed, the women and the young boys. He had watched the women go out with their baskets, had followed them in his miserable mind to the tomb. They were there now, anointing the wounded body of the man he had loved with his whole miserable, cowardly soul. Could he not go, at least to the place where he lay, on his way out of the city? Had Mary Magdalene loved Jesus of Nazareth with a love so much greater than his own? Was the boy John a man and he a child? That little lad had stood by the cross when he and the sons of Zebedee had stayed in hiding. He had not wavered in his allegiance even in face of that awful death and condemnation. Young John had not doubted and was not lost, even now. But he, Peter, was lost, utterly.

He would go and confess it. He would go to the tomb and beg forgiveness of the man he had loved and betrayed. He would go with all his doubts and acknowledge that he had no faith in him now, but

THE STORY OF JESUS

loved him still. Perhaps the one who was dead would understand and comfort him.

He had made up his mind to dare to do this, when he came down the stairs and saw Mary Magdalene running into the courtyard like one demented.

Her hair was streaming over her shoulders, she was all covered with dust. She cried out to him from below, "They have taken away the Lord out of the sepulchre and we know not where they have laid him."

He stared at her stupidly, and she stared up at him, panting for breath. But when he still hesitated, she cried out furiously, "The tomb is empty. Do you not understand? The body of the Lord is gone," and she made as if to drag him down the stairs. But now he ran. He leapt past her and ran out of the courtyard into the street and she ran after him. And the streets were filled with people, but Peter pounded his way through them with Mary Magdalene at his heels. And they passed the door of the house where the Lord's mother lay and the boy John was just coming out of it, and Mary called to him as they ran, "The tomb is empty. They have taken away the body of the Lord." And when John heard it, he came with them in a flash, and they ran all three back through the streets the way Mary had come. But John out-ran Peter, for he was a boy, light and swift on his feet as a young deer, and he knew the way.

It was much lighter now. The sky was glorious over the gulf of the wasteland. But a sound of lamentation rose from the garden as they ran up the path to the little gate. A great sighing wail, like the crying of a flock of birds, rose from the trees, and when they came in sight of the tomb, there were all the women gathered before it, bowed to the ground weeping, and the great stone that had closed the door of the tomb was rolled away, just as Mary Magdalene had said.

The lad John was the first to reach the sepulchre. He ran past the women to the gaping door in the rock, and the women saw him stoop down and look. But he did not go in. He fell back from the door, his young face white as death. And then Peter came rushing up and pushed past him and plunged into the tomb, and the boy John went in after him. And all the women held their breath when they went in. And Mary Magdalene, who had come after Peter, waited a little apart from the others.

The light was dim in the tomb. But when their eyes were accustomed to it, Peter and John saw the linen cloth that had wrapped him lying there and the napkin that had been about his head was not lying with the linen cloth, but folded together in a place by itself. But they found not the body of the Lord Jesus, and they came out of the tomb into the sunlight and the women saw in Peter's face that it was true, the body was gone.

They stared at him with stricken faces. The precious baskets lay forgotten on the ground. Some one had stolen their master. What could they do? What did it mean? Who had come in the night and taken the body?

They looked to Peter, waiting for him to speak and tell them who could have done this wicked thing. But Peter said nothing. He only stood there staring, with his mouth working as if he were muttering to himself or praying, but making no sound. And then they saw that all his great heavy body was shaking, and when they saw that, they began to be very frightened. And one whispered, "The Romans have done it. The guard must have taken him." But another said, "No, it was the High Priest who hated him and placed a guard at the tomb, so that we could not get near him." But still another said, "Perhaps the councillor himself has moved the body to another place," and they called out to Peter, "Let us find the Master! We must find the Master! Let us go in search of Joseph the councillor to question him." And one of them cried, "O poor Lord Jesus! Could they not have left his body in peace?" And at that they began to wail again, beating their breasts, and went on weeping louder and louder, till the little wood round the tomb throbbed with their wailing and a frenzy was like to have seized on them, for some began to knock their heads on the ground and tear their clothing; but Peter spoke suddenly, telling them in a stern voice to be silent.

They saw the boy John pluck Peter then by the arm. They couldn't hear what he said, but he was evidently arguing with Peter, for the disciple's face was dreadful as he spoke; and suddenly they saw the lad leave him and turn and run down the path and at that they started to wail again, crying:

"Where is he going? Oh, where is he going? Does he think he can find the Lord Jesus?" But Peter silenced them again with lifted hand, telling them to be gone to their homes.

"Go and warn your husbands," he said. "Go and

tell all the followers of Jesus what has happened. Go quickly, but go quietly, secretly. Let no man see aught in your faces."

They stared, appalled by the look of him and the sound of his voice. "Why?" they whispered. "Why do you speak so?"

"Because it will be said," he answered, "that we, the friends of Jesus of Nazareth, have stolen the body, and there is no knowing what the authorities will do to us."

None of them had thought of this. They didn't take in the meaning of it now. But they got to their feet obediently, for they were accustomed to obeying him. And they picked up the baskets that were of no use now with trembling hands and drew their shawls over their heads and began to creep away, and Peter said to them as they went:

"Let those of you who came from Galilee leave the city this day, if you value your lives. The boy John has gone to tell Mary of Nazareth. I go north to warn the disciples. May God have mercy on us all." And he watched them go down the path toward the city gate, then plunged into the bushes and disappeared. But Mary of Magdala did not move from her place.

She was alone in the garden when all the women were gone, and it was very still. There were only the little sounds of birds twittering in the trees, and the sun was just rising through the branches. She stood outside the sepulchre weeping and as she wept she stooped down and looked into the sepulchre. And there she saw two angels all in white sitting, the one at the head and the other at the foot, where the body of Jesus had lain. She was not surprised to see them there. Indeed, she paid little attention to them, for she had lost her master and could think of nothing but where she might find him. And the angels said to her, "Woman, why are you weeping?"

She answered, "Because they have taken away my Lord and I know not where they have laid him."

And when she had said this, she turned herself back, for she saw that there was indeed no sign of him in the tomb; there were only the two angels. So she turned away into the garden and there was a man standing there in the sunlight, and he said to her,

"Woman, why are you weeping? Whom do you seek?"

She, supposing him to be the gardener, said, "Sir,

if you have borne him hence, tell me where you have laid him and I will take him away."

But he said to her, "Mary," and she looked at him and whispered, "Rabboni," for she knew when he spoke her name that it was Jesus.

IN JERUSALEM

Anonymous

Dawns leaden day: a grey
  Wind moaning low;
Through empty streets no feet
  Echoing go;

Ways dank with breath of death,
  All day in gloom
Drift grim, white-draped, escaped
  Shapes from the tomb;

Men's doors fast-barred to guard
  Living from dead;
Cold-cramped, each head apart
  Crazes with dread;

Ten thousand groan and own
  Terror their guest;
One lying lone in stone
  Only knows rest.

HOLY SATURDAY

John Banister Tabb

O Earth, who daily kissed His feet
Like lowly Magdalen,—how sweet
(As oft His mother used) to keep

The silent watches of His sleep,
Till love demands the Prisoner,
And Death replies, "He is not here.
He passed my portal, where, afraid,
My footsteps faltered to invade
The region that beyond me lies:
Then, ere the dawn, I saw Him rise
In glory that dispelled my gloom
And made a Temple of the Tomb."

Renew thy youth, as eagle from the nest;
  O Master, who hast sown, arise to reap;—
No cock-crow yet, no flush on eastern crest:
  Our Master lies asleep.

NOW SLEEPS THE LORD

Margaret L. Woods

UPON THE SAVIOR'S TOMB

Richard Crashaw

How life and death in thee
        Agree!
Thou hadst a virgin womb,
        And tomb.
A Joseph did betroth
        Them both.

Now lies the Lord in a most quiet bed.
    Stillness profound
Steeps like a balm the wounded body wholly,
More still than the hushed night brooding around.
    The moon is overhead,
Sparkling and small, and somewhere a faint sound
Of water dropping in a cistern slowly.
Now lies the Lord in a most quiet bed.

Now rests the Lord in perfect loneliness.
One little grated window has the tomb,
    A patch of gloom
Impenetrable, where the moonbeams whiten
    And arabesque its wall
With leafy shadows, light as a caress.
The palms that brood above the garden brighten,
    But in that quiet room
Darkness prevails, deep darkness fills it all.
Now rests the Lord in perfect loneliness.

MARY MAGDALENE
AND THE OTHER MARY

Christina Rossetti

Our Master lies asleep and is at rest:
  His heart has ceased to bleed, his eye to weep:
The sun ashamed has dropped down in the west;
  Our Master lies asleep.

Now we are they who weep, and trembling keep
  Vigil, with wrung heart in a sighing breast,
While slow time creeps, and slow the shadows
    creep.

Now sleeps the Lord secure from human sorrow.
The sorrowing women sometimes fall asleep
    Wrapped in their hair,
Which while they slumber yet warm tears will steep,
Because their hearts mourn in them ceaselessly.
    Uprising, half-aware,
They myrrh and spices and rich balms, put by
For their own burials, gather hastily,
    Dreaming it is that morrow
When they the precious body may prepare.
Now sleeps the Lord secure from human sorrow.

Now sleeps the Lord unhurt by love's betrayal.
    Peter sleeps not,

He lies yet on his face and has not stirred
Since the iron entered in his soul red-hot.
The disciples trembling mourn their disillusion,
   That he whose word
Could raise the dead, on whom God had conferred
Power, as they trusted, to redeem Israel,
Had been that bitter day put to confusion,
   Crucified and interred.
Now sleeps the Lord unhurt by love's betrayal.

Now rests the Lord, crowned with ineffable peace.
Have they not peace tonight who feared him, hated
   And hounded to his doom,
The red thirst of their vengeance being sated?
No, they still run about and bite the beard,
   Confer, nor cease

To tease the contemptuous Pilate, are affeared
Still of him tortured, crushed, humiliated,
   Cold in a blood-stained tomb.
Now rests the Lord crowned with ineffable peace.

Now lies the Lord serene, august, apart,
That mortal life his mother gave him ended.
   No word save one
Of Mary more, but gently as a cloud
On her perdurable silence has descended.
   Hush! In her heart
Which first felt the faint life stir in her son,
   Perchance is apprehended
Even now dimly new mystery, grief less loud
Clamours, the Resurrection has begun.
Now lies the Lord serene, august, apart.

PART SEVEN

Christ as Redeemer
and Saviour

Does Christ save you from your sin?
Call Him Savior!

Does He free you from the slavery of
your passions?
Call Him Redeemer!

Does He teach you as no one else has
taught you?
Call Him Teacher!

Does He mould and master your life?
Call Him Master!

Does He shine upon the pathway that
is dark to you?
Call Him Guide!

Does He reveal God to you?
Call Him the Son of God!

Does He reveal man?
Call Him the Son of Man!

Or, in following Him, are your lips
silent in your incapacity to define
Him, and His influence upon you?
Call Him by no name, but follow
Him!

HOWARD S. BLISS

1. THE COSMIC DRAMA

AN HYMNE OF HEAVENLY LOVE

Edmund Spenser

Love, lift me up upon thy golden wings,
From this base world unto thy heavens hight,
Where I may see those admirable things
Which there thou workest by thy soveraine might,
Farre above feeble reach of earthly sight,
That I thereof an heavenly hymne may sing
Unto the God of Love, high heavens king.

Many lewd layes (ah, woe is me the more!)
In praise of that mad fit which fooles call love,
I have in th' heat of youth made heretofore,
That in light wits did loose affection move.
But all those follies now I do reprove,
And turned have the tenor of my string,
The heavenly prayses of true love to sing.

And ye that wont with greedy vaine desire
To reade my fault, and wondring at my flame,
To warme your selves at my wide sparckling fire,
Sith now that heat is quenched, quench my blame,
And in her ashes shrowd my dying shame:
For who my passed follies now pursewes,
Beginnes his owne, and my old fault renewes.

Before this worlds great frame, in which al things
Are now containd, found any being place,
Ere flitting Time could wag his eyas wings
About that mightie bound, which doth embrace
The rolling spheres, and parts their houres by
        space,
That high eternall Powre, which now doth move
In all these things, mov'd in it selfe by love.

It lov'd it selfe, because it selfe was faire;
(For faire is lov'd;) and of it selfe begot
Like to it selfe his eldest Sonne and Heire,
Eternall, pure, and voide of sinfull blot,
The firstling of his joy, in whom no jot
Of loves dislike or pride was to be found,
Whom he therefore with equall honour crownd.

With him he raignd, before all time prescribed,
In endlesse glorie and immortall might,
Together with that third from them derived,
Most wise, most holy, most almightie Spright,
Whose kingdomes throne no thought of earthly
        wight
Can comprehend, much lesse my trembling verse
With equall words can hope it to reherse.

Yet, O most blessed Spirit, pure lampe of light,
Eternall spring of grace and wisedome trew,
Vouchsafe to shed into my barren spright
Some little drop of thy celestiall dew,
That may my rymes with sweet infuse embrew,
And give me words equall unto my thought,
To tell the marveiles by thy mercie wrought.

Yet being pregnant still with powrefull grace,
And full of fruitfull love, that loves to get
Things like himselfe, and to enlarge his race,
His second brood, though not in powre so great,
Yet full of beautie, next he did beget,
An infinite increase of angels bright,
All glistring glorious in their Makers light.

To them the heavens illimitable hight
(Not this round heaven, which we from hence be-
    hold,
Adornd with thousand lamps of burning light,
And with ten thousand gemmes of shyning gold)
He gave as their inheritance to hold,
That they might serve him in eternall blis,
And be partakers of those joyes of his.

There they in their trinall triplicities
About him wait, and on his will depend,
Either with nimble wings to cut the skies,
When he them on his messages doth send,
Or on his owne dread presence to attend,
Where they behold the glorie of his light,
And caroll hymnes of love both day and night.

Both day and night is unto them all one,
For he his beames doth still to them extend,
That darknesse there appeareth never none;
Ne hath their day, ne hath their blisse an end,
But there their termelesse time in pleasure spend;
Ne ever should their happinesse decay,
Had not they dar'd their Lord to disobay.

But pride, impatient of long resting peace,
Did puffe them up with greedy bold ambition,
That they gan cast their state how to increase
Above the fortune of their first condition,
And sit in Gods owne seat without commission:
The brightest angell, even the Child of Light,
Drew millions more against their God to fight.

Th' Almighty, seeing their so bold assay,
Kindled the flame of his consuming yre,
And with his onely breath them blew away
From heavens hight, to which they did aspyre,
To deepest hell, and lake of damned fyre;
Where they in darknesse and dread horror dwell,
Hating the happie light from which they fell.

So that next off-spring of the Makers love,
Next to himselfe in glorious degree,
Degendering to hate, fell from above
Through pride; (for pride and love may ill agree)
And now of sinne to all ensample bee:
How then can sinfull flesh it selfe assure,
Sith purest angels fell to be impure?

But that Eternal Fount of love and grace,
Still flowing forth his goodnesse unto all,
Now seeing left a waste and emptie place
In his wyde pallace, through those angels fall,
Cast to supply the same, and to enstall
A new unknowen colony therein,
Whose root from earths base groundworke shold
    begin.

Therefore of clay, base, vile, and next to nought,
Yet form'd by wondrous skill, and by his might,
According to an heavenly patterne wrought,
Which he had fashiond in his wise foresight,
He man did make, and breathd a living spright
Into his face most beautifull and fayre,
Endewd with wisedomes riches, heavenly, rare.

Such he him made, that he resemble might
Himselfe, as mortall thing immortall could;
Him to be lord of every living wight
He made by love out of his owne like mould,
In whom he might his mightie selfe behould:
For love doth love the thing belov'd to see,
That like it selfe in lovely shape may bee.

But man, forgetfull of his Makers grace,
No lesse then angels, whom he did ensew,
Fell from the hope of promist heavenly place,
Into the mouth of death, to sinners dew,
And all his off-spring into thraldome threw:
Where they for ever should in bonds remaine
Of never dead, yet ever dying paine.

Till that great Lord of Love, which him at first
Made of meere love, and after liked well,
Seeing him lie like creature long accurst
In that deepe horror of despeyred hell,
Him, wretch, in doole would let no lenger dwell,
But cast out of that bondage to redeeme,
And pay the price, all were his debt extreeme.

Out of the bosome of eternall blisse,
In which he reigned with his glorious Syre,
He downe descended, like a most demisse
And abject thrall, in fleshes fraile attyre,
That he for him might pay sinnes deadly hyre,
And him restore unto that happie state
In which he stood before his haplesse fate.

In flesh at first the guilt committed was,
Therefore in flesh it must be satisfyde:
Nor spirit, nor angell, though they man surpas,
Could make amends to God for mans misguyde,
But onely man himselfe, who selfe did slyde.
So, taking flesh of sacred virgins wombe,
For mans deare sake he did a man become.

And that most blessed bodie, which was borne
Without all blemish or reprochfull blame,
He freely gave to be both rent and torne
Of cruell hands, who with despightfull shame
Revyling him, that them most vile became,
At length him nayled on a gallow tree,
And slew the just by most unjust decree.

O huge and most unspeakable impression
Of loves deepe wound, that pierst the piteous hart
Of that deare Lord with so entyre affection,
And sharply launching every inner part,
Dolours of death into his soule did dart;
Doing him die, that never it deserved,
To free his foes, that from his heast had swerved!

What hart can feele least touch of so sore launch,
Or thought can think the depth of so deare wound,
Whose bleeding sourse their streames yet never
    staunch,
But stil do flow, and freshly still redound,
To heale the sores of sinfull soules unsound,
And clense the guilt of that infected cryme,
Which was enrooted in all fleshly slyme?

O blessed Well of Love! O Floure of Grace!
O glorious Morning Starre! O Lampe of Light!
Most lively image of thy Fathers face,
Eternall King of Glorie, Lord of Might,
Meeke Lambe of God, before all worlds behight,
How can we thee requite for all this good?
Or what can prize that thy most precious blood?

Yet nought thou ask'st in lieu of all this love,
But love of us, for guerdon of thy paine.
Ay me! what can us lesse then that behove?
Had he required life of us againe,
Had it beene wrong to aske his owne with gaine?
He gave us life, he it restored lost;
Then life were least, that us so little cost.

But he our life hath left unto us free,
Free that was thrall, and blessed that was band;
Ne ought demaunds, but that we loving bee,
As he himselfe hath lov'd us afore hand,
And bound therto with an eternall band,
Him first to love, that us so dearely bought,
And next, our brethren, to his image wrought.

Him first to love, great right and reason is,
Who first to us our life and being gave;
And after, when we fared had amisse,
Us wretches from the second death did save;
And last, the food of life, which now we have,
Even himselfe in his deare sacrament,
To feede our hungry soules, unto us lent.

Then next, to love our brethren, that were made
Of that selfe mould and that selfe Makers hand
That we, and to the same againe shall fade,
Where they shall have like heritage of land,
How ever here on higher steps we stand;
Which also were with selfe same price redeemed
That we, how ever of us light esteemed.

And were they not, yet since that loving Lord
Commaunded us to love them for his sake,
Even for his sake, and for his sacred word,
Which in his last bequest he to us spake,
We should them love, and with their needs par-
    take;
Knowing that whatsoere to them we give,
We give to him, by whom we all doe live.

Such mercy he by his most holy reede
Unto us taught, and to approve it trew,
Ensampled it by his most righteous deede,
Shewing us mercie, miserable crew!
That we the like should to the wretches shew,
And love our brethren; thereby to approve
How much himselfe, that loved us, we love.

Then rouze thy selfe, O Earth, out of thy soyle,
In which thou wallowest like to filthy swyne,
And doest thy mynd in durty pleasures moyle,
Unmindfull of that dearest Lord of thyne;
Lift up to him thy heavie clouded eyne,
That thou his soveraine bountie mayst behold,
And read through love his mercies manifold.

Beginne from first, where he encradled was
In simple cratch, wrapt in a wad of hay,
Betweene the toylefull oxe and humble asse,
And in what rags, and in how base aray.
The glory of our heavenly riches lay,
When him the silly shepheards came to see,
Whom greatest princes sought on lowest knee.

From thence reade on the storie of his life,
His humble carriage, his unfaulty wayes,
His cancred foes, his fights, his toyle, his strife,
His paines, his povertie, his sharpe assayes
Through which he past his miserable dayes,
Offending none, and doing good to all,
Yet being malist both of great and small.

And looke at last, how of most wretched wights
He taken was, betrayd, and false accused;
How with most scornefull taunts, and fell despights,
He was revyld, disgrast, and foule abused,
How scourgd, how crownd, how buffeted, how
    brused;
And lastly, how twixt robbers crucifyde,
With bitter wounds through hands, through feet,
    and syde.

Then let thy flinty hart, that feeles no paine,
Empierced be with pittifull remorse,
And let thy bowels bleede in every vaine,
At sight of his most sacred heavenly corse,
So torne and mangled with malicious forse,
And let thy soule, whose sins his sorrows wrought,
Melt into teares, and grone in grieved thought.

With sence whereof whilest so thy softened spirit
Is inly toucht, and humbled with meeke zeale,
Through meditation of his endlesse merit,
Lift up thy mind to th' author of thy weale,
And to his soveraine mercie doe appeale;
Learne him to love, that loved thee so deare,
And in thy brest his blessed image beare.

With all thy hart, with all thy soule and mind,
Thou must him love, and his beheasts embrace;
All other loves, with which the world doth blind
Weake fancies, and stirre up affections base,
Thou must renounce, and utterly displace,
And give thy selfe unto him full and free,
That full and freely gave himselfe to thee.

Then shalt thou feele thy spirit so possest,
And ravisht with devouring great desire
Of his deare selfe, that shall thy feeble brest
Inflame with love, and set thee all on fire
With burning zeale, through every part entire,
That in no earthly thing thou shalt delight,
But in his sweet and amiable sight.

Thenceforth all worlds desire will in thee dye,
And all earthes glorie, on which men do gaze,
Seeme durt and drosse in thy pure sighted eye,
Compar'd to that celestiall beauties blaze,
Whose glorious beames all fleshly sense doth daze
With admiration of their passing light,
Blinding the eyes and lumining the spright.

Then shall thy ravisht soule inspired bee
With heavenly thoughts, farre above humane skil,
And thy bright radiant eyes shall plainely see
Th' idee of his pure glorie present still
Before thy face, that all thy spirits shall fill
With sweete enragement of celestiall love,
Kindled through sight of those faire things above.

THE SCHEME OF REDEMPTION *

John Milton

Now had the Almighty Father from above,
From the pure Empyrean where He sits
High throned above all highth, bent down his eye,
His own works and their works at once to view:
About him all the Sanctities of Heaven
Stood thick as stars, and from his sight received
Beatitude past utterance; on his right
The radiant image of his glory sat,
His only Son. On Earth he first beheld
Our two first parents, yet the only two
Of mankind, in the Happy Garden placed,
Reaping immortal fruits of joy and love,
Uninterrupted joy, unrivalled love,
In blissful solitude. He then surveyed
Hell and the gulf between, and Satan there

* From *Paradise Lost*, Book III, lines 56-343.

Coasting the wall of Heaven on this side Night,
In the dun air sublime, and ready now
To stoop, with wearied wings and willing feet,
On the bare outside of this World, that seemed
Firm land imbosomed without firmament,
Uncertain which, in ocean or in air.
Him God beholding from his prospect high,
Wherein past, present, future, he beholds,
Thus to His only Son foreseeing spake:—

"Only-begotten Son, seest thou what rage
Transports our Adversary? whom no bounds
Prescribed, no bars of Hell, nor all the chains
Heaped on him there, nor yet the main Abyss
Wide interrupt, can hold; so bent he seems
On desperate revenge, that shall redound
Upon his own rebellious head. And now,
Through all restraint broke loose, he wings his way
Not far off Heaven, in the precincts of light,
Directly towards the new-created World,
And Man there placed, with purpose to assay
If him by force he can destroy, or, worse,
By some false guile pervert: and shall pervert;
For Man will hearken to his glozing lies,
And easily transgress the sole command,
Sole pledge of his obedience: so will fall
He and his faithless progeny. Whose fault?
Whose but his own? Ingrate, he had of me
All he could have; I made him just and right,
Sufficient to have stood, though free to fall.
Such I created all the Ethereal Powers
And Spirits, both them who stood and them who
        failed;
Freely they stood who stood, and fell who fell.
Not free, what proof could they have given sincere
Of true allegiance, constant faith, or love,
Where only what they needs must do appeared,
Not what they would? What praise could they
        receive,
What pleasure I, from such obedience paid,
When Will and Reason (Reason also is Choice),
Useless and vain, of freedom both despoiled,
Made passive both, had served Necessity,
Not Me? They, therefore, as to right belonged
So were created, nor can justly accuse
Their Maker, or their making, or their fate,
As if Predestination overruled
Their will, disposed by absolute decree
Or high foreknowledge. They themselves decreed
Their own revolt, not I. If I foreknew,

Foreknowledge had no influence on their fault,
Which had no less proved certain unforeknown.
So without least impulse or shadow of fate,
Or aught by me immutably foreseen,
They trespass, authors to themselves in all,
Both what they judge and what they choose; for so
I formed them free, and free they must remain
Till they enthrall themselves: I else must change
Their nature, and revoke the high decree
Unchangeable, eternal, which ordained
Their freedom; they themselves ordained their fall.
The first sort by their own suggestion fell,
Self-tempted, self-depraved; Man falls, deceived
By the other first; Man, therefore, shall find grace;
The other, none. In mercy and justice both,
Through Heaven and Earth, so shall my glory excel;
But mercy, first and last, shall brightest shine."

Thus while God spake ambrosial fragrance filled
All Heaven, and in the blessèd Spirits elect
Sense of new joy ineffable diffused.
Beyond compare the Son of God was seen
Most glorious; in him all his Father shon
Substantially expressed; and in his face
Divine compassion visibly appeared,
Love without end, and without measure grace;
Which uttering, thus He to his Father spake:—

"O Father, gracious was that word which closed
Thy sovran sentence, that Man should find grace;
For which both Heaven and Earth shall high extol
Thy praises, with the innumerable sound
Of hymns and sacred songs, wherewith thy throne
Encompassed shall resound thee ever blest.
For, should Man finally be lost—should Man,
Thy creature late so loved, thy youngest son,
Fall circumvented thus by fraud, though joined
With his own folly—! That be from thee far,
That far be from thee, Father, who art judge
Of all things made, and judgest only right!
Or shall the Adversary thus obtain
His end, and frustrate thine? Shall he fulfil
His malice, and thy goodness bring to naught
Or proud return, though to his heavier doom
Yet with revenge accomplished, and to Hell
Draw after him the whole race of mankind,
By him corrupted? Or wilt thou thyself
Abolish thy creation, and unmake,
For him, what for thy glory thou hast made?—
So should thy goodness and thy greatness both
Be questioned and blasphemed without defence."

To whom the great Creator thus replied:—
"O Son, in whom my soul hath chief delight,
Son of my bosom, Son who art alone
My word, my wisdom, and effectual might,
All hast thou spoken as my thoughts are, all
As my eternal purpose hath decreed.
Man shall not quite be lost, but saved who will;
Yet not of will in him, but grace in me
Freely vouchsafed. Once more I will renew
His lapsèd powers, though forfeit, and enthralled
By sin to foul exorbitant desires:
Upheld by me, yet once more he shall stand
On even ground against his mortal foe—
By me upheld, that he may know how frail
His fallen condition is, and to me owe
All his deliverance, and to none but me.
Some I have chosen of peculiar grace,
Elect above the rest; so is my will:
The rest shall hear me call, and oft be warned
Their sinful state, and to appease betimes
The incensèd Deity, while offered grace
Invites; for I will clear their senses dark
What may suffice, and soften stony hearts
To pray, repent, and bring obedience due.
To prayer, repentance, and obedience due,
Though but endeavoured with sincere intent,
Mine ear shall not be slow, mine eye not shut.
And I will place within them as a guide
My umpire Conscience; whom if they will hear,
Light after light well used they shall attain,
And to the end persisting safe arrive.
This my long sufferance, and my day of grace,
They who neglect and scorn shall never taste;
But hard be hardened, blind be blinded more,
That they may stumble on, and deeper fall;
And none but such from mercy I exclude.—
But yet all is not done. Man disobeying,
Disloyal, breaks his fealty, and sins
Against the high supremacy of Heaven,
Affecting Godhead, and, so losing all,
To expiate his treason hath naught left,
But, to destruction sacred and devote,
He with his whole posterity must die;—
Die he or Justice must; unless for him
Some other, able, and as willing, pay
The rigid satisfaction, death for death.
Say, Heavenly Powers, where shall we find such
    love?
Which of ye will be mortal, to redeem

Man's mortal crime, and just, the unjust to save?
Dwells in all Heaven charity so dear?"
    He asked, but all the Heavenly Quire stood mute,
And silence was in Heaven: on Man's behalf
Patron or intercessor none appeared—
Much less that durst upon his own head draw
The deadly forfeiture, and ransom set.
And now without redemption all mankind
Must have been lost, adjudged to Death and Hell
By doom severe, had not the Son of God,
In whom the fulness dwells of love divine,
His dearest mediation thus renewed:—
    "Father, thy word is passed, Man shall find grace;
And shall Grace not find means, that finds her way,
The speediest of thy wingèd messengers,
To visit all thy creatures, and to all
Comes unprevented, unimplored, unsought?
Happy for Man, so coming! He her aid
Can never seek, once dead in sins and lost—
Atonement for himself, or offering meet,
Indebted and undone, hath none to bring.
Behold *me*, then: me for him, life for life,
I offer; on me let thine anger fall;
Account me Man: I for his sake will leave
Thy bosom, and this glory next to thee
Freely put off, and for him lastly die
Well pleased; on me let Death wreak all his rage.
Under his gloomy power I shall not long
Lie vanquished. Thou hast given me to possess
Life in myself for ever; by thee I live;
Though now to Death I yield, and am his due,
All that of me can die, yet, that debt paid,
Thou wilt not leave me in the loathsome grave
His prey, nor suffer my unspotted soul
For ever with corruption there to dwell;
But I shall rise victorious, and subdue
My vanquisher, spoiled of his vaunted spoil.
Death his death's wound shall then receive, and
    stoop
Inglorious, of his mortal sting disarmed;
I through the ample air in triumph high
Shall lead Hell captive maugre Hell, and show
The powers of Darkness bound. Thou, at the sight
Pleased, out of Heaven shalt look down and smile,
While, by thee raised, I ruin all my foes—
Death last, and with his carcase glut the grave;
Then, with the multitude of my redeemed,
Shall enter Heaven, long absent, and return,
Father, to see thy face, wherein no cloud

Of anger shall remain, but peace assured
And reconcilement: wrauth shall be no more
Thenceforth, but in thy presence joy entire."
    His words here ended; but his meek aspect
Silent yet spake, and breathed immortal love
To mortal men, above which only shon
Filial obedience: as a sacrifice
Glad to be offered, he attends the will
Of his great Father. Admiration seized
All Heaven, what this might mean, and whither
    tend,
Wondering; but soon the Almighty thus replied:—
    "O thou in Heaven and Earth the only peace
Found out for mankind under wrauth, O thou
My sole complacence! well thou know'st how dear
To me are all my works; nor Man the least,
Though last created, that for him I spare
Thee from my bosom and right hand, to save,
By losing thee a while, the whole race lost!
Thou, therefore, whom thou only canst redeem,
Their nature also to thy nature join;
And be thyself Man among men on Earth,
Made flesh, when time shall be, of virgin seed,
By wondrous birth; be thou in Adam's room
The head of all mankind, though Adam's son.
As in him perish all men, so in thee,
As from a second root, shall be restored
As many as are restored; without thee, none.
His crime makes guilty all his sons; thy merit,
Imputed, shall absolve them who renounce
Their own both righteous and unrighteous deeds,
And live in thee transplanted, and from thee
Receive new life. So Man, as is most just,
Shall satisfy for Man, be judged and die,
And dying rise, and, rising, with him raise
His brethren, ransomed with his own dear life.
So Heavenly love shall outdo Hellish hate,
Giving to death, and dying to redeem,
So dearly to redeem what Hellish hate
So easily destroyed, and still destroys
In those who, when they may, accept not grace.

Nor shalt thou, by descending to assume
Man's nature, lessen or degrade thine own.
Because thou hast, though throned in highest bliss
Equal to God, and equally enjoying
God-like fruition, quitted all to save
A world from utter loss, and hast been found
By merit more than birthright Son of God,—
Found worthiest to be so by being good,
Far more than great or high; because in thee
Love hath abounded more than glory abounds;
Therefore thy humiliation shall exalt
With thee thy manhood also to this Throne:
Here shalt thou sit incarnate, here shalt reign
Both God and Man, Son both of God and Man,
Anointed universal King. All power
I give thee; reign for ever, and assume
Thy merits; under thee, as Head Supreme,
Thrones, Princedoms, Powers, Dominions, I reduce:
All knees to thee shall bow of them that bide
In Heaven, or Earth, or, under Earth, in Hell.
When thou, attended gloriously from Heaven,
Shalt in the sky appear, and from thee send
The summoning Archangels to proclaim
Thy dread tribunal, forthwith from all winds
The living, and forthwith the cited dead
Of all past ages, to the general doom
Shall hasten; such a peal shall rouse their sleep.
Then, all thy Saints assembled, thou shalt judge
Bad men and Angels; they arraigned shall sink
Beneath thy sentence; Hell, her numbers full,
Thenceforth shall be for ever shut. Meanwhile
The World shall burn, and from her ashes spring
New Heaven and Earth, wherein the just shall dwell,
And, after all their tribulations long,
See golden days, fruitful of golden deeds,
With Joy and Love triumphing, and fair Truth.
Then thou thy regal sceptre shalt lay by;
For regal sceptre then no more shall need;
God shall be All in All. But all ye Gods,
Adore Him who, to compass all this, dies;
Adore the Son, and honour him as me."

2. FAITH

CHRIST'S INCARNATION

Robert Herrick

Christ took our nature on Him, not that He
'Bove all things lov'd it, for the purity:
No but he drest Him with our human trim,
Because our flesh stood most in need of Him.

THE WORLD

George Herbert

Love built a stately house, where Fortune came;
  And spinning fancies, she was heard to say
That her fine cobwebs did support the frame,
Whereas they were supported by the same.
  But Wisdom quickly swept them all away.

Then Pleasure came, who, liking not the fashion,
  Began to make balconies, terraces,
Till she had weakened all by alteration;
But reverend laws, and many a proclamation,
  Reformed all at length with menaces.

Then entered Sin, and with that sycamore
  Whose leaves first sheltered man from drought
    and dew,

Working and winding slily evermore,
The inward walls and summers cleft and tore;
  But Grace shored these, and cut that as it grew.

Then Sin combined with Death in a firm band
  To raze the building to the very floor;
Which they effected, none could them withstand.
But Love and Grace took Glory by the hand,
  And built a braver palace than before.

REDEMPTION

George Herbert

Having been tenant long to a rich Lord,
  Not thriving, I resolved to be bold,
  And make a suit unto him to afford
A new small-rented lease, and cancel th'old.
In Heaven at his manor I him sought,
  They told me there, that he was lately gone
  About some land, which he had dearly bought
Long since on Earth, to take possession.
I straight return'd, and knowing his great birth,
  Sought him accordingly in great resorts,
  In cities, theaters, gardens, parks, and courts:
At length I heard a ragged noise and mirth
  Of thieves and murderers. There I him espied,
  Who straight, *Your suit is granted*, said, and died.

LOVE

George Herbert

Love bade me welcome; yet my soul drew back,
  Guilty of dust and sin.
But quick-eyed Love, observing me grow slack
  From my first entrance in,
Drew nearer to me, sweetly questioning,
  If I lacked anything.

"A guest," I answered, "worthy to be here:"
  Love said, "You shall be he."
"I, the unkind, ungrateful? Ah, my dear,
  I cannot look on Thee!"
Love took my hand and smiling did reply,
  "Who made the eyes but I?"

"Truth, Lord; but I have marred them; let my shame
  Go where it doth deserve."
"And know you not," says Love, "who bore the
    blame?"
  "My dear, then I will serve."
"You must sit down," says Love, "and taste my
    meat."
  So I did sit and eat.

A DIALOGUE ANTHEM

George Herbert

———

CHRISTIAN

DEATH

———

CHRISTIAN.
Alas, poor Death, where is thy glory?
Where is thy famous force, thy ancient sting?
  DEATH.
Alas poor Mortal, void of story,
Go spell and read, how I have kill'd thy King.
  CHRISTIAN.
Poor Death! and who was hurt thereby?
Thy curse being laid in him, makes thee accursed.
  DEATH.
Let losers talk; yet thou shalt die.
These arms shall crush thee.
  CHRISTIAN.
                          Spare not, do thy worst.
I shall be one day better than before:
Thou so much worse, that thou shalt be no more.

3. *FAITH, DOUBT, AND VICTORY*

From IN MEMORIAM

Alfred, Lord Tennyson

I

Strong Son of God, immortal Love,
  Whom we, that have not seen thy face,
  By faith, and faith alone, embrace,
Believing where we cannot prove;

Thine are these orbs of light and shade;
  Thou madest Life in man and brute;
  Thou madest Death; and lo, thy foot
Is on the skull which thou hast made.

Thou wilt not leave us in the dust:
  Thou madest man, he knows not why,
  He thinks he was not made to die;
And thou hast made him; thou art just.

Thou seemest human and divine,
  The highest, holiest manhood, thou.
  Our wills are ours, we know not how;
Our wills are ours, to make them thine.

Our little systems have their day;
  They have their day and cease to be;
  They are but broken lights of thee,
And thou, O Lord, art more than they.

II

Though truths in manhood darkly join,
  Deep-seated in our mystic frame,
  We yield all blessing to the name
Of Him that made them current coin;

For Wisdom dealt with mortal powers,
  Where truth in closest words shall fail,
  When truth embodied in a tale
Shall enter in at lowly doors.

And so the Word had breath, and wrought
  With human hands the creed of creeds
  In loveliness of perfect deeds,
More strong than all poetic thought;

Which he may read that binds the sheaf,
  Or builds the house, or digs the grave,
  And those wild eyes that watch the wave
In roarings round the coral reef.

Make Thou my spirit pure and clear
  As are the frosty skies,
Or this first snowdrop of the year
  That in my bosom lies.

As these white robes are soiled and dark,
  To yonder shining ground;
As this pale taper's earthly spark,
  To yonder argent round;
So shows my soul before the Lamb,
  My spirit before Thee;
So in mine earthly house I am,
  To that I hope to be.
Break up the heavens, O Lord! and far,
  Through all yon starlight keen,
Draw me, thy bride, a glittering star,
  In raiment white and clean.

He lifts me to the golden doors;
  The flashes come and go;
All heaven bursts her starry floors,
  And strows her lights below,
And deepens on and up! the gates
  Roll back, and far within
For me the Heavenly Bridegroom waits,
  To make me pure of sin.
The Sabbaths of Eternity,
  One Sabbath deep and wide—
A light upon the shining sea—
  The Bridegroom with his bride!

SAINT AGNES' EVE

Alfred, Lord Tennyson

Deep on the convent-roof the snows
  Are sparkling to the moon;
My breath to heaven like vapor goes;
  May my soul follow soon!
The shadows of the convent-towers
  Slant down the snowy sward,
Still creeping with the creeping hours
  That lead me to my Lord.

CROSSING THE BAR

Alfred, Lord Tennyson

Sunset and evening star,
  And one clear call for me!
And may there be no moaning of the bar,
  When I put out to sea,

But such a tide as moving seems asleep,
  Too full for sound and foam,
When that which drew from out the boundless deep
  Turns again home.

Twilight and evening bell,
  And after that the dark!
And may there be no sadness of farewell,
  When I embark;

For though from out our bourne of Time and Place
  The flood may bear me far,
I hope to see my Pilot face to face
  When I have crossed the bar.

From SAUL

Robert Browning

Browning's great poem "Saul" is not essentially a poem
about Jesus. But it is a poem about the great Christian
doctrine that God is Love; and David finds at its climax
that he cannot solve Saul's problem without reaching far
beyond the period of the historical David to grasp the
meaning of the Incarnation. The passage in which this
realization comes to him is given here.

I believe it! 'Tis Thou, God, that givest, 'tis I who
  receive:
In the first is the last, in Thy will is my power to
  believe.
All's one gift: Thou canst grant it, moreover, as
  prompt to my prayer
As I breathe out this breath, as I open these arms
  to the air.
From Thy will stream the worlds, life and nature,
  Thy dread Sabaoth:
I will?—the mere atoms despise me! Why am I not
  loth
To look that, even that, in the face too? Why is it
  I dare
Think but lightly of such impuissance? What stops
  my despair?
This:—'tis not what man Does which exalts him, but
  what man Would do!
See the King—I would help him but cannot, the
  wishes fall through.
Could I wrestle to raise him from sorrow, grow poor
  to enrich,—
To fill up His life, starve my own out,—I would;
  knowing which,

I know that my service is perfect. Oh, speak through
  me now!
Would I suffer for Him that I love? So wouldst
  Thou—so wilt Thou!
So shall crown Thee the topmost, ineffablest, utter-
  most crown—
And Thy love fill infinitude wholly, nor leave up nor
  down,
One spot for the creature to stand in! It is by no
  breath,
Turn of eye, wave of hand, that salvation joins issue
  with death!
As Thy Love is discovered almighty, almighty he
  proved
Thy power, that exists with and for it, of being
  Beloved!
He who did most, shall bear most: the strongest shall
  stand the most weak.
'Tis the weakness in strength, that I cry for! my flesh,
  that I seek
In the Godhead! I seek and I find it. O Saul, it
  shall be
A Face like my face that receives thee; a Man like
  to me,
Thou shalt love and be loved by, forever: a Hand
  like this hand
Shall throw open the gates of new Life to thee! See
  the Christ stand!

THE BETTER PART

Matthew Arnold

Long fed on boundless hopes, O race of man,
How angrily thou spurn'st all simpler fare!
"Christ," someone says, "was human as we are;
No judge eyes us from heaven, our sin to scan;
We live no more, when we have done our span."—
"Well, then, for Christ," thou answerest, "who can
  care?
From sin, which heaven records not, why forebear?
Live we like brutes our life without a plan!"
So answerest thou; but why not rather say:
"Hath man no second life?"—*Pitch this one high!*
Sits there no judge in heaven, our sin to see?

More strictly, then, the inward judge obey!
Was Christ a man like us? Ah, let us try
If we then, too, can be such men as he!"

EAST LONDON

Matthew Arnold

'Twas August and the fierce sun overhead
Smote on the squalid streets of Bethnal Green,
And the pale weaver, through his windows seen
In Spitalfields, look'd thrice dispirited.

I met a preacher there I knew, and said:
"Ill and o'erworked, how fare you in this scene?"—
"Bravely!" said he; "for I of late have been
Much cheer'd with thoughts of Christ, *the living
    bread.*"

O human soul! as long as thou canst so
Set up a mark of everlasting light,
Above the howling senses' ebb and flow,

To cheer thee, and to light thee if thou roam—
Not with lost toil thou labourest through the night
Thou mak'st the heaven thou hop'st indeed thy
    home.

PROGRESS

Matthew Arnold

The Master stood upon the mount, and taught,
He saw a fire in His disciples' eyes:
"The old law," they said, "is wholly come to naught!
    Behold the new world rise!"

"Was it," the Lord then said, "with scorn ye saw
The old law observed by Scribes and Pharisees?
I say unto you, see *ye* keep that law
    More faithfully than these!

"To hasty heads for ordering worlds, alas!
Think not that I to annul the law have will'd;
No jot, no tittle from the law shall pass,
    Till all hath been fulfill'd."

So Christ said eighteen hundred years ago,
And what then shall be said to those to-day,
Who cry aloud to lay the old world low
    To clear the new world's way?

"Religious fervours! ardor misapplied!
Hence, hence," they cry, "ye do but keep man blind!
But keep him self-immersed, preoccupied,
    And lame the active mind!"

Ah! from the old world let some one answer give:
"Scorn ye this world, their tears, their inward cares?
I say unto you, see that *your* souls live
    A deeper life than theirs!

"Say ye: The spirit of man has found new roads,
And we must leave the old faiths, and walk therein?—
Leave them the Cross as ye have left carved gods,
    But guard the fire within!

"Bright, else, and fast the stream of life may roll,
And no man may the other's hurt behold:
Yet each will have one anguish—his own soul
    Which perishes of cold."

Here let that voice make end; then let a strain,
From a far lonelier distance, like the wind
Be heard, floating through heaven, and fill again
    These men's profoundest mind:

"Children of men! the unseen Power, whose eye
For ever doth accompany mankind,
Hath looked on no religion scornfully
    That men did ever find.

"Which hath not taught weak wills how much they
    can?
Which has not fall'n on the dry heart like rain?
Which has not cried to sunk, self-weary man:
    Thou must be born again!

"Children of men! not that your age excel
In pride of life the ages of your sires,
But that *you* think clear, feel deep, bear fruit well
    The Friend of man desires."

A BETTER RESURRECTION

Christina Rossetti

I have no wit, no words, no tears;
    My heart within me like a stone
Is numbed too much for hopes or fears.
    Look right, look left, I dwell alone;
I lift mine eyes, but dimmed with grief
    No everlasting hills I see;
My life is in the falling leaf;
    O Jesus, quicken me.

My life is like a faded leaf,
    My harvest dwindled to a husk:
Truly my life is void and brief
    And tedious in the barren dusk;
My life is like a frozen thing,
    No bud nor greenness can I see;
Yet rise it shall—the sap of Spring;
    O Jesus, rise in me.

My life is like a broken bowl,
    A broken bowl that cannot hold
One drop of water for my soul
    Or cordial in the searching cold;
Cast in the fire the perished thing;
    Melt and remould it, till it be
A royal cup for Him, my King:
    O Jesus, drink of me.

DESIDERIUM INDESIDERATUM

Francis Thompson

O gain that lurk'st ungained in all gain!
O love we just fall short of in all love!
O height that in all heights art still above!
O beauty that dost leave all beauty pain!
Thou unpossessed that mak'st possession vain,
See these strained arms which fright the simple air,
And say what ultimate fairness holds thee, Fair!
They girdle Heaven, and girdle Heaven in vain;
They shut, and lo! but shut in their unrest.

Thereat a voice in me that voiceless was:—
"Whom seekest thou through the unmarged arcane,
And not discern'st to thine own bosom prest?"
I looked. My clasped arms athwart my breast
Framed the august embraces of the Cross.

E TENEBRIS

Oscar Wilde

Come down, O Christ, and help me! reach Thy hand,
For I am drowning in a stormier sea
Than Simon on the lake of Galilee:
The wine of life is spilt upon the sand,
My heart is as some famine-murdered land
Whence all good things have perished utterly,
And well I know my soul in Hell must lie
If I this night before God's throne should stand.
"He sleeps perchance, or rideth to the chase,
Like Baal, when his prophets howled that name
From morn to noon on Carmel's smitten height."
Nay, peace, I shall behold, before the night,
The feet of brass, the robe more white than flame,
The wounded hands, the weary human face.

THE EVERLASTING MERCY

John Masefield

The Everlasting Mercy, the story of Saul Kane's redemption through Christ, is one of the great studies of religious experience in contemporary literature. In its last eight pages, the poem rises to a magnificent climax, expressing the ecstasy of the redeemed soul. A portion of this climax is reprinted here.

———

O glory of the lighted mind.
How dead I'd been, how dumb, how blind.
The station brook, to my new eyes,
Was babbling out of Paradise,

The waters rushing from the rain
Were singing Christ has risen again.
I thought all earthly creatures knelt
From rapture of the joy I felt.
The narrow station-wall's brick ledge,
The wild hop withering in the hedge,
The lights in huntsman's upper storey
Were parts of an eternal glory,
Were God's eternal garden flowers.
I stood in bliss at this for hours.

O glory of the lighted soul.
The dawn came up on Bradlow Knoll,
The dawn with glittering on the grasses,
The dawn which pass and never passes.

"It's dawn," I said, "And chimney's smoking,
And all the blessed fields are soaking.
It's dawn, and there's an engine shunting;
And hounds, for huntsman's going hunting.
It's dawn, and I must wander north
Along the road Christ led me forth."

So up the road I wander slow
Past where the snowdrops used to grow
With celandines in early springs,
When rainbows were triumphant things
And dew so bright and flowers so glad,
Eternal joy to lass and lad.
And past the lovely brook I paced,
The brook whose source I never traced,
The brook, the one of two which rise
In my green dream of Paradise,
In wells where heavenly buckets clink
To give God's wandering thirsty drink,
By whose clean cots of carven stone

Where the clear water sings alone.
Then down, past that white-blossomed pond,
And past the chestnut trees beyond,
And past the bridge the fishers knew,
Where yellow flag flowers once grew,
Where we'd go gathering cops of clover,
In sunny June times long since over.
O clover-cops half white, half red,
O beauty from beyond the dead.
O blossom, key to earth and heaven,
O souls that Christ has new forgiven.

BEFORE THE CRUCIFIX *

Princess Gabrielle Wrede

Before Thy cross I'm kneeling,
 In penitence bowed down,
Where Thou for us hast suffered,
 And worn the martyr's crown.

On Calvary's cross Thou'rt hanging,
 Yet see I not thy pain,
And not the nail's deep traces,
 And not Thy blood's red stain.

The crown of thorns I see not
 Upon Thy brow entwined;
I see Thy arms outstretchèd
 In love to all mankind!

———————————————

* English version by Robert Huntington.

4. "THE GOSPEL ACCORDING TO BROWNING"

A DEATH IN THE DESERT

Robert Browning

In 1864 Robert Browning published *Dramatis Personae*. This volume contained, among others, three poems—"Abt Vogler," "Rabbi Ben Ezra," and "A Death in the Desert" —which have sometimes been described as "The Gospel According to Browning." Of these "A Death in the Desert" is richest in the exposition of Christian doctrine. It is also, by all means, the most difficult.

The situation at the beginning is this: St. John, a very old man, has fled from persecution in Ephesus, and a group of his disciples have brought him to a cave in the desert. Here they have been hiding for sixty days. The Apostle is in a kind of trance, but they hope he will come back to them long enough to deliver a last message. Various expedients to recall him are tried, but nothing succeeds until a boy in the company reads aloud from John's own Gospel the great words "I am the Resurrection and the Life."

For the purpose of this poem, Browning accepts the traditional ascription to John not only of the Fourth Gospel but also of the Book of Revelation and of three pastoral Epistles. In "A Death in the Desert" John explains why he wrote these works. The Epistles were informal, personal testimony. The Revelation was given to him; he was commanded to write; no interpretations of his own entered into it. But the Gospel was definitely an attempt to meet the heresies of the time. Certain matters were clear now that had not been clear before; certain facts had emerged into a clearer light. Now that few of those who had known Jesus when he was on earth were still living, a new approach was needed to the problems of a more critical age.

John's hearers, in these latter days, do not deny the practical value of his doctrines. But, they argue, he may still be preaching one of those myths that human imagi-nation has always loved to invent and to believe in. Man has always made God in his own image, progressing from lower to higher ideals. What reason is there to suppose that Christianity is on a different basis?

John's reply to this argument is as follows. The acknowledgment of God in Christ solves man's final problem. To search about the roots of what commends itself to the soul and becomes power and light within is to make the worst of all possible errors—to doubt life itself. This is to snatch loss from gain, and from life to fall back upon death. To argue that love is so human that it cannot be divine is to reject Christ through very need. It is impossible to believe that man has progressed beyond God.

Browning does not keep wholly within his alleged frame of reference in this poem. He was interested in the theological controversies of his own time, and attempting a reply to David Strauss, whose *Leben Jesu*, translated by George Eliot, had disturbed much Victorian thinking. The ideas he puts into John's mouth are often nineteenth century ideas.

———

[Supposed of Pamphylax the Antiochene:
It is a parchment, of my rolls the fifth,
Hath three skins glued together, is all Greek,
And goeth from *Epsilon* down to *Mu*;
Lies second in the surnamed Chosen Chest,
Stained and conserved with juice of terebinth,
Covered with cloth of hair, and lettered *Xi*,
From Xanthus, my wife's uncle now at peace;
Mu and *Epsilon* stand for my own name.
I may not write it, but I make a cross
To show I wait His coming, with the rest,
And leave off here; beginneth Pamphylax.]

I said, "If one should wet his lips with wine,
And slip the broadest plantain-leaf we find,
Or else the lappet of a linen robe,

Into the water-vessel, lay it right,
And cool his forehead just above the eyes,
The while a brother, kneeling either side,
Should chafe each hand and try to make it warm—
He is not so far gone but he might speak."

This did not happen in the outer cave,
Nor in the secret chamber of the rock—
Where, sixty days since the decree was out,
We had him, bedded on a camel-skin,
And waited for his dying all the while—
But in the midmost grotto, since noon's light
Reached there a little, and we would not lose
The last of what might happen on his face.
I at the head, and Xanthus at the feet,
With Valens and the Boy, had lifted him,
And brought him from the chamber in the depths,
And laid him in the light where we might see;
For certain smiles began about his mouth,
And his lids moved, presageful of the end.

Beyond, and halfway up the mouth o' the cave,
The Bactrian convert, having his desire,
Kept watch, and made pretense to graze a goat
That gave us milk, on rags of various herb,
Plantain and quitch, the rocks' shade keeps alive—
So that if any thief or soldier passed
(Because the persecution was aware),
Yielding the goat up promptly with his life,
Such man might pass on, joyful at a prize,
Nor care to pry into the cool o' the cave.
Outside was all noon and the burning blue.

"Here is wine," answered Xanthus—dropped a drop;
I stooped and placed the lap of cloth aright,
Then chafed his right hand, and the Boy his left;
But Valens had bethought him, and produced
And broke a ball of nard, and made perfume.
Only, he did—not so much wake, as—turn
And smile a little, as a sleeper does
If any dear one call him, touch his face—
And smiles and loves, but will not be disturbed.

Then Xanthus said a prayer, but still he slept.
It is the Xanthus that escaped to Rome,
Was burned, and could not write the chronicle.

Then the Boy sprang up from his knees, and ran,
Stung by the splendor of a sudden thought,

And fetched the seventh plate of graven lead
Out of the secret chamber, found a place,
Pressing with finger on the deeper dints,
And spoke, as 'twere his mouth proclaiming first,
"I am the Resurrection and the Life."

Whereat he opened his eyes wide at once,
And sat up of himself, and looked at us;
And thenceforth nobody pronounced a word.
Only, outside, the Bactrian cried his cry
Like the lone desert-bird that wears the ruff,
As signal we were safe, from time to time.

First he said, "If a friend declared to me,
This my son Valens, this my other son,
Were James and Peter—nay, declared as well
This lad was very John—I could believe!
—Could, for a moment, doubtlessly believe;
So is myself withdrawn into my depths,
The soul retreated from the perished brain
Whence it was wont to feel and use the world
Through these dull members, done with long ago.
Yet I myself remain; I feel myself—
And there is nothing lost. Let be, awhile!"

[This is the doctrine he was wont to teach,
How divers persons witness in each man,
Three souls which make up one soul: first, to wit,
A soul of each and all the bodily parts,
Seated therein, which works, and is what Does,
And has the use of earth, and ends the man
Downward; but, tending upward for advice,
Grows into, and again is grown into
By the next soul, which, seated in the brain,
Useth the first with its collected use,
And feeleth, thinketh, willeth—is what Knows;
Which, duly tending upward in its turn,
Grows into, and again is grown into
By the last soul, that uses both the first,
Subsisting whether they assist or no,
And, constituting man's self, is what Is—
And leans upon the former, makes it play,
As that played off the first: and, tending up,
Holds, is upheld by, God, and ends the man
Upward in that dread point of intercourse,
Nor needs a place, for it returns to Him.
What Does, what Knows, what Is; three souls, one
    man.
I give the glossa as Theotypas.]

And then, "A stick, once fire from end to end;
Now, ashes save the tip that holds a spark!
Yet, blow the spark, it runs back, spreads itself
A little where the fire was. Thus I urge
The soul that served me, till it task once more
What ashes of my brain have kept their shape,
And these make effort on the last o' the flesh,
Trying to taste again the truth of things"
(He smiled)—"their very superficial truth;
As that ye are my sons, that it is long
Since James and Peter had release by death,
And I am only he, your brother John,
Who saw and heard, and could remember all.
Remember all! It is not much to say.
What if the truth broke on me from above
As once and ofttimes? Such might hap again;
Doubtlessly He might stand in presence here,
With head wool-white, eyes flame, and feet like
    brass,
The sword and the seven stars, as I have seen—
I who now shudder only and surmise,
'How did your brother bear that sight and live?'

"If I live yet, it is for good, more love
Through me to men; be naught but ashes here
That keep awhile my semblance, who was John—
Still, when they scatter, there is left on earth
No one alive who knew (consider this!),
Saw with his eyes and handled with his hands
That which was from the first, the Word of Life.
How will it be when none more saith 'I saw'?

"Such ever was love's way: to rise, it stoops.
Since I, whom Christ's mouth taught, was bidden
    teach,
I went, for many years, about the world,
Saying 'It was so; so I heard and saw,'
Speaking as the case asked; and men believed.
Afterward came the message to myself
In Patmos isle; I was not bidden teach,
But simply listen, take a book and write,
Nor set down other than the given word,
With nothing left to my arbitrament
To choose or change. I wrote, and men believed.
Then—for my time grew brief, no message more,
No call to write again—I found a way,
And, reasoning from my knowledge, merely taught
Men should, for love's sake, in love's strength believe;
Or I would pen a letter to a friend

And urge the same as friend, nor less nor more.
Friends said I reasoned rightly, and believed.
But at the last, why, I seemed left alive
Like a sea-jelly weak on Patmos strand,
To tell dry sea-beach gazers how I fared
When there was mid-sea, and the mighty things;
Left to repeat, 'I saw, I heard, I knew,'
And go all over the old ground again,
With Antichrist already in the world,
And many Antichrists, who answered prompt,
'Am I not Jasper as thyself art John?
Nay, young, whereas through age thou mayest for-
    get;
Wherefore, explain, or how shall we believe?'
I never thought to call down fire on such,
Or, as in wonderful and early days,
Pick up the scorpion, tread the serpent dumb;
But patient stated much of the Lord's life
Forgotten or misdelivered, and let it work,
Since much that at the first, in deed and word,
Lay simply and sufficiently exposed,
Had grown (or else my soul was grown to match,
Fed through such years, familiar with such light,
Guarded and guided still to see and speak)
Of new significance and fresh result;
What first were guessed as points, I now knew stars,
And named them in the Gospel I have writ.
For men said, 'It is getting long ago;
Where is the promise of his coming?'—asked
These young ones in their strength, as loath to wait,
Of me who, when their sires were born, was old.
I, for I loved them, answered, joyfully,
Since I was there, and helpful in my age;
And, in the main, I think such men believed.
Finally, thus endeavoring, I fell sick;
Ye brought me here, and I supposed the end,
And went to sleep with one thought that, at least,
Though the whole earth should lie in wickedness,
We had the truth, might leave the rest to God.
Yet now I wake in such decrepitude
As I have slidden down and fallen afar,
Past even the presence of my former self,
Grasping the while for stay at facts which snap,
Till I am found away from my own world,
Feeling for foothold through a blank profound,
Along with unborn people in strange lands,
Who say—I hear said or conceive they say—
'Was John at all, and did he say he saw?
Assure us, ere we ask what he might see!'

"And how shall I assure them? Can they share—
They, who have flesh, a veil of youth and strength
About each spirit, that needs must bide its time,
Living and learning still as years assist
Which wear the thickness thin, and let man see—
With me who hardly am withheld at all,
But shudderingly, scarce a shred between,
Lie bare to the universal prick of light?
Is it for nothing we grow old and weak,
We whom God loves? When pain ends, gain ends too.
To me, that story—aye, that Life and Death
Of which I wrote 'it was'—to me, it is;
—Is, here and now; I apprehend naught else.
Is not God now i' the world his power first made?
Is not his love at issue still with sin,
Visibly when a wrong is done on earth?
Love, wrong, and pain, what see I else around?
Yea, and the Resurrection and Uprise
To the right hand of the throne—what is it beside,
When such truth, breaking bounds, o'erfloods my
    soul,
And, as I saw the sin and death, even so
See I the need yet transiency of both,
The good and glory consummated thence?
I saw the power; I see the Love, once weak,
Resume the Power; and in this world 'I see,'
Lo, there is recognized the Spirit of both,
That moving o'er the spirit of man, unblinds
His eye and bids him look. These are, I see;
But ye, the children, his beloved ones too,
Ye need—as I should use an optic glass
I wondered at erewhile, somewhere i' the world,
It had been given a crafty smith to make;
A tube, he turned on objects brought too close,
Lying confusedly insubordinate
For the unassisted eye to master once:
Look through his tube, at distance now they lay,
Become succinct, distinct, so small, so clear!
Just thus, ye needs must apprehend what truth
I see, reduced to plain historic fact,
Diminished into clearness, proved a point
And far away; ye would withdraw your sense
From out eternity, strain it upon time,
Then stand before that fact, that Life and Death,
Stay there at gaze, till it dispart, dispread,
As though a star should open out, all sides,
Grow the world on you, as it is my world.
For life, with all it yields of joy and woe,
And hope and fear—believe the aged friend—

Is just our chance o' the prize of learning love,
How love might be, hath been indeed, and is;
And that we hold thenceforth to the uttermost
Such prize despite the envy of the world,
And, having gained truth, keep truth; that is all.
But see the double way wherein we are led,
How the soul learns diversely from the flesh!
With flesh, that hath so little time to stay,
And yields mere basement for the soul's emprise,
Expect prompt teaching. Helpful was the light,
And warmth was cherishing, and food was choice
To every man's flesh, thousand years ago,
As now to yours and mine; the body sprang
At once to the height, and stayed: but the soul—no!
Since sages who, this noontide, meditate
In Rome or Athens, may descry some point
Of the eternal power, hid yestereve;
And, as thereby the power's whole mass extends,
So much extends the ether floating o'er
The love that tops the might, the Christ in God.
Then, as new lessons shall be learned in these
Till earth's work stop and useless time run out,
So duly, daily, needs provision be
For keeping the soul's prowess possible,
Building new barriers as the old decay,
Saving us from evasion of life's proof,
Putting the question ever, 'Does God love,
And will ye hold that truth against the world?'
Ye know there needs no second proof with good
Gained for our flesh from any earthly source;
We might go freezing, ages; give us fire—
Thereafter we judge fire at its full worth,
And guard it safe through every chance, ye know!
That fable of Prometheus and his theft,
How mortals gained Jove's fiery flower, grows old
(I have been used to hear the pagans own)
And out of mind; but fire, howe'er its birth,
Here is it, precious to the sophist now
Who laughs the myth of Æschylus to scorn,
As precious to those satyrs of his play,
Who touched it in gay wonder at the thing.
While were it so with the soul—this gift of truth,
Once grasped, were this our soul's gain safe, and sure
To prosper as the body's gain is wont—
Why, man's probation would conclude, his earth
Crumble; for he both reasons and decides,
Weighs first, then chooses: will he give up fire
For gold or purple, once he knows its worth?
Could he give Christ up were his worth as plain?

Therefore, I say, to test man, the proofs shift,
Nor may he grasp that fact like other fact,
And straightway in his life acknowledge it,
As, say, the indubitable bliss of fire.
Sigh ye, 'It had been easier once than now'?
To give you answer I am left alive;
Look at me who was·present from the first!
Ye know what things I saw; then came a test,
My first, befitting me who so had seen:
'Forsake the Christ thou sawest transfigured, him
Who trod the sea and brought the dead to life?
What should wring this from thee!'—ye laugh and
    ask.
What wrung it? Even a torchlight and a noise,
The sudden Roman faces, violent hands,
And fear of what the Jews might do! Just that.
And it is written, 'I forsook and fled.'
There was my trial, and it ended thus.
Aye, but my soul had gained its truth, could grow;
Another year or two—what little child,
What tender woman, that had seen no least
Of all my sights, but barely heard them told,
Who did not clasp the cross with a light laugh,
Or wrap the burning robe round, thanking God?
Well, was truth safe forever, then? Not so.
Already had begun the silent work
Whereby truth, deadened of its absolute blaze,
Might need love's eye to pierce the o'er-stretched
    doubt.
Teachers were busy, whispering 'All is true
As the aged ones report; but youth can reach
Where age gropes dimly, weak with stir and strain,
And the full doctrine slumbers till today.'
Thus, what the Roman's lowered spear was found,
A bar to me who touched and handled truth,
Now proved the glozing of some new shrewd tongue,
This Ebion, this Cerinthus, or their mates,
Till imminent was the outcry 'Save our Christ!'
Whereon I stated much of the Lord's life
Forgotten or misdelivered, and let it work.
Such work done, as it will be, what comes next?
What do I hear say, or conceive men say,
'Was John at all, and did he say he saw?
Assure us, ere we ask what he might see!'
Is this indeed a burden for late days,
And may I help to bear it with you all,
Using my weakness which becomes your strength?
For if a babe were born inside this grot,
Grew to a boy here, heard us praise the sun,

Yet had but yon sole glimmer in light's place—
One, loving him and wishful he should learn,
Would much rejoice himself was blinded first
Month by month here, so made to understand
How eyes, born darkling, apprehend amiss.
I think I could explain to such a child
There was more glow outside than gleams he caught,
Aye, nor need urge 'I saw it, so believe!'
It is a heavy burden you shall bear
In latter days, new lands, or old grown strange,
Left without me, which must be very soon.
What is the doubt, my brothers? Quick with it!
I see you stand conversing, each new face,
Either in fields, of yellow summer eves,
On islets yet unnamed amid the sea;
Or pace for shelter 'neath a portico
Out of the crowd in some enormous town
Where now the larks sing in a solitude;
Or muse upon blank heaps of stone and sand
Idly conjectured to be Ephesus;
And no one asks his fellow any more
'Where is the promise of his coming?' but
'Was he revealed in any of his lives,
As Power, as Love, as Influencing Soul?'

"Quick, for time presses, tell the whole mind out,
And let us ask and answer and be saved!
My book speaks on, because it cannot pass;
One listens quietly, nor scoffs but pleads,
'Here is a tale of things done ages since;
What truth was ever told the second day?
Wonders, that would prove doctrine, go for naught.
Remains the doctrine, love; well, we must love,
And what we love most, power and love in one,
Let us acknowledge on the record here,
Accepting these in Christ. Must Christ then be?
Has he been? Did not we ourselves make him?
Our mind receives but what it holds, no more.
First of the love, then; we acknowledge Christ—
A proof we comprehend his love, a proof
We had such love already in ourselves,
Knew first what else we should not recognize.
'Tis mere projection from man's inmost mind,
And, what he loves, thus falls reflected back,
Becomes accounted somewhat out of him;
He throws it up in air, it drops down earth's,
With shape, name, story added, man's old way.
How prove you Christ came otherwise at least?
Next try the power: he made and rules the world;

Certes there is a world once made, now ruled,
Unless things have been ever as we see.
Our sires declared a charioteer's yoked steeds
Brought the sun up the east and down the west,
Which only of itself now rises, sets,
As if a hand impelled it and a will—
Thus they long thought, they who had will and
    hands;
But the new question's whisper is distinct,
Wherefore must all force needs be like ourselves?
We have the hands, the will; what made and drives
The sun is force, is law, is named, not known,
While will and love we do know; marks of these,
Eye-witnesses attest, so books declare—
As that, to punish or reward our race,
The sun at undue times arose or set
Or else stood still: what do not men affirm?
But earth requires as urgently reward
Or punishment today as years ago,
And none expects the sun will interpose;
Therefore it was mere passion and mistake,
Or erring zeal for right, which changed the truth.
Go back, far, farther, to the birth of things;
Ever the will, the intelligence, the love,
Man's!—which he gives, supposing he but finds,
As late he gave head, body, hands, and feet,
To help these in what forms he called his gods.
First, Jove's brow, Juno's eyes were swept away,
But Jove's wrath, Juno's pride continued long;
As last, will, power, and love discarded these,
So law in turn discards power, love, and will.
What proveth God is otherwise at least?
All else, projection from the mind of man!'

"Nay, do not give me wine, for I am strong,
But place my gospel where I put my hands.

"I say that man was made to grow, not stop;
That help, he needed once, and needs no more,
Having grown but an inch by, is withdrawn:
For he hath new needs, and new helps to these.
This imports solely, man should mount on each
New height in view; the help whereby he mounts,
The ladder-rung his foot has left, may fall,
Since all things suffer change save God the Truth.
Man apprehends him newly at each stage
Whereat earth's ladder drops, its service done;
And nothing shall prove twice what once was proved.
You stick a garden-plot with ordered twigs

To show inside lie germs of herbs unborn,
And check the careless step would spoil their birth;
But when herbs wave, the guardian twigs may go,
Since should ye doubt of virtues, question kinds,
It is no longer for old twigs ye look,
Which proved once underneath lay store of seed,
But to the herb's self, by what light ye boast,
For what fruit's signs are. This book's fruit is plain,
Nor miracles need prove it any more.
Doth the fruit show? Then miracles bade 'ware
At first of root and stem, saved both till now
From trampling ox, rough boar, and wanton goat.
What? Was man made a wheelwork to wind up,
And be discharged, and straight wound up anew?
No!—grown, his growth lasts; taught, he ne'er for-
    gets;
May learn a thousand things, not twice the same.
This might be pagan teaching; now hear mine.

"I say, that as the babe, you feed awhile,
Becomes a boy and fit to feed himself,
So, minds at first must be spoon-fed with truth;
When they can eat, babe's nurture is withdrawn.
I fed the babe whether it would or no;
I bid the boy or feed himself or starve.
I cried once, 'That ye may believe in Christ,
Behold this blind man shall receive his sight!'
I cry now, 'Urgest thou, *for I am shrewd*
And smile at stories how John's word could cure—
Repeat that miracle and take my faith?'
I say, that miracle was duly wrought
When, save for it, no faith was possible.
Whether a change were wrought i' the shows o' the
    world,
Whether the change came from our minds which see
Of shows o' the world so much as and no more
Than God wills for his purpose—what do I
See now, suppose you, there where you see rock
Round us?—I know not; such was the effect,
So faith grew, making void more miracles
Because too much; they would compel, not help.
I say, the acknowledgment of God in Christ
Accepted by thy reason, solves for thee
All questions in the earth and out of it,
And has so far advanced thee to be wise.
Wouldst thou unprove this to re-prove the proved?
In life's mere minute, with power to use that proof,
Leave knowledge and revert to how it sprung?
Thou hast it; use it and forthwith, or die!

"For I say, this is death and the sole death,
When a man's loss comes to him from his gain,
Darkness from light, from knowledge ignorance,
And lack of love from love made manifest;
A lamp's death when, replete with oil, it chokes;
A stomach's when, surcharged with food, it starves.
With ignorance was surety of a cure.
When man, appalled at nature, questioned first,
'What if there lurk a might behind this might?'
He needed satisfaction God could give,
And did give, as ye have the written word;
But when he finds might still redouble might,
Yet asks, 'Since all is might, what use of will?'
—Will, the one source of might—he being man
With a man's will and a man's might, to teach
In little how the two combine in large—
That man has turned round on himself and stands,
Which in the course of nature is, to die.

"And when man questioned, 'What if there be love
Behind the will and might, as real as they?'—
He needed satisfaction God could give,
And did give, as ye have the written word;
But when, beholding that love everywhere,
He reasons, 'Since such love is everywhere,
And since ourselves can love and would be loved,
We ourselves make the love, and Christ was not'—
How shall ye help this man who knows himself
That he must love and would be loved again,
Yet, owning his own love that proveth Christ,
Rejecteth Christ through very need of him?
The lamp o'erswims with oil, the stomach flags
Loaded with nurture, and that man's soul dies.

"If he rejoin, 'But this was all the while
A trick; the fault was, first of all, in thee,
Thy story of the places, names, and dates,
Where, when, and how the ultimate truth had rise—
Thy prior truth, at last discovered none,
Whence now the second suffers detriment.
What good of giving knowledge if, because
O' the manner of the gift, its profit fail?
And why refuse what modicum of help
Had stopped the after-doubt, impossible
I' the face of truth—truth absolute, uniform?
Why must I hit of this and miss of that,
Distinguish just as I be weak or strong,
And not ask of thee and have answer prompt,
Was this once, was it not once?—then and now

And evermore, plain truth from man to man.
Is John's procedure just the heathen bard's?
Put question of his famous play again,
How, for the ephemerals' sake, Jove's fire was filched,
And carried in a cane and brought to earth;
The fact is in the fable, cry the wise,
Mortals obtained the boon, so much is fact,
Though fire be spirit and produced on earth.
As with the Titan's, so now with thy tale;
Why breed in us perplexity, mistake,
Nor tell the whole truth in the proper words?"

"I answer, Have ye yet to argue out
The very primal thesis, plainest law—
Man is not God, but hath God's end to serve,
A master to obey, a course to take,
Somewhat to cast off, somewhat to become?
Grant this, then man must pass from old to new,
From vain to real, from mistake to fact,
From what once seemed good, to what now proves
        best.
How could man have progression otherwise?
Before the point was mooted 'What is God?'
No savage man inquired 'What am myself?'
Much less replied, 'First, last, and best of things.'
Man takes that title now if he believes
Might can exist with neither will nor love,
In God's case—what he names now Nature's Law—
While in himself he recognizes love
No less than might and will: and rightly takes.
Since if man prove the sole existent thing
Where these combine, whatever their degree,
However weak the might or will or love,
So they be found there, put in evidence—
He is as surely higher in the scale
Than any might with neither love nor will,
As life, apparent in the poorest midge
(When the faint dust-speck flits, ye guess its wing),
Is marvelous beyond dead Atlas' self—
Given to the nobler midge for resting-place!
Thus, man proves best and highest—God, in fine,
And thus the victory leads but to defeat,
The gain to loss, best rise to the worst fall,
His life becomes impossible, which is death.

"But if, appealing thence, he cower, avouch
He is mere man, and in humility
Neither may know God nor mistake himself;
I point to the immediate consequence

And say, by such confession straight he falls
Into man's place, a thing nor God nor beast,
Made to know that he can know and not more;
Lower than God, who knows all and can all,
Higher than beasts, which know and can so far
As each beast's limit, perfect to an end,
Nor conscious that they know, nor craving more;
While man knows partly but conceives beside,
Creeps ever on from fancies to the fact,
And in this striving, this converting air
Into a solid he may grasp and use,
Finds progress, man's distinctive mark alone,
Not God's, and not the beasts'—God is, they are,
Man partly is and wholly hopes to be.
Such progress could no more attend his soul,
Were all it struggles after found at first
And guesses changed to knowledge absolute,
Than motion wait his body, were all else
Than it the solid earth on every side,
Where now through space he moves from rest to **rest**.
Man, therefore, thus conditioned, must expect
He could not, what he knows now, know at first;
What he considers that he knows today,
Come but tomorrow, he will find misknown;
Getting increase of knowledge, since he learns
Because he lives, which is to be a man,
Set to instruct himself by his past self:
First, like the brute, obliged by facts to learn,
Next, as man may, obliged by his own mind,
Bent, habit, nature, knowledge turned to law.
God's gift was that man should conceive of truth
And yearn to gain it, catching at mistake,
As midway help till he reach fact indeed.
The statuary, ere he mold a shape,
Boasts a like gift—the shape's idea—and next
The aspiration to produce the same;
So, taking clay, he calls his shape thereout,
Cries ever, 'Now I have the thing I see';
Yet all the while goes changing what was wrought,
From falsehood like the truth, to truth itself.
How were it had he cried, 'I see no face,
No breast, no feet i' the ineffectual clay'?
Rather commend him that he clapped his hands,
And laughed, 'It is my shape and lives again!'
Enjoyed the falsehood, touched it on to truth,
Until yourselves applaud the flesh indeed
In what is still flesh-imitating clay.
Right in you, right in him, such way be man's!
God only makes the live shape at a jet.

Will ye renounce this pact of creatureship?
The pattern on the Mount subsists no more,
Seemed awhile, then returned to nothingness;
But copies, Moses strove to make thereby,
Serve still and are replaced as time requires.
By these, make newest vessels, reach the type!
If ye demur, this judgment on your head,
Never to reach the ultimate, angels' law,
Indulging every instinct of the soul
There where law, life, joy, impulse are one thing!

"Such is the burden of the latest time.
I have survived to hear it with my ears,
Answer it with my lips; does this suffice?
For if there be a further woe than such,
Wherein my brothers struggling need a hand,
So long as any pulse is left in mine,
May I be absent even longer yet,
Plucking the blind ones back from the abyss,
Though I should tarry a new hundred years!"
But he was dead; 'twas about noon, the day
Somewhat declining. We five buried him
That eve, and then, dividing, went five ways,
And I, disguised, returned to Ephesus.

By this, the cave's mouth must be filled with sand.
Valens is lost, I know not of his trace;
The Bactrian was but a wild childish man,
And could not write nor speak, but only loved.
So, lest the memory of this go quite,
Seeing that I tomorrow fight the beasts,
I tell the same to Phœbas, whom believe!
For many look again to find that face,
Beloved John's to whom I ministered,
Somewhere in life about the world; they err—
Either mistaking what was darkly spoke
At ending of his book, as he relates,
Or misconceiving somewhat of this speech
Scattered from mouth to mouth, as I suppose.
Believe ye will not see him any more
About the world with his divine regard!
For all was as I say, and now the man
Lies as he lay once, breast to breast with God.

————————

[Cerinthus read and mused; one added this:

"If Christ, as thou affirmest, be of men
Mere man, the first and best but nothing more—
Account him, for reward of what he was,

Now and forever, wretchedest of all.
For see; himself conceived of life as love,
Conceived of love as what must enter in,
Fill up, make one with his each soul he loved:
Thus much for man's joy, all men's joy for him.
Well, he is gone, thou sayest, to fit reward.
But by this time are many souls set free,
And very many still retained alive;
Nay, should his coming be delayed awhile,
Say, ten years longer (twelve years, some compute),

See if, for every finger of thy hands,
There be not found, that day the world shall end,
Hundreds of souls, each holding by Christ's word
That he will grow incorporate with all,
With me as Pamphylax, with him as John,
Groom for each bride! Can a mere man do this?
Yet Christ saith, this he lived and died to do.
Call Christ, then, the illimitable God,
Or lost!"

　　　　But 'twas Cerinthus that is lost.]

5. "WHAT THINK YE OF CHRIST?"

EXCELLENCY OF CHRIST

Giles Fletcher

He is a path, if any be misled;
　He is a robe, if any naked be;
If any chance to hunger, he is bread;
　If any be a bondman he is free;
　If any be but weak, how strong is he!
To dead men life he is, to sick men health;
To blind men sight, and to the needy wealth;
A pleasure without loss, a treasure without stealth.

STILL THOU ART QUESTION

Anonymous

We place Thy sacred name upon our brows;
　Our cycles from Thy natal day we score:
Yet, spite of all our songs and all our vows,
　We thirst and ever thirst to know Thee more.

For Thou art Mystery and Question still;
　Even when we see Thee lifted as a sign
Drawing all men unto that hapless hill
　With the resistless power of Love Divine.

Still Thou art Question—while rings in our ears
　Thine outcry to a world discord-beset:
Have I been with thee all these many years,
　O World—dost thou not know Me even yet?

OUR CHRIST

Lucy Larcom

In Christ I feel the heart of God
　Throbbing from heaven through earth;
Life stirs again within the clod;
　Renewed in beauteous birth,
The soul springs up, a flower of prayer,
Breathing His breath out on the air.

In Christ I touch the hand of God,
  From His pure height reached down,
By blessed ways before untrod,
  To lift us to our crown;
Victory that only perfect is
Through loving sacrifice, like His.

Holding His hand, my steadied feet
  May walk the air, the seas;
On life and death His smile falls sweet,
  Lights up all mysteries:
Stranger nor exile can I be
In new worlds where He leadeth me.

Not my Christ only; He is ours;
  Humanity's close bond;
Key to its vast, unopened powers,
  Dream of our dreams beyond.
What yet we shall be none can tell:
Now are we His, and all is well.

OUR WARS ARE WARS OF LIFE

Robert Browning

Our wars are wars of life, and wounds of love,
With intellect spears and longwinged arrows of
  thought,
Mutual, in one another's wrath, all renewing
We live as One Man. For contracting our infinite
  senses
We behold multitude; or expanding, we behold as
  One,
As one man all the Universal Family; and that man
We call Jesus the Christ, and He in us, and we in
  Him,
Live in perfect harmony in Eden the land of life,
Giving, receiving, and forgiving each other's tres-
  passes.

CREDO

John Oxenham

Not what, but *Whom*, I do believe,
  That, in my darkest hour of need,
  Hath comfort that no mortal creed
  To mortal man may give;—
Not what, but *Whom!*
  For Christ is more than all the creeds,
  And His full life of gentle deeds
  Shall all the creeds outlive.
Not what I do believe, but *Whom!*
  Who walks beside me in the gloom?
  Who shares the burden wearisome?
  Who all the dim way doth illume,
  And bids me look beyond the tomb
  The larger life to live?—
Not what I do believe,
But *Whom!*
Not what,
But *Whom!*

THE SONG OF A HEATHEN

Sojourning in Galilee, A. D. 32

Richard Watson Gilder

If Jesus Christ is a man—
  And only a man,—I say
That of all mankind I cleave to him
  And to him will I cleave alway.

If Jesus Christ is a god,—
  And the only God,—I swear
I will follow Him through heaven and hell,
  The earth, the sea, and the air!

6. CHRIST'S REDEEMING POWER IN HISTORY
AND IN FICTION

GOD'S VAGABOND:
ST. FRANCIS OF ASSISI

Gamaliel Bradford

To illustrate the theme of Christ as Redeemer and Saviour, it seems wise, at this point, to go beyond the actual outlines of the Gospel narrative. I present, therefore, in order:

1. Gamaliel Bradford's psychographic study of St. Francis of Assisi, who is universally regarded as having come as close as any man ever came to living as Jesus lived;

2. A selection from *Dred,* by Harriet Beecher Stowe, in which the slave-woman Milly tells the heroine, Nina Gordon, how she learned to forgive the mistress who had sold Milly's children into slavery, how she comforted her mistress in her sorrow and helped her to save her soul alive;

3. Tolstoy's "Where Love Is, There God Is Also," a characteristic story by one of the great Nineteenth Century exponents of the Gospel;

4. Theodore Dreiser's "A Doer of the Word," a powerful piece of reporting about a modern Saint Francis.

I

In this developing twentieth century the immediate world of space and time has become so ample, so rich, so varied, in its hurrying, crowding luxury of interest and splendor, that it seems to absorb and engross us altogether, especially as the sense of any other world has grown more and more obscure and dim. It is, then, surely curious and perhaps profitable to turn back seven hundred years to a man like Francis of Assisi, to whom the things of the other world, eternal things, were so vivid and so real that he literally cast the joy and the splendor and the glory of this world under his feet and trod them in the dust.

Francis Bernardone, born about 1182, was the son of a well-to-do traveling merchant of Assisi. He was brought up in ease and luxury and seemed at first disposed to dissipation and riotous companionship. But he had a tender heart and a vivid imagination. These things soon made him sensitive to human misery, and above all keenly alive to the injustice of his having the good things of the world while so many others were wholly without them. Since his mind was as logical as his heart was sympathetic, the next step was to discard his own advantages utterly, and to stride right out into the empty world with the spirit of Christ as his only possession. Rich in this, he preached Christ, he practiced Christ, he lived Christ, and with the aid of the Church and of those in authority, he established an order of followers, whom he sent out from his little chapel in Assisi to preach the gospel as he saw it, all over the world. He himself, after two unsuccessful attempts, got as far as the Orient, in 1219, in the track of the Crusaders, and preached the gospel to the heathen and even to the Sultan, though without converting him or attaining the ideal of martyrdom which seemed so desirable. When Francis returned to Italy, the aura of sainthood had already gathered about him, and his death in 1226 is enveloped in the usual cloud of unprofitable miracles, culminating in the mysterious Stigmata, or impress of Christ's wounds upon the saint's body, a cloud of myth and legend from which it is almost as difficult to disentangle the real man as in the case of Jesus himself. Yet Francis, like Jesus, was so vividly and intensely human that even the adoration of seven centuries is not enough to obscure him entirely.

The first principle of Francis's religion was that of absolute, complete, uncompromising poverty. It seemed to him that not only the possession of money, but the desire for money and what it brings, was the root of all evil. And it is difficult not to agree with him that if you could get rid of that desire, most social and economic evils would settle themselves. Modern society, all human society, is composed of a few people who have a great deal, and who incidentally always want more than they have, and a vast number who violently, passionately want what belongs to, or, at any rate, is in the possession of, the others. If you could once thoroughly eradicate the fatal wanting, all the economic problems would be settled. Get rid of it, want nothing but Christ, said Francis. Seven hundred years later Tolstoy adopted much the same attitude. But Tolstoy hardly attempted to get beyond this world, while Francis had the immense compensating possibilities of the other world to support him. Naturally the abolition of wanting involves all sorts of contradictions and inconsistencies. Life would appear to be wanting and the abolition of wanting would come perilously close to death. Furthermore, if nobody has anything, who is to give to others, and how is the world to go on? But Francis had a practical and concrete mind. He did not foresee the slightest danger that the world in general would adopt his principles, and if it did, the world must take care of itself. He saw what was right for him, and he was going to do it, if the heavens fell.

When I was twenty and was engaged to be married, my love and I came to see the world for the time something as Saint Francis saw it. We, too, felt that we should give up luxury and wanting, should discard the comforting equipment of material life, to which we were accustomed, but of which so many millions were destitute, and adopt voluntary poverty for the good of the world and our own souls. As a letter of that time expresses it: "We should give up everything, live not only simply, but in poverty, with the poorest of clothes and the simplest of food, giving up everything material, everything tending to outward things, not because we want to be ascetic,

but because we will have nothing to draw us from the life within and because we want to set an example of forgetting all the luxuries and comforts of the body. We want to build a little house somewhere, perfectly plain and poor, and live there in every way just as peasants would live."

We were twenty, and simple, and foolish. Our parents and relatives and friends ridiculed us and scolded us and reasoned with us, and in the end forced us to let our ideals go—for better, for worse?—I wonder. The only point of importance is that Francis of Assisi did not let his ideals go; he let father and mother and home and wealth and friends all go hang, and followed God. When his father argued with him and bullied him and finally dragged him before the bishop to be rebuked for taking what did not belong to him, Francis came quietly into the assembled throng, tore off even every rag of clothing and threw it down at his father's feet, declaring that from that day on he had a father in heaven who would provide for him. There are times when I wish I had behaved as Francis did.

He had no doubts or hesitations or difficulties. Or if he had them he overcame them by the goodness of God. As for money, he spurned it, rejected it, cast it from him, from the beginning to the end. As the *Speculum Perfectionis* has it, "Francis, the true friend and imitator of Christ, despising all things which are of this world, above all detested money and by word and example led his followers to flee it as if it were the Devil." They were to subsist by God's loving support, and if they relied upon it, it would not fail them. This does not mean that Francis advocated direct beggary as the entire means of livelihood. On the contrary, he was always insistent upon honest labor. Those who followed him should work as they had been accustomed to do and should receive proper reward for it. Only the reward should not go beyond the bare means of subsistence, and, if there was any superfluity, it should be immediately passed on to those who were in greater need.

For Francis not only condemned and contemned money in its immediate form. He was still more hostile to the accumulation of it in possessions of any kind. No radical of the present day could be more bitter in his denunciations of capital, not only in its far-reaching aspects of vaster ownership, but even, perhaps still more, in the petty grasp on small visible holdings to which men cling with a madder grip than they extend to airy claims which they cannot see but only imagine. The owner of a cottage or a cow is a capitalist just as much as is a Rockefeller or a Ford, and he hates to have the cow or the cottage taken away from him, just as they would hate to lose their millions. All wrong, says Francis, and he speaks right out about the whole business: "I don't want to be a thief, and to have what others lack is to be a sheer thief and nothing else." Those who followed him were to count nothing as belonging to them except the clothes on their backs, and even those were often to be turned over to any who might be more greatly in need of them.

Evidently Francis was starting the greatest fight in the world, the one that all fundamental reformers have undertaken, the fight against human nature. Even before his death he saw the huge forces of greed and avarice, the desire for gain and the desire for power, breaking in on the Rule he sought to establish. Over and over he enjoined upon his disciples that they must keep the simple principles before them—love, quiet, faithful labor, persistent self-sacrifice, above all the fundamental idea of not wanting, not wanting the things of this world, rooting them out of your spirit altogether. Poverty, living without money, and all the accursed things which money brings, which cannot be had without it and are of no real profit when you get them, that was the lesson that he tried to teach, by preaching and by example. And with the high-wrought, lyrical, imaginative touch that makes so much of his charm, he breaks out into a hymn of rapture to his spiritual bride, our Holy Lady Poverty: "To trample under foot is to condemn, and Poverty tramples all things under foot, therefore she is queen of all things. But, oh, my holy Lord Jesus Christ, pity me and my Lady Poverty, for I am tortured with the love of her, nor without her can I find repose. . . . Oh, who would not love this Lady Poverty above all others? Of thee, dear Jesus of the Poor, I ask to be honored with this privilege, to be enriched with this treasure, that it may be the eternal distinction of me and mine in thy name to possess nothing whatever under heaven of our own, but to be sustained always by the scanty use of others' benefits, so long as this miserable flesh endures."

Undeniably in these raptures and vehement assertions and injunctions of Francis there is the touch of extravagance and excess which sometimes repels and estranges. There is the mediæval quaintness of expression, there is the ascetic forcing, which makes you feel the ideal to be elevated beyond human reach. What tempers and sweetens all this in Francis is the peculiar flavor and relish of sympathy and tenderness. When his demands seem most impossible, you feel that his penetrating eyes look right down into your heart and see the weakness as well as the strength. Does not the whole depth of the tenderness shine out in this lovely sentence from a letter of his later years? "And I shall know whether you love God and me, his servant and yours, if you do this: see to it that there shall be no brother in the world, no matter how much he has sinned, who if he has once met your eyes, shall go away without your pity. And if he does not ask pity of you, do you ask it of him." No harsh injunction about poverty could ever chill the infinite loving-kindness of that.

II

The second great fundamental principle of Francis's religion was the principle of obedience, and it seems hardly likely that this would be any more to the taste of the twentieth century than the principle of poverty. The vast individualism that has developed during the last hundred years does not greatly relish the notion of blind obedience to anyone for any purpose. Yet it must be admitted that the ideal of obedience is a very restful thing. When one has struggled long with doubtful courses, anxious above all things to do the right, but utterly unable to see where the right lies; when one has come to have a hopeless mistrust of one's reason for guiding one anywhere and to feel that the responsibility for action is the most terrible burden in the world, the dream of obedience to someone who will take all the responsibility and all the burden, to someone who knows, to someone who even thinks he knows, is an exceedingly alluring one. Moreover, obedience is one of the greatest agents in the world for getting things done. The supreme organizing saints, Dominic, Ignatius, understood this perfectly, and built their world-power upon it. Also, obedience is the very best training for command, and those who have formed the habit of taking orders quickly, intelligently, unquestioningly, are often the ones who end by giving the most effective orders themselves.

It may appear that what is apt to be the earliest phase of obedience, the submission to paternal authority, was not very conspicuous in the case of Saint Francis. But as he went on with his life and work, he came to feel that obedience was a most essential virtue, not only for others, but for himself. Great heretics in the religious sphere, like great radicals in the political, are apt to have the instinct of rebellion, even of destruction. They have often the blind impulse to root up and overthrow existing institutions to get rid of their defects, with a secure confidence that the dynamic creative force of mankind will provide something better in their places. The history of Francis's forerunners in that turbulent twelfth century, so effectively told by Miss Davison and Miss Richards, is a history of rebellion at many points. But Saint Francis was by no manner of means a rebel, either by instinct or by practice. Like Abraham Lincoln, he was essentially constructive rather than destructive. He wanted to make over the world, but he wanted to make it over by love, and love does not destroy.

From the beginning of his career he showed his profound respect and submission to the authority of the Church. There might be errors, there might be defects, but such a magnificent power in the world was to be used, not to be battled with. Therefore he approached Pope Innocent III, and Pope Honorius III, and his intimate friend Cardinal Hugolino, who afterwards became Pope Gregory IX, with an inimitable combination of reverent tact and straightforward simplicity, which repeatedly secured for him the permissions and the authorizations he required.

Nor was the obedience or the submission confined to the higher powers or to those whose exalted rank necessarily imposed. Francis enjoined upon all who loved him at all times the profoundest respect for even humble representatives of the Church. They were to be honored and heeded for their office, independent of what they might be in themselves. Even when the hand that ministered at the altar was corrupt and unclean, you were to kiss it, not for what it was, but for what it did. And in the most authentic and undisputed of all his written words, his final Testament, Francis expressly records his feeling on the subject: "If I had the wisdom of Solomon and should come into contact with the poor parish priests of today, dwelling in their parishes, I would not preach against their wishes. And I would reverence,

love, and honor them, and all like them, as if they were my lords and masters."

Never did Francis miss an opportunity to impress this duty of obedience and submission upon all who followed him. In one of his letters to the faithful he writes: "We should never desire to be above others, but should rather be submissive and subject to every human creature for the sake of God." It cannot be denied that here, as in other things, there are elements of the fantastic, of extravagance and excess. Such, for example, is his likening of complete and implicit obedience to death, since a dead body at least does absolutely what is required of it. And the story runs that he ordered an erring brother to be buried up to the neck, till death seemed immediately imminent, then asked him if he was dead, and on his agreeing, let him go with the injunction to obey his superiors as a dead man would: "I want my followers to be dead, not living." But here again it is not the extreme illustration but the principle that counts.

To Francis there were two roots of the supreme, self-resigning obedience. The first root was intellectual. You were to give up, to eschew, to rid yourself utterly of, the pride and exaltation of your intelligence. There has been endless controversy on this point. It has sometimes been urged that Francis was quite ignorant, even of the Scriptures, that he rejected human learning altogether. On the other side it is answered, with good appearance of reason, that he lived with the Bible and that no one could have so perfectly practiced it who was not intimately familiar with its precepts. As later scholarship inevitably made its way into Franciscan pulpits, as into all others, innumerable pleas and explanations have been offered for departing from the Founder's uncompromising attitude. But that attitude is really simple enough. Francis knew what the pride of the intellect is, knew also its abysmal weakness: he had probably had example in himself of both. Learning and scholarship have their place, and he appreciated that place. But learning and scholarship are always too ready to exalt themselves, and they are of no account when once they are placed in competition with the light and the power of the spirit. Francis lived by the spirit, and he wanted others to do the same.

And as the first root of obedience is the humility of the intellect, the obliteration of intellectual pride, so the second root is the abasement of the will. It is the determination to do things simply because you want to do them that kills. This is what you must root out and tear up and overcome. You are told to go and do things. Go and do them, no matter whether every impulse of poor, fragile human nature rebels or not. You are to face ridicule and scorn and discomfort and torture and death, simply because you are ordered to do so, without debate or dispute or discussion or delay.

After which, even for saints like Francis, or rather supremely for the saints, there remains the qualification that when human obedience grows too distasteful, you can fall back upon the will of God, beside which all human command is dwarfed and insignificant. Thus, when the highest authority of the Church suggested that he should make some alteration in his Rule, Francis gently but absolutely declined to comply: "I, most Holy Father, did not place those precepts or words in the Rule, but Christ. . . . Therefore I must not and I cannot change or remove the words of Christ in any way whatever." For there is degree in obedience as in other things.

Yet all the time I confess that what most appeals to me in Francis's gospel of obedience is the getting rid of responsibility, throwing the burden of settling life upon someone else. It seems to me that this is what I have always longed for, and yet I wonder if, after fifty years of erratic independence, I should really relish it. So, alas, of all Francis's virtues. In him they appear exquisite, but an old and weary body, saturated with this world, might find them onerous in practice. The marvel of Francis is that he practiced what he preached. But then he believed in God and in a future life, and perhaps that makes all the difference.

III

The third great principle of Francis's religion was that of chastity, symbolizing in its most vehement form the conflict between the baser, more animal instincts, and the obedience to the higher, spiritual self, an obedience even more difficult and even more significant than the submission to the external will and commands of others.

As with Francis's other principles, there is something about this one also strange, if not quite repellent, to the whole intellectual attitude of the present day. The growing tendency of the later nineteenth and opening twentieth century is to establish a unified human nature, to recognize all the natural instincts as not only respectable but normal and desirable, not to be fought with and repressed and restrained into unnatural fury and turbulence, but to be directed and guided and developed to their fullest satisfaction, limited only by the simple dictates of expediency and common-sense. It is needless to say that the view of Francis and of his age was totally different from this. The animal elements in our nature were the province of the Devil, at any rate the Devil was given power over us by means of them. It was our duty, our highest religious function and divine privilege, to control and subdue these elements by the power of God working through conscience to a higher, remote, future end, an end conforming to God's will and leading to our own supreme final happiness, beside which the mere immediate gratification of the animal instincts seemed ineffably tame and poor.

At any rate, such self-conquest meant everything to Saint Francis of Assisi. And from the hour of his first conversion his effort was to subdue and overcome the weaknesses of the flesh in every possible way. As to the grosser temptations of sex, there is the strange legend, so much associated with other saints that it is difficult to give it more than a legendary character, of his rushing out naked and burying himself in snow-banks to teach the rebellious passions the indispensable lesson of frigidity. Much more valid and significant are the general comments and warnings as to the danger of association with the opposite sex: "Dear brethren, we ought to avoid the intimacy, the conversation, even the sight of women, which are the occasion of ruin to so many, all the more zealously when we realize how such things disturb the weak and weaken the strong."

Yet it is interesting to find that, for all these general injunctions, which no doubt were rigidly applied and acted upon, women played a considerable part in the Saint's life, as was only natural with a temperament so sensitive and so quickly and obviously responsive to all the more delicate emotions. There was the somewhat shadowy Roman lady, Madame Jacopa di Settesoli, to whom Francis seems to have turned for comfort and advice when he was in the Capital and who was opportunely present with him in almost his very last moments. Still more, there was the exquisite Saint Clara, who in her youth cast aside wealth and worldly happiness as Francis did and made it her glory to establish an order of feminine piety in intimate association and affiliation with his. And to Clara even more than to Jacopa, Francis turned for encouragement and inspiration in some of the darkest moments of his career. As Sabatier puts it, in one such moment, "Clara, by urging him to persevere, instilled into him a new enthusiasm. One word of hers sufficed to restore to him all his energy, and from that time on we find in his life more poetry and more love than ever before."

But Francis's subdual of the lower instincts extended far beyond any contest of sex. All immediate fleshly pleasures and indulgences were to be rooted out and got rid of, for the mere power of overcoming them, if for nothing else. There were the temptations of good living, warm housing, luxurious habitations, delicate food. Francis's scheme of holiness allowed for none of these things. Others could not have them, and why should you? If by any chance any little rag or shred of comfort came in your way, what better could you do with it than dispose of it to someone who needed it more? The body, this wretched body, which must so soon be food for worms, why cater to it, why pamper it, why caress it? And in his strange, quaint fashion, he sometimes abused it familiarly, chiding it as "Brother Body"; sometimes he spoke of it as "the ass," to be whipped and bullied and made to travel and bear burdens just exactly as its spirit owner might desire.

Doubtless this abuse of the body went to the usual excesses. It was not only denied, it was tormented. Doubtless there were extravagances of penance and self-humiliation which seem almost childish, as when the Saint ate a bit of chicken for the good of his health and then, in an agony of remorse, had one of his followers hale him into church with a rope around his neck to do penance for his weakness. And the abstinence and the privations were destructive to a physique which was never of the best, so that Francis's last years were a story of physical suffering which would be painful to read about if the sufferings were not borne with such complete spiritual tranquillity even to his final death on the bare ground with nothing beneath him but one poor garment.

But the acme and climax of Francis's self-struggle was undoubtedly his experience with the lepers.

These unhappy creatures were at that time to be found in Italy in considerable numbers, and of course collected in the usual colonies. Francis had always regarded them with the peculiar horror of a sensitive nature, had pitied them, had been ready to aid them as he could—from a distance—but had shunned all intimate contact with them in instinctive disgust. Then one day, about the time of his conversion, he was riding in the country when a leper came in his way. His first, natural, impulse was to throw the man a gratuity, give him his blessing, and pass by on the other side. But the whole power of the new life that had come upon him said no. Here was the opportunity to show the stuff that was in him at its fullest and richest. He went right up to the leper, not only gave him what he had about him, but embraced him, and treated him in every respect as a brother and a friend. From that hour he felt that he had fought the great fight and won, and ever after the lepers were an object of peculiar tenderness and respect and of his constant injunctions to those who followed him. For the lepers merely symbolized the highest victory that a man can win in this world, the victory summed up in the exquisite phrase of the *Fioretti*, "*perfetta letizia. . . . vincere se medesimo,*" the victory over self, which, alas, some of us never achieve at all.

IV

It would be an entire mistake to assume that the religious life of Saint Francis was in any way centered in the effort to apply these cardinal principles to himself. On the contrary, his first, unfailing impulse was to extend his rich possession to others, all others. At the same time it would be an equal mistake not to emphasize adequately in him the richness and depth of the inner spiritual life which must always be the perennial source of any inspiration that is imparted.

This inward ardor appears in him from the day of his conversion until the end. It is manifest in every line of the story of the conversion as told by Bonaventure: "One day, while he was praying thus apart and through intensity of fervor wholly absorbed in God, the image of Christ Jesus crucified appeared to him. At this sight his soul was melted within him and the memory of the passion of Christ was so inwardly impressed upon the bowels of his heart that from that hour, whenever the crucifixion of Christ came into his mind, he could hardly refrain from breaking out into tears and groans." The height, the ecstasy of mystical rapture penetrates passage after passage of the indisputable writings of the Saint himself, as in this sentence of prayer and exhortation: "Let us therefore desire nothing else, let us wish for nothing else, let nothing else please us and delight us, except our Creator and Redeemer and our Saviour, the true and only God." Again and again in the midst of his most active labors, Francis withdrew into himself, buried himself in the solitary communion with his Creator from which alone he could draw the vigor and the power to do his work. Sometimes such isolation had its moments of despair. Demons tormented him, actual external demons as he appeared to think, at any rate demons of doubt and question and hesitating uncertainty, as to his powers, as to his accomplishment, as to his salvation. Then the sweet, compelling, involving rapture of God would once more overcome him, and he would return to the world more than ever determined to give all that was in him to making it over and making it what it ought to be and what God would have it.

For the essence of the man, after all, was action, to be up and doing something, for God and other men. It is charmingly typical that the first manifestation of the religious influence in him was the effort to repair a church. When he saw the house of God tottering to decay, he gave what little money he had to save it, then he went out and begged and solicited, and worked with his own hands and got others to work, till he achieved final and satisfying success. That was the kind of man he was. Prayer and contemplation and adoration were all very well. Nobody could have too much of them—provided they did not crowd out other things. But this was a world of work. You could not live in it without working. Above all you could not save it without working, and he was going to work, as long as he had life in him, to help see that it was saved.

There are winning accounts in the different Lives of the characteristic frankness with which Francis laid before his friends the problem as to whether he should devote his life to prayer or preaching: "In prayer we talk with God and listen to him and we mingle with the angels, leading as it were an angel's life, whereas in preaching we have to descend to mortality and, living as a man among men, we have

to think and speak and see and hear human things." The truth was, he liked human things, for all his love of the divine, and when the difficult debate arose in his soul, he settled it forever by the example of his Lord and Master. Christ came down from heaven to preach and teach. Are we not bound to do all things as he did? "Therefore it seems to be the will of God that, casting repose away from us, we should go forth to labor in the world without (*intermissa quiete foras egrediamur ad laborem*)." And he did go forth and labor mightily.

When a man gets to dealing with men, to influencing them, to acquiring power over them, so that he can lead them whither he will, it becomes a matter of singular interest to analyze his sense of that power and his motive in acquiring it and using it. In other words, how much of his own personal ambition, his own glorification, enters into his desire and his effort to benefit his fellows? If it be said that it is ungrateful and ungracious to probe so deeply and so closely into the more human and perhaps the baser side of those who have given their lives to apparently unselfish labor, the answer is that, if we find them somewhat akin to ourselves, we shall be better able to imitate them, and also for some of us there is the further sufficing answer, that the investigation is profoundly curious. As Sainte-Beuve said: "Let us not be afraid to surprise the human heart naked, in its incurable duplicity, even in the most saintly." For the saints, if they really are saints, are sure to come well out of the trial, and to be left more lovable and more imitable, if not more admirable.

There is no doubt that Francis in his youth cherished dreams of vast and vague ambition and greatness. He was interested in large projects, he was interested in chivalry and soldiership and the chivalric ideal. At one time, when there was strife between Assisi and the neighboring Perugia, Francis with some of his friends was captured and detained as prisoner in the rival city. His fellow captives wondered at his constant cheerfulness and contentment. "Why should I not be cheerful?" he answered. "Here, to be sure, we are in prison, but the day will come when I shall be adored by the whole world." The same secure, cloudy, dream confidence seems to have inspired much of the effort and agitation of his early life.

Then God got hold of him and in appearance at least he cast all these visions and hallucinations away. He, the humblest and meanest of God's servants, had been chosen to do God's work. As he puts it in the *Fioretti*, "God has called us in his holy Religion for the salvation of the world and has made this bargain between us and the world: that we should set the world a good example and that the world should furnish us a living." When there was such a mission and such a calling, how could there be any thought of worldly exaltation or glory? The servant of Christ had enough to do to promote the cause of his Lord without thinking of any advantage or future reputation for himself: "So did this man abjure all glory which did not savor of Christ; so did he pour eternal anathema upon all the adoration of men," says the adoring biographer. And yet—and yet —one wonders. When you assure an inquiring disciple that you owe such leading position as you may have to the fact that you are "a greater sinner than anyone else in the whole world," is there not still a lingering satisfaction in the sense of being the greatest something? When you abase yourself in the depths of humility, is there not always a suggestion of the saying of another distinguished Italian of recent years, Mussolini, "I am not intoxicated with grandeur; I should like to be intoxicated with humility?" And is there such a great difference in the two intoxications, after all? Again and again in Francis himself we seem to get gleams of this bitter struggle with the devouring, persistent ego which will make its own self-glory out of what honestly means to be the bitterest denial of itself. And is there not the profoundest possible depth of human meaning in the lovely words of Thomas of Celano, who is not generally the loveliest of Francis's biographers? *"Sic totum in laudibus hominum vivimus, quia nichil aliud quam homines sumus.* Thus we live all over in the praises of men, because we are men and nothing else."

This strain, or perhaps remote savor and relish, of earthly glory appears, or is suggested, in the most active agency of Francis's mission to his fellow-men, his gift of speech. Unfortunately, we cannot judge of this agency as fully as we should wish, since we have no record of what the preacher actually said, but only of some of the effects he produced upon his auditors. It is clear that he was not impressive in appearance—a little, sallow, insignificant person to look at. Yet the minute he began speaking, there was such a pervading earnestness in his words that all sorts of hearers were carried away; "even the most learned men, weighted and freighted with dignities and glories, wondered at his sermons and were overcome with a profitable awe in his presence." And it is evident that Francis himself felt the danger in such success. Again and again he cries out that those who would follow him must eschew the vain glory of speech, must use their gifts only to magnify God and to perform wonders in his service: "Blessed is that servant who does not speak with the hope of reward, who does not take pride in showing his own powers and is not glib in speech, but considers sagely what ought to be spoken and answered." Yet with it all one realizes perfectly that a sensitive temperament like his must have felt in every nerve the superb exaltation which comes with the power to sway men whither you will by your tongue and your imagination. It is God working through you, no doubt, but it is God working through you and not through anybody else.

And as the sense of power and the exaltation of the ego comes with the exercise of oratory, so with some temperaments it comes in the habit of leadership and the practice of wide and systematic governmental organization. It does not appear that this was so much the bent of Francis as of some others, Saint Ignatius for example. His method and his instinct were rather for quiet labor with individual souls. Yet as his Order grew and his mission developed, the necessity of organization was almost imposed upon him and he met it with the ability of his clear intelligence and the tremendous zeal of his working force. Just how far the different Rules and the organization of the Three Orders, male, female, and lay, as they come to us, are to be attributed to him, it is difficult to say, but it is manifest that he had at any rate large cognizance of them. The thought that he had given to the whole subject is conspicuous in his description of the ideal leader of an order such as he would have liked to see. But what strikes me most here again is the significance of the phrase given to him in the *Speculum Perfectionis*: "There is no prelate in the whole world who would be so feared by his subordinates as God would make me feared by my brethren if I so wished. But God has given me this grace, to be content with all things as if I were the humblest." "Let us not be afraid to surprise the human heart naked, in its incurable duplicity, even in the most saintly."

And Francis's management and ruling of men was not free from the strain and irritation and friction which such ruling almost necessarily involves. It was obvious that his extreme ideals could hardly become popular or practical without considerable modification. When men of the world, men of affairs and executive capacity, took hold of the Order, they were impelled to modify it, almost insensibly, and even when they were as sympathetic as Pope Honorius and Cardinal Hugolino. Francis himself felt that the modification was inevitable, yet he protested with his whole soul against yielding an inch. The change seems to have chiefly centered in Brother Elias, and it is interesting to see the different views of this figure taken by those who take different views of the Order and its purposes. To the strict followers of Francis, Elias, in spite of his undisputed devotion to Francis himself, is anathema, little short of a traitor, while those who interpret more freely feel that Elias's action really established the Order as a great working power in the world. The main interest of the controversy is that it to some extent distressed and darkened the last days of the Saint, though Sabatier probably exaggerates this element of tragedy: Francis, after all, was born joyous and with an enduring confidence in the triumphant goodness of God.

What is most interesting in Francis's human relations is not his larger executive efforts, but his immediate contact with individual souls. Here his touch was instinctive, exquisite, and prevailing. Spirits of diametrically opposite tempers clung to him and adored him with equal devotion. The tender Masseo, the ardent Leo, the volatile Juniper, the haughty Elias, and innumerable others, all alike submitted to that warmly dominating spiritual ascendency. The master understood, he penetrated into the deepest and most hidden corners of men's hearts and saw what went on there and knew and recognized that nothing darker or more shameful went on there than went on in his own. In the simple, direct language of the *Fioretti*, "As our Lord Jesus Christ says in the Gospel, I know my sheep, and they know me, so the blessed Saint Francis, like a good shepherd, knew all the merits and the virtues of his companions by a divine revelation, and so also he knew their defects." Like the other great Saint Francis, him of Sales, and like Fénelon, Saint Francis of Assisi was a supreme director of souls, and could turn them into the right way, sometimes by sharp and severe rebuke when it was needed—as when he bade the erring brother, who had soiled his fingers with dirty money, to fill his mouth with ass's dung—more often by supreme sympathy and the loving, comforting touch, which eases burdens and lightens the dark places, and makes the troubled, groping footing more firm and more secure.

For the man's mission in life was incontestably the gathering and garnering and saving of souls. And if there is a more joyous and more satisfying occupation, I do not know where you will find it. As D. L. Moody, who was perhaps an American Francis, seven hundred years later, expressed it: "There is no joy in the world like that: the luxury of winning a soul to Christ, the luxury of being used by God in building up his kingdom." And if Moody and Francis got a certain personal glory out of it, who shall grudge it to them?

V

But the freshest and most delightful of all the elements of Francis's character is unquestionably the impulse of wandering, of joyous, untiring, inexhaustible, vagrant peregrination. It is one of the basic impulses of human nature, perhaps the basic impulse, the desire of new things and fresh experiences, of turning perpetually from one phase of life to another. It is the splendid impulse of youth. Only in most of us the swift flight of years, the clouding conventions of civilized life, the involving burden of social prejudice, numb and kill the original impulse in this case as in so many others. But the sweet, sunny, vagrant ardor crops out at least in the aspirations of the poets, as in the lovely spring cry of Catullus,

> *Jam mens praetrepidans avet vagari,*

or the wilder murmur of the rash hero of the old dramatist,

> *Let rogues be staid that have no habitation;*
> *A gentleman may wander.*

And again there is the musical travel sentence of old Burton, "For peregrination hath such an infinite and sweet variety that some call him unhappy who never traveled, but beholdeth from his cradle to his old age the same, still, still the same." Only Burton traveled but in spirit, like so many of us. Francis's restless limbs wanted to waft his spirit all over the world. When he was young, he was fascinated by the wandering dreams of chivalry and knight errantry, and again by the vagrant music of the troubadours, and in later years he used to call his proselyting followers the chivalry of God and used to pour out his religious ecstasies in the troubadour's form.

With this instinct of sweet general vagrancy, with the pleasure of letting one's feet stray whither they will, there is the further delight of varied human contact, of seeing endless human faces, and exploring endless human souls. There was once a social-minded lady who said, "I should like to meet everybody in the world." In the same way we feel with the great human poets, the Chaucers and the Shakespeares, the wide love of human nature and human beings, just because they are human. Saint and sinner, doer and dreamer, all are interesting, all are acceptable, because we find something of all of them in our own hearts. The essential elements of this far-traveling human interest are, first, a limitless, inexhaustible curiosity and, second, a considerable indifference to one's own personal comfort; in other words, a constant tendency to forget one's self in the lives of others. And both these elements are undyingly conspicuous in Saint Francis. He had the vast curiosity, the interest in all human souls, where they came from, what their nature was, where they were going to. And he had the instinct, the formed habit of making himself comfortable wherever he might be. To be sure, in later years, he seemed to show a growing attachment to the home center, the Portiuncula at Assisi, and he enjoined upon his followers that they should forget or desert it. But in the vigorous and active portion of his life, when "for the space of eighteen years his body never had rest, circulating through varied and far-flung regions," his principle seems to have been that which he loudly proclaimed, *"Nam ubicumque sumus et ambulamus, habemus semper cellam nobiscum"*; or, in the words of the old poet Donne, holding up the snail as an example,

Be thou thine own home and in thyself dwell;
Inn anywhere; continuance maketh hell.

Also, besides the pure pleasure of vagrancy in itself and the interest in humanity, there is the infinite delight in out-of-doors, and this is always evident in Saint Francis. He was willing to meet the crowds in cities, he did not shrink from lepers in body or from lepers in spirit, but what he above all loved was wandering in the fields and woods, the bright air, the broad sky, the sun, the wind, the clouds, and the living creatures inhabiting all this. There is a sunny sweet old play of Richard Brome, called *The Merry Beggars,* which breathes all through it the delicious spirit of vagrancy. The central figure has the charming name Springlove. He is a steward, and a faithful servant, and spends his winter hours over his master's accounts and the tedious minutiæ of daily care. But when spring comes, and the blossoms burst, and the nightingale and the cuckoo begin calling, calling, the blood in Springlove calls too, and he must up and away, leaving master and duty behind him, and follow the cuckoo and the nightingale.

Saint Francis had something of Springlove in his soul, and he too heard the cuckoo and the nightingale when they began their calling. He too felt the charm of the spring flowers and the lure of narrow, winding paths leading perhaps nowhere, or perhaps anywhere. When the call came, he was ready to arise and follow. And he loved all the living creatures and even the creatures that might appear not to have life. With his usual quaint exaggeration, he cherished and reverenced even the stones on which he trod and the water he had to use for washing. He loved the flowers and the birds and the cicadas. In that strange, unearthly canticle in which he poured out his lyrical, poetical aspiration, he hailed all the works of God with exuberant praise: "Praised be my Lord God with all his creatures; and specially our brother the sun, who brings us the day, and who brings us the light; fair is he, and shining with a very great splendour: O Lord, he signifies to us Thee!" And there is the delicious story of his preaching to the birds, which appears in so many different forms. When Francis was preparing to discourse one evening out-of-doors, he was interrupted by the mad twitter of the swallows, who gathered in clouds all about him. And at first he smiled and let them twitter. But finally he remonstrated: "Sister swallows, you might let me have my turn." And the swallows were suddenly silent, there was not one single twitter, while the Saint held forth to them on the goodness of God.

For all this out-of-doors of Francis is penetrated, permeated with God. It reminds me always of the sweet story of the two young lovers, sitting on an open hillside, watching the light grasses bent all one way in the light south wind, like a group of Fra Angelico angels. And the lady murmured, "You know, my soul also is swayed gently, like the grasses, in the wind of your love. Only that would make me the flower and you the wind. And I had rather we should both be flowers and God the wind. What could be more exquisite than to be swayed forever hither and thither in the wind of his love?"

It is this pervading presence of God that gives Francis's spirit of vagrancy the final and crowning touch. It is perhaps delicious enough to roam and wander for the pure joy and revel of it. But how much of depth and delicacy and grandeur is added when you feel that it is your duty to wander, that you are called by God to travel over the wide earth, seeing all things, and visiting all men, so that you may enlarge the boundaries of God's kingdom. This is what Francis felt. He lived all his life in the intoxication of it. He imparted the intoxication to thousands who have followed him. Go forth, and do my bidding, and bear my message to the whole wide world. That was Saint Francis of Assisi, God's Vagabond, and prouder in that title than in the glory of kings or the resonant splendor of conquerors. And because the charm of inexhaustible itinerance, physical and spiritual, was blended with the God-impulse, inextricably, the religion of Francis and his preaching have always a singular and delightful touch of joy. There was no gloom about him, no pressure of misery or hell, no touch of asceticism in the tortured sense. As Renan puts it, admirably, "Note well that Francis forbids us to possess, he does not forbid us to enjoy"; and the experience of humanity, even without Francis, has long ago taught us that possession and enjoyment are by no means identical. Francis wanted his followers to find endless joy in their religion, in their God, and in all the delightful things that their God had scattered about them in such abundant profusion. He was even ready to carry joy to the point of a sweet and sacred merriment, and when Brother Juniper made his careless and trivial jests, Brother Juniper, who is stamped with the magnificent phrase, *"egregius Domini joculator,"* the egregious jester of God, Francis smiled and sympathized, for, he said, "What are the servants of God but as it were merry-makers who should stir the hearts of men and impel them to spiritual joy?"

So this illimitable roamer and dreamer went on

wandering and wondering and loving. With such an inborn tendency, is it not hard to imagine that the wandering should ever stop? Rather you feel that he would go on eternally, traveling, soaring, adventuring, through the vast unplumbed depths of the spiritual universe, always, always, always, touching, enjoying, engrossing—and dominating souls.

FORGIVENESS

Harriet Beecher Stowe

"Ah, ah, honey! ladies born have some bad stuff in dem, sometimes, like de rest of us. But, den, honey, it was de most natural thing in de world, come to look on't; for now, see here, honey, dere was your aunt—she was poor, and she was pestered for money. Dere was Mas'r George's bills and Peter's bills to pay, and Miss Susy's; and every one of 'em must have everything, and dey was all calling for money, money; and dere has been times she didn't know which way to turn. Now, you see, when a woman is pestered to pay two hundred here and tree hundred dere, and when she has got more niggers on her place dan she can keep, and den a man calls in and lays down eight hundred dollars in gold and bills before her, and says, 'I want dat ar Lucy or George of yourn,' why, don't you see? Dese yer soul-drivers is always round, tempting folks dey know is poor; and dey always have der money as handy as de devil has his. But, den, I oughtn't fur to be hard upon dem poor soul-drivers, neither, 'cause dey an't taught no better. It's dese yer Christians, dat profess Christ, dat makes great talks 'bout religion, dat has der Bibles, and turns der backs upon swearing soul-drivers, and tinks dey an't fit to speak to—it's *dem*, honey, dat's de root of de whole business. Now, dere was dat uncle of hern,—mighty great Christian he was, with his prayer-meetings, and all dat!—he was always a putting her up to it. Oh, dere's been times—dere was times 'long first, Miss Nina, when my first chil'en was sold—dat, I tell you, I poured out my soul to Miss Harrit, and I've seen dat ar woman cry so dat I was sorry for her.

And she said to me, 'Milly, I'll never do it again.' But, Lord! I didn't trust her,—not a word on't,—'cause I knowed she would. I knowed dere was dat in her heart dat de devil wouldn't let go of. I knowed he'd no kind of objection to her 'musing herself with meetin's, and prayers, and all dat; but he'd no notion to let go his grip on her heart.

"But, Lord! she wasn't *quite* a bad woman,—poor Miss Harrit wasn't,—and she wouldn't have done so bad, if it hadn't been for *him*. But he'd come and have prayers, and exhort, and den come prowling round my place like a wolf, looking at my chil'en.

"'And, Milly,' he'd say, 'how do you do now? Lucy is getting to be a right smart girl, Milly. How old is she? Dere's a lady in Washington has advertised for a maid,—a nice woman, a pious lady. I suppose you wouldn't object, Milly? Your poor mistress is in great trouble for money.'

"I never said nothing to that man. Only once, when he asked me what I thought my Lucy would be worth, when she was fifteen years old, says I to him:—

"'Sir, she is worth to me just what your daughter is worth to you.'

"Den I went in and shut de door. I didn't stay to see how he took it. Den he'd go up to de house, and talk to Miss Harrit. 'Twas her duty, he'd tell her, to take proper care of her goods. And dat ar meant selling my chil'en. I 'member, when Miss Susy came home from boarding-school, she was a pretty girl: but I didn't look on her very kind, I tell you, 'cause three of my chil'en had been sold to keep her at school. My Lucy,—ah, honey!—she went for a lady's maid. I knowed what dat ar meant, well enough. De lady had a son grown, and he took Lucy with him to Orleans, and dere was an end of dat. Dere don't no letters go 'tween us. Once gone, we can't write, and it is good as being dead. Ah, no, chile, not so good! Paul used to teach Lucy little hymns, nights, 'fore she went to sleep. And if she'd a died right off after one of dem, it would have been better for her. Oh, honey, 'long dem times I used to rave and toss like a bull in a net—I did so!

"Well, honey, I wasn't what I was. I got cross and ugly. Miss Harrit, she grew a great Christian, and joined de church, and used to have heaps of ministers and elders at her house; and some on 'em used to try and talk to me. I told 'em I'd seen enough of der old religion, and I didn't want to hear no more. But

Paul, he was a Christian; and when he talked to me, I was quiet, like, though I couldn't be like what he was. Well, last, my missis promised me one. She'd give me my youngest child, sure and certain. His name was Alfred. Well, dat boy!—I loved dat child better dan any of de rest of 'em. He was all I'd got left to love; for, when he was a year old, Paul's master moved away down to Louisiana, and took him off, and I never heard no more of him. So it 'peared as if dis yer child was all I had left. Well, he *was* a bright boy. Oh, he was most uncommon! He was so handy to anything, and saved me so many steps! Oh, honey, he had such ways with him—dat boy!—would always make me laugh. He took after larnin' mighty, and he larned himself to read; and he'd read de Bible to me, sometimes. I just brought him up and teached him de best way I could. All dat made me 'fraid for him was, dat he was so spirity. I's 'fraid 'twould get him into trouble.

"He war'nt no more spirity dan white folks would like der chil'en fur to be. When white chil'en holds up der heads, and answers back, den de parents laugh, and say, 'He's got it in him! He's a bright one!' But, if one of ourn does so, it's a drefful thing. I was allers talking to Alfred 'bout it, and telled him to keep humble. It 'peared like there was so much in him, you couldn't keep it down. Laws, Miss Nina, folks may say what dey like about de black folks, dey'll never beat it out of my head;—dere's some on 'em can be as smart as any white folks, if dey could have de same chance. How many white boys did you ever see would take de trouble for to teach theirselves to read? And dat's what my Alfred did. Laws, I had a mighty heap of comfort in him, 'cause I was thinkin' to get my missis to let me hire my time; den I was going to work over hours, and get money, and buy him; because, you see, chile, I knowed he was too spirity for a slave. You see he couldn't *learn to stoop;* he wouldn't let nobody impose on him; and he always had a word back again to give anybody as good as dey sent. Yet, for all dat, he was a dear, good boy to me; and when I used to talk to him, and tell him dese things was dangerous, he'd always promise fur to be kerful. Well, things went on pretty well while he was little, and I kept him with me till he got to be about twelve or thirteen years old. He used to wipe de dishes, and scour de knives, and black de shoes, and such-like work. But, by and by, dey said it was time dat he should go to de reg'lar work; and dat was de time I felt feared. Missis had an overseer, and he was real aggravating, and I felt feared dere'd be trouble; and sure enough dere was, too. Dere was always somethin' brewing 'tween him and Alfred; and he was always running to missis with tales, and I was talking to Alfred. But 'peared like he aggravated de boy so, dat he couldn't do right. Well, one day, when I had been up to town for an errand, I come home at night, and I wondered Alfred didn't come home to his supper. I thought something was wrong; and I went to de house, and dere sat Miss Harrit by a table covered with rolls of money, and dere she was a counting it.

"'Miss Harrit,' says I, 'I can't find Alfred. An't you seen him?' says I.

"At first she didn't answer, but went on counting—fifty-one, fifty-two, fifty-three. Finally I spoke again.

"'I hope there an't nothing happened to Alfred, Miss Harrit?'

"She looked up, and says she to me,—

"'Milly,' says she, 'de fact is, Alfred has got too much for me to manage, and I had a great deal of money offered for him: and I sold him.'

"I felt something strong coming up in my throat, and I just went up and took hold of her shoulders, and said I,—

"'Miss Harrit, you took de money for thirteen of my chil'en, and you promised me, sure enough, I should have dis yer one. You call dat being a Christian?' says I.

"'Why,' says she, 'Milly, he an't a great way off; you can see him about as much. It's only over to Mr. Jones's plantation. You can go and see him, and he can come and see you. And you know you didn't like the man who had the care of him here, and thought he was always getting him into trouble.'

"'Miss Harrit,' says I, 'you may cheat yourself saying dem things; but you don't cheat me, nor de Lord neither. You folks have de say all on your side, with your ministers preaching us down out of de Bible; you won't teach us to read. But I'm going straight to de Lord with dis yer case. I tell you, if de Lord is to be found, I'll find him; and I'll ask him to look on't,—de way you've been treating me, —selling *my* chil'en, all de way 'long, to pay for *your* chil'en, and now breaking your word to me, and taking dis yer boy, de last drop of blood in my heart!

I'll pray de Lord to curse every cent of dat ar money to you and your chil'en!'

"'Dat ar was de way I spoke to her, child. I was poor, ignorant cretur, and didn't know God, and my heart was like a red-hot coal. I turned and walked right straight out from her. I didn't speak no more to her, and she didn't speak no more to me. And when I went to bed at night, dar, sure 'nough, was Alfred's bed in de corner, and his Sunday coat hanging up over it, and his Sunday shoes I had bought for him with my own money; 'cause he was a handsome boy, and I wanted him always to look nice. Well, so, come Sunday morning, I took his coat and his shoes, and made a bundle of 'em, and I took my stick, and says I, 'I'll just go over to Jones's place and see what has 'come of Alfred.' All de time, I hadn't said a word to missis, nor she to me. Well, I got about half-way over to de place, and dere I stopped under a big hickory-tree to rest me a bit, and I looked along and seed some one a coming; and pretty soon I knowed it was Huldah. She was one that married Paul's cousin, and she lived on Jones's place. And so I got up and went to meet her, and told her I was going over to see 'bout Alfred.

"'Lord!' says she, 'Milly, haven't you heard dat Alfred's dead?'

"Well, Miss Nina, it seemed as if my heart and everything in it stopped still. And said I, 'Huldah, has dey killed him?'

"And said she, 'Yes.' And she told me it was dis yer way: Dat Stiles—he dat was Jones's overseer—had heard dat Alfred was dreadful spirity; and when boys is so, sometimes dey aggravates 'em to get 'em riled, and den dey whips 'em to break 'em in. So Stiles, when he was laying off Alfred's task, was real aggravating to him; and dat boy—well, he answered back, just as he allers would be doing, 'cause he was smart, and it 'peared like he couldn't keep it in. And den dey all laughed round here, and den Stiles was mad, and swore he'd whip him; and den Alfred, he cut and run. And den Stiles he swore awful at him, and he told him to 'come here, and he'd give him hell, and pay him de cash.' Dem is de very words he said to my boy. And Alfred said he wouldn't come back; he wasn't going to be whipped. And just den young Master Bill come along, and wanted to know what was de matter. So Stiles told him, and he took out his pistol, and said, 'Here, young dog, if you don't come back before I count five, I'll fire!'

"'Fire ahead!' says Alfred; 'cause you see, dat boy never knowed what fear was. And so he fired. And Huldah said he just jumped up and gave one scream, and fell flat. And dey run up to him, and he was dead; 'cause you see, de bullet went right through his heart. Well, dey took off his jacket and looked, but it wa'nt of no use; his face settled down still. And Huldah said dat dey just dug a hole and put him in. Nothing on him—nothing round him—no coffin; like he'd been a dog. Huldah showed me de jacket. Dere was de hole, cut right round in it, like it was stamped, and his blood running out on it. I didn't say a word. I took up de jacket, and wrapped it up with his Sunday clothes, and I walked straight —straight home. I walked up into missis' room, and she was dressed for church, sure enough, and sat dere reading her Bible. I laid it right down under her face, dat jacket. 'You see dat *hole*!' said I; 'you see dat blood! Alfred's killed! *You* killed him; his blood be on you and your chil'en! O Lord God in heaven, hear me, and *render unto her double*!'"

Nina drew in her breath hard, with an instinctive shudder. Milly had drawn herself up, in the vehemence of her narration, and sat leaning forward, her black eyes dilated, her strong arms clenched before her, and her powerful frame expanding and working with the violence of her emotion. She might have looked, to one with mythological associations, like the figure of a black marble Nemesis in a trance of wrath. She sat so for a few minutes, and then her muscles relaxed, her eyes gradually softened; she looked tenderly, but solemnly, down on Nina. "Dem was awful words, chile; but I was in Egypt den. I was wandering in de wilderness of Sinai. I had heard de sound of de trumpet, and de voice of words; but, chile, I hadn't seen de Lord. Well—I went out, and I didn't speak no more to Miss Harrit. Dere was a great gulf fixed 'tween us; and dere didn't no words pass over it. I did my work—I scorned not to do it; but I didn't speak to her. Den it was, chile, dat I thought of what my mother told me, years ago; it came to me, all fresh—'Chile, when trouble comes, you ask de Lord to help you;' and I saw dat I hadn't asked de Lord to help me; and now, says I to myself, de Lord can't help me; 'cause he couldn't bring back Alfred, no way you could fix it; and yet I wanted to find de Lord, 'cause I was so tossed up and down. I wanted jist to go and say, 'Lord, you see what dis woman has done.' I wanted to put it to

him, if he'd stand up for such a thing as that. Lord, how de world, and everything, looked to me in dem times! Everything goin' on in de way it did; and dese yer Christians, dat said dat dey was going into de kingdom, doing as dey did! I tell you, I sought de Lord early and late. Many nights I have been out in de woods and laid on de ground till morning, calling and crying, and 'peared like nobody heerd me. Oh, how strange it used to look, when I looked up to de stars! winking at me, so kind of still and solemn, but never saying a word! Sometimes I got dat wild, it seemed as if I could tear a hole through de sky, 'cause I must find God; I had an errand to him, and I must find him.

"Den I heard 'em read out de Bible, 'bout how de Lord met a man on a threshing-floor, and I thought maybe if I had a threshing-floor he would come to me. So I threshed down a place just as hard as I could under de trees; and den I prayed dere—but he didn't come. Den dere was coming a great camp-meeting; and I thought I'd go and see if I could find de Lord dere; because, you see, missis, she let her people go Sunday to de camp-meeting. Well, I went into de tents and heerd dem sing; and I went afore de altar, and I heerd preaching; but it 'peared like it was no good. It didn't touch me nowhere; and I couldn't see nothing to it. I heerd 'em read out of de Bible, 'Oh, dat I knew where I might find him. I would come even to his seat. I would order my cause before him. I would fill my mouth with arguments'; and I thought, sure enough, dat ar's just what I want. Well, came on dark night, and dey had all de camp-fires lighted up, and dey was singing de hymns round and round, and I went for to hear de preaching. And dere was a man—pale, lean man he was, with black eyes and black hair. Well, dat ar man, he preached a sermon, to be sure, I shall never forget. His text was, 'He that spared not his own Son, but freely delivered him up for us all, how shall he not with him freely give us all things?' Well, you see, the first sound of dis took me, because I'd lost my son. And the man, he told us who de son of God was,—Jesus,—Oh, how sweet and beautiful he was! How he went round doing for folks. O Lord, what a story dat ar was! And, den, how dey took him, and put de crown of thorns on his head, and hung him up bleeding, bleeding, and bleeding! God so loved us dat he let his own dear Son suffer all dat for us. Chile, I got up, and I went to de altar, and

I kneeled down with de mourners; and I fell flat on my face, and dey said I was in a trance. Maybe I was. Where I was, I don't know; but I saw de Lord! Chile, it seemed as if my very heart was still. I saw him, suffering, bearing with us, year in and year out—bearing—bearing—bearing so patient! 'Peared like, it wasn't just on de cross; but, bearing, always, everywhar! Oh, chile, I saw how he loved us!—us *all* —all—every one on us!—we dat hated each other so! 'Peared like he was using his heart up for us, all de time—bleedin' for us like he did on Calvary, and willin' to bleed! Oh, chile, I saw what it was for me to be hatin', like I'd hated. 'O Lord,' says I, 'I give up! O Lord, never see you afore; I didn't know. Lord, I's a poor sinner! I won't hate no more!' And oh, chile, den dere come such a rush of love in my soul! Says I, 'Lord, I ken love even de white folks!' And den came another rush; and says I, 'Yes, Lord, I love poor Miss Harrit, dat's sole all my chil'en, and been de death of my poor Alfred! I loves her.' Chile, I overcome—I did so—I overcome by de blood of de *Lamb*—de Lamb!—Yes, de Lamb, Chile!—cause if he'd been a lion I could a kept in; 'twas de *Lamb* dat overcome.

"When I come to, I felt like a chile. I went home to Miss Harrit; and I hadn't spoke peaceable to her since Alfred died. I went in to her. She'd been sick, and she was in her room, looking kinder pale and yaller, poor thing; 'cause her son, honey, he got drunk and 'bused her awful. I went in, and says I, 'Oh, Miss Harrit, I's seen de Lord! Miss Harrit, I aw't got no more hard feelin's; I forgive ye, and loves ye with all my heart, jest as de Lord does.' Honey, ye ought to see how dat woman cried! Says she, 'Milly, I's a great sinner.' Says I. 'Miss Harrit, we's sinners, both on us, but de Lord gives hisself for us both; and if he loves us poor sinners, we mustn't be hard on each other. Ye was tempted, honey,' says I (for you see I felt like makin' 'scuses for her); 'but de Lord Jesus has got a pardon for both on us.'

"After dat, I didn't have no more trouble with Miss Harrit. Chile, we was sisters in Jesus. I bore her burdens, and she bore mine. And, dear, de burdens was heavy; for her son he was brought home a corpse; he shot hisself right through de heart trying to load a gun when he was drunk. Oh, Chile, I thought den how I'd prayed de Lord to render unto her double; but I had a better mind den. Ef I could have brought poor Mas'r George to life, I'd a done it; and I

held de poor woman's head on my arm all dat ar night, and she a screamin' every hour. Well dat ar took her down to de grave. She didn't live much longer; but she was ready to die. She sent and bought my daughter Lucy's son, dis here Tom, and gin him to me. Poor thing! she did all she could.

"I watched with her de night she died. Oh, Miss Nina, if ever ye're tempted to hate anybody, think how 't'll be with 'em when dey comes to die.

"She died hard, poor thing! and she was cast down, 'bout her sins. 'Oh, Milly,' says she, 'the Lord and you may forgive me, but I *can't* forgive myself.'

"'And,' says I to her, 'Oh, missis, don't think of it no more! *de Lord's hid it in his own heart!*' Oh, but she struggled long, honey; she was all night dyin', and 'twas 'Milly! Milly!' all de time; 'Oh, Milly, stay with me!'

"And, chile, I felt I loved her like my own soul; and when de day broke de Lord set her free, and I laid her down like she'd been one o' my babies. I took up her poor hand. It was warm, but the strength was all gone out on't; and, 'Oh,' I thought, 'ye poor thing, how could I ever have hated ye so?' Ah, chile, we mustn't hate nobody; we's all poor creaturs, and de dear Lord he loves us all."

WHERE LOVE IS, THERE GOD IS ALSO

Leo N. Tolstoy

In the city lived Martuin Avdyéitch, a shoemaker. He lived in a basement, in a little room with one window. The window looked out on the street. Through the window he used to watch the people passing by: although only their feet could be seen, yet by the boots Martuin Avdyéitch recognized their owners. Martuin Avdyéitch had lived long in one place, and had many acquaintances. Few pairs of boots in his district had not been in his hands once and again. Some he would half-sole, some he would patch, some he would stitch around, and occasionally he would also put on new uppers. And through the window he quite often recognized his work. Avdyéitch had plenty to do, because he was a faithful workman,

THE STORY OF JESUS

used good material, did not make exorbitant charges, and kept his word. If he can finish an order by a certain time, he accepts it: if not, he will not deceive you,—he tells you so beforehand. And all knew Avdyéitch, and he was never out of work.

Avdyéitch had always been a good man; but as he grew old, he began to think more about his soul, and get nearer to God. Martuin's wife had died when he was still living with his master. His wife left him a boy three years old. None of their other children had lived. All the eldest had died in childhood. Martuin at first intended to send his little son to his sister in the village, but afterwards he felt sorry for him: he thought to himself, "It will be hard for my Kapitoshka to live in a strange family. I shall keep him with me."

And Avdyéitch left his master, and went into lodgings with his little son. But, through God's will, Avdyéitch had no luck with children. As Kapitoshka grew older, he began to help his father, and would have been a delight to him, but fell sick, went to bed, suffered a week, and died. Martuin buried his son, and fell into despair. So deep was this despair, that he began to complain of God. Martuin fell into such a melancholy state, that more than once he prayed to God for death, and reproached God because he did not take away him who was an old man, instead of his beloved only son. Avdyéitch also ceased to go to church.

And once a little old man, a fellow-countryman, came from Troïtsa (Trinity) to see Avdyéitch: for seven years he had been absent. Avdyéitch talked with him, and began to complain about his sorrows.

"I have no more desire to live," he said. "I only wish I was dead. That is all I pray God for. I am a man without any thing to hope for now."

And the little old man said to him,—

"You don't talk right, Martuin: we must not judge God's doings. The world moves, not by your skill, but by God's will. God decreed for your son to die, —for you—to live. Consequently, it is for the best. And you are in despair, because you wish to live for your own happiness."

"But what shall one live for?" asked Martuin.

And the little old man said, "We must live for God, Martuin. He gives you life, and for his sake you must live. When you begin to live for him, you will not grieve over any thing, and all will seem easy to you."

Martuin kept silent for a moment, and then said, "But how can one live for the sake of God?"

And the little old man said, "Christ has taught us how to live for God. You know how to read? Buy a Testament, and read it: there you will learn how to live for God. Every thing is explained there."

And these words kindled a fire in Avdyéitch's heart. And he went that very same day, bought a New Testament in large print, and began to read. At first Avdyéitch intended to read only on holidays; but as he began to read, it so cheered his soul that he used to read every day. At times he would become so absorbed in reading, that all the kerosene in the lamp would burn out, and still he could not tear himself away. And so Avdyéitch used to read every evening. And the more he read, the clearer he understood what God wanted of him, and how one should live for God; and his heart constantly grew easier and easier. Formerly, when he lay down to sleep, he used to sigh and groan, and always think of his Kapitoshka; and now he only exclaimed, "Glory to thee! glory to thee, Lord! Thy will be done."

And from that time Avdyéitch's whole life was changed. In other days he, too, used to drop into a saloon, as a holiday amusement, to drink a cup of tea; and he was not averse to a little brandy either. He would take a drink with some acquaintance, and leave the saloon, not intoxicated exactly, yet in a happy frame of mind, and inclined to talk nonsense, and shout, and use abusive language at a person. Now he left off this sort of thing. His life became quiet and joyful. In the morning he sits down to work, finishes his allotted task, then takes the little lamp from the hook, puts it on the table, gets his book from the shelf, opens it, and sits down to read. And the more he reads, the more he understands, and the brighter and happier it is in his heart.

Once it happened that Martuin read till late into the night. He was reading the Gospel of Luke. He was reading over the sixth chapter; and he was reading the verses, "And unto him that smiteth thee on the one cheek offer also the other; and him that taketh away thy cloak forbid not to take thy coat also. Give to every man that asketh of thee; and of him that taketh away thy goods ask them not again. And as ye would that men should do to you, do ye also to them likewise." He read further also those verses, where God speaks: "And why call ye me, Lord, Lord, and do not the things which I say? Whosoever cometh to me, and heareth my sayings, and doeth them, I will shew you to whom he is like: he is like a man which built an house, and digged deep, and laid the foundation on a rock: and when the flood arose, the stream beat vehemently upon that house, and could not shake it: for it was founded upon a rock. But he that heareth, and doeth not, is like a man that without a foundation built an house upon the earth; against which the stream did beat vehemently, and immediately it fell; and the ruin of that house was great."

Avdyéitch read these words, and joy filled his soul. He took off his spectacles, put them down on the book, leaned his elbows upon the table, and became lost in thought. And he began to measure his life by these words. And he thought to himself,—

"Is my house built upon the rock, or upon the sand! 'Tis well if on the rock. It is so easy when you are alone by yourself; it seems as if you had done every thing as God commands: but when you forget yourself, you sin again. Yet I shall still struggle on. It is very good. Help me, Lord!"

Thus ran his thoughts: he wanted to go to bed, but he felt loath to tear himself away from the book. And he began to read further in the seventh chapter. He read about the centurion, he read about the widow's son, he read about the answer given to John's disciples, and finally he came to that place where the rich Pharisee desired the Lord to sit at meat with him; and he read how the woman that was a sinner anointed his feet, and washed them with her tears, and how he forgave her. He reached the forty-fourth verse, and began to read,—

"And he turned to the woman, and said unto Simon, Seest thou this woman? I entered into thine house, thou gavest me no water for my feet: but she hath washed my feet with tears, and wiped them with the hairs of her head. Thou gavest me no kiss: but this woman since the time I came in hath not ceased to kiss my feet. My head with oil thou didst not anoint: but this woman hath anointed my feet with ointment." He finished reading these verses, and thought to himself, *"Thou gavest me no water for my feet, thou gavest me no kiss. My head with oil thou didst not anoint."*

And again Avdyéitch took off his spectacles, put them down upon the book, and again he became lost in thought.

"It seems that Pharisee must have been such a

man as I am. I, too, apparently have thought only of myself,—how I might have my tea, be warm and comfortable, but never to think about my guest. He thought about himself, but there was not the least care taken of the guest. And who was his guest? The Lord himself. If he had come to me, should I have done the same way?"

Avdyéitch rested his head upon both his arms, and did not notice how he fell asleep.

"Martuin!" suddenly seemed to sound in his ears.

Martuin started from his sleep: "Who is here?"

He turned around, glanced toward the door—no one.

Again he fell into a doze. Suddenly he plainly heard,—

"Martuin! Ah, Martuin! look to-morrow on the street. I am coming."

Martuin awoke, rose from the chair, began to rub his eyes. He himself did not know whether he heard those words in his dream, or in reality. He turned down his lamp, and went to bed.

At daybreak next morning, Avdyéitch rose, made his prayer to God, lighted the stove, put on the *shchi**and the *kasha,*† put the water in the samovar, put on his apron, and sat down by the window to work.

Avdyéitch is working, and at the same time thinking about all that had happened yesterday. He thinks both ways: now he thinks it was a dream, and now he thinks he really heard a voice. "Well," he thinks, "such things have been."

Martuin is sitting by the window, and does not work as much as he looks through the window: when any one passes by in boots that he does not know, he bends down, looks out of the window, in order to see, not only the feet, but also the face.

The *dvornik* ‡ passed by in new *valenki;* ** the water-carrier passed by; then came alongside of the window an old soldier of Nicholas's time, in an old pair of laced felt boots, with a shovel in his hands. Avdyéitch recognized him by his felt boots. The old man's name was Stepánuitch; and a neighboring merchant, out of charity, gave him a home with him. He was required to assist the *dvornik.* Stepánuitch began to shovel away the snow from in front of Avdyéitch's window. Avdyéitch glanced at him, and took up his work again.

"Pshaw! I must be getting crazy in my old age,"

---

* Cabbage-soup.   ‡ House-porter.
† Gruel.   ** Felt boots.

said Avdyéitch, and laughed at himself. "Stepán-uitch is clearing away the snow, and I imagine that Christ is coming to see me. I was entirely out of my mind, old dotard that I am!"

Avdyéitch sewed about a dozen stitches, and then felt impelled to look through the window again. He looked out again through the window, and saw that Stepánuitch had leaned his shovel against the wall, and was warming himself, and resting. He was an old, broken-down man: evidently he had not strength enough, even to shovel the snow. Avdyéitch said to himself:—

"I will give him some tea: by the way, the samovar must be boiling by this time." Avdyéitch laid down his awl, rose from his seat, put the samovar on the table, poured out the tea, and tapped with his finger at the glass. Stepánuitch turned around, and came to the window. Avdyéitch beckoned to him, and went to open the door.

"Come in, warm yourself a little," he said. "You must be cold."

"May Christ reward you for this! my bones ache," said Stepánuitch.

Stepánuitch came in, and shook off the snow, tried to wipe his feet, so as not to soil the floor, but staggered.

"Don't trouble to wipe your feet. I will clean it up myself: we are used to such things. Come in and sit down," said Avdyéitch. "Drink a cup of tea."

And Avdyéitch filled two glasses, and handed one to his guest; while he himself poured his tea into a saucer, and began to blow it.

Stepánuitch finished drinking his glass of tea, turned the glass upside down,* put upon it the half-eaten lump of sugar, and began to express his thanks. But it was evident he wanted some more.

"Have some more," said Avdyéitch, filling both his own glass and his guest's. Avdyéitch drank his tea, but from time to time kept glancing out into the street.

"Are you expecting any one?" asked his guest.

"Am I expecting any one? I am ashamed even to tell whom I expect. I am, and I am not, expecting some one; but one word has impressed itself upon my heart. Whether it is a dream, or something else, I do not know. Don't you see, brother, I was reading yesterday the gospel about Christ, the *Bátiushka*,† how he suffered, how he walked on the earth. I suppose you have heard about it?"

---
* A custom among the Russians.   † Little father.

"Indeed I have," replied Stepánuitch: "but we are people in darkness; we can't read."

"Well, now, I was reading about that very thing, —how he walked upon the earth: I read, you know, how he comes to the Pharisee, and the Pharisee did not treat him hospitably. Well, and so, my brother, I was reading, yesterday, about this very thing, and was thinking to myself how he did not receive Christ, the Bátiushka, with honor. If, for example, he should come to me, or any one else, I think to myself, I should not even know how to receive him. And he gave him no reception at all. Well! while I was thus thinking, I fell asleep, brother, and I hear some one call me by name. I got up: the voice, just as though some one whispered, says, 'Be on the watch: I shall come tomorrow.' And this happened twice. Well! would you believe it, it got into my head? I scold myself—and yet I am expecting him, the Bátiushka."

Stepánuitch shook his head, and said nothing: he finished drinking his glass of tea, and put it on the side; but Avdyéitch picked up the glass again, and filled it once more.

"Drink some more for your good health. You see, I have an idea, that, when the Bátiushka went about on this earth, he disdained no one, and had more to do with the simple people. He always went to see the simple people. He picked out his disciples more from among our brethren, sinners like ourselves from the working-class. He, says he, who exalts himself, shall be humbled, and he who is humbled shall become exalted. You, says he, call me Lord, and I, says he, wash your feet. Whoever wishes, says he, to be the first, the same shall be a servant to all. Because, says he, blessed are the poor, the humble, the kind, the generous." And Stepánuitch forgot about his tea: he was an old man, and easily moved to tears. He is sitting listening, and the tears are rolling down his face.

"Come, now, have some more tea," said Avdyéitch; but Stepánuitch made the sign of the cross, thanked him, turned up his glass, and arose.

"Thanks to you," he said, "Martuin Avdyéitch, for treating me kindly, and satisfying me, soul and body."

"You are welcome; come in again: always glad to see a friend," said Avdyéitch.

Stepánuitch departed; and Martuin poured out the rest of the tea, drank it up, put away the dishes, and sat down again by the window to work, to stitch on a patch. He was stitching, and at the same time looking through the window. He was expecting Christ, and was all the while thinking of him and his deeds, and his head was filled with the different speeches of Christ.

Two soldiers passed by: one wore boots furnished by the Crown, and the other one, boots that he had made; then the master of the next house, passed by in shining galoshes; then a baker with a basket passed by. All passed by; and now there came also by the window a woman in woollen stockings and wooden shoes. She passed by the window, and stood still near the window-case.

Avdyéitch looked up at her from the window, saw it was a strange woman poorly clad, and with a child: she was standing by the wall with her back to the wind, trying to wrap up the child, and she had nothing to wrap it up in. The woman was dressed in shabby summer clothes: and from behind the frame, Avdyéitch heard the child crying, and the woman trying to pacify it; but she was not able to pacify it. Avdyéitch got up, went to the door, ascended the steps, and cried, "Hey! my good woman!" The woman heard him and turned around.

"Why are you standing in the cold with the child? Come into my room, where it is warm: you can manage it better. Right in this way!"

The woman was astonished. She saw an old, old man in an apron, with spectacles on his nose, calling her to him. She followed him. They descended the steps, entered the room: the old man led the woman to his bed.

"There," said he, "sit down, my good woman, nearer to the stove: you can get warm, and nurse the child."

"I have no milk for him. I myself have not eaten any thing since morning," said the woman; but, nevertheless, she took the child to her breast.

Avdyéitch shook his head, went to the table, brought out the bread and a dish, opened the oven-door, poured into the dish some cabbage-soup, took out the pot with the gruel, but it was not done yet; so he filled the dish with *shchi* only, and put it on the table. He got the bread, took the towel down from the hook, and put it upon the table.

"Sit down," he said, "and eat, my good woman; and I will mind the little one. You see, I once had children of my own: I know how to handle them."

The woman crossed herself, sat down at the table, and began to eat; while Avdyéitch took a seat on the

bed near the infant. Avdyéitch kept smacking and smacking to it with his lips; but it was a poor kind of smacking, for he had no teeth. The little one still cried. And it occurred to Avdyéitch to threaten the little one with his finger: he waved, waved his finger right before the child's mouth, and hastily withdrew it. He did not put it to its mouth, because his finger was black, and soiled with wax. And the little one looked at his finger, and became quiet: then it began to smile, and Avdyéitch also was glad. While the woman ate, she told who she was, and whither she was going.

"I," said she, "am a soldier's wife. It is now seven months since they sent my husband away off, and no tidings. I lived out as cook; the baby was born; no one cared to keep me with a child. This is the third month that I have been struggling along without a place. I ate up all I had. I wanted to engage as a wet-nurse—no one would take me—I am too thin, they say. I have just been to the merchant's wife, where lives our *bábotchka*,* and so they promised to take us in. I thought this was the end of it. But she told me to come next week. And she lives a long way off. I got tired out; and it tired him, too, my heart's darling. Fortunately, our landlady takes pity on us for the sake of Christ, and gives us a room, else I don't know how I should manage to get along."

Avdyéitch sighed, and said, "Haven't you any warm clothes?"

"Now is the time, friend, to wear warm clothes; but yesterday I pawned my last shawl for a twenty-kopek piece."

The woman came to the bed, and took the child; and Avdyéitch rose, went to the little wall, and succeeded in finding an old coat.

"Na!" said he: "it is a poor thing, yet you may turn it to some use."

The woman looked at the coat, looked at the old man; she took the coat, and burst into tears: and Avdyéitch turned away his head; crawling under the bed, he pushed out a little trunk, rummaged in it, and sat down again opposite the woman.

And the woman said, "May Christ bless you, *diédushka*! † He must have sent me himself to your window. My little child would have frozen to death. When I started out, it was warm, but now it is terribly cold. And he, Bátiushka, led you to look through the window, and take pity on me, an unfortunate."

---

* Little grandmother.   † Little grandfather.

Avdyéitch smiled, and said, "Indeed, he did that! I have been looking through the window, my good woman, not without cause." And Martuin told the soldier's wife his dream, and how he heard the voice, —how the Lord promised to come and see him that day.

"All things are possible," said the woman. She rose, put on the coat, wrapped up her little child in it; and, as she started to take leave, she thanked Avdyéitch again.

"Take this, for Christ's sake," said Avdyéitch, giving her a twenty-kopek piece: "redeem your shawl." She made the sign of the cross. Avdyéitch made the sign of the cross, and went with her to the door.

The woman left. Avdyéitch ate some shchi, washed some dishes, and sat down again to work. While he worked he still remembered the window: when the window grew darker, he immediately looked out to see who was passing by. Both acquaintances and strangers passed by, and there was nothing out of the ordinary.

But here Avdyéitch saw that an old apple-woman had stopped right in front of his window. She carried a basket with apples. Only a few were left, as she had nearly sold them all out; and over her shoulder she had a bag full of chips. She must have gathered them up in some new building, and was on her way home. One could see that the bag was heavy on her shoulder: she wanted to shift it to the other shoulder. So she lowered the bag upon the sidewalk, stood the basket with the apples on a little post, and began to shake down the splinters in the bag. And while she was shaking her bag, a little boy in a torn cap came along, picked up an apple from the basket, and was about to make his escape; but the old woman noticed it, turned around, and caught the youngster by his sleeve. The little boy began to struggle, tried to tear himself away; but the old woman grasped him with both hands, knocked off his cap, and caught him by the hair.

The little boy screamed, the old woman scolded. Avdyéitch lost no time in putting away his awl; he threw it upon the floor, sprang to the door,—he even stumbled on the stairs, and dropped his eye-glasses,—and rushed out into the street.

The old woman was pulling the youngster by his hair, and scolding, and threatening to take him to the policeman: the youngster defended himself, and denied the charge. "I did not take it," he said: "what are you licking me for? let me go!" Avdyéitch tried to separate them. He took the boy by his arm, and said,—

"Let him go, bábushka; forgive him, for Christ's sake."

"I will forgive him so that he won't forget till the new broom grows. I am going to take the little villain to the police."

Avdyéitch began to entreat the old woman:—

"Let him go, bábushka," he said, "he will never do it again. Let him go, for Christ's sake."

The old woman let him loose: the boy tried to run, but Avdyéitch kept him back.

"Ask the bábushka's forgiveness," he said, "and don't you ever do it again: I saw you taking the apple."

With tears in his eyes, the boy began to ask forgiveness.

"Nu! that's right; and now, here's an apple for you." Avdyéitch got an apple from the basket, and gave it to the boy. "I will pay you for it, bábushka," he said to the old woman.

"You ruin them that way, the good-for-nothings," said the old woman. "He ought to be treated so that he would remember it for a whole week."

"Eh, bábushka, bábushka," said Avdyéitch, "that is right according to our judgment, but not according to God's. If he is to be whipped for an apple, then what do we deserve for our sins?"

The old woman was silent.

Avdyéitch told her the parable of the master who forgave a debtor all that he owed him, and how the debtor went and began to choke one who owed him.

The old woman listened, and the boy stood listening.

"God has commanded us to forgive," said Avdyéitch, "else we, too, may not be forgiven. All should be forgiven, and the thoughtless especially."

The old woman shook her head, and sighed.

"That's so," said she; "but the trouble is, that they are very much spoiled."

"Then, we, who are older, must teach them," said Avdyéitch.

"That's just what I say," remarked the old woman. "I myself had seven of them,—only one daughter is left." And the old woman began to relate where and how she lived with her daughter, and how many grandchildren she had. "Here," she says, "my strength is only so-so, and yet I have to work. I pity the youngsters—my grandchildren—how nice they are! No one gives me such a welcome as they do. Aksíntka won't go to any one but me. (Bábushka, dear bábushka, loveliest)"—and the old woman grew quite sentimental.

"Of course, it is a childish trick. God be with him," said she, pointing to the boy.

The woman was just about to lift the bag upon her shoulder, when the boy ran up, and says, "Let me carry it, bábushka: it is on my way."

The old woman nodded her head, and put the bag on the boy's back.

Side by side they both passed along the street. And the old woman even forgot to ask Avdyéitch to pay for the apple.

Avdyéitch stood motionless, and kept gazing after them; and he heard them talking all the time as they walked away. After Avdyéitch saw them disappear, he returned to his room; he found his eye-glasses on the stairs,—they were not broken; he picked up his awl, and sat down to work again.

After working a little while, it grew darker, so that he could not see to sew: he saw the lamplighter passing by to light the street-lamps.

"It must be time to make a light," he thought to himself; so he fixed his little lamp, hung it up, and betook himself again to work. He had one boot already finished; he turned it around, looked at it: "Well done." He put away his tools, swept off the cuttings, cleared off the bristles and ends, took the lamp, put it on the table, and took down the Gospels from the shelf. He intended to open the book at the very place where he had yesterday put a piece of leather as a mark, but it happened to open at another place; and the moment Avdyéitch opened the Testament, he recollected his last night's dream. And as soon as he remembered it, it seemed as though he heard some one stepping about behind him. Avdyéitch looked around, and sees—there, in the dark corner, it seemed as though people were standing: he was at a loss to know who they were. And a voice whispered in his ear,—

"Martuin—ah, Martuin! did you not recognize me?"

"Who?" uttered Avdyéitch.

"Me," repeated the voice. "It's I;" and Stepán-uitch stepped forth from the dark corner; he smiled,

and like a little cloud faded away, and soon vanished.

"And this is I," said the voice. From the dark corner stepped forth the woman with her child: the woman smiled, the child laughed, and they also vanished.

"And this is I," continued the voice; both the old woman and the boy with the apple stepped forward; both smiled and vanished.

Avdyéitch's soul rejoiced: he crossed himself, put on his eye-glasses, and began to read the Evangelists where it happened to open. On the upper part of the page he read,—

"For I was an hungered, and ye gave me meat: I was thirsty, and ye gave me drink: I was a stranger, and ye took me in." . . .

And on the lower part of the page he read this:—

"Inasmuch as ye have done it unto one of the least of these my brethren, ye have done it unto me." (St. Matthew, chap. xxv.)

And Avdyéitch understood that his dream did not deceive him; that the Saviour really called upon him that day, and that he really received him.

A DOER OF THE WORD

Theodore Dreiser

Noank is a little played-out fishing town on the south-eastern coast of Connecticut, lying half-way between New London and Stonington. Once it was a profitable port for mackerel and cod fishing. Today its wharves are deserted of all save a few lobster smacks. There is a shipyard, employing three hundred and fifty men, a yacht-building establishment, with two or three hired hands: a sail-loft, and some dozen or so shops or sheds, where the odds and ends of fishing life are made and sold. Everything is peaceful. The sound of the shipyard axes and hammers can be heard for miles over the quiet waters of the bay. In the sunny lane which follows the line of the shore, and along which a few shops struggle in happy-go-lucky disorder, may be heard the voices and noises of the workers at their work. Water gurgling about the stanchions of the docks, the whistle of some fisherman as he dawdles over his nets, or puts his fish ashore, the whirr of the single high-power sewing machine in the sail-loft, often mingle in a pleasant harmony, and invite the mind to repose and speculation.

I was in a most examining and critical mood that summer, looking into the nature and significance of many things, and was sitting one day in the shed of the maker of sailboats, where a half-dozen characters of the village were gathered, when some turn in the conversation brought up the nature of man. He is queer, he is restless; life is not so very much when you come to look upon many phases of it.

"Did any of you ever know a contented man?" I inquired idly, merely for the sake of something to say.

There was silence for a moment, and one after another met my roving glance with a thoughtful, self-involved and retrospective eye.

Old Mr. Main was the first to answer.

"Yes, I did. One."

"So did I," put in the sailboat maker, as he stopped in his work to think about it.

"Yes, and I did," said a dark, squat, sunny, little old fisherman, who sold cunners for bait in a little hut next door.

"Maybe you and me are thinking of the same one, Jacob," said old Mr. Main, looking inquisitively at the boat-builder.

"I think we've all got the same man in mind, likely," returned the builder.

"Who is he?" I asked.

"Charlie Potter," said the builder.

"That's the man!" exclaimed Mr. Main.

"Yes, I reckon Charlie Potter is contented, if any-body be," said an old fisherman who had hitherto been silent.

Such unanimity of opinion struck me forcibly. Charlie Potter—what a humble name; not very re-markable, to say the least. And to hear him so spoken of in this restless, religious, quibbling com-munity made it all the more interesting.

"So you really think he is contented, do you?" I asked.

"Yes, sir! Charlie Potter is a contented man," re-plied Mr. Main, with convincing emphasis.

"Well," I returned, "that's rather interesting. What sort of a man is he?"

"Oh, he's just an ordinary man, not much of any-

body. Fishes and builds boats occasionally," put in the boat-builder.

"Is that all? Nothing else?"

"He preaches now and then—not regularly," said Mr. Main.

A-ha! I thought. A religionist!

"A preacher is expected to set a good example," I said.

"He ain't a regular preacher," said Mr. Main, rather quickly. "He's just kind of around in religious work."

"What do you mean?" I asked curiously, not quite catching the import of this "around."

"Well," answered the boat-builder, "he don't take any money for what he does. He ain't got anything."

"What does he live on then?" I persisted, still wondering at the significance of "around in religious work."

"I don't know. He used to fish for a living. Fishes yet once in a while, I believe."

"He makes models of yachts," put in one of the bystanders. "He sold the New Haven Road one for two hundred dollars here not long ago."

A vision of a happy-go-lucky Jack-of-all-trades arose before me. A visionary—a theorist.

"What else?" I asked, hoping to draw them out. "What makes you all think he is contented? What does he do that makes him so contented?"

"Well," said Mr. Main, after a considerable pause and with much of sympathetic emphasis in his voice, "Charlie Potter is just a good man, that's all. That's why he's contented. He does as near as he can what he thinks he ought to by other people—poor people."

"You won't find anybody with a kinder heart than Charlie Potter," put in the boat-builder. "That's the trouble with him, really. He's too good. He don't look after himself right, I say. A fellow has to look out for himself some in this world. If he don't, no one else will."

"Right you are, Henry," echoed a truculent sea voice from somewhere.

I was becoming both amused and interested, in-tensely so.

"If he wasn't that way, he'd be a darned sight better off than he is," said a thirty-year-old helper, from a far corner of the room.

"What makes you say that?" I queried. "Isn't it better to be kind-hearted and generous than not?"

"It's all right to be kind-hearted and generous, but

that ain't sayin' that you've got to give your last cent away and let your family go hungry."

"Is that what Charlie Potter does?"

"Well, no, maybe he don't, but he comes mighty near to it at times. He and his wife and his adopted children have been pretty close to it at times."

You see, this was the center, nearly, for all village gossip and philosophic speculation, and many of the most important local problems, morally and intellectually speaking, were here thrashed out.

"There's no doubt but that's where Charlie is wrong," put in old Mr. Main a little later. "He don't always stop to think of his family."

"What did he ever do that struck you as being over-generous?" I asked of the young man who had spoken from the corner.

"That's all right," he replied in a rather irritated and peevish tone; "I ain't going to go into details now, but there's people around here that hang on him, and that he's give to, that he hadn't orter."

"I believe in lookin' out for Number One, that's what I believe in," interrupted the boat-maker, laying down his rule and line. "This givin' up everything and goin' without yourself may be all right, but I don't believe it. A man's first duty is to his wife and children, that's what I say."

"That's the way it looks to me," put in Mr. Main.

"Well, does Potter give up everything and go without things?" I asked the boat-maker.

"Purty blamed near it at times," he returned definitely, then addressing the company in general he added, "Look at the time he worked over there on Fisher's Island, at the Ellersbie farm—the time they were packing the ice there. You remember that, Henry, don't you?"

Mr. Main nodded.

"What about it?"

"What about it! Why, he give his rubber boots away, like a darned fool, to old drunken Jimmy Harper, and him loafin' around half the year drunk, and worked around on the ice without any shoes himself. He might 'a' took cold and died."

"Why did he do it?" I queried, very much interested by now.

"Oh, Charlie's naturally big-hearted," put in the little old man who sold cunners. "He believes in the Lord and the Bible. Stands right square on it, only he don't belong to no church like. He's got the biggest heart I ever saw in a livin' being."

"Course the other fellow didn't have any shoes for to wear," put in the boat-maker explanatorily, "but he never would work, anyhow."

They lapsed into silence while the latter returned to his measuring, and then out of the drift of thought came this from the helper in the corner:

"Yes, and look at the way Bailey used to sponge on him. Get his money Saturday night and drink it all up, and then Sunday morning, when his wife and children were hungry, go cryin' around Potter. Dinged if I'd 'a' helped him. But Potter'd take the food right off his breakfast table and give it to him. I saw him do it! I don't think that's right. Not when he's got four or five orphans of his own to care for."

"His own children?" I interrupted, trying to get the thing straight.

"No, sir; just children he picked up around, here and there."

Here is a curious character, sure enough, I thought—one well worth looking into.

Another lull, and then as I was leaving the room to give the matter a little quiet attention, I remarked to the boat-maker:

"Outside of his foolish giving, you haven't anything against Charlie Potter, have you?"

"Not a thing," he replied, in apparent astonishment. "Charlie Potter's one of the best men that ever lived. He's a good man."

I smiled at the inconsistency and went my way.

A day or two later the loft of the sail-maker, instead of the shed of the boat-builder, happened to be my lounging place, and thinking of this theme, now uppermost in my mind, I said to him:

"Do you know a man around here by the name of Charlie Potter?"

"Well, I might say that I do. He lived here for over fifteen years."

"What sort of a man is he?"

He stopped in his stitching a moment to look at me, and then said:

"How d'ye mean? By trade, so to speak, or religious-like?"

"What is it he has done," I said, "that makes him so popular with all you people? Everybody says he's a good man. Just what do you mean by that?"

"Well," he said, ceasing his work as though the subject were one of extreme importance to him, "he's a peculiar man, Charlie is. He believes in giving nearly everything he has away, if any one else needs it. He'd give the coat off his back if you asked him for it. Some folks condemn him for this, and for not giving everything to his wife and them orphans he has, but I always thought the man was nearer right than most of us. I've got a family myself—but, then, so's he, now, for that matter. It's pretty hard to live up to your light always."

He looked away as if he expected some objection to be made to this, but hearing none, he went on. "I always liked him personally very much. He ain't around here now any more—lives up in Norwich, I think. He's a man of his word, though, as truthful as kin be. He ain't never done nothin' for me, I not bein' a takin' kind, but that's neither here nor there."

He paused, in doubt apparently, as to what else to say.

"You say he's so good," I said. "Tell me one thing that he ever did that struck you as being preëminently good."

"Well, now, I can't say as I kin, exactly, offhand," he replied, "there bein' so many of them from time to time. He was always doin' things one way and another. He give to everybody around here that asked him, and to a good many that didn't. I remember once"—and a smile gave evidence of a genial memory—"he give away a lot of pork that he'd put up for the winter to some colored people back here—two or three barrels, maybe. His wife didn't object, exactly, but my, how his mother-in-law did go on about it. She was livin' with him then. She went and railed against him all around."

"She didn't like to give it to them, eh?"

"Well, I should say not. She didn't set with his views, exactly—never did. He took the pork, though—it was right in the coldest weather we had that winter—and hauled it back about seven miles here to where they lived, and handed it all out himself. Course they were awful hard up, but then they might 'a' got along without it. They do now, sometimes. Charlie's too good that way. It's his one fault, if you might so speak of it."

I smiled as the evidence accumulated. Houseless wayfarers, stopping to find food and shelter under his roof, an orphan child carried seven miles on foot from the bedside of a dead mother and cared for all winter, three children, besides two of his own, being raised out of a sense of affection and care for the fatherless.

One day in the local postoffice I was idling a half hour with the postmaster, when I again inquired:

"Do you know Charlie Potter?"

"I should think I did. Charlie Potter and I sailed together for something over eleven years."

"How do you mean sailed together?"

"We were on the same schooner. This used to be a great port for mackerel and cod. We were wrecked once together."

"How was that?"

"Oh, we went on rocks."

"Any lives lost?"

"No, but there came mighty near being. We helped each other in the boat. I remember Charlie was the last one in that time. Wouldn't get in until all the rest were safe."

A sudden resolution came to me.

"Do you know where he is now?"

"Yes, he's up in Norwich, preaching or doing missionary work. He's kind of busy all the time among the poor people, and so on. Never makes much of anything out of it for himself, but just likes to do it, I guess."

"Do you know how he manages to live?"

"No, I don't, exactly. He believes in trusting to Providence for what he needs. He works though, too, at one job and another. He's a carpenter for one thing. Got an idea the Lord will send 'im whatever he needs."

"Well, and does He?"

"Well, he lives." A little later he added:

"Oh, yes. There's nothing lazy about Charlie. He's a good worker. When he was in the fishing line here there wasn't a man worked harder than he did. They can't anybody lay anything like that against him."

"Is he very difficult to talk to?" I asked, meditating on seeking him out. I had so little to do at the time, the very idlest of summers, and the reports of this man's deeds were haunting me. I wanted to discover for myself whether he was real or not—whether the reports were true. The Samaritan in people is so easily exaggerated at times.

"Oh, no. He's one of the finest men that way I ever knew. You could see him, well enough, if you went up to Norwich, providing he's up there. He usually is, though, I think. He lives there with his wife and mother, you know."

I caught an afternoon boat for New London and Norwich at one-thirty, and arrived in Norwich at five. The narrow streets of the thriving little mill city were alive with people. I had no address, could not obtain one, but through the open door of a news-stall near the boat landing I called to the proprietor:

"Do you know any one in Norwich by the name of Charlie Potter?"

"The man who works around among the poor people here?"

"That's the man."

"Yes, I know him. He lives out on Summer Street, Number Twelve, I think. You'll find it in the city directory."

The ready reply was rather astonishing. Norwich has something like thirty thousand people.

I walked out in search of Summer Street and finally found a beautiful lane of that name climbing upward over gentle slopes, arched completely with elms. Some of the pretty porches of the cottages extended nearly to the sidewalk. Hammocks, rocking-chairs on verandas, benches under the trees—all attested the love of idleness and shade in summer. Only the glimpse of mills and factories in the valley below evidenced the grimmer life which gave rise mayhap to the need of a man to work among the poor.

"Is this Summer Street?" I inquired of an old darky who was strolling cityward in the cool of the evening. An umbrella was under his arm and an evening paper under his spectacled nose.

"Bress de Lord!" he said, looking vaguely around. "Ah couldn't say. Ah knows dat street—been on it fifty times—but Ah never did know de name. Ha, ha, ha!"

The hills about echoed his hearty laugh.

"You don't happen to know Charlie Potter?"

"Oh, yas, sah. Ah knows Charlie Potter. Dat's his house right ovah dar."

The house in which Charlie Potter lived was a two-story frame, overhanging a sharp slope, which descended directly to the waters of the pretty river below. For a mile or more, the valley of the river could be seen, its slopes dotted with houses, the valley itself lined with mills. Two little girls were upon the sloping lawn to the right of the house. A stout, comfortable-looking man was sitting by a window on the left side of the house, gazing out over the valley.

"Is this where Charlie Potter lives?" I inquired of one of the children.

"Yes, sir."

"Did he live in Noank?"

"Yes, sir."

Just then a pleasant-faced woman of forty-five or fifty issued from a vine-covered door.

"Mr. Potter?" she replied to my inquiry. "He'll be right out."

She went about some little work at the side of the house, and in a moment Charlie Potter appeared. He was short, thick-set, and weighed no less than two hundred pounds. His face and hands were sunburned and brown like those of every fisherman of Noank. An old wrinkled coat and a baggy pair of gray trousers clothed his form loosely. Two inches of a spotted, soft-brimmed hat were pulled carelessly over his eyes. His face was round and full, but slightly seamed. His hands were large, his walk uneven, and rather inclined to a side swing, or the sailor's roll. He seemed an odd, pudgy person for so large a fame.

"Is this Mr. Potter?"

"I'm the man."

"I live on a little hummock at the east of Mystic Island, off Noank."

"You do?"

"I came up to have a talk with you."

"Will you come inside, or shall we sit out here?"

"Let's sit on the step."

"All right, let's sit on the step."

He waddled out of the gate and sank comfortably on the little low doorstep, with his feet on the cool bricks below. I dropped into the space beside him, and was greeted by as sweet and kind a look as I have ever seen in a man's eyes. It was one of perfect courtesy and good nature—void of all suspicion.

"We were sitting down in the sailboat maker's place at Noank the other day, and I asked a half dozen of the old fellows whether they had ever known a contented man. They all thought a while, and then they said they had. Old Mr. Main and the rest of them agreed that Charlie Potter was a contented man. What I want to know is, are you?"

I looked quizzically into his eyes to see what effect this would have, and if there was no evidence of a mist of pleasure and affection being vigorously restrained I was very much mistaken. Something seemed to hold the man in helpless silence as he gazed vacantly at nothing. He breathed heavily, then drew himself together and lifted one of his big hands, as if to touch me, but refrained.

"Yes, brother," he said after a time, "I am."

"Well, that's good," I replied, taking a slight

mental exception to the use of the word brother. "What makes you contented?"

"I don't know, unless it is that I've found out what I ought to do. You see, I need so very little for myself that I couldn't be very unhappy."

"What ought you to do?"

"I ought to love my fellowmen."

"And do you?"

"Say, brother, but I do," he insisted quite simply and with no evidence of chicane or make-believe— a simple, natural enthusiasm. "I love everybody. There isn't anybody so low or so mean but I love him. I love you, yes, I do. I love you."

He reached out and touched me with his hand, and while I was inclined to take exception to this very moral enthusiasm, I thrilled just the same as I have not over the touch of any man in years. There was something effective and electric about him, so very warm and foolishly human. The glance which accompanied it spoke, it seemed, as truthfully as his words. He probably did love me—or thought he did. What difference?

We lapsed into silence. The scene below was so charming that I could easily gaze at it in silence. This little house was very simple, not poor, by no means prosperous, but well-ordered—such a home as such a man might have. After a while I said:

"It is very evident that you think the condition of some of your fellowmen isn't what it ought to be. Tell me what you are trying to do. What method have you for improving their condition?"

"The way I reason is this-a-way," he began. "All that some people have is their feelings, nothing else. Take a tramp, for instance, as I often have. When you begin to sum up to see where to begin, you find that all he has in the world, besides his pipe and a little tobacco, is his feelings. It's all most people have, rich or poor, though a good many think they have more than that. I try not to injure anybody's feelings."

He looked at me as though he had expressed the solution of the difficulties of the world, and the wonderful, kindly eyes beamed in rich romance upon the scene.

"Very good," I said, "but what do you do? How do you go about it to aid your fellowmen?"

"Well," he answered, unconsciously overlooking his own personal actions in the matter, "I try to bring them the salvation which the Bible teaches.

You know I stand on the Bible, from cover to cover."

"Yes, I know you stand on the Bible, but what do you do? You don't merely preach the Bible to them. What do you do?"

"No, sir, I don't preach the Bible at all. I stand on it myself. I try as near as I can to do what it says. I go wherever I can be useful. If anybody is sick or in trouble, I'm ready to go. I'll be a nurse. I'll work and earn them food. I'll give them anything I can— that's what I do."

"How can you give when you haven't anything? They told me in Noank that you never worked for money."

"Not for myself alone. I never take any money for myself alone. That would be self-seeking. Anything I earn or take is for the Lord, not me. I never keep it. The Lord doesn't allow a man to be self-seeking."

"Well, then, when you get money what do you do with it? You can't do and live without money."

He had been looking away across the river and the bridge to the city below, but now he brought his eyes back and fixed them on me.

"I've been working now for twenty years or more, and, although I've never had more money than would last me a few days at a time, I've never wanted for anything and I've been able to help others. I've run pretty close sometimes. Time and time again I've been compelled to say, 'Lord, I'm all out of coal,' or 'Lord, I'm going to have to ask you to get me my fare to New Haven tomorrow,' but in the moment of my need He has never forgotten me. Why, I've gone down to the depot time and time again, when it was necessary for me to go, without five cents in my pocket, and He's been there to meet me. Why, He wouldn't keep you waiting when you're about His work. He wouldn't forget you—not for a minute."

I looked at the man in open-eyed amazement.

"Do you mean to say that you would go down to a depot without money and wait for money to come to you?"

"Oh, brother," he said, with the softest light in his eyes, "if you only knew what it is to have faith!"

He laid his hand softly on mine.

"What is car-fare to New Haven or to anywhere, to Him?"

"But," I replied materially, "you haven't any car-fare when you go there—how do you actually get it? Who gives it to you? Give me one instance."

"Why, it was only last week, brother, that a woman wrote me from Malden, Massachusetts, wanting me to come and see her. She's very sick with consumption, and she thought she was going to die. I used to know her in Noank, and she thought if she could get to see me she would feel better.

"I didn't have any money at the time, but that didn't make any difference.

"'Lord,' I said, 'here's a woman sick in Malden, and she wants me to come to her. I haven't got any money, but I'll go right down to the depot, in time to catch a certain train,' and I went. And while I was standing there a man came up to me and said, 'Brother, I'm told to give you this,' and he handed me ten dollars."

"Did you know the man?" I exclaimed.

"Never saw him before in my life," he replied, smiling genially.

"And didn't he say anything more than that?"

"No."

I stared at him, and he added, as if to take the edge off my astonishment:

"Why, bless your heart, I knew he was from the Lord, just the moment I saw him coming."

"You mean to say you were standing there without a cent, expecting the Lord to help you, and He did?"

"'He shall call upon me, and I shall answer him,'" he answered simply, quoting the Ninety-first Psalm.

This incident was still the subject of my inquiry when a little colored girl came out of the yard and paused a moment before us.

"May I go down across the bridge, papa?" she asked.

"Yes," he answered, and then as she tripped away, said:

"She's one of my adopted children." He gazed between his knees at the sidewalk.

"Have you many others?"

"Three."

"Raising them, are you?"

"Yes."

"They seem to think, down in Noank, that living as you do and giving everything away is satisfactory to you but rather hard on your wife and children."

"Well, it is true that she did feel a little uncertain in the beginning, but she's never wanted for anything. She'll tell you herself that she's never been

without a thing that she really needed, and she's been happy."

He paused to meditate, I presume, over the opinion of his former fellow townsmen, and then added:

"It's true, there have been times when we have been right where we had to have certain things pretty badly, before they came, but they never failed to come."

While he was still talking, Mrs. Potter came around the corner of the house and out upon the sidewalk. She was going to the Saturday evening market in the city below.

"Here she is," he said. "Now you can ask her."

"What is it?" she inquired, turning a serene and smiling face to me.

"They still think, down in Noank, that you're not very happy with me," he said. "They're afraid you want for something once in a while."

She took this piece of neighborly interference in better fashion than most would, I fancy.

"I have never wanted for anything since I have been married to my husband," she said. "I am thoroughly contented."

She looked at him and he at her, and there passed between them an affectionate glance.

"Yes," he said, when she had passed after a pleasing little conversation, "my wife has been a great help to me. She has never complained."

"People are inclined to talk a little," I said.

"Well, you see, she never complained, but she did feel a little bit worried in the beginning."

"Have you a mission or a church here in Norwich?"

"No, I don't believe in churches."

"Not in churches?"

"No. The sight of a minister preaching the word of God for so much a year is all a mockery to me."

"What do you believe in?"

"Personal service. Churches and charitable institutions and societies are all valueless. You can't reach your fellowman that way. They build up buildings and pay salaries—but there's a better way." (I was thinking of St. Francis and his original dream, before they threw him out and established monasteries and a costume or uniform—the thing he so much objected to.) "This giving of a few old clothes that the moths will get anyhow, that won't do. You've got to give something of yourself, and that's affection. Love is the only thing you can really give in all this world. When you give love, you give everything. Everything comes with it in some way or other."

"How do you say?" I queried. "Money certainly comes handy sometimes."

"Yes, when you give it with your own hand and heart—in no other way. It comes to nothing just contributed to some thing. Ah!" he added, with sudden animation, "the tangles men can get themselves into, the snarls, the wretchedness! Troubles with women, with men whom they owe, with evil things they say and think, until they can't walk down the street any more without peeping about to see if they are followed. They can't look you in the face; can't walk a straight course, but have got to sneak around corners. Poor, miserable, unhappy—they're worrying and crying and dodging one another!"

He paused, lost in contemplation of the picture he had conjured up.

"Yes," I went on catechistically, determined, if I could, to rout out this matter of giving, this actual example of the modus operandi of Christian charity. "What do you do? How do you get along without giving them money?"

"I don't get along without giving them some money. There are cases, lots of them, where a little money is necessary. But, brother, it is so little necessary at times. It isn't always money they want. You can't reach them with old clothes and charity societies," he insisted. "You've got to love them, brother. You've got to go to them and love them, just as they are, scarred and miserable and bad-hearted."

"Yes," I replied doubtfully, deciding to follow this up later. "But just what is it you do in a needy case? One instance?"

"Why, one night I was passing a little house in this town," he went on, "and I heard a woman crying. I went right to the door and opened it, and when I got inside she just stopped and looked at me.

"'Madam,' I said, 'I have come to help you, if I can. Now you tell me what you're crying for.'

"Well, sir, you know she sat there and told me how her husband drank and how she didn't have anything in the house to eat, and so I just gave her all I had and told her I would see her husband for her; and the next day I went and hunted him up and said to him, 'Oh, brother, I wish you would open your eyes and see what you are doing. I wish you wouldn't do that any more. It's only misery you are creating.' And, you know, I got to telling about how badly his wife felt about it, and how I intended to work and try and help her, and bless me if he didn't up and promise me before I got through that he wouldn't do that any more. And he didn't. He's working today, and it's been two years since I went to him, nearly."

His eyes were alight with his appreciation of personal service.

"Yes, that's one instance," I said.

"Oh, there are plenty of them," he replied. "It's the only way. Down here in New London a couple of winters ago we had a terrible time of it. That was the winter of the panic, you know. Cold—my, but that was a cold winter, and thousands of people out of work—just thousands. It was awful. I tried to do what I could here and there all along, but finally things got so bad there that I went to the mayor. I saw they were raising some kind of a fund to help the poor, so I told him that if he'd give me a little of the money they were talking of spending that I'd feed the hungry for a cent-and-a-half a meal."

"A cent-and-a-half a meal!"

"Yes, sir. They all thought it was rather curious, not possible at first, but they gave me the money and I fed 'em."

"Good meals?"

"Yes, as good as I ever eat myself," he replied.

"How did you do it?" I asked.

"Oh, I can cook. I just went around to the markets, and told the market-men what I wanted—heads of mackerel, and the part of the halibut that's left after the rich man cuts off his steak—it's the poorest part that he pays for, you know. And I went fishing myself two or three times—borrowed a big boat and got men to help me—oh, I'm a good fisherman, you know. And then I got the loan of an old covered brick-yard that no one was using any more, a great big thing that I could close up and build fires in, and I put my kettle in there and rigged up tables out of borrowed boards, and got people to loan me plates and spoons and knives and forks and cups. I made fish chowder, and fish dinners, and really I set a very fine table, I did, that winter."

"For a cent-and-a-half a meal!"

"Yes, sir, a cent-and-a-half a meal. Ask any one in New London. That's all it cost me. The mayor said he was surprised at the way I did it."

"Well, but there wasn't any particular personal

service in the money they gave you?" I asked, catching him up on that point. "They didn't personally serve—those who gave you the money?"

"No, sir, they didn't," he replied dreamily, with unconscious simplicity. "But they gave through me, you see. That's the way it was. I gave the personal service. Don't you see? That's the way."

"Yes, that's the way," I smiled, avoiding as far as possible a further discussion of this contradiction, so unconscious on his part, and in the drag of his thought he took up another idea.

"I clothed 'em that winter, too—went around and got barrels and boxes of old clothing. Some of them felt a little ashamed to put on the things, but I got over that, all right. I was wearing them myself, and I just told them, 'Don't feel badly, brother. I'm wearing them out of the same barrel with you—I'm wearing them out of the same barrel.' Got my clothes entirely free for that winter."

"Can you always get all the aid you need for such enterprises?"

"Usually, and then I can earn a good deal of money when I work steadily. I can get a hundred and fifty dollars for a little yacht, you know, every time I find time to make one; and I can make a good deal of money out of fishing. I went out fishing here on the Fourth of July and caught two hundred blackfish—four and five pounds, almost, every one of them."

"That ought to be profitable," I said.

"Well, it was," he replied.

"How much did you get for them?"

"Oh, I didn't sell them," he said. "I never take money for my work that way. I gave them all away."

"What did you do?" I asked, laughing—"advertise for people to come for them?"

"No. My wife took some, and my daughters, and I took the rest and we carried them around to people that we thought would like to have them."

"Well, that wasn't so profitable, was it?" I commented amusedly.

"Yes, they were fine fish," he replied, not seeming to have heard me.

We dropped the subject of personal service at this point, and I expressed the opinion that his service was only a temporary expedient. Times changed, and with them, people. They forgot. Perhaps those he aided were none the better for accepting his charity.

"I know what you mean," he said. "But that don't make any difference. You just have to keep on giv-

ing, that's all, see? Not all of 'em turn back. It helps a lot. Money is the only dangerous thing to give—but I never give money—not very often. I give myself, rather, as much as possible. I give food and clothing, too, but I try to show 'em a new way—that's not money, you know. So many people need a new way. They're looking for it often, only they don't seem to know how. But God, dear brother, however poor or mean they are—He knows. You've got to reach the heart, you know, and I let Him help me. You've got to make a man over in his soul, if you want to help him, and money won't help you to do that, you know. No, it won't."

He looked up at me in clear-eyed faith. It was remarkable.

"Make them over?" I queried, still curious, for it was all like a romance, and rather fantastic to me. "What do you mean? How do you make them over?"

"Oh, in their attitude, that's how. You've got to change a man and bring him out of self-seeking if you really want to make him good. Most men are so tangled up in their own errors and bad ways, and so worried over their seekings, that unless you can set them to giving it's no use. They're always seeking, and they don't know what they want half the time. Money isn't the thing. Why, half of them wouldn't understand how to use it if they had it. Their minds are not bright enough. Their perceptions are not clear enough. All you can do is to make them content with themselves. And that, giving to others will do. I never saw the man or the woman yet who couldn't be happy if you could make them feel the need of living for others, of doing something for somebody besides themselves. It's a fact. Selfish people are never happy."

He rubbed his hands as if he saw the solution of the world's difficulties very clearly, and I said to him:

"Well, now, you've got a man out of the mire, and 'saved,' as you call it, and then what? What comes next?"

"Well, then he's saved," he replied. "Happiness comes next—content."

"I know. But must he go to church, or conform to certain rules?"

"No, no, no!" he replied sweetly. "Nothing to do except to be good to others. 'True religion and undefiled before our God and Father is this,'" he quoted, "'to visit the widow and the orphan in their affliction and to keep unspotted from the world.'

Charity is kind," you know. " 'Charity vaunteth not itself, is not puffed up, seeketh not its own.' "

"Well," I said, rather aimlessly, I will admit, for this high faith staggered me. (How high! How high!) "And then what?"

"Well, then the world would come about. It would be so much better. All the misery is in the lack of sympathy one with another. When we get that straightened out we can work in peace. There are lots of things to do, you know."

Yes, I thought, looking down on the mills and the driving force of self-interest—on greed, lust, love of pleasure, all their fantastic and yet moving dreams.

"I'm an ignorant man myself, and I don't know all," he went on, "and I'd like to study. My, but I'd like to look into all things, but I can't do it now. We can't stop until this thing is straightened out. Some time, maybe," and he looked peacefully away.

"By the way," I said, "whatever became of the man to whom you gave your rubber boots over on Fisher's Island?"

His face lit up as if it were the most natural thing that I should know about it.

"Say," he exclaimed, in the most pleased and confidential way, as if we were talking about a mutual friend, "I saw him not long ago. And, do you know, he's a good man now—really, he is. Sober and hard-working. And, say, would you believe it, he told me that I was the cause of it—just that miserable old pair of rubber boots—what do you think of that?"

I shook his hand at parting, and as we stood looking at each other in the shadow of the evening I asked him:

"Are you afraid to die?"

"Say, brother, but I'm not," he returned. "It hasn't any terror for me at all. I'm just as willing. My, but I'm willing."

He smiled and gripped me heartily again, and, as I was starting to go, said:

"If I die tonight, it'll be all right. He'll use me just as long as He needs me. That I know. Good-by."

"Good-by," I called back.

He hung by his fence, looking down upon the city. As I turned the next corner I saw him awakening from his reflection and waddling stolidly back into the house.

7. TWO PARABLES

CHRIST IN FLANDERS

Honoré de Balzac

At a time somewhat indeterminate in Brabantine history, connection between the island of Cadzant and the coast of Flanders was kept up by a boat used for passengers to and fro. The capital of the island, Middleburg, afterwards so celebrated in the annals of Protestantism, counted them hardly two or three hundred hearths. Rich Ostend was then an unknown harbor, flanked by a village thinly peopled by a few fisherfolk, and poor dealers, and pirates who plied their trade with impunity. Nevertheless, the borough of Ostend, composed of about twenty houses and three hundred cottages, cabins, and hovels—made with the remains of wrecked ships—rejoiced in a governor, a militia, a gallows, a convent, and a burgomaster, in fact, all the institutions of advanced civilization. Who was reigning at that time in Brabant, Belgium, and Flanders? On this point tradition is mute.

Let us admit that this story is strangely imbued with that vagueness, indefiniteness, and love of the marvelous which the favorite orators of Flemish vigils love to intermingle in their legends, as varied in poetry as they are contradictory in detail. Told from age to age, repeated from hearth to hearth, by grandmothers and by storytellers night and day, this chronicle has received each century a different coloring. Like those buildings planned according to the architectural caprice of each epoch, whose dark, crumbling masses are a pleasure to poets alone, this legend would drive commentators, and wranglers over facts, words, and dates, to desperation. The narrator believes in it, as all superstitious souls in Flanders have believed in it, without being for that reason either more learned or more weak-minded. Admitting the impossibility of harmonizing all the different versions, here is the story, stripped perhaps of its romantic naïveté—for this it is impossible to reproduce—but still, with its daring statements disproved by history, and its morality approved by religion, its fantastic flowers of imagination, and hidden sense which the wise can interpret each to his own liking. Let each one seek his pasture herein and take the trouble to separate the good grain from the tares.

The boat which served to carry over the passengers from the island of Cadzant to Ostend was just about to leave the village. Before undoing the iron chain which held his boat to a stone on the little jetty where people embarked, the skipper blew his horn several times to call the loiterers, for this journey was his last. Night was coming on, the last fires of the setting sun scarcely gave enough light to distinguish the coast of Flanders or the tardy passengers on the island wandering along the earthen walls which surrounded the fields or among the tall reeds of the marshes. The boat was full. "What are you waiting for? Let us be off!" they cried. Just then a man appeared a few steps from the jetty. The pilot, who had neither heard nor seen him approaching, was somewhat surprised. The passenger seemed to have risen from the earth on a sudden. He might have been a peasant sleeping in a field, waiting for the hour for starting, whom the horn had wakened up. Was it a thief, or was it someone from the Customs House or police? When he arrived on the jetty to which the boat was moored, seven persons who were standing in the stern hastened to sit down on the benches, in order to have

them to themselves and prevent the stranger from seating himself among them. It was a sudden instinctive feeling, one of those aristocratic instincts which suggest themselves to rich people. Four of these personages belonged to the highest nobility of Flanders.

First of all, there was a young cavalier, with two beautiful greyhounds, wearing over his long hair a cap decked with jewels. He clinked his gilded spurs, and now and again curled his mustache, as he cast disdainful looks at the rest of the freight.

Then there was a proud damosel, who carried a falcon on her wrist and spoke only to her mother or to an ecclesiastic of high rank, a relative, no doubt. These persons made as much noise talking together as if they were the only people on the boat. All the same, next to them sat a man of great importance in the country, a fat merchant from Bruges, enveloped in a large mantle. His servant, armed to the teeth, kept by his side two bags full of money. Beside them was a man of science, a doctor of the University of Louvain, with his clerk. These people, who all despised one another, were separated from the bows by the rower's bench.

When the late passenger put his foot into the boat he gave a swift look at the stern, but when he saw no room there he went to seek a place among the people in the bows. It was the poor who sat there. At the sight of a man bareheaded, whose brown cloth coat and fine linen shirt had no ornament, who held in his hand neither hat nor cap, with neither purse nor rapier at his girdle, all took him for a burgomaster—a good and gentle man, like one of those old Flemings whose nature and simple character have been so well rendered by the painters of their country. The poor passengers welcomed the stranger with a respectful demeanor, which excited mocking whispers among the people in the stern. An old soldier, a man of toil and trouble, gave him his place on the bench, and sat himself at the end of the boat, keeping himself steady by putting his feet against one of the transverse beams which knit the planks together like the backbone of a fish.

A young woman, a mother with her little child, who seemed to belong to the working class of Ostend, moved back to make room for the newcomer. In this movement there was no trace either of servility or disdain. It was merely a mark of that kindliness by which the poor, who know so well how to appreciate a service, show their frank and natural disposition—so simple and obvious in the expression of all their qualities, good or bad.

The stranger thanked them with a gesture full of nobility, and sat down between the young mother and the old soldier. Behind him was a peasant with his son, ten years old. A poor old woman, with a wallet almost empty, old and wrinkled, and in rags—a type of misery and neglect—lay in the prow, crouched upon a coil of ropes. One of the rowers, an old sailor, who had known her when she was rich and beautiful, had let her get in for what the people so beautifully call "the love of God." "Thank you kindly, Thomas," the old woman had said; "I will say two *Paters* and two *Aves* for you in my prayers this evening."

The skipper blew his horn once more, looked at the silent country, cast the chain into his boat, ran along the side to the helm, took the tiller, and stood erect; then, having looked at the sky, called out in a loud voice to the rowers, when they were well in the open sea, "Row hard, make haste; the sea smiles evilly—the witch! I feel the swell at the helm and the storm at my wound." These words, spoken in the language of the sea—a tongue only understood of those accustomed to the sound of the waves—gave to the oars a hastened but ever-cadenced movement, as different from the former manner of rowing as the gallop of a horse from its trot. The fine people sitting at the stern took pleasure in seeing the sinuous arms, the bronzed faces with eyes of fire, the distended muscles, and the different human forms working in unison, just to get *them* the quicker over this narrow strait. So far from being sorry for their labor, they pointed out the rowers to each other, and laughed at the grotesque expressions which their exertion printed on their anxious faces. In the prow the soldier, the peasant, and the old woman regarded the mariners with that kind of compassion natural to people who, living by toil, know its hard anguish and feverish fatigue. Besides, being accustomed to life in the open air, they all divined by the look of the sky the danger which threatened them; so *they* were serious. The young mother was rocking her child to sleep, singing to it some old hymn of the church.

"If we *do* get over," said the old soldier to the peasant, "God will have taken a deal of trouble to keep us alive."

"Ah! He is master," said the old woman; "but I think it is His good pleasure to call us to Himself. Do you see that light, there?" and by a gesture of the head she pointed out the setting sun. Bands of fire streaked vividly the brown-red tinted clouds, which seemed just about to unchain a furious wind. The sea gave forth a suppressed murmur, a sort of internal groan, something like the growling of a dog whose anger will not be appeased.

After all Ostend was not far off. Just now the sky and the sea showed one of those sights to which it is impossible for words or painting to give longer duration than they have in reality. Human creations like powerful contrasts, so artists generally demand from nature its most brilliant aspects, despairing perhaps to be able to render the great and beautiful poetry of her ordinary appearance, although the human soul is often as profoundly moved by calm as by motion, by the silence as much as by the storm.

There was one moment when everyone on the boat was silent and gazed on the sea and sky, whether from presentiment or in obedience to that religious melancholy which comes over nearly all of us at the hour of prayer, at the fall of day, at the moment when nature is silent and the bells speak. The sea cast up a faint, white glimmer, but changing like the color of steel; the sky was mostly gray; in the west, long, narrow spaces looked like waves of blood, whereas in the east, glittering lines, marked as by a fine pencil, were separated from one another by clouds, folded like the wrinkles on an old man's forehead. Thus the sea and the sky formed a neutral background, everything in half tints, which made the fires of the setting sun glare ominously. The face of nature inspired a feeling of terror. If it is allowable to interweave the daring hyperboles of the people into the written language, one might repeat what the soldier said, "Time is rolling away," or what the peasant answered, that the sky had the look of a hangman. All of a sudden the wind rose in the west, and the skipper, who never ceased to watch the sea, seeing it swell toward the horizon, cried, "Ho, ho!" At this cry the sailors stopped immediately, and let their oars float.

"The skipper is right," said Thomas. The boat, borne on the top of a huge wave, seemed to be descending to the bottom of the gaping sea. At this extraordinary movement and this sudden rage of the ocean the people in the stern turned pale, and gave a terrible cry, "We perish!"

"Not yet," answered the skipper quietly. At this moment the clouds were rent in twain by the force of the wind exactly above the boat. The gray masses spread out with ominous quickness from east to west, and the twilight, falling straight down through a rent made by the storm wind, rendered visible every face. The passengers, the rich and the noble, the sailors and the poor, all stopped one moment in astonishment at the aspect of the last comer. His golden hair, parted in the middle on his tranquil, serene forehead, fell in many curls on his shoulders, and outlined against the gray sky a face sublime in its gentleness, radiant with divine love. He did not despise death; he was certain not to perish. But if at first the people at the stern had forgotten for an instant the tempest whose implacable fury menaced them, they soon returned to their selfish sentiments and lifelong habits.

"It's lucky for him, that dolt of a burgomaster, that he does not know the danger we are all in. There he stands like a dog, and doesn't seem to mind dying," said the doctor.

Hardly had he completed this judicious remark when the tempest unchained its legions; wind blew from every side, the boat spun round like a top, and the sea swamped it.

"Oh, my poor child! my child! who will save my child?" cried the mother, in a heartrending voice.

"You yourself," replied the stranger. The sound of this voice penetrated the heart of the young woman and put hope therein. She heard this sweet word, in spite of the raging of the storm, in spite of the shrieks of the passengers.

"Holy Virgin of Perpetual Succor, who art at Antwerp, I promise you twenty pounds of wax and a statue if you will only get me out of this," cried the merchant, falling on his knees upon his bags of gold.

"The Virgin is no more at Antwerp than she is here," replied the doctor.

"She is in heaven," said a voice, which seemed to come forth from the sea.

"Who spoke?"

"The devil," said the servant; "he's mocking the Virgin of Antwerp."

"Shut up with your blessed Virgin," said the skipper to the passengers; "take hold of the bowls and help me get the water out of the boat. As to you," he continued, addressing the sailors, "row hard, we have a moment's grace, and in the devil's name, who has left you in this world until now, let us be our own Providence. This little strip of water is horribly dangerous, I know from thirty years' experience. Is this evening the first time I have had a storm to deal with?" Then standing at the helm, the skipper continued to look alternately at the boat, the sea, and the sky.

"The skipper mocks at everything," said Thomas in a low voice.

"Will God let *us* die with these wretched people?" asked the proud damosel of the handsome cavalier.

"No! no! Noble damsel, listen to me." He put his arm round her waist, and spoke in her ear. "I can swim—don't say anything about it; I will take you by your beautiful hair and bring you safely to the shore; but I can save you only."

The damosel looked at her old mother; the dame was on her knees asking absolution from the bishop, who was not listening to her. The cavalier read in the eyes of his beautiful mistress some faint sentiment of filial piety, so he said to her in a low voice, "Submit yourself to the will of God; if He wishes to call your mother to Himself, it will doubtless be for her happiness—in the other world," he added, in a voice still lower, "and for ours in this."

The dame Rupelmonde possessed seven fiefs, besides the barony of Gâvres. The damosel listened to the voice of life, to the interests of love, speaking through the mouth of the handsome adventurer, a young miscreant, who haunted churches, seeking for prey—either a girl to marry or else good ready money.

The bishop blessed the waves and ordered them to be calm, not knowing exactly what to do; he was thinking of his concubine awaiting him with a delicate feast, perhaps at this moment in her bath perfuming herself, or arraying herself in velvet, and fastening on her necklaces and jewels. So far from thinking of the powers of the Church, and consoling these Christians, and exhorting them to trust in God, the perverse bishop mingled worldly regrets and words of lust with the sacred words of the Breviary.

The light, which lit up the pale faces, showed all their varying expressions, when the boat was borne up into the air by a wave, or cast down to the bottom of the abyss; then, shaken like a frail leaf, a plaything of the autumn wind, it cracked its shell, and seemed nigh to break altogether. Then there were horrible cries alternating with awful silence.

The demeanor of the people seated in the prow of the boat contrasted singularly with that of the rich and powerful in the stern. The young mother strained her child to her bosom every time that the waves threatened to engulf the frail bark; but she held to the hope with which the words of the stranger had filled her heart: each time she turned her eyes toward this man she drank in from his face a new faith, the strong faith of a weak woman, the faith of a mother. Living by the divine word, the word of love, which had gone forth from this man, the simple creature awaited trustfully the fulfillment of the sort of promise he had given her, and scarcely feared the tempest any more. Sticking to the side of the boat, the soldier ceased not to contemplate this singular being, on whose impassibility he sought to model his own rough, tanned face, bringing into play all his intelligence and strength of will, whose powerful springs had not been vitiated in the course of a passive mechanical life. He was emulous to show himself tranquil and calm, after the manner of this superior courage; he ended by identifying himself in some measure with the secret principle of its interior power. Then his imagination became an instinctive fanaticism, a love without limit, a faith in this man, like that enthusiasm which soldiers have for their commander when he is a man of power, surrounded with the glory of victories, marching in the midst of the splendid prestige of genius. The poor old woman said in a low voice, "Ah! what a miserable sinner I am! Have I not suffered enough to expiate the pleasures of my youth? Miserable one, why hast thou led the gay life of a Frenchwoman? Why hast thou consumed the goods of God with the people of the Church, the goods of the poor 'twixt the drink shop and the pawn shop? Ah! how wicked I was! Oh! my God! my God! let me finish my hell in this world of misery. Holy Virgin, Mother of God, take pity on me."

"Console yourself, mother, God is not a Lombard; although I have killed here and there good people and wicked, I do not fear for the resurrection."

"Ah! Sir, how happy they are, those beautiful ladies who are near the bishop, holy man!" the old woman went on; "they will have absolution from their sins. Oh! if I could only hear the voice of a priest saying to me, 'Your sins are forgiven you,' I could believe him."

The stranger turned toward her, and his look, full of charity, made her tremble. "Have faith," he said, "and you will be saved."

"May God reward you, good sir," she answered. "If you speak truly, I will go for you and for me on a pilgrimage to Our Lady of Loretto, barefooted."

The two peasants, father and son, remained silent, resigned, and submitting to the will of God, as people accustomed to follow instinctively, like animals, the convulsions of nature.

So on one side there were riches, pride, knowledge, debauchery, crime, all human society such as it is made by arts, thought, and education, the world and its laws; but also on this side, only shrieks, terror, the struggles of a thousand conflicting feelings, with horrible doubt—naught but the anguish of fear. And, towering above these, one powerful man, the skipper of the boat, doubting nothing, the chief, the fatalist king, making his own Providence, crying out for bailing bowls and not on the Virgin to save him, defying the storm, and wrestling with the sea, body to body.

At the other end of the boat, the weak: The mother, holding to her bosom a little child, who smiled at the storm. A wanton once gay, now given over to horrible remorse. A soldier, scarred with wounds, without other reward than his mutilated life, as a price for indefatigable devotion—he had hardly a morsel of bread, steeped in tears; all the same, he laughed at everything, and marched on without care, happy when he could drown his glory at the bottom of a pot of beer, or was telling stories thereof to wondering children; he commended gaily to God the care of his future. Lastly, two peasants, people of toil and weariness, labor incarnate, the work on which the world lives; these simple creatures were guileless of thought and its treasures, but ready to lose themselves utterly in a belief; having a more robust faith, in that they had never discussed or analyzed it; virgin natures, in whom conscience had remained pure and feeling strong. Contrition, misery, love, work had exercised, purified, concentrated, disculpated their will, the only thing which in man resembles that which sages call the soul.

When the boat, piloted by the marvelous dexterity of the skipper, came almost in view of Ostend, fifty paces from the shore, it was driven back by the convulsion of the storm, and suddenly began to sink. The stranger with the light upon his face then said to this little world of sorrow, "Those who have faith shall be saved; let them follow me." This man stood up and walked with a firm step on the waves. At once the young mother took her child in her arms and walked with him on the sea. The soldier suddenly stood at attention, saying in his rough language, "By my pipe! I follow you to the devil." Then, without seeming astonished, he marched on the sea.

The old prostitute, believing in the omnipotence of God, followed the man, and walked on the sea. The two peasants said, "As they are walking on the sea, why should not *we*?" So they got up and hastened after the others, walking on the sea.

Thomas wished to do likewise; but his faith wavered, and he fell several times into the sea, but got out again; and after three failures he too walked upon the sea.

The daring pilot stuck like a leech to the bottom of his boat. The merchant had faith, and had risen, but he wanted to take his gold with him, and his gold took him to the bottom of the sea. Mocking at the charlatan and the imbeciles who listened to him, at the moment when he saw the stranger proposing to the passengers to walk on the sea, the man of science began to laugh, and was swallowed up in the ocean. The damosel was drawn down into the abyss by her lover. The bishop and the old lady went to the bottom, heavy with sin perhaps, heavier still with unbelief and confidence in false images; heavy with devotional practices, light of alms and true religion.

The faithful troop, who trod with firm, dry feet on the plain of the raging waters, heard around them the horrible howling of the storm; great sheets of water broke in their path; irresistible force rent the ocean in twain. Through the mist these faithful ones perceived on the shore a little feeble light, which flickered in the window of a fisherman's cabin. Each one as he marched bravely toward this light seemed to hear his neighbor crying through the roaring sea, "Courage!" Nevertheless, absorbed each in his own danger, no one said a single word. And so they reached the shore. When they were all seated at the hearth of the fisherman, they sought in vain the guide who had a light upon his face. From his seat upon the summit of a rock, at the base of which the hurricane had cast the pilot clinging to

his plank with all the strength of a sailor in the throes of death, the MAN descended, picked up the shipwrecked man almost dashed to pieces; then he said, as he held out a helping hand over his head, "It is well this once, but do as thou *hast* done no more; the example would be too bad." He took the mariner on his shoulders, and carried him to the fisherman's cottage. He knocked for the unfortunate man, so that someone would open the door of this humble refuge to him; then the Savior disappeared.

In this place the sailors built the Convent of Mercy, where were long to be seen the prints that the feet of JESUS CHRIST had, it was said, left on the sand.

Afterward, when the French entered Belgium, some monks took away with them this precious relic, the testimony of the last visit JESUS ever paid to the earth.

CHRIST IN THE CUPBOARD

T. F. Powys

Mr. John Pie, a sober and a worthy man, was now in a good way of business. Mr. Pie possessed a large face, heavy hands, and a keen look—and he had once been poor.

When Mr. Pie was poor and worked as a day-labourer for Farmer Told, he, with the help of Betty, his wife, spent generously what they earned. When any one begged of them—and old Mrs. Crapper was always begging—they would bid her, or any others, share their meat, and Mrs. Crapper would say, after hoping first that she wasn't taking away the bread from the children, that "John Pie didn't put Christ into the cupboard like some folk, but always had Him to sit at table."

"And thee daren't refuse no beggar a crust with 'e here," old Mrs. Crapper would shout out with her usual boisterous laugh that made the plates upon the dresser rattle and shake.

It is well understood that wealth is not increased by large acts of charity, and, though a man may believe that whoso giveth lendeth unto the Lord, it is easy for him also to wonder how soon the Lord will repay.

Mr. Pie began to change his manners as soon as his master gave him a young sow as a gift, because John had worked so industriously. This sow, as is the habit with lowly creatures, increased and multiplied. Within a year Mr. Pie held twenty pounds in his hand through selling his young pigs, with which money he purchased a horse and trap and commenced trade as a dealer.

One gain leads to another when a man is industrious and busy, and it wasn't long before Mr. Pie became a dairyman and then again a farmer.

At Grange Farm Mrs. Betty Pie churned the butter, and in the evening she would darn the socks for her children, Tommy and Winnie, who were six and eight years old.

As one might expect, while the riches were being acquired the beggars were forgotten, for Mrs. Crapper couldn't walk into a large farmhouse as she used to do into a little cottage, because now that the family had got on so well she felt that it wouldn't be proper to eat bread at their table, but would only go to the back door and ask for it. Mrs. Crapper didn't have a kind welcome when she came, for Mr. Pie would be bringing in the milk with a great clatter and banging of cans, and the old woman's whispered request for a bite of food would pass unheeded. . . .

Although Mr. Pie never gave anything away now that he was rich, he still liked to think that he was a religious man, who would give a very warm welcome to Christ if He ever came to visit him.

Upon the first Sunday in Advent after the evening service held in Norbury Church, Mr. and Mrs. Pie were sitting in the farmhouse parlour, where a large fire burned. Mrs. Pie had laid the supper, and had, by chance, set out an extra plate. When she noticed her mistake she said, as is usual in the country when such an error occurs, "That's for the Devil."

In the parlour at Grange Farm there was a large, empty cupboard that had no use except for Tommy and Winnie to be frightened about, for they would take turns to lift the latch and peep in, and then run away to hide behind their parents' chairs.

It chanced that this evening the winds of heaven were very boisterous and gusts of rain lashed the windows so that the old house shook. No one would wish to be out upon such a night, and certainly no knock was expected at the rich farmer's door.

But as soon as the blue cheese and the old ale were ready, there came a soft knocking at the door, that made the children run and hide, for they remembered what their mother had said about the Devil being expected because an extra plate had been laid.

Mr. John Pie opened the door.

The Man who presented himself, and who came in as soon as He was invited, was easy to recognise, for His face all the family had seen either in a church window or else in a picture. He wore a crown of thorns, the usual robe, and His feet were bare.

He sat down at once in the vacant place, and, looking at the table, He blessed the food. While He ate He gazed lovingly upon the children and even stroked the cat that had jumped upon His knee. But the Visitor hadn't been there for more than a few moments before another knock came, but this time it was at the back door.

This knocker was Mrs. Crapper, who had come to beg a little food, for she had nothing to eat in her cottage that was away in a wide and distant field.

"Oh, she's always begging!" said Betty Pie. "She's always asking for things, and we should be certainly ruined if we gave to every one."

Mr. Pie looked nervously at the Visitor, who, in a quiet tone, commanded Mrs. Pie to give the best she had to the beggar.

As soon as Mrs. Pie returned from doing so, she looked ruefully at her husband, who remarked angrily that, however pleasant it was to have Christ amongst them, yet if He always commanded them to give to every old woman who came, they might as well go back to the cottage again and work for Farmer Told, as they used to do before he gave them the pig.

"But we want to keep Christ in the house," replied Betty Pie, "for if either Winnie or Tommy happen to die of measles He would bring them to life again as He did the daughter of the Roman centurion."

"Yes, that's very true," answered John Pie, "but if He sits with us at table He will be soon telling us not only to give away our food, but also to sell all we have and give the proceeds to the poor."

"Then we will put Christ into the cupboard," said Betty Pie.

The Visitor didn't wait to be asked twice to go there, for, as soon as ever Betty Pie had made her request, He rose of His own accord and, stepping to the cupboard, He went in.

One can easily imagine that, with Christ in the cupboard, all things would go well with Mr. Pie's worldly affairs. His cows yielded quantities of milk, and his large flock of sheep that, at this season of Advent, were lambing, had all of them twins.

But such a place of prosperity was no suitable begging-ground for Mrs. Crapper. She, indeed, had been very much surprised when Mrs. Pie carried to her, the first evening of Christ's visit, all the best of food. As one may well suppose, she came the very next evening, hoping that the old times were come again when John Pie never refused any poor woman a place at his table.

Mrs. Pie was skimming the cream when Mrs. Crapper called, but she never looked round when the old woman begged, and Mr. Pie, who was bringing in two great cans of milk, told her rudely to go. . . .

As Christmas drew near, the family that thrived so well could talk merrily, and even the children joined in, about their guest whom they were so glad to have safe in the cupboard.

Every evening they would pile the fire high, and Mr. Pie, after tending the cows in the yards and giving them large quantities of sweet meadow hay, would sit amongst his family and, heating the poker red-hot, would plunge it into the large jug of ale to warm it, and Mrs. Pie would even give the children a little sip out of her own glass.

Of course they would often speak of the pleasure of having so grand a guest in the house, though He was but in the cupboard, and Tommy, warmed by the ale, thought one evening that he might take a peep to see if He was there still.

Mrs. Crapper had just been to the back door, but the dog roaming in the yard had torn her clothes that were but rags, and she had gone away. Mr. Pie was smiling into the fire and telling of all the fine lambs that were born in the turnip field, when little Tommy crept to the cupboard and peeped in.

As soon as he returned to the fire his father asked him whether Christ was still there.

"Oh yes, He's there," said Tommy, taking another sip of ale from his mother's glass. "His face is as kind and loving as ever and the marks of the nails are in His hands, but His feet look a little different."

Mr. Pie laughed. He was so well off now that he could afford a bottle of brandy, which he mixed with the old ale.

"Ah!" he said, emptying his glass and smacking his lips, "it's pleasant to know that He's there, for, if any of us were to fall ill, it's a comfort to think that we have only to open the cupboard door to have Him by our bedside."

About Christmas-time it is usual for those who are poor to expect gifts from those whom God has blessed with greater plenty, and more than one poor person besides Mrs. Crapper, as the holy day drew nigh, came to Grange Farm to ask for a little. But each of them was driven from the door.

The cold came with severe frost, and snow covered the fields, and Mrs. Crapper, trying to find her way to the farm to ask for a little skim milk, found herself too ill to reach the gate and lay down in a snowdrift to die.

When the cold froze her and she breathed her last, yielding up her soul to the still comfort of the frozen air, Winnie Pie, in the warm farmhouse parlour, after taking a sip at her mother's glass, thought that she, too, would like to have a little peep at the Christ who, she remembered very well, had looked so lovingly at her when He sat at their table.

Winnie opened the cupboard and looked, but she quickly shut it again, and retired to the fire and told her mother that she had seen no marks of the nails, and that His face, though He still had those mild eyes, looked rather queer.

Tommy peeped the next, but he came back quick enough and said that Christ had a tail and that His feet were like a cow's.

Mr. Pie laughed heartily.

"That's from standing so long in the cupboard," he said. "He hasn't been wanted yet, but the day may come when we shall be glad of Him!"

Mrs. Pie laughed too. It seemed so pleasant to her to have Christ in the cupboard, while they could drink warm ale and brandy and count the gains that had come to them while Christ was there.

On Christmas Eve, when the path to Mr. Pie's front gate was so slippery that one might easily fall, a knock came at the back door that was so like Mrs. Crapper's that Mrs. Pie was startled and upset her glass.

"Oh, I'm not one to be afraid of a ghost, with Christ in the cupboard," said Mr. Pie, and with an oath, he rushed out to drive the spectre away.

A figure moved along the path in the moonlight, and Mr. Pie followed, but he had not gone far before he slipped and fell heavily upon the frozen ground.

He was carried in and laid upon the bed, where it was soon evident that a fractured rib had pierced his lung and that he must die.

The family gathered round, and Mr. Pie whispered faintly that the time had come to let the Divine Guest out of the cupboard to save His host's life.

Tommy ran down to open the cupboard door. The dying man grew weaker, while the family waited in hopeful expectation for Christ to save.

Although the dead of winter had come there was a sudden flash of lightning outside and the thunder rolled. The children cowered and Betty Pie screamed.

A hot breath of sulphurous air filled the room. Presently an ugly thing appeared in the doorway, with flashing, fiery eyes, horrid horns, a tail, and a beast's feet.

"You hid Christ in the cupboard," exclaimed the Devil, "but your mean deeds have changed Him."

PART EIGHT

Afterwards

———————

The people who love Christ are set apart. Like the soft, glorious Pleiades that keep together in the sky.

STORM JAMESON

1. VICTORY

EASTER

Edmund Spenser

Most glorious Lord of lyfe, that on this day
Didst make thy triumph over death and sin,
And having harrowd hell, didst bring away
Captivity thence captive, us to win:
This joyous day, deare Lord, with joy begin,
And grant that we, for whom thou diddest dye,
Being with thy deare blood clene washt from sin,
May live for ever in felicity:
And that thy love we weighing worthily,
May likewise love thee for the same againe;
And for thy sake, that all lyke deare didst buy,
With love may one another entertayne.
So let us love, deare love, lyke as we ought:
Love is the lesson which the Lord us taught.

Hasting to Heaven, would, that he might allow
Himselfe unto all stations, and fill all,
For these three daies become a minerall;
Hee was all gold when he lay downe, but rose
All tincture, and doth not alone dispose
Leaden and iron wills to good, but is
Of power to make even sinfull flesh like his.
Had one of those, whose credulous pietie
Thought, that a Soule one might discerne and see
Goe from a body, 'at this sepulcher been,
And, issuing from the sheet, this body seen,
He would have justly thought this body a soule,
If not of any man, yet of the whole.

RESURRECTION

John Donne

Sleep, sleep old Sun, thou canst not have repast
As yet, the wound thou took'st on friday last;
Sleepe then, and rest; The world may beare thy stay,
A better Sun rose before thee to day,
Who, not content to'enlighten all that dwell
On the earth's face, as thou, enlightened hell,
And made the darke fires languish in that vale,
As, at thy presence here, our fires grow pale.
Whose body having walk'd on earth, and now

EASTER HYMN

Henry Vaughan

Death and darkness get you packing,
Nothing now to man is lacking;
All your triumphs now are ended,
And what Adam marred is mended;
Graves are beds now for the weary,
Death a nap, to wake more merry;
Youth now, full of pious duty,
Seeks in thee for perfect beauty;
The weak and aged, tir'd with length

Of days, from thee look for new strength;
And infants with thy pangs contest
As pleasant, as if with the breast.
  Then, unto Him, who thus hath thrown
Even to contempt thy kingdom down,
And by His blood did us advance
Unto His own inheritance,
To Him be glory, power, praise,
From this, unto the last of days!

TWO EASTER LILIES

John Banister Tabb

Behold the reed of scorn,
  Like Aaron's rod,
Hath blossomed to adorn
  The risen GOD.

And she, the broken bloom
  That balmed His feet,
Is first before His tomb,
  Her LORD to greet.

CHRIST'S VICTORY

Richard Crashaw

Christ when He died
Deceived the cross,
And on death's side
Threw all the loss:
The captive world awak'd and found
The prisoners loose, the jailor bound.

O dear and sweet dispute
'Twixt death's and love's far different fruit,
Different as far
As antidote and poisons are:
By the first fatal Tree
Both life and liberty
Were sold and slain,
By this they both look up, and live again.

O strange and mysterious strife,
Of open death and hidden life:
When on the cross my King did bleed,
Life seemed to die, Death died indeed.

EASTER NIGHT

Alice Meynell

All night had shout of men and cry
  Of woeful women filled His way;
Until that noon of sombre sky
  On Friday, clamor and display
Smote Him; no solitude had He,
No silence, since Gethsemane.

Public was Death; but Power, but Might,
  But Life again, was Victory,
Were hushed within the dead of night,
  The shutter'd dark, the secrecy.
And all alone, alone, alone
  He rose again behind the stone.

A GUARD OF THE SEPULCHER

Edwin Markham

I was a Roman soldier in my prime;
Now age is on me and the yoke of time.
I saw your Risen Christ, for I am he
Who reached the hyssop to Him on the tree;
And I am one of two who watched beside
The Sepulcher of Him we crucified.
All that last night I watched with sleepless eyes;
Great stars arose and crept across the skies.
The world was all too still for mortal rest,
For pitiless thoughts were busy in the breast.
The night was long, so long, it seemed at last
I had grown old and a long life had passed.
Far off, the hills of Moab, touched with light,
Were swimming in the hollow of the night.
I saw Jerusalem all wrapped in cloud,
Stretched like a dead thing folded in a shroud.

Once in the pauses of our whispered talk
I heard a something on the garden walk.
Perhaps it was a crisp leaf lightly stirred—
Perhaps the dream-note of a waking bird.
Then suddenly an angel burning white
Came down with earthquake in the breaking light,
And rolled the great stone from the Sepulcher,
Mixing the morning with a scent of myrrh.
And lo, the Dead had risen with the day:
The Man of Mystery had gone his way!

Years have I wandered, carrying my shame;
Now let the tooth of time eat out my name.
For we, who all the wonder might have told,
Kept silence, for our mouths were stopt with gold.

A consecration ne'er forgot,
  For where His hand had lain
The shining breast grew crimson red,
  Blessed by the holy stain.

That Easter morn is sacred since,
  For with each verdant spring,
Our faith and hope return to us
  Whenever robins sing.

THE EASTER ROBIN

Geraldine Farrar

You oft have heard of that dark night
  When our dear Christ and Lord
Was laid away by tender hands,
  While those who loved Him mourned.

Then in the hush of rosy dawn,
  The earth began to sing,
And by the Saviour's resting place,
  A robin preened his wing.

He lifted high his little head
  And saw the angel bright,
Who rolled the heavy stone away
  To let in God's sweet light.

There came a gracious Presence forth,
  With gentle tread and mien;
He halted at the budding tree,
  Where sat the bird unseen.

A bruised hand, scarce healed of wounds,
  Caressed the feathered throat,
And from the robin's swelling heart
  There burst a joyous note!

THE EMPTY TOMB

Toyohiko Kagawa

As they climbed the slope to the sepulcher, the four women went, in unspoken accord, more slowly. The journey through Jerusalem's narrow and deserted streets had been black and desolate beyond the telling. They had reached the outskirts of the city when a sharp earthquake occurred and the sky overhead took on a queer unfamiliar color. They had huddled together for long frightened moments, rolling eyes upward at the great heaped clouds and feeling the road tremble as if with palsy. Salome had suggested turning back, but Mary Magdalene would have none of it. With resolution now she led the way up the twisting path to the garden of Joseph of Arimathea, a dark silent figure in the gloom. Salome and Mary, the mother of James, wept and moaned a little as they mounted the incline, their grief steady and resigned. All rebellion had gone out of them when they had watched with Jesus' mother at the foot of the cross. Only the sorrow, deep and beyond human stemming, remained.

Joanna, like Mary Magdalene, could not weep. A great heaviness was upon her, the weight of spirit and of body and of the night. Her thoughts were slow as words thickly spoken in alien tongue. Her feet dragged as if shackled. The jars of spices which she bore were an almost intolerable burden. She could go no farther. She could not. Yet—she must. She, with those faithful others, must minister to the broken body of her Master.

"But who will roll us away the stone from before the sepulcher?" wailed Salome in sudden anxiety.

"Perhaps the guards will help us when they see we mean no trouble," said Mary, the mother of James.

Joanna thought of the size of the boulder. "It will take at least three score."

Only Mary Magdalene said nothing. Rounding a group of thick-leaved trees, they stopped. There were lights in the garden ahead, and much confusion. Nay, there was one light, a strange radiance from the sepulcher. Soldiers were running toward them, away from the tomb. Others stood huddled together in groups. Some knelt with faces covered, sobbing like children.

Joanna was stricken with consternation. The stone was rolled away from the cave's mouth! Father in heaven, what had happened? She started forward with her companions. No voice challenged them. None of the guards made any attempt to halt them.

Mary Magdalene was first at the sepulcher. Joanna followed her, stooping down to look into the cavern. She heard Mary Magdalene's quick intake of breath, and then she herself felt the quickening of her startled heart. The body of Jesus was not there!

The jar of sweet ointment fell from Joanna's nerveless hands with a crash. She looked down blindly at the shattered pieces on the cave's floor, and fragrance drifted up to her slowly. Her throat was painfully tight. Her two fists ached. Was it not enough that they had crucified him? Could they not let the dead rest in peace?

Beside her, she heard Salome breathe: "Behold!"

She lifted her head and through eyes blurred with moisture saw, in the dimness of the tomb, two white figures, one at the head and one at the foot, where the body of Jesus had lain.

For the shaking of her lips, Joanna could utter no sound. Nor could she look longer upon the figures, for the strange glistening of their raiment.

There came a voice from the sepulcher, and it was like no voice which Joanna had ever heard.

"Fear not: for I know you seek Jesus which was crucified. He is not here, for he is risen, as he said. Go quickly and tell his disciples that he goes before you into Galilee. There shall you see him. Lo, I have told you."

When Joanna came to herself she was with Salome and Mary the mother of James hastening along the road back to Jerusalem. How or when she had left the sepulcher, she knew not. Only one thing she knew. They must find Peter and John and the others. They must tell them of the astounding events.

Salome said suddenly: "But—but where is Mary Magdalene?"

"Is she not with us?" asked Joanna. She turned her head, half expecting to see a figure hurrying to overtake them. But there was nought upon that road but the pale dawn.

Mary Magdalene could not leave. She stood without at the sepulcher and the tears she could not shed before, fell now. She was frightened, bewildered and, above everything, desolate. In her agony, she knew not what to think. Were those gleaming figures in the sepulcher part of a dream or vision, or were they representatives of evil men who had robbed the tomb of the body of her beloved master? She walked blindly in the garden, not able to see her way because of tears. She stumbled into bushes. Branches caught at her garments, and she bruised her sandaled feet on sharp, upthrusting stones. Dimly, she was aware of a man approaching and turned a little away from him, bowing her face in her hands.

"Woman," said the stranger, "why do you weep?"

She did not answer. Why did she weep? There was reason in plenty. None, she moaned inwardly, had ever known such cause for grief. She had been thrust from a height into a pit where no light came and out of which she could never climb.

"Whom do you seek?"

The man's voice seemed to her far away, and she wished that he would go away and leave her with her sorrow. Yet, he might know something of what had occurred here. Perhaps he was the gardener.

"Sir," she said pleadingly, "if you have borne him hence, tell me where you have laid him, and I will take him away."

"Mary!"

That voice! That voice of infinite compassion. That tone of tender rebuke. Father in heaven, who was it spoke thus to her—who? She turned, shaking from head to foot, and blinked the tears from her eyes.

"Rabboni!"

It was he! It was her Master! It was Jesus of Nazareth. Joy crowded into her heart. There was room for nought else. She flung herself forward to touch him, to hold him. . . .

Jesus said to her: "Touch me not, for I am not yet ascended to my Father: but go to my brethren, and say to them that I ascend to my Father and your Father; and to my God, and your God."

Mary Magdalene sank to her knees in the dew-wet grass, and her prayer had no words, for it needed none. . . . When she lifted her head, Jesus had disappeared. Nevertheless, she doubted not that she had indeed seen him, and returned to Jerusalem with rejoicing to seek out the disciples.

2. THE EXPERIENCE AND ITS CONSEQUENCES

THE CROWNING WONDER

John Oxenham

His followers had fled like frightened sheep,
Their hopes all wrecked by the catastrophe;
And yet, within a little span of days,
They were all bound together and to him
In fellowship far closer than before;
And, bold beyond their natures, and aflame
With new-born zeal that burned like pure white fire,
They faced the world prepared to live and die
To bring to man the Kingdom of God's Love.
They were new men, remade, and wholly filled
With that great spirit that had been their Chief's.

They had sore doubted; they had feared and fled;
Their hearts had turned to water when he died;
They had lost hope; and faith, too hardly tried,
Had sped and left them bruised and stupefied;—
But now . . . they knew!—they knew!—

They had been weak,—but now they were like gods,
Performing wonders in the name of God,
And preaching everywhere their risen Lord
In words that pierced like lightning to men's hearts.
And all with such vast plenitude of power
That all men marvelled.

And why?
How had this wonder come?—
Hear now the crowning glory of it all!—

He had made promise on that fatal night
To come again and be with them awhile,
To cheer and hearten them for his great work.

They saw him die the malefactor's death,
They saw his body sealed within the tomb,
They saw the guard that watched it night and day.

But His true self was not to bind nor hold,
And three days later, as He had foretold,
He came again among them as of old,—
Came in His own marred body, bearing still
The ragged nail-wounds in His hands and feet,—
Came in the flesh, and ate and drank with them;
And not of them alone was He thus seen,
But unto many who had known Him well.
Unto His own, he spoke full lovingly,
And pledged them all anew to do His will,
Till all men everywhere should know
God's love for man,
And His eternal longing for man's good.

No man may see the face of God and live;
His Love enfolds us like the air and light;

His wonders are about us everywhere;
But finite cannot grasp the infinite
And so He vailed His Godhead in the flesh,
That all might see and know Him in His Son,—
Might see in Him the fulness of His love
And share with Him the victory He won.

So died the mortal of this son of man,
Whose body shrined the immortal love of God.
He lived that His fair life might be to man
A perfect mirror of the Love of God,
The full expression of His Fatherhood.

He died that Love might live for evermore,
And find in Him its ever-open door,
And we in Him find God still more and more.

He rose to show that Death is not the end
But the beginning of a life that will transcend
Man's highest hopes, and will in full amend,
By God's sweet grace, life's woe.
An end? An end? Nay, then, there is no end!
Death vanquished is no more man's foe
But his good friend.

He rose to show that Death is but The Gate
To Life Immortal, where He still doth wait
To welcome man with love impassionate.

And now He lives and loves and pleads as then,
And in His own good time will come again,
To dwell once more among the sons of men.

THE WALK TO EMMAUS

William Cowper

It happened, on a solemn eventide,
Soon after he that was our surety died,
Two bosom friends, each pensively inclined,
The scene of all those sorrows left behind,
Sought their own village, busied, as they went,
In musings worthy of the great event:
They spake of him they loved, of him whose life,
Though blameless, had incurred perpetual strife,
Whose deeds had left, in spite of hostile arts,

A deep memorial graven on their hearts.
The recollection, like a vein of ore,
The farther traced, enriched them still the more;
They thought him, and they justly thought him, one
Sent to do more than He appeared t'have done;
To exalt a people, and to place them high
Above all else, and wondered he should die.
Ere yet they brought their journey to an end,
A Stranger joined them, courteous as a friend,
And asked them, with a kind engaging air,
What their affliction was, and begged a share.
Informed, he gathered up the broken thread,
And, truth and wisdom gracing all he said,
Explained, illustrated, and searched so well
The tender theme, on which they chose to dwell,
That reaching home, "The night," they said, "is near,
We must not now be parted, sojourn here."
The new acquaintance soon became a guest,
And, made so welcome at their simple feast,
He blessed the bread, but vanished at the word,
And left them both exclaiming, " 'Twas the Lord!
Did not our hearts feel all he deigned to say,
Did they not burn within us by the way?"

CHRIST TO THOMAS

Richard Crashaw

"EXCEPT I SHALL PUT MY FINGER." JOHN 20:25

Thy impious finger, would it, then, reborrow
The nails, the spear, each circumstance of sorrow?
That on a living Christ thou mayst rely,
Cruel, wouldst thou thy Christ recrucify?

THE GREEN BOUGH

Mary Austin

It was the season of the green bough. On into the
night, emanations from the warm, odorous earth
kept the chill from the air, and the sky, steeped in
the full Spring suns, retained, almost until dawn,

light enough to show the pale undersides of the olive branches where they stirred with the midnight currents. It was not until the hours fell into the very pit of the night that the morning coolness began to strike shivers along the bodies of those whose business kept them sleeping on the open slopes outside the city walls.

It would have been about that time that he awoke. For more than an hour past he had swung from point to point of consciousness on successive waves of pain; now he was carried almost to the verge of recovery, and now he felt the dragging clutch of the Pit from which hardly he had escaped. By degrees as he was borne toward life his passages in and out of insensibility began to approach more nearly the normal phases of waking and sleeping; the pangs of his body separated from the obsessions of spiritual distress, and recurrent memory began to ply.

It began with the agony in the garden and the falling away of all human support from that inexplicable wrestling of great souls with foreknowledge, which must always seem to the generality, unnecessary if not a little absurd. More pitiably than all that had rolled between, he felt the empty reach of his affections toward the uncomprehending sleep of his companions. . . . Could ye not watch one little hour! He remembered the futility of trial, the scoffings and the betrayals, through the crisis of which his quick spirit had lived so long before that at last it broke upon him harmlessly. Pain by pain, his body picked out for him other memories of the way, the cross, the tearing nails . . . more than all else the impotence of purely human impulses under the larger vision which kept him even in the midst of anguish, profoundly aware of how little they knew the thing they did. It came back upon him as the stiffness of his wounds, the burden of understanding that loses even the poor human relief of bitterness and blame. As he fell away again into the trough of bodily pain it was to measure the full horror of that drop, which when the racked consciousness that had sustained him in the knowledge of Fatherliness, had failed like a splitten sail and left him beating blindly in the void. "My God, my God why hast thou forsaken me?" He came strangely up to life in the anguish of that cry. . . . Suddenly he put up his hand and touched the cold stones of his sepulchre. He was dead then, and was alive. Lying very still for pure weakness, his spirit returned half unwittingly

by the old track and traveled toward God . . . fumblingly, as a drowsy child at the breast, he sucked comfort, the ineffable, divine support. It flowed. Slowly the slacked spirit filled. . . . Power came upon him. God was not dead . . . nor forsaking. . . . He hung upon that and waited for a word. Outside in the dawn dusk a bird, awakened by the swaying of his bough in the first waft of the morning, bubbled over with the joyous urge of the Spring. The sound of it filtered through the rock crevices in a thin, clear trickle of song. He laid off the grave cloth and began to feel for the round stone which he knew should close the mouth of the grave. Wounded as he was, it was still no more than many suffer in battle, with the cheerful promise of recovery; calling on those reserves of power for which he had always been remarkable, he applied his shoulder to the stone . . . it yielded to the pressure and slid along the groove.

He made out the soft bulk of the olive trees, all awake and astir to catch the first streak of the morning, and the *tink, tink* of water falling from a pipe into a stone basin. Following it he came to the fountain from which the garden was watered, and drank and bathed his wounds. He was startled for a moment by the swaying of a garment against him, and then he perceived it to be the gardener's cloak left hanging in the tree, the long, brown hooded garment of the time. He drew its folds around him as a protection against the warning chill of dawn. He was a working man also, and knew the ways of working folk; he groped in the split hollow of the ancient olive tree, and far under the roots behind the gardener's spade he found a lump of figs tied in a cloth and a common flask which had yet a few swallows of wine in it. When he had eaten and drunk he bound up his feet with the cloth and sat down on the stone bench of the fountain to think what had befallen him.

He was dead—else why had they buried him?— and he was alive again. This then was the meaning of those glimmers and intimations of a life so abundant that he could not imagine even the shock of death to separate him from it. . . . For a long time he had known what he must face if he came up to Jerusalem, yet he had faced it, urged by that inward impulse too deep and imperative for human withstanding . . . and he had died . . . witness the gaping wound in his side . . . and now he walked among the olives. Vestiges and starts of the broken images of pain and returning consciousness, advised where he had been. He turned his mind deliberately away from that and laid hold on God . . . he was alive again. . . . The currents of the Eternal Being circulated through him with peace and healing.

The dusk of the dawn cleared to ineffable blueness, in which the domes and towers of Jerusalem swam, islanded in light. Round about, single high peaks, which still retained the winter whiteness, glowed like outposts of the heavenly host. The gates of the city clattered to let in the hordes of market gardeners with their donkeys, camped since the night before outside the walls, and presently in the cool dimness he saw the women stealing out by a postern and beginning to climb the hill path toward the place of sepulchres. They came peering through the dawn, for they were not certain of any mark by which they should know it, except that it was a new tomb wherein never man was laid. Their voices came up to him clearly through the morning stillness, and he knew at once what their errand was when he heard them troubling lest they had come so early there would be no one about to take away the stone from the door; but when they came to the place where it should be, and saw that it was already rolled away, they were amazed and a little afraid. Then Mary the mother of James and Salome, and the other Mary, put down the spices they had brought, to go and carry word to the disciples, but Mary Magdalene stayed weeping by the sepulchre.

When he saw that she was alone he went to her and inquired why she wept. She, supposing him to be the gardener, for she saw little because of her weeping and it was not yet full light—"Oh, sir," she said, "if you have borne him hence, tell me where you have laid him that I may take him away."

"Mary!" he said, and as he spoke he put back the gardener's hood from his head.

"Rabboni," the old title came back half consciously in answer to the tone, and suddenly she saw that it was he, and fell a trembling, for she could not understand but that he was a spirit. She sunk in the wet grass of the orchard, for the quaking of her limbs would not sustain her.

"Why seek ye the living among the dead?" he questioned with the old tender irony, but she scarcely heard him. She worked toward him on her knees; tremblingly her hands went out to touch the beloved feet, half to prove it were his very self or a vision of thin air.

"Nay, touch me not, Mary." He drew back with the sensitiveness of the newly wounded. "I am not yet ascended to my Father," he assured her as he raised her from the ground.

Louder now they heard the stir of Jerusalem awake, and knew that the broadening day might soon bring the rabble about them. When he had questioned her a little hurriedly concerning the state of the city and his disciples, he bade her tell them to come to him in Galilee in a place known to them of old, and so saying drew the folds of his cloak about him and went down by the hill trail away from Jerusalem.

It was twilight of the same day when he came near to the village of Emmaus and heard the cheerful barking of the dogs and the lowing of the cattle at the byres. There was a good Spring smell of tillage in the inlets of the hills and the cry of the nightjar shaken out over the stony places in a shrill fine spray of sound. Half an hour from the village he came upon two who had followed him up to Jerusalem in the beginning of Passover, and as they walked they reasoned together concerning the things that had come to pass there. When he had entered into conversation he saw that they were sad, and inquired of them the reason for it; and they, taking him for a stranger, told him how but a short time since there had gone a man up to Jerusalem with a great company, preaching the Kingdom of Heaven at hand, and what had been done to him by the authorities.

"But," said they, "we trusted it had been he should redeem Israel."

"O slow of heart," cried he, "that you should believe not all that the prophets have spoken!"

All day as he had come, against the pangs of his torn body, his spirit had beat up toward God with the rhythm of his walking, calling on Power by all the names of Jehovah, until he went veiled in it as in a cloud, which now by the mere added effort of communication, burst into splendor. But a few days since he had walked up to Jerusalem, battling, in the midst of the presages of betrayal and disaster, with the incomplete revelation of Messiahship. This morning waking at once to a knowledge of the practical defeat and to a new and extraordinary security of Divine continuance, he had felt his way, like a true Hebrew, back through the maze of intimations by the words of the Prophets; starlighted sayings shot like meteors across the dark of Israel's history. They lit far inward past the shames and consternations of the crucifixion.

This, then, was the Kingdom; not the overthrow of one form by another, but the flux of all forms, empires, pomps, societies, in the eternal facts of existence . . . the redemption of life from the bondage of Things. He was dead and was alive again.

How indeed was a Messiahship to prove its divine origin by merely setting up in the room of thrones and principalities? Say rather, the last word as to the futility of the Kingdoms of the world was pronounced when they wrecked themselves against its immortal quality.

As he held up the events of the last few days to the familiar scriptures, new meanings came out in them like secret writing held before a flame, and as he talked the hearts of his companions burned within them. As they drew near to their house the speaker made as if he would have gone further, but they urged that he should come in to supper, for the way was hard and the dark had fallen. So as they sat at table, still talking, the mistress of the house set food before them and a little oil-fed lamp. Then the guest put back the hood from his head and stretching forth his hand broke the bread and blessed it, as was his custom, and at once they knew him, but for very fear and astonishment they spoke neither to him nor to one another. As soon as he saw that he was recognized he rose and went forth from them, disappearing in the night.

So little anticipated by his disciples had been the overthrow of the Messianic Hope, that the stroke of it fell upon them like a wolf upon the flock. It scattered them into nooks and corners, into the hill places and villages round about Jerusalem, there to huddle, pressing together for relief from consternation, loath to believe that the miraculous powers which had so often served them, had failed him on his own account, and wholly unable to accept the whispered word brought by the women from the sepulchre. He was gone; power and personality, his body even risen or spirited away. All during that day there had been fearful stealers about the precincts of the burial place for a view of the deserted tomb, stealing back again to whisper and wonder or to handle the dropped grave cloth which lay treasured in the house of Mary.

And now, here were two come back from Emmaus with extraordinary new proof of a resurrection, which when they had heard it neither did they believe. But as some few of them sat together talking of these things, secretly behind shut doors for fear of authorities, he of whom they spoke, advised by that mysterious inward leading that his name passed among them with the old reverent tenderness, sought them out by it, and while they were yet speaking appeared among them. Wounded and pale from his vigils and his pains, the voice of his customary salutation struck terror through them. There were men there who had unbound him dead, as they believed, from the cross and bestowed him in the tomb!

"Behold my hands and feet," he said; "handle me and see; for a spirit hath not flesh and bones." But seeing they hung between terror and wonder, he understood that they still supposed that they had seen a spirit. Then he sat at table and asked that he be served with what food they had, the broiled fish and honey in the comb, upon which they had been at supper, talking quietly the while. Seeing him eat they grew secure, and as they began to realize that he was with them in flesh, they were glad.

So by such simple means as they were able to receive he made them to know that he was the very man whom with their own hands they had laid away, in no wise changed or altered; but of the new meaning which his life had taken on by the fact, he spoke very little, for their minds were not opened to it; neither was it at all times and altogether plain to himself.

In the hills beyond the Sea of Tiberias there was a hut built in a secret and solitary place by one of those wild anchorites not infrequently met with in the borders of Judea. None knew of it except perhaps a runaway slave or two, and shepherds who used it at lambing time. Here in the beginning of his ministry he had drawn apart for seasons of prayer and meditation, that the Word might be plain in him; here, then, he remained resting of God, subsisting in the body by what the hills afforded him and by the gifts of a few poor followers who had their homes hereabout, as yet scarcely apprised of the tragic termination of his mission to Jerusalem. Here he saw the passing of the rains, and flowers come out, flame like, on low piney shrubs; wandering shepherds went by him with their new-washed flocks, and whiter clouds led flockwise in the draws between the hills. . . . By all these things knowledge flowed into him.

He saw with chastening how it was that he, so near at all times to the Divine mind, should suffer these things. Lying so close there, as a child to its parent, he had been pushed off the better to measure its reach and fullness. He had clung to that breast which in his ministry had nourished him, until torn from it by betrayals, mockings, tortures of his body, he had dropped despairingly into the gulf of death, and lo, he was fallen into the lap of God! "The Kingdom of Heaven is in the midst of you," he had said to his disciples, and now suddenly he had discovered it in the midst of himself—this profound inward clutch upon Being, from which not the breaking of his body could divide him.

Here in the weakness of shock and wounds, much that had perplexed him in his own life, the fullness of Power straining at his human limitations, came out clearly like the contour of a coast at ebb, but it left him more than ever groping for that communicating touch by which the gained knowledge could be made serviceable to men.

"As my father hath sent me," he had said to his disciples when his new-found resistance to wounding and the malice of men was at flood, "even so I send you." Now as his body frailed before the inundation of revelation, he yearned for Peter and that John whom he had loved, all the company of humble folk who had heard him gladly, following up to Jerusalem trustfully as the great bands of sheep that passed him almost daily, roving the Galilean hills at the heels of the shepherd.

How was he to reach them now, scattered and leaderless, with the significance of his persistence in the body which he accepted at its humanest interpretation. Lying close in the cover of the hills he sent out his thoughts in a strong cry toward his best loved disciples, and Peter and John and the others picking up again the dropped thread of their humble avocations about Gennesareth, heard him. They heard him inwardly, but read it so humanly awry that they made excuse to one another that they went a fishing. They entered into the fishing boats and all night, though they caught nothing, they beat toward the coast where the cry was; and when it was early

light they heard his very voice calling to them that they should cast in their net on the side where he had seen the silver schools floating under the morning mist. When Peter knew the voice he girt on his fisher's coat and came ashore through the shallows, for they were close in, and he had the quickest faith of all the twelve.

Then the others came in with the nets full to breaking, and found that he had made a fire, for the nights along the lake borders were chill, and prepared bread. So they took fish and broiled it and broke their fast together as they had done so many times before when in the beginning of his ministry he had often no other food than the shared bread of the working people. The naturalness of the morning meal restored to them a little of their former reverent familiarity, and served as the medium by which he undertook to lay upon them the obligation of the gospel which he could now no more in this frame and presence preach about the world.

Of this he seems to have been certain. Daily as he reached inward on great tides of prayer for the word born of his late experience, he was aware of being carried so far out of his wracked body that it was inevitable that he should finally leave it there tumbled like weed along the shore of Things. Beyond that episode lay the full light for which he panted more than a hart for the waterbrook.

He had known, evidently, how his visit to Jerusalem must terminate; he seems now to have understood that his further usefulness must wait upon the dropping off of the tortured frame which he had brought up through the tomb with him, but he missed knowing how to convey to the remnant of his disciples, who came together about him in the hills, the spiritual values of his return.

He failed, perhaps because he was not himself yet sure that it might not come that way, to rid them of the expectation of Jewish Autonomy; he was concerned, as always, with the preaching of his Word, rather than what came of it. On this morning the flocks rounding the lake fronting hills furnished the figure of his admonition.

"Feed my sheep," he said to Peter, and again; and then "Feed my lambs." One thing he had not brought back out of the tomb with him was the fear by which his church was afterward corrupted, that the Truth of God could not be trusted to do its Perfect Work in man.

On a mountain, in a place appointed for them, he flamed forth for the last time, with that message, the faint, misread recollection of which as it lay in the minds of his disciples has become the ultimate hope of all our science and all untoward questionings—the assurance of the supremacy of Spirit. What they got from it chiefly was the certainty of the continuance of his personal power. It was the green bough presented to them among the desolating blasts of human experience. "For, lo, I am with you always," he said, "even to the end of the world."

That they did not treasure more these last words, preserve them with that meticulous accuracy for which that body of religionists, from whom they were shorn by the sword of Christ's teaching, were notable, was due in part to their having no apparent belief in this being the last. They had seen him in the flesh, they expected to see him in the flesh again. Nothing else could account for the boldness with which these timid and easily shaken peasant souls faced so soon again the possibility of persecution and death in that Jerusalem whither he had told them to await the confirming visitation of the spirit. They faced it. They went while the city still rang with the story of his defeat, to confirm his triumph; they preached what they had known and seen.

It seems likely, then, that on that last occasion when he went with them a little way on the road toward Jerusalem, they had no notion that it was the last they should see of him in the body. They said unto him, "Lord, dost thou at this time restore the Kingdom to Israel?"

"It is not for you," said he, "to know times and seasons." In his own time he should come again and in no other guise than Counselor and Friend. When he had blessed them they saw him pass up the hill trail toward his chosen place and the mountain mists receive him.

Afterward in the long time when they expected him in vain, they said, in the manner of speaking of that country, that he had ascended to Heaven, so that long afterward it came to be reported that they had seen him ascending there in the company of clouds of angels. But so long as they lived who had seen him, they looked out for him every day . . . any knock at the door . . . any solitary figure on the hill paths about Bethany. . . . For they had laid him in the tomb, and he had come to them in the very flesh.

THE ASCENSION

Edwin Markham

In the gray dawn they left Jerusalem,
And I rose up to follow after them.
He led toward Bethany by the narrow bridge
Of Kedron, upward to the olive ridge.
Once on the camel path beyond the City,
He looked back, struck at heart with pain and pity—
Looked backward from the two lone cedar trees
On Olivet, alive to every breeze—
Looked in a rush of sudden tears, and then
Went steadily on, never to turn again.

Near the green quiets of a little wood
The Master halted silently and stood.
The figs were purpling, and a fledgling dove
Had fallen from a windy bough above,
And lay there crying feebly by a thorn,
Its little body bruisèd and forlorn.
He stept aside a moment from the rest
And put it safely back into the nest.

Then mighty words did seem to rise in Him
And die away; even as white vapors swim
A moment on Mount Carmel's purple steep,
And then are blown back rainless to the deep.
And once He looked up with a little start:
Perhaps some loved name passed across his heart,
Some memory of a road in Galilee,
Or old familiar rock beside the Sea.

And suddenly there broke upon our sight
A rush of angels terrible with light—
The high same host the Shepherds saw go by,
Breaking the starry night with lyric cry—
A rush of angels, wistful and aware,
That shook a thousand colors on the air—
Colors that made a music to the eye—
Glories of lilac, azure, gold, vermilion,
Blown from the air-hung delicate pavilion.

And now his face grew bright with luminous will:
The great grave eyes grew planet-like and still.
Yea, in that moment, all his face, fire-white,
Seemed struck out of imperishable light.
Delicious apprehension shook his spirit,
With song so still that only the heart could hear it.

A sense of something sacred, starry, vast,
Greater than earth, across his spirit passed.

Then with a stretching of his hands to bless,
A last unspeakable look that was caress,
Up through the vortice of bright cherubim
He rose until the august form grew dim—
Up through the blue dome of the day ascended,
By circling flights of seraphim befriended.
He was uplifted from us, and was gone
Into the darkness of another dawn.

TOLD IN THE STARS

Manuel Komroff

Out of the deep far East came the old oracle Xado. His skin was brown, scorched by the hot sun of the Indies and dried by the winds of desert Persia. He carried a staff cut from the holy acacia wood and with this rod he journeyed the hundreds of leagues from the great mysterious lands of the East. From India, dotted with its fierce stone gods, through the vast snow-covered mountains and into Persia the land of mystery he journeyed. He had climbed the mountain of Elam and spent the night on the very top studying the stars in the heavens. He journeyed through the rocky wilderness of Paran and the hot sands of the wilderness of Zin. And now with staff in hand he walked through the open gate and into the busy paved streets of Jerusalem.

The cloth of his tattered garment, his burnt skin and even the staff in his hand gave him the stamp of one who had come from the far far East. And it was not long before the people of Jerusalem discovered that the great oracle Xado was in their midst.

As he was washing himself at the public fountain rich merchants sent their servants to bow before him and invite him to their homes for rest and refreshment. But he thanked them and sent them away saying he had need of nothing. There was a proud toss of his head.

The servants of the high-priests also came to him

but these too he sent away. "I must journey now to the land of Egypt," he said.

The hunch-backed female slave of Pilate came before the oracle and said: "My master sends me. Though he is Governor of all Judea he offers the holy and wise man from the East nothing."

"You come to tell me this?"

"In haste I have been sent."

"Then return," spoke the oracle Xado, "and thank your governor for the nothing he offers. I ask for nothing and I am truly grateful if what I ask for is given me."

"Ah!" said Buncha with a twinkle in her eye. "I see I am no match for you, for the years of my life are only forty and yours are twice forty, and I can barely read the alphabet while you can read the stars in the heavens; and so if my master can give you nothing, then perhaps you could give my master something."

"What have I so precious?"

"Words and prophecy."

"Your master does not believe in the stars."

"He would listen to your words for he has heard of the fame of Xado even in Rome."

"And he sent you to bring me before him?"

"That is it."

"And if I refuse to appear in his presence he will probably send his soldiers to bring me. And what I would not do willingly I will have to do by compulsion."

"No. You are wrong. That is what I said he should do but he has another plan. If you do not come to him, then he will come to you."

"This he said?"

"Yes."

"Then lead the way and take me to him. When governors are humble, then they deserve to hear words of faith and prophecy."

The hunch-backed slave led the way through the streets of Jerusalem and brought the venerable oracle Xado into the presence of Pontius Pilate.

"Long have I heard of the wonders of your prophecies," said Pilate. "Your fame has even traveled to Rome."

The old man bowed in acknowledgment of this compliment.

"Tell me, wise Xado, what brings you into Jerusalem?"

"For the past forty nights have I watched the stars

in the sky. I am on my way to the land of Egypt. In Egypt my fathers were born and died and there I will remain the rest of my days and be buried beside my own people. Here in Jerusalem I hoped to see some of those whose names I read clearly in the stars."

"You have but to command, my good Xado, and I will order that they be brought before you. This would be little service indeed for a guest so renowned."

"Ah, Pilate! It is not so easy. Only eleven of the true followers remain and they have already left Jerusalem."

"Then someone else surely you desire to see?"

"No one else."

"You know," said Pilate, "many years ago, it must have been about thirty years ago, when I was still a young man in Rome, little did I imagine I would ever be sitting face to face with the oracle Xado . . . At that time we heard stories in Rome how once three Eastern kings came to you. And you pointed out a star to them and told them to follow this star for under it a certain child was born. And this child was destined to be king over all. Tell me, Xado, was this a tale of a story-teller or was it true?"

"It was true, Pilate."

"Then what happened to this king?"

"Alas, he is dead."

"Dead? Born only thirty years ago and already dead?"

"Yes. By your command."

"No, no! It could not be. No king came before me. Five years have I been in this wretched hole and . . ."

"By your command," repeated the oracle.

"When? Tell me when I condemned a king."

"Forty days ago. Before the Passover holidays."

"Ah! That was no king. Your stars could not have told the truth."

"The stars have no reason to speak falsely."

"He was one from the desert and the priests arrested him. They called him the King of the Jews only in mockery. I remember clearly now. I could find no guilt in the man. But they cried aloud for him. And I washed my hands of the whole business."

"He was the one. Forty days ago I read the news in the heavens. And because of this innocent man whom you condemned . . ."

"I wanted only peace."

"Because of him, your name will be immortal."

"Because of him?"

"Yes. Only that and nothing else."

"Immortal! . . . Tell me this, wise Xado. Here I have been Procurator of Judea these five long years. How many more years will I remain here as procurator?"

"Five more."

"And after me?"

"You are the last of all. No other governors will Rome send to Jerusalem."

"And those who served as procurators here before me . . . Will their names be forgotten?"

"Perhaps on some dusty page of history their names may be preserved. But only your name will be truly known in all the ages to come."

"The first procurator to come to Jerusalem from Rome was Coponius and soon after there was Marcus Ambivius and he was followed by Annius Rufus. These three were all very distinguished. And they did very well for themselves and went back to Rome laden with wealth."

"They will be forgotten."

"And before me there was Valerius Gratus. He spent six years here in this wretched hole and is now a senator in Rome."

"Only one name of all these will be immortal and that name is Pontius Pilate."

"How strange! And you say five years more I will remain in this place?"

"Yes."

"And then?"

"Wars will drive you out."

"And I will return to Rome?"

"Yes, in poverty and disgrace."

"But you say I will be renowned and my name will be immortal."

"Not in your days, but in the years to come."

"And when you say immortal you mean my name will really be known everywhere?"

"Everywhere and in every land. It will be known as well as Cæsar's."

"And all because . . ."

"Because of him."

"How strange are the stars. One could really never imagine such a thing. It is like a dream. Tell me more. What else do you read in the stars?"

"Herod Antipas, the son of the old tyrant Herod

who killed the innocents, will fall from his high place. And with him will fall Herodias who plotted for the head of the Baptist John. The Arabian king Aretas, father of the first wife of Herod Antipas, will invade the lands and defeat him. He will flee to Rome to plead before the Emperor but he will not win favor. And he and his dark wife will end their evil days in banishment."

"What else do you read in the stars? The Temple of the Jews . . . Will it remain standing?"

"For forty years more it will stand. And then it will be laid in ruin, as will all the great buildings of Jerusalem."

"And the victors?"

"Rome. The great altar candlesticks and other golden relics sacred to the Jews will be paraded in a march of triumph through the streets of Rome."

"Then out of all this Rome will be the victor?"

"No, not really. The true conquest is of a different order. It will stem from those who have survived. From the eleven faithful followers. Theirs will be the victory and a new faith will be born."

"But they are without arms and can conquer no one."

"Without arms, true. But little by little a great part of the world will come over to their faith. And the teachings of their Master they will make known over the entire world."

"You seem to make this incident into a very big affair."

"Not I. The stars so proclaim. And your name is caught in this net of destiny and will endure the ages."

"And that is why you seek the eleven followers of this one who was condemned?"

"Yes. I hoped to find them here and learn from their own lips how they saw their Master after he rose out of the tomb. He spoke with them as man to man and he commanded them to believe and go out into the world and teach the word that is the true word."

"And what word could be a true word?" asked Pilate.

"Love is a true word. Faith is another word that might well be true."

"I must admit, Xado, that the stars are filled with a great confusion of strange things."

"Out of the confusion comes order and the destiny of all things."

With these words the venerable oracle rose to depart.

"Stay, Xado. I will make a feast for you."

"My eyes have feasted with forty nights of heaven. And such a feast has never been before. In peace I leave you. Egypt calls."

"Come, I will give you beasts of burden that your journey may be less wearisome."

"My heart is light and my staff dots a long track. As I came so I will depart."

He held his acacia staff aloft as a signal of a long farewell and with this gesture left the presence of the Procurator of Judea. When he reached the street, Buncha the slave woman came running after him with a bag of dried dates and other fruit. She pressed it quickly into his hands and without a single word she ran away.

PART NINE

Christ Universal

———

"Well, sir," I says, pretty humble, "I don't seem to make out which world it is I'm from. But you may know it from this—it's the one the Saviour saved."

He bent his head at the Name. Then he says, gently—

"The worlds He has saved are like to the gates of heaven in number—none can count them."

MARK TWAIN
CAPTAIN STORMFIELD'S VISIT
TO HEAVEN

1. CHRIST IN NATURE

SYMBOL

David Morton

My faith is all a doubtful thing,
  Wove on a doubtful loom,
Until there comes, each showery spring,
  A cherry tree in bloom;

And Christ, who died upon a tree
  That death had stricken bare,
Comes beautifully back to me,
  In blossoms everywhere.

I SEE HIS BLOOD
UPON THE ROSE

Joseph Mary Plunkett

I see his blood upon the rose
And in the stars the glory of His eyes,
His body gleams amid eternal snows,
His tears fall from the skies.

I see His face in every flower;
The thunder and the singing of the birds
Are but His voice—and carven by His power
Rocks are His written words.

All pathways by His feet are worn,
His strong heart stirs the ever-beating sea,
His crown of thorns is twined with every thorn,
His cross is every tree.

THE LILIES OF THE FIELD

Daniel Henderson

When I went up to Nazareth—
  A pilgrim of the spring—
When I went up to Nazareth
  The earth was blossoming!
I saw the blue flower of the flax
  Beside a shepherd's fold!
Along the hillsides' stony tracks
  I found the marigold!
The iris raised a shimmering spire
  Of beauty at my feet!
The poppy was a cup of fire
  Among the cooling wheat!

When I went up to Nazareth
  I marked how time came down
With blighting dust and withering breath
  Upon the hallowed town!

[463]

The years that buried Babylon
 Were drifting to efface
The steps of Mary's Heavenly Son,
 His dwelling and His face!
But still I read His permanence
 By signs that never dim;
With all their ancient eloquence
 The lilies spoke of Him!

HIS LAUREATE

Joyce Kilmer

Before Christ left the Citadel of Light,
To tread the dreadful way of human birth,
His shadow sometimes fell upon the earth
And those who saw it wept with joy and fright.
"Thou art Apollo, than the sun more bright!"
They cried, "Our music is of little worth,
But thrill our blood with thy creative mirth
Thou god of song, thou lord of lyric might!"

O singing pilgrim! who could love and follow
Your lover Christ, through even love's despair,
You knew within the cypress-darkened hollow
The feet that on the mountain are so fair.
For it was Christ that was your own Apollo,
And thorns were in the laurel on your hair.

THE DEATHLESS TALE

Charles Hanson Towne

Had He not breathed His breath
Truly at Nazareth;
Had not His very feet
Roamed many a hill and street;

Had Mary's story gone
To Time's oblivion;
Had the sweet record paled
And the truth not prevailed;
Dormant and bleak had been
This transitory scene,
And dark, thrice dark our earth
Unknowing of His birth.

The flowers beheld His face,
The stars knew His white grace.
The grass was greener for
His humble stable door;
The rose upon its stem
Redder for Bethlehem.
And we—are we not wise
To cling with avid eyes
To the old tale, and be
Moved by its memory?
Unutterably dim
Our bright world, lacking Him.

"WHAT THINK YE OF CHRIST?"

Geraldine Farrar

My Christ is the sweep of the lofty elm
That reaches the deep blue sky,
The swaying nest of a fearless bird
In its tiny cradle so high.

My Christ is the shining star above,
The cooling breeze of the night,
The afternoon of a glowing sun,
As it sinks in a misty night.

My Christ is the eye of a little child,
With its earnest glance so clear,
The touch of a dear and friendly hand,
The heart that knows no fear.

My Christ is the sparkling waterfall
That tumbles in merry play,

The fragrant bush of a sweet wild rose
That brightens a summer day.

My Christ is music and human song,
The marble dreams that delight,
The treasured page of a favorite book,
Or a palette of colors so bright.

My Christ is the beauty of gardens fair,
The lilac of early Spring,
The pungent sap of the evergreen,
A humming-bird's jeweled wing.

My Christ is the softness of falling snow
That dazzles in shining white,
The moon aloft in silver sheen,
As she sheds her radiant light.

My Christ is the growing, happy thing,
Be it Earth, Soul, Spirit, or Heart;
For all are His gracious gifts bestowed,
And of His Kingdom our part.

HOLY LAND

Richard Watson Gilder

This is the earth he walked on; not alone
    That Asian country keeps the sacred stain;
    Ah, not alone the far Judaean plain,
    Mountain and river! Lo, the sun that shone
On him, shines now on us; when day is gone
    The moon of Galilee comes forth again
    And lights our path as his; an endless chain
    Of years and sorrows makes the round world one.
The air we breathe, he breathed—the very air
    That took the mold and music of his high
    And godlike speech. Since then shall mortal dare
With base thought front the ever-sacred sky—
    Soil with foul deed the ground whereon he laid
    In holy death his pale, immortal head!

CHRIST AND THE WINDS

John Banister Tabb

From Bethlehem to Calvary,
By night and day, by land and sea,
His closest followers were we.

We soothed Him on His mother's breast;
We shared with John the place of rest;
With Magdalen His feet we pressed.

We saw His twilight agony;
To us He breathed His latest sigh;
With us He sought again the sky.

And now of all to whom His tone,
His face and gesture once were known,
We, wanderers, remain alone.

WHERE THE BLESSED FEET
HAVE TROD

Michael Field

Not alone in Palestine those blessed Feet have trod,
For I catch their print,
I have seen their dint
On a plot of chalky ground,
    Little villas dotted round;
On a sea-worn waste,
Where a priest, in haste,
Passeth with the Blessèd Sacrament to one dying,
    frail,
Through the yarrow, past the tamarisk, and the
    plaited snail:
Bright upon the grass I see
    Bleeding Feet of Calvary—
And I worship, and I clasp them round!
    On this bit of chalky, English ground,
Jesu, Thou art found: my God I hail,
    My Lord, my God!

ONE THERE WAS

Stella Fisher Burgess

One there was Who, passing by,
Touched all life with alchemy,
Grass of field or birds of air
Made His heart of God aware
Of common salt or smooth-worn yoke
A figure patterned for eager folk;
Of wayside spring or granary
Symbols He made which never die;
From mustard seed or branching vine,
Similitudes of things divine.
Meaning to leavening dough He lent;
He made, of bread, a sacrament.

IMMANENCE

Evelyn Underhill

I come in the little things,
Saith the Lord:
Not borne on morning wings
Of majesty, but I have set My Feet
Amidst the delicate and bladed wheat
That springs triumphant in the furrowed sod.
There do I dwell, in weakness and in power;
Not broken or divided, saith our God!
In your strait garden plot I come to flower:
About your porch My Vine
Meek, fruitful, doth entwine;
Waits, at the threshold, Love's appointed hour.
I come in the little things,
Saith the Lord:
Yea! on the lancing wings
Of eager birds, the softly pattering feet
Of furred and gentle beasts, I come to meet
Your hard and wayward heart. In brown bright
    eyes
That peep from out the brake, I stand confest.
On every nest
Where feathery Patience is content to brood
And leaves her pleasure for the high emprise
Of motherhood—
There doth My Godhead rest.

I come in the little things,
Saith the Lord:
My starry wings
I do forsake,
Love's highway of humility to take:
Meekly I fit my stature to your need.
In beggar's part
About your gates I shall not cease to plead—
As man, to speak with man—
Till by such art
I shall achieve My Immemorial Plan,
Pass the low lintel of the human heart.

CORPUS CHRISTI

Evelyn Underhill

Come, dear Heart!
The fields are white to harvest: come and see
As in a glass the timeless mystery
Of love, whereby we feed
On God, our bread indeed.
Torn by the sickles, see him share the smart
Of travailing Creation: maimed, despised,
Yet by his lovers the more dearly prized
Because for us he lays his beauty down
Last toll paid by Perfection for our loss!

Trace on these fields his everlasting Cross,
And o'er the stricken sheaves the Immortal Victim's
    crown.

From far horizons came a Voice that said,
Lo! from the hand of Death take thou thy daily
    bread.
Then I, awakening, saw
A splendour burning in the heart of things:
The flame of living love which lights the law
Of mystic death that works the mystic birth.
I knew the patient passion of the earth,
Maternal, everlasting, whence there springs
The Bread of Angels and the life of man.

Now in each blade
I, blind no longer, see
The glory of God's growth: know it to be

An earnest of the Immemorial Plan.
Yea, I have understood
How all things are one great oblation made:
He on our altars, we on the world's rood.
Even as this corn,

Earth-born,
We are snatched from the sod;
Reaped, ground to grist,
Crushed and tormented in the Mills of God,
And offered at Life's hands, a living Eucharist.

2. CHRIST IN HUMAN LIFE

WITHOUT AND WITHIN

Norman Ault

"If I ascend to heaven, thou art there;
There too, thou, if I make my bed in hell;
And if I take the wings of morning, there
Within the sea's most utmost parts to dwell,
Thy hand shall lead and hold me, even there."
Of old, thy singer thus; and in my heart
I hid myself from thee, long years apart.

"Raise but the stone, and thou shalt find me there;
Or cleave the wood, and there am I. I say
Wherever there is one alone, yea, there
Am I in him.' These thy new words, to-day
I heard, still darkly hid, and looked, and there—
Where I so long had thought thou hadst my part,—
I found thee hiding with me in my heart.

LOST AND FOUND

George MacDonald

I missed him when the sun began to bend;
I found him not when I had lost his rim;
With many tears I went in search of him,

Climbing high mountains which did still ascend,
And gave me echoes when I called my friend;
Through cities vast and charnel-houses grim,
And high cathedrals where the light was dim,
Through books and arts and works without an end,
But found him not—the friend whom I had lost.
And yet I found him—as I found the lark,
A sound in fields I heard but could not mark;
I found him nearest when I missed him most;
I found him in my heart, a life in frost,
A light I knew not till my soul was dark.

WRITTEN 1811

William Blake

Jesus said, "Wouldst thou love one who never died
For thee, or ever die for one who had not died for
   thee?
And if God dieth not for Man and giveth not Himself
Eternally for Man, Man could not exist; for Man
   is Love
As God is Love: every kindness to another is a little
   death
In the Divine Image, nor can Man exist but by
   Brotherhood."

He who would see the Divinity must see Him in
His Children.
One first, in friendship and love; then a Divine
Family, and in the midst
Jesus will appear; and so he who wishes to see a
Vision, a perfect Whole
Must see it in its Minute Particulars.

CITIZEN OF THE WORLD

Joyce Kilmer

No longer of Him be it said,
"He hath no place to lay His head."

In every land a constant lamp
Flames by His small and mighty camp.

There is no strange and distant place
That is not gladdened by His face.

And every nation kneels to hail
The Splendor shining through its veil.

Cloistered beside the shouting street,
Silent, He calls me to His feet.

Imprisoned for His love of me
He makes my spirit greatly free.

And through my lips that uttered sin
The King of Glory enters in.

JESUS OF NAZARETH
PASSETH BY

Lydia H. Sigourney

Watcher, who watch'st by the bed of pain,
While the stars sweep on in their midnight train;
Stifling the tear for thy loved one's sake;

Holding thy breath, lest his sleep should break;
In thy loneliest hours, there is a helper nigh,
"Jesus of Nazareth passeth by."

Stranger, afar from thy native land,
Whom no one takes with a brother's hand,
Table, and hearthstone are glowing free,
Casements are sparkling, but not for thee,
There is one who can tell of a home on high,
"Jesus of Nazareth passeth by."

Sad one, in secret, bending low,
A dart in thy breast, that the world may not know.
Striving the favor of God to win,—
Asking his pardon for days of sin;
Press on, press on, with thy earnest cry,
"Jesus of Nazareth passeth by."

Mourner, who sits in the church-yard lone,
Scanning the lines on that marble stone,—
Plucking the weeds from thy children's bed,
Planting the myrtle, the rose instead—
Look up, look up, with thy tearful eye,
"Jesus of Nazareth passeth by."

Fading one, with the hectic streak,
With thy vein of fire, and thy burning cheek,
Fear'st thou to tread the darkened vale
Look unto One, who can never fail.
He hath trod it Himself, He will hear thy sigh,
"Jesus of Nazareth passeth by."

HYMN FOR A HOUSEHOLD

Daniel Henderson

Lord Christ, beneath Thy starry dome
We light this flickering lamp of home,
And where bewildering shadows throng
Uplift our prayer and evensong.
Dost Thou, with heaven in thy ken
Seek still a dwelling-place with men,
Wandering the world in ceaseless quest?
O Man of Nazareth, be our guest!

Lord Christ, the bird his nest has found,
The fox is sheltered in his ground,
But dost Thou still this dark earth tread
And have no place to lay Thy head?
Shepherd of mortals, here behold
A little flock, a wayside fold
That wait thy presence to be blest—
O Man of Nazareth, be our guest!

THE HOUSEWIFE

Catherine Cate Coblentz

Jesus, teach me how to be
Proud of my simplicity.

Sweep the floors, wash the clothes,
Gather for each vase a rose.

Iron and mend a tiny frock,
Keeping one eye on the clock.

Always having time kept free
For childish questions asked of me.

Grant me wisdom Mary had
When she taught her little Lad.

CHRIST IN WOOLWORTH'S

Teresa Hooley

I did not think to find You there—
Crucifixes, large and small,
Sixpence and threepence, on a tray,
Among the artificial pearls,
Paste rings, tin watches, beads of glass.
It seemed so strange to find You there
Fingered by people coarse and crass,
Who had no reverence at all.
Yet—what is it that You would say?

"For these I hang upon My cross,
For these the agony and loss,
Though heedlessly they pass Me by."
Dear Lord, forgive such fools as I,
Who thought it strange to find You there,
When You are with us everywhere.

TO AND FRO ABOUT THE CITY

John Drinkwater

Shakespeare is dust, and will not come
To question from his Avon tomb,
And Socrates and Shelley keep
An Attic and Italian sleep.

They will not see us, nor again
Shall indignation light the brain
Where Lincoln on his woodland height
Tells out the spring and winter night.

They see not. But, O Christians, who
Throng Holborn and Fifth Avenue,
May you not meet, in spite of death,
A traveler from Nazareth?

DESPISED AND REJECTED

Christina Rossetti

My sun has set, I dwell
In darkness as a dead man out of sight;
And none remains, not one, that I should tell
To him mine evil plight
This bitter night.
I will make fast my door
That hollow friends may trouble me no more.

"Friend, open to Me."—Who is this that calls?
Nay, I am deaf as are my walls:
Cease crying, for I will not hear

Thy cry of hope or fear.
Others were dear,
Others forsook me: what art thou indeed
That I should heed
Thy lamentable need?
Hungry should feed,
Or stranger lodge thee here?

"Friend, My Feet bleed.
Open thy door to Me and comfort Me."
I will not open, trouble me no more.
Go on thy way footsore,
I will not rise and open unto thee.

"Then is it nothing to thee? Open, see
Who stands to plead with thee.
Open, lest I should pass thee by, and thou
One day entreat My Face
And howl for grace,
And I be deaf as thou art now.
Open to Me."

Then I cried out upon him: Cease,
Leave me in peace:
Fear not that I should crave
Aught thou mayst have.
Leave me in peace, yea trouble me no more,
Lest I arise and chase thee from my door.
What, shall I not be let
Alone, that thou dost vex me yet?

But all night long that voice spake urgently:
"Open to Me."
Still harping in mine ears:
"Rise, let Me in."
Pleading with tears:
"Open to Me that I may come to thee."
While the dew dropped, while the dark hours were
    cold:
"My Feet bleed, see My Face,
See My Hands bleed that bring thee grace,
My Heart doth bleed for thee,
Open to Me."

So till the break of day:
Then died away
That voice, in silence as of sorrow;
Then footsteps echoing like a sigh
Passed me by,

Lingering footsteps slow to pass.
On the morrow
I saw upon the grass
Each footprint marked in blood, and on my door
The mark of blood forevermore.

THREE CROSSES

Leila Avery Rotherburger

Three crosses stood on Calvary
    Stark against the sky.
Roman soldiers laughed to see
    Three ways a man may die.

Crosses still stand on Calvary
    Stark against the sky,
And some still laugh to see
    Men die . . . hear little children cry.

Who builds the cross on Calvary
    Stark against the sky?
Who laughs at pain and want?
    Can it be you—or I?

TO HIM THAT WAS CRUCIFIED

Walt Whitman

My spirit to yours, dear Brother,
Do not mind because many sounding Your name
    do not understand You,
I do not sound Your name, but I understand You,
I specify You with joy, O my Comrade, to salute
    You, and to salute those who are with You be-
    fore and since, and those to come also,
That we all labor together transmitting the same
    charge and succession,

We few equals indifferent of lands, indifferent of
    times,
We, enclosers of all continents, all castes, allowers
    of all theologies,
Compassionaters, perceivers, rapport of men,
We walk silent among disputes and assertions, but
    reject not the disputers nor any thing that is
    asserted,
We hear the bawling and din, we are reach'd at by
    divisions, jealousies, recriminations on every
    side,
They close peremptorily upon us to surround us, my
    Comrade,
Yet we walk unheld, free, the whole earth over,
    journeying up and down till we make our in-
    effaceable mark upon time and the diverse eras,
Till we saturate time and eras, that the men and
    women of races, ages to come, may prove
    brethren and lovers as we are.

OUR MASTER

John Greenleaf Whittier

Immortal Love, forever full,
    Forever flowing free,
Forever shared, forever whole,
    A never-ebbing sea!

Our outward lips confess the name
    All other names above;
Love only knoweth whence it came
    And comprehendeth love.

Blow, winds of God, awake and blow
    The mists of earth away!
Shine out, O Light Divine, and show
    How wide and far we stray!

Hush every lip, close every book,
    The strife of tongues forbear;
Why forward reach, or backward look,
    For love that clasps like air?

We may not climb the heavenly steeps
    To bring the Lord Christ down:
In vain we search the lowest deeps,
    For Him no depths can drown.

Nor holy bread, nor blood of grape,
    The lineaments restore
Of Him we know in outward shape
    And in the flesh no more.

He cometh not a king to reign;
    The world's long hope is dim;
The weary centuries watch in vain
    The clouds of heaven for Him.

Death comes, life goes; the asking eye
    And ear are answerless;
The grave is dumb, the hollow sky
    Is sad with silentness.

The letter fails, and systems fall,
    And every symbol wanes;
The Spirit over-brooding all
    Eternal Love remains.

And not for signs in heaven above
    Or earth below they look,
Who know with John His smile of love,
    With Peter His rebuke.

In joy of inward peace, or sense
    Of sorrow over sin,
He is His own best evidence,
    His witness is within.

No fable old, nor mythic lore,
    Nor dream of bards and seers,
No dead fact stranded on the shore
    Of the oblivious years;—

But warm, sweet, tender, even yet
    A present help is He;
And faith has still its Olivet,
    And love its Galilee.

The healing of His seamless dress
    Is by our beds of pain;
We touch Him in life's throng and press,
    And we are whole again.

Through Him the first fond prayers are said
  Our lips or childhood frame,
The last low whispers of our dead
  Are burdened with His name.

Our Lord and Master of us all!
  Whate'er our name or sign,
We own Thy sway, we hear Thy call,
  We test our lives by Thine.

Thou judgest us; Thy purity
  Doth all our lusts condemn;
The love that draws us nearer Thee
  Is hot with wrath to them.

Our thoughts lie open to Thy sight;
  And, naked to Thy glance,
Our secret sins are in the light
  Of Thy pure countenance.

Thy healing pains, a keen distress
  Thy tender light shines in;
Thy sweetness is the bitterness,
  Thy grace the pang of sin.

Yet, weak and blinded though we be,
  Thou dost our service own;
We bring our varying gifts to Thee,
  And Thou rejectest none.

To Thee our full humanity,
  Its joys and pains, belong;
The wrong of man to man on Thee
  Inflicts a deeper wrong.

Who hates, hates Thee, who loves becomes
  Therein to Thee allied;
All sweet accords of hearts and homes
  In Thee are multiplied.

Deep strike Thy roots, O heavenly Vine,
  Within our earthly sod,
Most human and yet most divine,
  The flower of man and God!

O Love! O Life! Our faith and sight
  Thy presence maketh one,
As through transfigured clouds of white
  We trace the noon-day sun.

So, to our mortal eyes subdued,
  Flesh-veiled, but not concealed,
We know in Thee the fatherhood
  And heart of God revealed.

We faintly hear, we dimly see,
  In differing phrase we pray!
But, dim or clear, we own in Thee
  The Light, the Truth, the Way!

The homage that we render Thee
  Is still our Father's own;
No jealous claim or rivalry
  Divides the Cross and Throne.

To do Thy will is more than praise,
  As words are less than deeds,
And simple trust can find Thy ways
  We miss with chart of creeds.

No pride of self Thy service hath,
  No place for me and mine;
Our human strength his weakness, death
  Our life, apart from Thine.

Apart from Thee all gain is loss,
  All labor vainly done;
The solemn shadow of Thy Cross
  Is better than the sun.

Alone, O Love ineffable!
  Thy saving name is given;
To turn aside from Thee is hell,
  To walk with Thee is heaven!

How vain, secure in all Thou art,
  Our noisy championship!
The sighing of the contrite heart
  Is more than flattering lip.

Not Thine the bigot's partial plea,
  Nor Thine the zealot's ban;
Thou well canst spare a love of Thee
  Which ends in hate of man.

Our Friend, our Brother, and our Lord,
  What may Thy service be?—
Nor name, nor form, nor ritual word,
  But simply following Thee.

We bring no ghastly holocaust,
  We pile no graven stone;
He serves thee best who loveth most
  His brothers and Thy own.

Thy litanies, sweet offices
  Of love and gratitude;
Thy sacramental liturgies
  The joy of doing good.

In vain shall waves of incense drift
  The vaulted nave around,
In vain the minster turret lift
  Its brazen weights of sound.

The heart must ring Thy Christmas bells,
  Thy inward altars raise;
Its faith and hope Thy canticles,
  And its obedience praise!

3. L'ENVOI: CHRIST IN THE UNIVERSE

CHRIST IN THE UNIVERSE

Alice Meynell

With this ambiguous earth
His dealings have been told us. These abide:
The signal to a maid, the human birth,
The lesson, and the young Man crucified.

But not a star of all
The innumerable host of stars has heard
How He administered this terrestrial ball.
Our race have kept their Lord's entrusted Word.

Of His earth-visiting feet
None knows the secret, cherished, perilous,
The terrible, shamefast, frightened, whispered,
  sweet,
Heart-shattering secret of His way with us.

No planet knows that this
Our wayside planet, carrying land and wave,
Love and life multiplied, and pain and bliss
Bears, as chief treasure, one forsaken grave.

Nor, in our little day,
May His devices with the heavens be guessed,
His pilgrimage to thread the Milky Way,
Or His bestowals there be manifest.

But in the eternities,
Doubtless we shall compare together, hear
A million alien Gospels, in what guise
He trod the Pleiades, the Lyre, the Bear.

O, be prepared, my soul!
To read the inconceivable, to scan
The million forms of God those stars unroll
When, in our turn, we show to them a Man.

INDEX OF AUTHORS

INDEX OF TITLES